GUINNESS

CRICKET
FACTS & FEATS

BILL FRINDALL

Editor: Beatrice Frei
Design and Layout: Martin Bronkhorst

Published in Great Britain by Guinness Superlatives Ltd,
33 London Road, Enfield, Middlesex

First Published in 1983

Typeset in Cheltenham ITC Book
by Angel Graphics Ltd, London
Printed and bound in Great Britain by
Redwood Burn Ltd.

British Library Cataloguing in Publication Data

Frindall, Bill
Guinness cricket facts & feats. —— New ed.
1. Cricket —— Records
I. Title   II. Frindall, Bill. Guinness
book of cricket facts and feats
796.35'8'09   GV925

ISBN 0-85112-456-9

BILL FRINDALL, Editor of *Playfair Cricket Annual* and Cricket Correspondent of the *Mail on
Sunday*, is a regular contributor to the *Daily Telegraph*, *The Guardian*, *The Cricketer* and *The
Cricketer Quarterly Facts and Figures*. He has compiled eleven titles (notably *The Guinness
Book of Cricket Facts and Feats*, 1st ed.; the *Test Cricket* and *Cricket Records* volumes of the
Wisden Library, and six volumes of *Frindall's Score Book*), besides providing statistics and
appendices for numerous other publications.

In 1966 he succeeded Arthur Wrigley as the BBC Radio scorer and after 21 seasons, has enjoyed
an unbroken run of 109 home Test matches with the Test Match Special Radio 3 ball-by-ball
commentary team. Dubbed 'The Bearded Wonder' by Brian Johnston, he has also scored 20
Tests in Australia and six for TVNZ in New Zealand.

He still plays regularly for his own touring team (the Maltamaniacs), and in charity matches for
the Lord's Taveners and SPARKS when he also assists with the public address commentaries.

CONTENTS

PREFACE AND ACKNOWLEDGEMENTS

Four years have passed since I first added a Cricket edition to the *Guinness Facts and Feats* series. Congratulations and thanks are due not only to the publishers and purchasers of that initial offering but also to the world's first-class cricketers for making an updated edition necessary.

This is not just a catalogue of records. It is intended to be a rewarding read for those not besotted with statistics; providing, I hope, as much interest and entertainment for readers with only the flimsiest interest in cricket as for the game's many aficionados.

The contents have been completely revised to the end of the 1986 English season (16 September). With the lengthy process of book production taking more than six months from delivery of manuscript, it is inevitable that some of the career aggregates will be almost a year out of date by the time of publication. Until we progress to more highly electronic methods this must remain a compiler's dilemma.

Although the overseas season of 1986-87 has seen a further and, in my view, dangerous proliferation of international cricket of both the Test match and the smash-and-grab variety, no major records have changed hands. The outstanding and historic performance has been that of Sunil Gavaskar becoming the first to score 10 000 runs in Test cricket. He has mastered all the world's outstanding bowlers of the last two decades and now holds most of the major Test batting records: most Tests (125), most consecutive appearances (106), most innings (214), most runs (10 122), most hundreds (34), most fifties (79), and most shares in century partnerships (58). With the ever-increasing amount of Test cricket being staged, it seems inevitable that all his records will be surpassed before the end of the century. After all, if Sir Donald Bradman had enjoyed as many completed Test innings (i.e. 198 – excluding Gavaskar's 16 'not outs'), and maintained his average of 99.94, he would have reached the phenomenal totals of 19 788 runs and 77 hundreds.

Since the last edition was completed Sri Lanka has been granted full membership of the ICC, achieved Test status and defeated both of its nearest neighbours. I have included a new section on first-class cricket in Serendip and am grateful to Mohamed Kamardeen, S.S. Perera and Mahinda Wijesinghe for their help.

With just eight exceptions, all the earlier edition's illustrations have been changed. Their selection has provided huge enjoyment and several headaches. The process has been greatly abetted by the kindness of Bobbie Ross, wife of the late Gordon, who substantially increased my own hoard of material by generously presenting me with her husband's library of cricket photographs. All uncredited illustrations are from my collection. Thanks are due to Sue Harley, Don Neely, Roy Perry, John Reader, Netta Rheinberg, Sa'adi Thawfeeq, Tom Troman and Chris Warne, all of whom have donated pictures for this edition.

I am delighted that Martin Bronkhorst, a near-neighbour and a collaborator on other publications, has undertaken the design and layout of this edition. Robert Heesom is to be equally commended for his evocative jacket design.

The Names Index has been compiled as a major feature of this book and includes, where ascertainable, the birth – and death – dates and full names of every cricketer mentioned.

Unless specified otherwise an asterisk (*) denotes either a 'not out' score or an unbroken partnership. Other symbols are explained where they appear.

In addition to those mentioned either above or in my acknowledgements in the first edition, I should like to record my thanks to John English for checking the proofs.

BILL FRINDALL
London

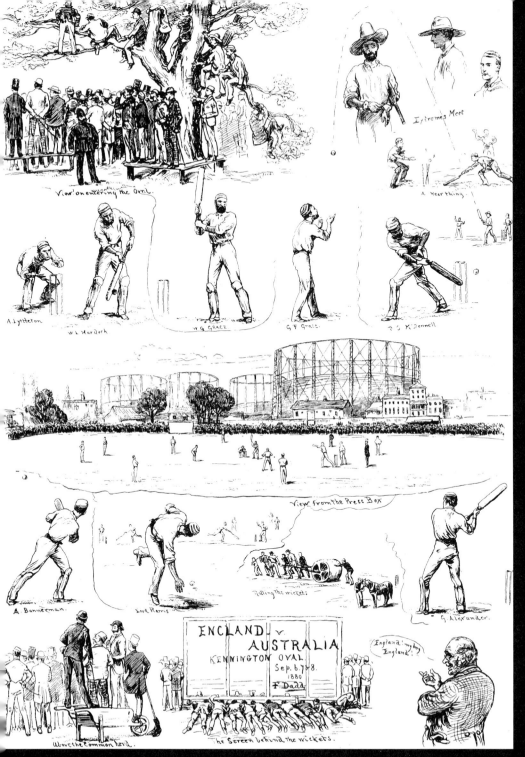

Impressions of Australia's defeat in the first Test match staged in England. (Illustrated London News)

FIRST NOTCHES

Origins

The origins of cricket are obscure, unrecorded, and the source of much speculation. There are two major theories concerning the derivation of the word cricket.

One concerns the Anglo-Saxon word *cricce*, meaning a crooked staff, ie a staff with a crook or with a club at one end. In the Saxon rendering of the 23rd Psalm, 'Thy staff' appears as 'cricc thin'. Developing this theory results in the supposed origins of the game being among shepherds hitting some appropriate object (a stone or pine cone perhaps) with their crooks and, at the same time, defending the wicket gate into the sheep fold.

The other theory traces the word 'criquet' to the Flemish or Dutch *krickstoel*, a piece of furniture on which one kneels in church. A low stool between 18 inches and 2 feet in length once generally called a 'cricket' in England, its profile is very similar to that of the long, low wicket in early cricket, or of the early stool in stool-ball. The word 'stool' is old Sussex dialect for a tree stump.

Other theories attribute the game's origins to club-ball, where the striker defends a hole in the ground, or to a game played in the churchyard.

Earliest References

The first probable reference to cricket appears in the Wardrobe accounts for the 28th year of the reign of Edward I (1299-1300), published in 1787 by the London Society of Antiquaries, and first brought to notice by 'H.P.-T' (P.F. Thomas) in *Old English Cricket*, a collection of five pamphlets issued between 1923 and 1929. Thomas's translation of the Latin reads:

> 'To Master John of Leek, Chaplain of Prince Edward, the King's son, for ready money disbursed for the said Prince's playing at **Creag'** and other sports, out of his own and deputies' hands (was paid) at Westminster, on the 10th day of March (1300) the sum of 100 shillings. And to his Chamberlain Hugo, at Newenton, in the month of March 20 shillings. In all £6.'

The apostrophe after Creag is a shorthand method of showing the diminutive 'et'. 'Creaget', probably pronounced 'craiget', was almost certainly cricket; no alternative explanation has ever been offered. Prince Edward, the first Prince of Wales who was to become Edward II, was 16 years old in 1300. A Gascon youth, Piers Gaveston, was maintained at Court to provide company for the young prince. If Newenton was the village of Newenden in the Weald on the Kent/Sussex border of today, this document would show that Prince Edward and his friend were the first pair of known cricketers and that the Weald was its first known ground.

The first certain reference to cricket is contained in a document dated December 1478 and refers to '**criquet**' near St Omer, in what is now north-eastern France.

The earliest certain reference to cricket being played in England occurs in a document dated 16 January 1598, recording the evidence of John Derrick in a court case concerning a disputed piece of land in Guildford, Surrey. Then aged 59 and a coroner, Derrick attested that 'when he was a scholler in the free school of Guldeford, he and several of his fellowes did runne and play there at **krickett** and other plaies'. This means that cricket was being played there in the 1550s, just before the reign of Elizabeth I.

The earliest known dictionary to mention cricket was *A Worlde of Words*, compiled by Giovanni Florio, an Italian then living in England, and published in 1598. His Italian/English translation of *sgrillare* was 'to play cricket-a-wicket, to make merry'. In 1611, Randle Cotgrave's French-English dictionary (the first such ever compiled) translated *crosse* as 'a crosier', or 'Bishop's staffe', also a 'cricket-staffe', or the 'crooked staffe wherewith boys play at cricket'.

The first recorded cricket match took place at Coxheath in Kent in 1646. This match also produced the first record of betting on cricket.

The earliest known reference to cricket being played abroad dates back to 1676 and is contained in the diary of a naval chaplain, Henry Teonge, who had visited Aleppo in what is now Syria:

> 'May 6, 1676. This morning early (as it is the custom all summer longe) at the least 40 of the English, with his worship the Consull, rod out of the cytty about 4 miles, to the Greene Platt, a fine vally by a river-syde, to recreate themselves. Where a princely tent was pitched; and we had several pastimes and sports, as duck-hunting, fishing, shooting, hand-ball, krickett, scrofilo . . .'

The first full description of a cricket match appeared in a Latin poem *In certamen pilae*, written by William Goldwin of Eton and King's College, Cambridge.

The first match between two counties took place on 29 June 1709 when Kent played Surrey at Dartford Brent.

The first great match of which the full score has survived was played between Kent and All-England on the Artillery Ground near Finsbury Square, London, on 18 June 1744.

The first cricket illustration was drawn by a Frenchman, Hubert d'Anville Bourguignon dit Gravelot (1699-1773) during his few years in England and was published on 7 May 1739 as *The Game of Cricket*. Depicting youngsters playing, it was one of a small collection of children's games and was re-issued in France 20 years later as *Le jeu de la crosse*.

The oldest surviving painting of a cricket match is *Cricket in Marylebone Fields* by Francis Hayman, R.A. (1708-76) and dates from *c* 1743. It was used for the illustration of the earliest printed version of the 1744 code of the Laws, on a handker-chief now in the MCC collection.

The earliest known cricket photographs were taken in 1857 by Roger Fenton at the Artillery Ground when the Royal Artillery played Hunsdonbury.

Evolution of Modern Cricket

EQUIPMENT

The earliest bats were sticks and, probably, shepherds' crooks. These gave way to clubs and clubbed sticks before the introduction of the *batte*, with its long, thin shaft and curved thicker end not unlike a slightly straightened-out hockey stick. The clubbed design of these first bats was dictated by the type of bowling encountered, which was similar to that in the game of bowls – underarm and all along the ground.

By the early 18th century the batte had developed into a longer, heavier, curved version of the modern item; it had a handle and a blade but was carved out of a single piece of wood.

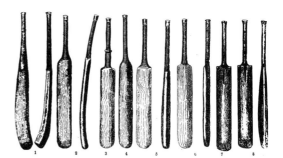

Bats ancient and Victorian. Dates: 1-1743; 2-1771; 3-1790; 4-1792; 5-*c*.1800; 6-1827; 7 and 8 owned by W.G. Grace (1848-1915). (MCC)

The oldest surviving cricket bat is inscribed 'J.C. 1729' – J.C. was John Chitty of Knaphill – and can be seen in the pavilion at The Oval.

There has never been any restriction on a bat's weight. Some used in the 1770s weighed as much as 5 pounds and many 19th-century players used 4-pound bats. The average weight of a modern bat is 2 pounds 5 ounces.

The bat used today consists of a willow blade with a cane handle (invented *c* 1853), layered with thin strips of rubber and bound with twine. This is covered by a tight rubber sheath – the grip. The 'V' shaped extension of the handle into the blade is the splice.

Until Thomas ('Shock' or 'Daddy') White of Reigate took guard with a bat wider than the wicket in 1771, there was no restriction on the implement's dimensions. Following White's inventiveness, the Hambledon Club, who were then the game's law-givers, limited the bat's width to $4\frac{1}{2}$ inches. They constructed an iron gauge through which any suspect bat had to pass. White, incidentally, does not appear to have suffered any severe remorse as he lived actively until 1831 when he was 91.

The bat's length has been limited to 38 inches since 1835 and its maximum width is now $4\frac{1}{4}$.

THE BALL

Earliest cricket was played with stones, pieces of wood and probably sundry other available missiles. The first 'manufactured' ball was made by interlacing narrow strips of hide and was first mentioned in 1658.

The first six-seamed ball was made in 1775 by Dukes, a family firm at Penshurst in Kent, who presented it to the Prince of Wales (later George IV).

The ball's colour is first mentioned in 1753 in *Sevenoke: A poem* which describes a match on the Sevenoaks Vine ground and refers to 'the crimson ball'. Probably by accident the colour at the opposite end of the spectrum from green was adopted, but this happens to be the perfect contrast as the human eye cannot focus the two colours simultaneously.

Balls are made of hand-stitched leather quarters dyed red, covering an interior of cork wound round with twine.

Dimensions have altered little. The 1744 code laid down merely that 'ye ball must weigh between 5 and 6 ounces'. The present weight of between $5\frac{1}{2}$ and $5\frac{3}{4}$ ounces was established in 1774. The circumference was established as between 9 and $9\frac{1}{4}$ inches in 1838. This was changed to the present measurements of between $8\frac{13}{16}$ and 9 inches in 1927, to legalize the smaller ball that had been used for some years without anyone noticing.

The oldest surviving cricket ball in the Lord's collection was used in the MCC v Norfolk match of 1820, when William Ward scored 278, the highest innings at Lord's until 1925.

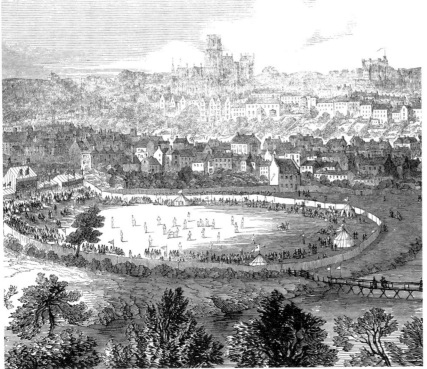

William Clarke's All England Eleven at Durham in May 1849. Twenty-Two of Durham were dismissed for 67 and 51, losing by 42 runs. (Mary Evans Picture Library)

THE STUMPS

Wickets in the early 17th century were up to 6 feet wide and often under 12 inches high. By 1700 they had narrowed to 2 feet wide and 1 foot high.

The third stump is believed to have been introduced in 1775 when Hambledon Players were engaged in a match in London. Not until 1785 did the third stump become mandatory.

By 1775 the wicket had narrowed to 6 inches and was 22 inches high. After being increased to 24×7 inches in 1798, an additional 2 inches was added to its height in 1819, and a further inch to both dimensions in 1823. No other tampering occurred until 1931. Then, in response to a general horror of high scores and drawn matches in the county championship, the wicket was enlarged by one inch in both directions. Although various experiments have taken place behind the scenes, including one involving a fourth stump, today's wickets are the same measurement as those of 1931, namely 28 inches high and 9 inches wide.

THE BAILS

The wicket in its early form carried only one bail, sometimes several feet long. The first mention of two bails for each wicket occurred in 1786 when an 'unofficial' version of the Laws was issued in Maidstone.

THE PITCH

The first known measurement for the length of the pitch wicket-to-wicket is the 23 yards given in the 1727 Articles of Agreement between the second Duke of Richmond and Mr Brodrick of Peper Harow in Surrey.

The 1744 code stipulates 22 yards, a distance which has remained steadfast for more than two centuries despite the vast and fundamental changes in the techniques of bowling and batting. It is also the length of the agricultural chain invented by Gunter in the early 17th century and derived from four rods, poles or perches.

THE LAWS

The first known Laws were issued in 1744 as a result of a meeting of 'the London Star and Garter' Club. This was a full set of Laws and the ones under which Kent played All–England in the first match for which the full score has survived.

The earliest known documented playing regulations are to be found in a copy of the 1727 Articles of Agreement between the Duke of Richmond and Mr Brodrick. These were really instructions to the umpires and team managers, and they obviously were an attempt to clarify certain points of dispute arising from an earlier full code of Laws which has not been found.

The first 'Laws' of which any documentary evidence exists are two which have survived from the 17th century: a batsman could be out 'caught', and, if he was in danger of being caught, he could charge down the fielder attempting the catch.

In 1755 the Laws were revised by the 'Star and Garter' Club, some of whose members were to form (c 1782) the White Conduit Club, which was to merge with the new Marylebone Cricket Club in 1787.

The latest revision was drafted by S.C. ('Billy') Griffith, Secretary of the MCC 1962-74, and was issued as a new code in 1980.

SCORING AND RECORDS

The earliest method of scoring did not involve paper and pen but the cutting of notches in wooden staves. Every tenth notch was cut larger than the previous nine to facilitate a tally at the end of the innings.

No doubt there were other ingenious methods. Certainly none could match the simplicity of an early West Indian method whereby leaves were put into a hat during the first innings and removed during the second. Either one run was required for victory when the hat was emptied or the winning margin of runs remained in it when the last wicket fell.

The first great match of which a full score survives was played on 18 June 1744 between Kent and All-England on the Artillery Ground, London. The score also survives of a less important match played a few days earlier.

The first known stroke-by-stroke score of a match was kept on 31 August 1769 when the Duke of Dorset's XI played Wrotham. It included the first known century, 107 by John Minshull who batted at number three. Soon afterwards, the Duke engaged Minshull as his gardener at 8 shillings a week.

The first recorded hundred partnership was scored in 1769: 128 for the first wicket by Thomas Sueter and George Leer for Hampshire against Surrey at Broadhalfpenny Down, Hambledon.

The first record of a bowler being credited with a catch off his own bowling appeared in 1777. In the same year James Aylward scored 167 for Hampshire against England and batted on all three days. This was the highest score in an important match until 1820 and Hampshire's total of 403 was the first on record of 400.

The first recorded lbw dismissal is to be found in the scores of the match between Surrey and Thirteen of England at Moulsey Hurst on 12-15 August 1795. Batting at number three for England, the Hon John Tufton was lbw b Wells 3. Previously lbw dismissals had been recorded as 'bowled'.

The first evidence of a full bowling analysis being kept including maiden overs for the first time, is in the scores of the match between Yorkshire and Norfolk at Hyde Park, Sheffield, on 14-18 July 1834.

Wides were first recorded as such in 1827, three years before **no-balls**. Not until 1848 did **the first leg-bye** go on record. Wides (introduced in 1816) had been treated as byes, and no-balls as 'dead'.

The earliest known matchcard or scorecard was printed by the Sevenoaks Vine scorer for the match between Kent and Hampshire in 1776.

The telegraph scoreboard was introduced at Lord's in 1846, scorecards being sold there that season also for the first time.

Although scoreboards showing extended batting details had been used in Australia for many season before, **the first board to give full bowling analyses** as well did not appear until that designed by E.J. ('Ned') Gregory was brought into use in 1895. Gregory, the eldest of five brothers who played for New South Wales, played in the first-ever Test match and made the first duck in Test cricket. A useful right-handed all-rounder, he became curator of the Sydney Cricket Ground.

The standard technique of scoring has changed little over the years and is still used by most official scorers employed by first-class teams. A far more informative method is that invented in 1905 by W.H. Ferguson, the Australian scorer who recorded 208 Test matches and acted as scorer and baggage-master for Australia, England, South Africa, West Indies and New Zealand on 43 tours. 'Fergie's' method involved vertical fools'cap sheets with columns for each batsman and for each bowling end. Each line across the columns is one over, starting with a record of the time when it begins. All the action is noted in the column of the batsman facing the bowling, and various columns of totals are completed at the end of each over. From this system it is possible to tell who bowled each ball, at what time, from which end, to which batsman, and, with the aid of various symbols, exactly how it was dealt with. This is the system which radio and television scorers have used since the introduction of ball-by-ball broadcasting in 1957.

The first radial scoring chart was devised in 1905 by Bill Ferguson while he was official scorer

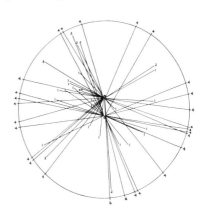

Radial scoring chart of Botham's audacious innings against Australia in 1981. (Author)

for Australia in England and on his first overseas tour.

The first cricket annual was published in 1791 by Samuel Britcher. Containing full scores of important and other matches for each season, Britcher's books of scores appeared regularly until 1805. Seasonal batting averages were not published until 1793.

BOWLING

Originally bowling in cricket was exactly the same as the bowling in bowls, with the ball rolled under-arm along the ground. This method of bowling was unchallenged by experiment until the middle of the 18th century. Some time after 1744 bowlers began to pitch the ball and two new weapons, length and direction, had been added to their armoury. Before the advent of lob bowling the only variation possible had been in the degree of speed at which the ball travelled along the ground. Bats-men did not need to move their feet; they simply stood where they were, swung their long clubbed sticks and despatched the ball like golfers. The introduction of pitching compelled the batsman to play forward or back. It was arguably the most significant technical advance in the entire evolution of cricket.

One historian, G.B. Buckley, has suggested that during the 1744 match between Kent and England, the first match for which we have the complete scores, the ball was 'thrown' so that it described a low but airborne trajectory before bouncing. If so, then that match, already historically important, also marked the inception of length bowling at the highest playing level.

By 1773 length bowling had replaced true bowl-ing. It soon led to further experiments. In the 1780s Thomas Walker of Hambledon tried out a form of round-arm delivery but was specifically warned against it. Gradually others tried to bowl it and in 1816 a Law was introduced to prohibit it:

> 'The ball must be bowled (not thrown or jerked), and be delivered underhand, with the hand below the elbow. But if the ball be jerked, or the arm extended from the body horizontally, and any part of the hand be uppermost, or the hand horizontally extended when the ball is delivered, the Umpire shall call "No Ball".'

Opponents of round-arm bowling feared that it would restrict scoring and lead to an imbalance in favour of the bowler. Statistics were to prove them right.

The first exponent of round-arm bowling was probably John Willes of Kent. He used to prac-tise batting against the bowling of his sister, Chris-tina. Because of her full skirt of the period she could only deliver the ball round-arm and Willes found it very difficult to play. When he opened the

William Lillywhite (1792-1854) who perfected round-arm bowling.

bowling round-arm for Kent against the MCC at Lord's on 15 July 1822, he became **the first bowler in the game's history to be no-balled for throwing.** *Bell's Life* describes him leaving the ground 'in high dudgeon' and his place had to be taken by another player.

By 1827 many bowlers had tried out the round-arm method and the Sussex pair, William Lilly-white and James Broadbridge, had perfected it. Three experimental matches that season between Sussex and England, in which the effect on scoring was studied, led to the MCC authorising round-arm bowling the following year. Bowlers were allowed to raise their hand level with their elbow. The change was incorporated into a revision of the Laws in 1835 but with 'shoulder' replacing 'elbow'.

Some were already experimenting with overarm bowling and it was frequently employed in matches when the umpires allowed. Edgar Will-sher of Kent was **the first to be no-balled for bowling overarm**, by John Lillywhite at The Oval on 26 August 1862. Opening England's bowling against Surrey, he was called six times and the England team left the field causing play to be aban-doned for the rest of the day. Lillywhite refused to change his mind and he was replaced as umpire for the final day. Thus reprieved, Willsher took 6 for 49.

Overarm bowling was legalized when an amendment to the Laws was passed on 10 June 1864. It did not lead to a wholesale overnight change in bowling actions. Most raised their arms to shoulder height. The 1878 Australians were **the first team to employ a specialist overarm attack** and another decade was to pass before the new style became prevalent.

The first underarm bowler to spin the ball deliberately was Lamborn who played just five seasons for Surrey and England (1777-82). No one knew his first name and he was always called 'The Little Farmer'. He invented the off-break by bowling for hours at a time against hurdles while tending his father's sheep. 'He was, it is believed, a Surrey man; but his christian name, native village, date of death, and age, could not be discovered. He was a regular country bumpkin, a very civil and inoffensive young fellow, but did not continue the game long, why is not recorded'. (*Scores and Biographies*)

The only other bowler known to have invented a new type of delivery was Bernard Bosanquet, the Middlesex and England all-rounder who introduced the 'googly' to the first-class game at Lord's in 1900. An off-break bowled with a leg-break action, it is known in Australia as the 'Bosie'.

Bernard Bosanquet (1877-1936) who devised the googly.

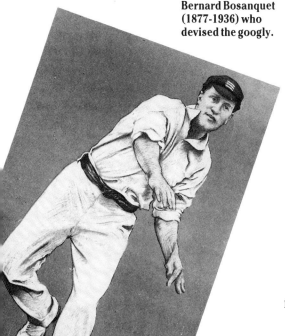

Other important notches

Two Clubs have influenced the game more than any others: **Hambledon** and the **MCC**:

Formed in about 1767, **the Hambledon Club** with its ground on Broadhalfpenny Down, a strip of Hampshire heathland high above the village of Hambledon a mile away, was the centre of the cricketing world for more than two decades. Most of the Club's founders were old boys of Westminster School, influential gentlemen who were able to attract wealthy patrons to the game. The Hambledon Club became adept at promoting important matches and the great sides of the day, England, Sussex and Kent, were regular visitors. Frequently they were defeated by a team that was generally called Hampshire although it has been subsequently listed in some publications as Hambledon.

The Marylebone Club was formed in the late 18th century as an offshoot of a club at the Star and Garter tavern in Pall Mall, London, whose members frequented the White Conduit House and played cricket in the adjoining fields near Islington. Thomas Lord, a Thirsk-born Yorkshireman employed at the White Conduit Club as a bowler and general attendant, was persuaded to start a new private ground at what is now Dorset Square. It staged its first great match on 31 May-1 June 1787 when Middlesex defeated Essex. When the lease ended after the 1810 season, Lord had already moved his turf, so that 'the nobleman and Gentlemen of the MCC' should be able 'to play on the same footing as before', to a field at North Bank Regent's Park, on the St John's Wood Estate. In 1813 a third and final ground had to be found when Parliament decreed that the Regent's Canal would be cut through the middle of Lord's field. Now on its present site in St John's Wood, Lord's much-travelled turf staged its third great inaugural match on 22 June 1814 when the MCC beat Hertfordshire by an innings.

The present practice ground, 'The Nursery', was bought in the Club's centenary year, 1887. It had been the site of Henderson's Nursery Gardens and famous for its tulips and pineapples.

From its earliest days the MCC appears to have assumed, and have been conceded, lawmaking

The first overseas tour: George Parr's All England Team aboard *Novia Scotian* September 1859.
STANDING: **R.P. Carpenter, W. Caffyn, T. Lockyer, H.H. Stephenson, G. Parr, J. Grundy, J. Caesar, T. Hayward.**
SEATED: **J. Wisden, A.J.D. Diver, John Lillywhite, J. Jackson.**

powers. The habitués of the Star and Garter tavern, who became known as the White Conduit Club, had revised the Laws in 1755 and 1774. When they formed the MCC the accepted powers of legislation were transferred to the new Club. Its membership, in terms of social status, patronage of the game and playing distinction, commanded universal and unrivalled prestige as the game's sole authority.

In 1903 the MCC became responsible for selection and administration of all overseas tours. Until the 1977-78 season, England teams overseas played under the MCC banner except during official Test matches.

In 1898 the MCC established The Board of Con-

trol at the request of the counties to administer Test cricket in England. In 1904 they were similarly invited to form an Advisory County Cricket Committee to provide an equivalent service for county cricket. In 1968 both bodies were replaced by the Test and County Cricket Board (TCCB) under the newly-constituted Cricket Council. The latter was formed as a democratic official body which the Government could recognize and thus grant financial aid to, for the game's development through the new Sports Council.

Since 1909 the MCC has hosted and secretarily administered the Imperial Cricket Conference. Renamed the International Cricket Conference in 1965, its delegates meet annually at Lord's to discuss current problems affecting the well-being of cricket.

The first overseas cricket tour was to have been undertaken in August 1789 by an English team to Paris. The Duke of Dorset, a great patron of cricket responsible for many matches at Hambledon and elsewhere, was Ambassador in Paris when the French Revolution began. He asked the Duke of Leeds, another cricket enthusiast who was then Foreign Secretary, for an assurance of goodwill to France from the British Government. The tour seems to have been arranged as a 'goodwill' visit. The project was abandoned when the team, arriving at Dover, were confronted by the sight of the Duke of Dorset fleeing from his post.

The first touring team actually to reach its objective overseas was the English expedition to Canada and the United States in the autumn of 1859. Organized by Fred Lillywhite, it was captained by George Parr, William Clarke's successor as leader of the All-England Eleven, and included John Wisden, founder of the rival United All-England Eleven. Six players from each of those professional Elevens constituted the 12-man touring team which left Liverpool on 7 September and arrived, via storms, ice-bergs, gales, fog and sea-sickness, in Quebec on 22 September. **The first match involving an overseas touring team** was played at Montreal on 24-27 September 1859 between 22 of Lower Canada and 11 of England, the tourists winning by eight wickets. Having won all its five matches, the team returned to England on 11 November after travelling approximately 7500 miles in slightly over two months. The expedition prompted the publication of the first 'tour book', *The English Cricketers' Trip to Canada and the United States in 1859* by Fred Lillywhite.

The first match between teams from two different countries was played between Toronto Cricket Club and St George's Cricket Club of New York in 1840, the latter winning by ten wickets.

The first international match was played between the United States and Canada, involving players from the same two clubs who contested the 1840 encounter, in New York in 1844. It was played for a $1000 stake and won by Canada by 23 runs.

The first overseas team to visit England arrived from Australia in 1868 and played 47 matches (14 wins, 14 defeats, 19 draws) between 25 May and 17 October. The team was organized, promoted, coached, managed and captained by Charles Lawrence, an all-rounder who, after occasional appearances for Surrey, Middlesex and the All-England Eleven, had been a member of **the first English expedition to Australia** in 1861-62. He had accepted an invitation to coach the newly-founded Albert Club in Sydney and to play for New South Wales. The 13 Australians he brought to England in 1868, just four years after overarm bowling had been legalized, were all Aborigines. Their playing attire included white flannels and red Garibaldi shirts with blue sashes and neckties. They gave many exhibitions of their native skills; dressed in possum skin they staged various field and track events (flat sprints, hurdling, high jumping, pole-vaulting, water bucket races), as well as demonstrating the art of throwing spears, boomerangs, and 'kangaroo rats' (a 2-foot handle with a knob on the end used for bringing down birds or small animals). Their native names and the nicknames under which they played were:

Arrahmunijarrimun	*Peter*
Ballrinjarrimin	*Sundown*
Bonnibarngeet	*Tiger*
Brimbunyah	*Red Cap*
Brippokei	*King Cole*
Bullchanach	*Bullocky*
Grongarrong	*Mosquito*
Jallachmurrimin	*Jim Crow*
Jungunjinanuke	*Dick-a-Dick*
Murrumgunarriman	*Twopenny*
Pripumuarraman	*Charley Dumas*
Unaarrimin	*Mullagh*
Zellanach	*Cuzens*

Only ten of the Aborigines completed the arduous tour. King Cole died of tuberculosis in Guy's Hospital London, on 24 June, and Sundown and Jim Crow returned in August. Their departure left a tremendous workload for the survivors. Red Cap and Tiger played in all 47 matches, a record for any tour.

TEST CRICKET

	Tests	Won	Lost	Drawn	Tied	Toss Won
England	628	227	167	234	·	309
Australia	464	193	137	133	1	231
South Africa	172	38	77	57	·	80
West Indies	246	90	60	95	1	132
New Zealand	179	25	75	79	·	88
India	235	38	83	114	·	119
Pakistan	157	36	39	82	·	81
Sri Lanka	21	2	11	8	·	11

Key to abbreviations

A Australia
E England
I India
NZ New Zealand

P Pakistan
SA South Africa
SL Sri Lanka
WI West Indies

* not out (unless otherwise stated)

Results summary of all Test matches (1876-77 to 1986†)

		Tests Won by	E	A	SA	WI	NZ	I	P	SL	Tied	Drawn
England	v Australia	257	86	96	·	·	·	·	·	·	·	75
	v South Africa	102	46	·	18	·	·	·	·	·	·	38
	v West Indies	90	21	·	·	35	·	·	·	·	·	34
	v New Zealand	63	30	·	·	·	4	·	·	·	·	29
	v India	75	30	·	·	·	·	11	·	·	·	34
	v Pakistan	39	13	·	·	·	·	·	3	·	·	23
	v Sri Lanka	2	1	·	·	·	·	·	·	0	·	1
Australia	v South Africa	53	·	29	11	·	·	·	·	·	·	13
	v West Indies	62	·	27	·	19	·	·	·	·	1	15
	v New Zealand	21	·	9	·	·	5	·	·	·	·	7
	v India	42	·	20	·	·	·	8	·	·	·	14
	v Pakistan	28	·	11	·	·	·	·	8	·	·	9
	v Sri Lanka	1	·	1	·	·	·	·	·	0	·	0
South Africa	v New Zealand	17	·	·	9	·	2	·	·	·	·	6
West Indies	v New Zealand	21	·	·	·	7	3	·	·	·	·	11
	v India	54	·	·	·	22	·	5	·	·	·	27
	v Pakistan	19	·	·	·	7	·	·	4	·	·	8
New Zealand	v India	25	·	·	·	·	4	10	·	·	·	11
	v Pakistan	27	·	·	·	·	3	·	10	·	·	14
	v Sri Lanka	5	·	·	·	·	4	·	·	0	·	1
India	v Pakistan	35	·	·	·	·	·	4	6	·	·	25
	v Sri Lanka	4	·	·	·	·	·	0	·	1	·	3
Pakistan	v Sri Lanka	9	·	·	·	·	·	·	5	1	·	3
		1051	227	193	38	90	25	38	36	2	1	401

† Up to and including 1 September 1986

Charles William Alcock (1842-1907): Surrey secretary 1872-1907; Football Association secretary 1867-1896 (captained England v Scotland 1875); founder of the FA Cup; organizer of the first Test in England.

The first Test match

This was **the first match played on level terms** (eleven-a-side) between an English touring side and a representative Australian team. It was not until Clarence Moody classified the early matches some fifteen years later in his *Australian Cricket and Cricketers* , that this encounter was given the accolade of 'Test' match. Moody's list was quoted by C.W. Alcock, instigator and organizer of the first Test match in England (1880) and a leading English authority of the day, in his weekly magazine *Cricket*. In 1895 J.N. Pentelow published his *England v. Australia – The Story of the Test Matches* with full scores and a commentary on each of the first 43 Tests played between the two countries. This book of 180 small pages, firmly established Moody's list and assured the 1877 contest a unique place in cricket history.

Neither team was fully representative. James Lillywhite's men were all professionals; their strength would have been increased by the inclusion of such amateurs as W.G. Grace whose 3669 runs in all matches during the 1876 season had included a little matter of 318 not out against Yorkshire. Dave Gregory's side was composed entirely of Sydney and Melbourne players, even though South Australia had recently thrashed Victoria by an innings and plenty. Almost five years were to pass before the first Adelaide cricketer, George Giffen, forced his way into the Australian team. Gregory was without three of his best bowlers, including 'The Demon' Spofforth who refused to play when his own wicket-keeper, Billy Murdoch, was not picked. Some of Lillywhite's side were still sea-sick after their return voyage from New Zealand when the match started and their wicket keeper, Ted Pooley, had been confiscated by the authorities during that interim tour. They were the fourth English team to visit Australia following those led by H.H. Stephenson (1861-62), George Parr (1863-64) and W.G. Grace (1873-74).

Play on the first day of Test cricket began at 1.05 pm on a warm and sunny Thursday (15 March 1877), with a 34-year-old Nottinghamshire professional bowling the first ball to a 25-year-old Kentish man playing his tenth first-class innings. Bannerman scored the first run off Shaw's second ball. Before lunch was taken from 2.00 until 2.40

pm, Nat Thompson had become the first Test batsman to lose his wicket and Allen Hill the first bowler to capture one. Hill also held the first Test match catch.

Bannerman reached **the only first-class hundred of his career** in 160 minutes and had scored 126 out of Australia's 166 for 6 when play ended at 5.00 pm. Resuming at 12.45 pm on Friday, he advanced to 159 at lunch (2.00 pm). Soon afterwards a rising ball from Ulyett coincided with a damaged part of his right batting glove and badly split his second finger. Bannerman thus added the first 'retired hurt' to all his other unique achievements. He had offered no chance during his 4 hours 45 minutes at the crease and had hit 15 fours. Perhaps most notably he had scored his 165 runs out of a total of 240 for 7. His score represented 67 per cent of his side's eventual total and remains the **highest individual contribution to any Test innings.** No other Australian exceeded 20.

Shaw's match figures appear remarkable (89.3 overs, 50 maidens, 89 runs, 8 wickets), but it must be remembered that the over consisted of four balls. It is this analysis which lends most weight to Sir Donald Bradman's opinion 'that any reference to maiden overs has long since become anachronistic and serves no useful purpose'.

England, needing only 154 for victory when Australia's second innings had folded after Bannerman's early dismissal, fell to the left-arm slow bowling of Tom Kendall. **Australia won by 45 runs** on the Monday afternoon, 19 March 1877, a crowd of 3000 watching the final stages of their first victory against England in an eleven-a-side match.

One hundred years later this result and the victory margin were repeated exactly, and on the same ground.

Six of the team were from Sydney clubs, including the youngest player in the match, Tom Garrett, a right-arm medium-fast bowler and aggressive batsman. He was 18 years 232 days old when Test cricket began and remained its youngest participant for nearly 53 years, until Derek Sealy (17 years 122 days) was introduced into the West Indies team. Garrett outlived every other player in this match by more than ten years.

Billy Midwinter subsequently played four times

THE SCORES

AUSTRALIA v ENGLAND 1876-77 (1st Test)

Played at Melbourne Cricket Ground on 15, 16, 17, 19 March.
Toss: Australia.   Result: AUSTRALIA won by 45 runs.
Debuts: All.

Close of play scores: 1st day—Australia 166 for 6 (Bannerman 126*, Blackham 3*); 2nd day—
England 109 for 4 (Jupp 54*); 3rd day—Australia 83 for 9 (Kendall 5*, Hodges 3*).

AUSTRALIA

C. Bannerman	retired hurt	165	b Ulyett	4
N. Thompson	b Hill	1	c Emmett b Shaw	7
T.P. Horan	c Hill b Shaw	12	c Selby b Hill	20
D.W. Gregory*	run out	1	(9) b Shaw	3
B.B. Cooper	b Southerton	15	b Shaw	3
W.E. Midwinter	c Ulyett b Southerton	5	c Southerton b Ulyett	17
E.J. Gregory	c Greenwood b Lillywhite	0	c Emmett b Ulyett	11
J.M. Blackham†	b Southerton	17	lbw b Shaw	6
T.W. Garrett	not out	18	(4) c Emmett b Shaw	0
T. Kendall	c Southerton b Shaw	3	not out	17
J.H. Hodges	b Shaw	0	b Lillywhite	8
Extras	(B 4, LB 2, W 2)	8	(B 5, LB 3)	8
Total		**245**		**104**

ENGLAND

H. Jupp	lbw b Garrett	63	(3) lbw b Midwinter	4
J. Selby†	c Cooper b Hodges	7	(5) c Horan b Hodges	38
H.R.J. Charlwood	c Blackham b Midwinter	36	(4) b Kendall	13
G. Ulyett	lbw b Thompson	10	(6) b Kendall	24
A. Greenwood	c E.J. Gregory b Midwinter	1	(2) c Midwinter b Kendall	5
T. Armitage	c Blackham b Midwinter	9	(8) c Blackham b Kendall	3
A. Shaw	b Midwinter	10	st Blackham b Kendall	2
T. Emmett	b Midwinter	8	(9) b Kendall	9
A. Hill	not out	35	(1) c Thompson b Kendall	0
James Lillywhite*	c and b Kendall	10	b Hodges	4
J. Southerton	c Cooper b Garrett	6	not out	1
Extras	(LB 1)	1	(B 4, LB 1)	5
Total		**196**		**108**

ENGLAND	O	M	R	W	O	M	R	W
Shaw	55.3	34	51	3	34	16	38	5
Hill	23	10	42	1	14	6	18	1
Ulyett	25	12	36	0	19	7	39	3
Southerton	37	17	61	3				
Armitage	3	0	15	0				
Lillywhite	14	5	19	1	1	0	1	1
Emmett	12	7	13	0				
AUSTRALIA								
Hodges	9	0	27	1	7	5	7	2
Garrett	18.1	10	22	2	2	0	9	0
Kendall	38	16	54	1	33.1	12	55	7
Midwinter	54	23	78	5	19	7	23	1
Thompson	17	10	14	1				
D.W. Gregory					5	1	9	0

FALL OF WICKETS

Wkt	A 1st	E 1st	A 2nd	E 2nd
1st	2	23	7	0
2nd	40	79	27	7
3rd	41	98	31	20
4th	118	109	31	22
5th	142	121	35	62
6th	143	135	58	68
7th	197	145	71	92
8th	243	145	75	93
9th	245	168	75	100
10th	–	196	104	108

Umpires: C.A. Reid and R.B. Terry.

THE FIRST TEST CRICKETERS

AUSTRALIA

	Born	Died
Bannerman, Charles (New South Wales)	Woolwich, England 23 July 1851	Surry Hills, Sydney 20 August 1930
Blackham, John McCarthy (Victoria)	North Fitzroy, Melbourne 11 May 1854	Melbourne 28 December 1932
Cooper, Bransby Beauchamp (Victoria)	India 15 March 1844	Geelong, Victoria 7 August 1914
Garrett, Thomas William (New South Wales)	Wollongong, NSW 26 July 1858	Warrawee, Sydney 6 August 1943
Gregory, David William (New South Wales)	Fairy Meadow, NSW 15 April 1845	Turramurra, Sydney 4 August 1919
Gregory, Edward James (New South Wales)	Waverley, Sydney 29 May 1839	SCG, Sydney 22 April 1899
Hodges, John Henry (Victoria)	Collingwood, Victoria 31 July 1856	Collingwood, Victoria 17 January 1933
Horan, Thomas Patrick (Victoria)	Midleton, Ireland 8 March 1854	Malvern, Melbourne 16 April 1916
Kendall, Thomas (Victoria)	Bedford, England 24 August 1851	Hobart, Tasmania 17 August 1924
Midwinter, William Evans (Victoria)	St Briavels, Glos., England 19 June 1851	Kew, Melbourne 3 December 1890
Thompson, Nathaniel (New South Wales)	Birmingham, England 21 April 1838	Burwood, Sydney 2 September 1896

ENGLAND

	Born	Died
Armitage, Thomas (Yorkshire)	Walkley, Sheffield, Yorkshire 25 April 1848	Pullman, Chicago, USA 21 September 1922
Charlwood, Henry Rupert James (Sussex)	Horsam, Sussex 19 December 1846	Scarborough, Yorkshire 6 June 1888
Emmett, Thomas (Yorkshire)	Halifax, Yorkshire 3 September 1841	Leicester 29 June 1904
Greenwood, Andrew (Yorkshire)	Cowmes Lepton, Yorkshire 20 August 1847	Huddersfield, Yorkshire 12 February 1889
Hill, Allen (Yorkshire)	Kirkheaton, Yorkshire 14 November 1843	Leyland, Lancashire 29 August 1910
Jupp, Henry (Surrey)	Dorking, Surrey 19 November 1841	Bermondsey, London 8 April 1889
Lillywhite, James, Jr (Sussex)	Westhampnett, Sussex 23 February 1842	Westerton, Sussex 25 October 1929
Selby, John (Nottinghamshire)	Nottingham 1 July 1849	Nottingham 11 March 1894
Shaw, Alfred (Nottinghamshire)	Burton Joyce, Nottinghamshire 29 August 1842	Gedling, Nottinghamshire 16 January 1907
Southerton, James (Surrey)	Petworth, Sussex 16 November 1827	Mitcham, Surrey 16 June 1880
Ulyett, George (Yorkshire)	Pitsmoor, Sheffield, Yorkshire 21 October 1851	Pitsmoor, Yorkshire 18 June 1898

Jack Blackham who kept wicket for Australia in the first 17 Test matches. (Mary Evans Picture Library)

James Southerton, the first Test cricketer to die. (Illustrated London News)

for England before resuming his career for Australia. He is the only cricketer to have played both for and against Australia.

All but Southerton were currently professionals for the counties of their birth. At 49 years 119 days, James Southerton remains **the oldest man ever to begin a Test career.**

A round-arm bowler of off-breaks who spun the ball considerably, he was also **the first Test cricketer to die** (16 June 1880).

Team records

The highest innings total in all Test cricket

is 903 for 7 wickets declared by England against Australia on 20, 22 and 23 August 1938. Compiled on an over-prepared and lifeless Kennington Oval pitch in a timeless Test, it lasted 15 hours 17 minutes until tea on the third day. Len Hutton (364 in 13 hours 17 minutes), Maurice Leyland (187 in 6 hours 21 minutes in his final Test), and Joe Hardstaff (169 not out in 5 hours 26 minutes) were the main contributors.

The highest second innings total in Test cricket, the highest total by a side following-on, and the longest innings in all first-class cricket (16 hours 53 minutes) is Pakistan's 657 for 8 wickets declared against West Indies at

HIGHEST INNINGS TOTALS

		Opponents	Venue	Series
England	903-7d	Australia	Oval	1938
West Indies	790-3d	Pakistan	Kingston	1957-58
Australia	758-8d	West Indies	Kingston	1954-55
Pakistan	674-6	India	Faisalabad	1984-85
India	644-7d	West Indies	Kanpur	1978-79
South Africa	622-9d	Australia	Durban	1969-70
New Zealand	553-7d	Australia	Brisbane	1985-86
Sri Lanka	491-7d	England	Lord's	1984

Bridgetown on 20-23 January 1958 in the very first Test between those teams.

The only instance of both sides scoring 600 runs in an innings in 1051 Test matches to the end of the 1986 English season occurred at Manchester on 23-28 July 1964, England scoring 611 in reply to Australia's 656 for 8 declared.

There have been only eleven totals of over 400 runs in the fourth innings of Test matches. Two of those batting sides won (India at Port-of-Spain, Trinidad in 1975-76 and Australia at Leeds in 1948), four drew and the other five lost.

The highest aggregate of runs in a Test match is 1981 by South Africa (530 and 481) and England (316 and 654 for 5) in a timeless Test at Kingsmead, Durban in March 1939. The match began when the author was 3½ hours old and ended when rain stopped play with England only 42 runs away from victory some eleven days later when the touring side had to begin their two-day train journey to rejoin their ship, the *Athlone Castle,* at Cape Town. It remains **the longest first-class match** ever staged with play taking place on nine days (March 3,4,6,7,8,9,10,13 and 14 – rain prevented play on 11 March). Time actually played amounted to 43 hours 16 minutes.

The longest match in England in terms of hours played is the drawn six-day Fourth Test between England and Australia at The Oval in 1975. Actual playing time, excluding 187 minutes lost and breaks between innings, totalled 32 hours 17 minutes. Two other six-day matches have been staged in England, both Test matches against Australia at The Oval. In 1930 Australia won at 3.50 pm on the last day after rain had prevented play on the penultimate one. Forty-two years later Australia repeated their victory at 2.49 pm on the sixth day.

The highest match aggregate by one side is 1121 by England who scored 849 and 272 for 9

declared against West Indies at Sabina Park, Kingston, Jamaica in April 1930.

The lowest innings total in Test cricket is 26 by New Zealand at Eden Park, Auckland, on 28 March 1955. Playing the second of two Tests against Hutton's England team which had just retained the Ashes in Australia, New Zealand had contained the tourists to a first innings lead of 46. A crowd of 14 000 saw the home side reduced to 14 for 5 and eventually dismissed in 27 overs by Tyson (2 for 10), Statham (3 for 9), Appleyard (4 for 7) and Wardle (1 for 0). Opening batsman Bert Sutcliffe (11) achieved the only double-figure score of an innings which lasted 106 minutes either side of the tea interval on the third day. Appleyard took three wickets in four balls and narrowly missed the hat-trick. It was Hutton's last Test.

LOWEST INNINGS TOTALS

		Opponents	Venue	Series
New Zealand	26	England	Auckland	1954-55
South Africa	30	England	Port Elizabeth	1895-96
	30	England	Birmingham	1924
Australia	36	England	Birmingham	1902
India	42	England	Lord's	1974
England	45	Australia	Sydney	1886-87
Pakistan	62	Australia	Perth	1981-82
West Indies	76	Pakistan	Dacca	1958-59
Sri Lanka	93	N. Zealand	Wellington	1982-83

The lowest declared total is 32 for 7 wickets by Australia against England at Woolloongabba, Brisbane, on 4 December 1950. Caught on a 'sticky' wicket, Australia declared their innings when only 192 runs ahead, took six England second innings wickets for 30 runs before the close, and went on to win by 70 runs.

The shortest completed Test innings in terms of time was recorded by South Africa either at St

HIGHEST FOURTH INNINGS TOTALS

To Win	406-4	India v West Indies	Port-of-Spain	1975-76
To Draw	654-5	England v South Africa	Durban	1938-39
To Lose	445	India v Australia	Adelaide	1977-78

George's Park in Port Elizabeth on 14 February 1896, or at Edgbaston, Birmingham, on 16 June 1924. On both occasions they were routed by England for totals of 30. Unfortunately, as contemporary match accounts loosely describe the length of both innings as being 'three-quarters of an hour', it is not possible to determine which instance was the shorter. Although the scorebook containing the 1924 match has survived to reveal that Arthur Gilligan (6 for 7) and Maurice Tate (4 for 12) in fact took 48 minutes to complete their destruction, no such record exists from which to measure the 1896 debacle exactly.

The shortest completed Test match was that played between Australia and South Africa on a vicious Melbourne 'sticky' on 12 and 15 February 1932. The total playing time in this Fifth Test amounted to 5 hours 53 minutes.

The shortest completed Test match in England was the Third of the 1888 series against Australia at Old Trafford, Manchester, on 30-31 August. The match ended before lunch, at 1.52 pm, on the second day, the total playing time being 6 hours 34 minutes. Australia's second innings of 70 lasted only 69 minutes and remains their shortest in all Test cricket.

The lowest aggregate of runs scored in a completed Test match is 234 by Australia (153) and South Africa (36 and 45) at Melbourne on 12 and 15 February 1932. South Africa's aggregate of 81 remains the lowest by any side losing all 20 wickets in a Test.

The greatest margin of victory in Test cricket was achieved by England at the Oval on 24 August 1938 when they defeated Australia by an innings and 579 runs on the fourth day. After amassing the record total of 903 for 7 in 15 hours 17 minutes before Hammond declared at tea on the third day, England dismissed Australia twice in 4¾ hours of play. With Fingleton and Bradman both injured and unable to bat, Australia scored 201 and 123.

The record margin of victory by runs alone was also achieved by England against Australia. On 5 December 1928 they won the first Test staged in Brisbane (and their only encounter at the Exhibition Ground) by 675 runs on the fifth day. After scoring 521, they bowled out Australia for 122, scored 342 for 8 before Chapman made **the first declaration in a Test in Australia,** and finally routed the home side for 66. After bowling 41 overs in the first innings, Jack Gregory damaged his knee so severely that he was unable to bat and never played cricket again.

The only Test match to result in a tie was played between Australia and West Indies at Woolongabba, Brisbane, and ended on 14 December 1960. Australia, requiring 233 runs to win in 310 minutes, lost their last wicket to a run out off the seventh ball of the final over. After much confusion the scores were found to be level.

Six Test matches have been won by a single wicket, one of them – between Australia and England at Melbourne in January 1908 – almost resulting in a tie. This was the first of 61 Test match appearances by Jack Hobbs who scored 83 and 28. When England's ninth wicket fell, 39 runs were still needed for victory. Sydney Barnes and Arthur Fielder, 'to the astonishment of everyone concerned' (*Wisden*), levelled the scores before risking a desperately quick run from a push to cover point. Gerry Hazlitt threw wildly at the stumps, missed, and delayed the first tie in Test cricket by almost 53 years. That was the second-highest tenth-wicket partnership to win a Test match; the highest is 48 by Dave Nourse, who scored 93 not out batting at Number 8, and Percy Sherwell (22 not out), for South Africa against England at the Old Wanderers ground, Johannesburg, on 4 January 1906. It was South Africa's first victory. Sherwell, their captain and wicket-keeper, was playing in his first Test match.

Only one of the 1051 Test matches played up to the end of the 1986 season has been won off the last possible ball. At Kingsmead in Durban on 20 December 1948, England's ninth-wicket pair, Alec Bedser and Cliff Gladwin, needed eight runs from the final eight-ball over from Lindsay Tuckett. Before Bedser brought the scores level off the sixth ball, all four results were possible. Gladwin missed the seventh ball. He also missed the last ball. It bounced off his thigh and the batsmen managed to scamper a leg bye.

VICTORIES BY ONE WICKET

Victor	Opponents	Venue	Tenth Wicket Partnership	Series
England	Australia	The Oval	15*	1902
South Africa	England	Johannesburg	48*	1905-06
England	Australia	Melbourne	39*	1907-08
England	South Africa	Cape Town	5*	1922-23
Australia	West Indies	Melbourne	38*	1951-52
New Zealand	West Indies	Dunedin	4*	1979-80

The narrowest victory by a team fielding last was achieved by Australia when they beat England by just three runs at Old Trafford, Manchester, on 26 July 1902. England required 124 runs to win on a rain-affected wicket with showers threatening and occasionally interrupting play. They seemed certain of victory when only 32 runs were wanted with six wickets in hand, but fine bowling by Hugh Trumble and Jack Saunders, supported by superb fielding, captured five wickets for 24 runs. Heavy rain then caused a delay of 45 minutes before England's last man, Fred Tate, faced Saunders with eight runs needed to win. After scoring a legside boundary off his first ball, Tate was beaten and bowled by the fourth.

Eighty year later, on 30 December 1982, England avenged that defeat by winning the Fourth Test against Australia at Melbourne by an identical margin. During their last-wicket partnership of 70 in 128 minutes, Allan Border (62*) and Jeff Thomson (21) declined to run 29 comfortable singles offered to Border. This remains the only Test in which all 40 wickets have fallen where the four innings totals have ranged within ten runs: England 284 and 294; Australia 287 and 288.

England have provided **the only two instances of a team winning a Test match after being forced to follow on.** At Sydney in December 1894, England followed on 261 runs behind on first innings, scored 437 and dismissed Australia for

England celebrate their 3-run victory at Melbourne on 30 December 1982. (Adrian Murrell/All-Sport)

166 to win by ten runs. It was **the first Test to go into a sixth day.** In July 1981 at Headingley, Leeds, England were 135 for 7, after following on 227 runs behind on first innings when Ian Botham was joined by Graham Dilley. They scored 117 in 80 minutes before Dilley was bowled for 56. Botham (149 not out) then added another 114 runs with the aid of Chris Old (29) and Bob Willis (2). On the fifth and final day, Australia needing 130 runs to win, reached 56 for 1 before Willis (8 for 43) achieved the best analysis in a Test at Headingley and bowled England to victory by 18 runs against bookmakers' odds of 500-1.

The most runs scored in a single day of Test cricket is 588 by England (398) and India (190) on the second day (27 July) of the Manchester Test of 1936. That record aggregate was scored for the loss of six wickets at a rate of over 90 runs per hour in 6½ hours.

The highest number of runs by one team in a day is 503 scored by England on the second day of the Lord's Test against South Africa on 30 June 1924. When Arthur Gilligan declared the innings closed 66 minutes before stumps, Hobbs (whose 211 equalled the highest Test innings in England at that time), Sutcliffe, Woolley and Hendren had attained an average scoring rate of 93 runs per hour while losing only two wickets.

The fewest runs scored in a full day of Test cricket is 95. This bizarre record was established on the matting pitch of the National Stadium in Karachi on 11 October 1956, the first day of Test cricket between Pakistan and Australia. After a strenuous and unsuccessful tour of England's grass pitches, Australia's batsmen had been allowed no preliminary match practice in the different conditions. Shortly after tea they were all out for 80, the lowest total in Karachi Tests. It was compiled from 53.1 overs bowled by Fazal Mahmood (6 for 34) and Khan Mohammad (4 for 43). This remains **the only post-war instance of two bowlers operating unchanged throughout a completed Test innings.** By the close Pakistan had reached 15 for 2.

The least number of runs scored in a full day of Test cricket in England is 151 at Lord's on Saturday, 26 August 1978. England, resuming at 175 for 2, added 67 for 2 by lunch and were all out for 289 at 4.21 pm when tea was taken. At the 6.30 pm close, New Zealand had reached 37 for 7 off 25 overs. A total of 82.3 overs was bowled during this third day.

The highest number of wickets to fall in a day of Test cricket is 27 on 17 July 1888. The wicket of W.G. Grace, the champion cricketer of the day – some would argue of all time – featured twice in that incredible tally. The record was set on a farcically difficult mud pitch at Lord's on the second day of the First Test against Australia. At the start of play, England were 18 for 3 in reply to Australia's 116 all out. In under an hour they had lost their remaining seven wickets for 35 runs. Australia, at one stage 18 for 7, totalled 60 and set England 124 runs to win. By 4.25 pm they had bowled out England for 62 and were being heartily cheered by thousands of spectators massed in front of the pavilion. Grace, the only England batsman to reach double figures in both innings, recorded the highest score of the match: 24. In just over three hours of actual play, 27 wickets had fallen for 157 runs.

Six weeks later those two teams set the record for losing **the most wickets before lunch in a Test match.** At Old Trafford, Manchester, on 31 August 1888, 18 wickets fell before lunch. Hot sun on a soft, wet pitch made batting conditions impossible. Australia, resuming at 32 for 2 in reply to England's 172, were all out for 81, followed on, and recovered from losing their first six wickets for seven runs to total 70. The match was completed at 1.55 pm (before lunch on the second day) and remains **the shortest Test match in which there was a result.**

The only Test team to be dismissed twice in a day is India. At Old Trafford, Manchester, on 19 July 1952, they were bowled out by England for 58 and 82 in a total batting time of 3¾ hours, 22 wickets falling in the day.

Only eight uninterrupted days of Test cricket have failed to produce the fall of a wicket; five of them have occurred in the West Indies, one in Australia, one in India, one in Sri Lanka and none in England.

The only pair of batsmen to bat throughout

Arjuna Ranatunga and Asanka Gurusinha – the first Sri Lankans to bat throughout a day of Test cricket.
(Ceylon Daily News/Sa'adi Thawfeeq)

two consecutive days of Test cricket are Gary Sobers (226) and Frank Worrell (197 not out) on 9 and 11 January 1960, the fourth and fifth days of the First Test between West Indies and England at Kensington Oval in Bridgetown, Barbados. The final hour of the fourth day was lost to rain and a rest day intervened. Their fourth-wicket partnership of 399 occupied 9 hours 39 minutes – **the longest stand in Test cricket.**

The only Test match in which batsmen averaged over 100 runs per wicket lost took place at Delhi in December 1955. In five days New Zealand (450 for 2d and 112 for 1) and India (531 for 7d) amassed 1093 runs for the loss of only ten wickets.

The most hundreds scored in a Test innings

is five by Australia against West Indies at Kingston, Jamaica in June 1955. In reply to a total of 357, Australia compiled their highest total of 758 for 8 declared, with centuries from Colin McDonald (127), Neil Harvey (204), Keith Miller (109), Ron Archer (128) and Richie Benaud (121). Benaud reached his humdred in 78 minutes – the third-fastest in Tests.

The record number of fifties in a Test innings is seven by England (627 for 9d) against Australia at Manchester, in July 1934.

No country has won every Test in a six-match series, although Australia beat West Indies 5-1 in Australia in 1975-76 and were themselves beaten by England by a similar margin in 1978-79.

There have been six instances of teams win-

BATTING PARTNERSHIPS THAT HAVE SURVIVED A FULL DAY'S PLAY

Batsmen	Match	Day	Venue	Series
J.B. Hobbs, H. Sutcliffe	E v A	3rd	Melbourne	1924-25
D. St E. Atkinson, C.C. Depeiza	WIv A	4th	Bridgetown	1954-55
M.H. ('Vinoo') Mankad, Pankaj Roy	Iv NZ	1st	Madras	1955-56
C.C. Hunte, G. St A. Sobers	WIv P	3rd	Kingston	1957-58
G. St A. Sobers, F.M.M. Worrell	WIv E	5th	Bridgetown	1959-60
W.M. Lawry, R.B. Simpson	Av WI	1st	Bridgetown	1964-65
G.R. Viswanath, Yashpal Sharma	Iv E	2nd	Madras	1981-82
A.P. Gurusinha, A. Ranatunga	SLv P	5th	Colombo (SO)	1985-86

ning every Test in a five-match series, West Indies in England in 1984 being the only team to achieve this feat abroad: Australia beat England in 1920-21 and South Africa in 1931-32; England defeated India in 1959; West Indies beat India in 1961-62, and demolished England in successive series in 1984 and 1985-86.

West Indies hold the record for winning most consecutive Tests – they gained eleven successive victories between 4 April and 11 December 1984: three against Australia at home, five in England and another three in Australia.

The most successive victories against the same opponent is ten by West Indies against England in 1984 and 1985-86.

West Indies enjoyed a run of 27 matches without a defeat between January 1982 and December 1984. England were unbeaten in 26 matches between June 1968 and August 1971. At the other end of the scale, New Zealand failed to win any of their first 44 matches. Their first victory came on 13 March 1956 when they beat West Indies at Auckland by 190 runs – 26 years after starting their first Test match, against England at Christchurch on 10 January 1930.

Surprisingly, in view of their reputation for playing positive cricket, **West Indies drew a record ten successive Tests** between 1970-1 and 1972-73.

The most players to appear for one team during a single rubber is 30 for England in the 1921 five-match series. Whitewashed in the five Tests in Australia the previous winter, England lost the first three matches before drawing the last two. South Africa employed 20 players when they lost all three matches of their 1895-96 rubber against England.

Only twice has a **team remained unchanged**

The unchanged 1905 South Africans. BACK: J. Phillips *umpire*, A.W. Nourse, J.M. Reid *manager*, A.E.E. Vogler, F. Hearne *umpire*. CENTRE: S.J. Snooke, R.O. Schwarz, C.M.H. Hathorn, P.W. Sherwell *captain*, J.H. Sinclair, L.J. Tancred. FRONT: W.A. Shalders, G.C. White, G.A. Faulkner. (MCC)

throughout a **five-match series,** England winning 3-2 in Australia in 1884-85 and South Africa beating England 4-1 at home in 1905-06.

On only two occasions has **an entire eleven bowled during a Test innings.** The first was at The Oval in August 1884 when Australia scored the then monumental total of 551 off 311 four-ball overs. Declarations were not permitted until 1889. The tenth bowler called upon by Lord Harris was England's wicket-keeper, the Hon Alfred Lyttelton. His first spell with Walter Read behind the stumps was unsuccessful and Australia ended the first day at 363 for 2, with three batsmen scoring centuries. Lyttelton's lobs were not reintroduced until the total reached 532 for 6. This time Grace kept wicket and he held a good legside catch off the first ball of this second spell. Lyttelton, still wearing his pads, took the last four wickets for only eight runs in eight overs to finsh with 4 for 19 – **the best analysis in Test cricket by a player who began the innings as wicket-keeper.**

The second instance occurred more than 95 years later on a perfect batting pitch at the Iqbal Stadium, Faisalabad in March 1980. Rain had washed out the first day and delayed the start of the second. By the time Australia's innings of 617 had ended, only 7 hours 15 minutes of play remained. Pakistan scored 382 for 2 in this time and only one of Greg Chappell's eleven bowlers, Geoff Dymock, took a wicket.

The most players to bowl in a Test match is 20, both South Africa and England calling upon ten in the drawn Third Test at Cape Town in January 1965.

There have been eight instances of all eleven batsmen reaching double figures in a Test innings. England, at Melbourne in January 1895, were the first to do so, whilst India, against New Zealand at Kanpur in November 1976, provided the most recent instance. In the latter case, India's innings of 524 for 9d was **the highest total in Test cricket in which no batsman scored a century.**

Although there have been 15 totals of under 50 in Test matches, **only one completed innings has failed to produce a double figure score.** When South Africa were bowled out for 30 at Edgbaston, Birmingham, on 16 June 1924, their highest scorer was Herbie Taylor, their captain and opening batsman, who made seven. The main contribution came from eleven extras as Arthur Gilligan (6 for 7) and Maurice Tate (4 for 12) bowled unchanged. The Sussex pair took just 48 minutes and only 75 balls to complete the devastation.

Batting records

The highest individual aggregate of runs in Test cricket is 9367 (average 50.63) by Sunil Gavaskar for India in 115 Tests (201 innings) between 6 March 1971 and 8 July 1986. He passed the previous record of 8114 runs, scored for England in 193 innings by Geoffrey Boycott, when he glanced a ball from Michael Holding of West Indies soon after tea on 13 November 1983 at Ahmedabad.

Gavaskar also holds the world Test records for **most matches** (115), **most innings** (201), **most hundreds** (32), **most innings of fifty and**

EXTRAS TOP-SCORING IN A COMPLETED INNINGS

	Total	Highest Score	Extras	Opponents	Venue	Series
South Africa	58	13	17	England	Lord's	1912
South Africa	30	7	11	England	Birmingham	1924
New Zealand	97	19	20	England	Nottingham	1973
England	126	24	25	West Indies	Manchester	1976
England	227	33	46	Pakistan	Lord's	1982
Australia	200	29	36	West Indies	St John's	1983-84
England	315	47	59	West Indies	Port-of-Spain	1985-86

The most recent instance established a record for **the highest total (315) in which no batsman had scored a fifty.**

Sunil Gavaskar – Test cricket's most prolific batsman.
(Author)

over (72), and has shared in **the most hundred partnerships** (52).

Only one batsman has scored more than 4000 runs against one country: Don Bradman amassed 5028 runs (average 89.78) in 37 Tests for Australia against England between November 1928 and August 1948. **The highest aggregate for England against another country** is 3636 runs (average 54.26) by Jack Hobbs in 41 Tests against Australia between January 1908 and August 1930.

The highest batting average in a Test career involving more than five innings is 99.94 by Bradman for Australia. In 52 Tests he scored 6996 from 80 innings, ten of them undefeated. He averaged a century every 2.8 innings. He needed to score just four runs in his final Test innings on Saturday, 14 August 1948, in the Fifth Test at The Oval, to become the second (after Hammond) to score 7000 runs and the first to attain a career average of 100. Given a standing ovation by the crowd throughout his progress to the middle, Bradman was then saluted by three cheers from the England team. Shortly before six o'clock he took guard and

safely negotiated the first ball, a leg-break from Eric Hollies. The next was pitched on a perfect length, a googly which spun past Bradman's forward defensive stroke and bowled him.

The first batsman to score 1000 runs in Test cricket was Arthur Shrewsbury of Nottinghamshire. He reached that landmark during the last of his three centuries for England, against Australia at Lord's on 17 July 1893.

Clem Hill, the Australian left-hander, was **the first to score both 2000 and 3000 runs in Tests.** He reached the 2000-mark against England on his home ground, the Adelaide Oval, on 15 January 1904. He completed his third thousand on the same ground almost exactly seven years later against South Africa.

Having exceeded Hill's final and record aggregate of 3412, Jack Hobbs went on to become **the first to reach both 4000** (at Lord's against Australia on 28 June 1926) **and 5000 runs** (on 14 March 1929 at Melbourne).

Wally Hammond continued this sequence by **taking the record beyond 6000** (against South Africa at Johannesburg on 24 December 1938) and, after an interval for Hitler, **past the 7000-mark** (on 19 August 1946 at The Oval against India).

Hammond's record of 7249 survived until 29 November 1970 when Cowdrey overtook it at Brisbane. Then, against England at Kingston, Jamaica, on 20 February 1974, Gary Sobers became **the first to score 8000 runs in Test cricket.**

The only batsman to score 9000 runs in Tests is Sunil Gavaskar. He achieved this feat during his innings of 166 not out against Australia at Adelaide on 17 December 1985.

1000 RUNS IN FEWEST INNINGS

Runs	Batsman	Team	Innings
1000	H. Sutcliffe	England	12
	E. de C. Weekes	West Indies	12
2000	D.G. Bradman	Australia	22
3000	D.G. Bradman	Australia	33
4000	D.G. Bradman	Australia	48
5000	D.G. Bradman	Australia	56
6000	D.G. Bradman	Australia	68
7000	W.R. Hammond	England	131
8000	G. St A. Sobers	West Indies	157
9000	S.M. Gavaskar	India	192

MOST RUNS IN A TEST MATCH

380	G.S. Chappell (247*, 133)	Australia v New Zealand	Wellington	1973-74
375	A. Sandham (325, 50)	England v West Indies	Kingston	1929-30
365	G. St A. Sobers (365*)	West Indies v Pakistan	Kingston	1957-58
364	L. Hutton (364)	England v Australia	The Oval	1938
354	Hanif Mohammad (17, 337)	Pakistan v West Indies	Bridgetown	1957-58

The highest aggregate of runs by a batsman in Test cricket during a calendar year is 1710 (average 90.00) by Viv Richards in eleven matches for West Indies in 1976. His 19 innings were: 44, 2, 30, 101, 50 and 98 in Australia; 142, 130, 20, 177, 23 and 64 v India in the West Indies; 232, 63, 4, 135, 66, 38 and 291 in England.

The record individual aggregate in one rubber or series is 974 (average 139.14) by Bradman in only seven innings during Australia's five-match series in England in 1930. His scores were: 8, 131, 254, 1, 334, 14, and 232. The only other batsman to exceed 900 runs in a series is Hammond who totalled 905 runs (average 113.12) for England in Australia in 1928-29. The record for a three-match series in 583 runs (average 194.33) by Zaheer Abbas in five innings for Pakistan in their home rubber against India in 1978-79.

The most runs by a batsman playing in his first Test series is 774 (average 154.80) by Sunil Gavaskar in four matches for India in the West Indies in 1971. His eight innings were: 65, 67 not out, 116, 64 not out, 1, 117 not out, 124 and 220. Surgery on a septic finger prevented his playing in the First Test.

The highest individual aggregate in a Test match is 380 runs by Greg Chappell, who scored 247 not out and 133 for Australia against New Zealand at Wellington on 1-6 March 1974.

The highest individual Test innings is 365 not out by Garfield Sobers for West Indies against Pakistan during the Third Test at Sabina Park, Kingston, Jamaica on 27 February to 1 March 1958. Sobers, aged 21 years 216 days and **the youngest to score a triple century in Test cricket,** batted 10 hours 14 minutes (3 hours 3 minutes less than Hutton, whose record he beat by one run) and hit 38 fours. It was his 29th innings and his 17th match for West Indies, his previous highest Test score being 80. His partnership of 446 with Conrad Hunte (260) for the second wicket remains the second-highest for any wicket in Test cricket, just five runs short of the world record. His innings ended when Gerry Alexander declared with the scoreboard

Gary Sobers – Test cricket's youngest triple century-maker.

How the record individual Test score has progressed since Charles Bannerman faced the first ball bowled in Test cricket, scored the first century and became the first batsman to retire hurt:

Score	Batsman	Minutes		Match	Series
165*	C. Bannerman	285	A v E	Melbourne	1876-77
211	W.L. Murdoch	485	A v E	The Oval	1884
287	R.E. Foster	419	E v A	Sydney	1903-04
325	A. Sandham	600	E v WI	Kingston	1929-30
334	D.G. Bradman	383	A v E	Leeds	1930
336*	W.R. Hammond	318	E v NZ	Auckland	1932-33
364	L. Hutton	797	E v A	The Oval	1938
365*	G. St A. Sobers	614	WI v P	Kingston	1957-58

BOY BATSMAN WHO MAKES NO MISTAKES: By M. D. LYON

DAILY SKETCH

INCORPORATING THE DAILY GRAPHIC

LAST DAY £1,200 PUZZLE

No. 6,626. | [Registered as a newspaper.] | SATURDAY, JULY 12, 1930. | ONE PENNY.

BRADMAN'S 100 BEFORE LUNCH—& A NEW RECORD

Another picture of the man who has been described as a run-making machine. Here he is hitting a ball from Leyland.—(Daily Sketch.)

Bradman signalling with his bat his acknowledgment of the roars of cheering that greeted his 200th run.—(Daily Sketch.)

The 200th run came from a ball from Dick Tyldesley. Bradman starting on the run.—(Daily Sketch.)

Chapman tosses his lucky coin—

—and finds Woodfull has called right.—(Daily Sketch.)

Don Bradman, who yesterday in the Test Match at Leeds beat R. E. Foster's Test Match record score of 287. Australia's boy batsman scored a century before lunch and at the close was 309 not out, the tourists' total being 458 for 3.—(Daily Sketch.)

The wonder batsman slips—but the ball was safely out of the way.—(Daily Sketch.)

Don Bradman's most productive day of Test cricket. (John Frost)

proudly exhibiting **the record West Indies total** of 790 for 3. Sobers was favoured by a small and extremely fast outfield and by a Pakistan attack reduced to just two uninjured specialist bowlers.

The most runs and only instance of over 300 in a day by one batsman is 309 by Bradman for Australia against England at Headingley, Leeds, on 11 July 1930. He scored 105 before lunch, 115 between lunch and tea, and 89 in the final session.

Bradman is alone in holding the record scores for two batting positions in Test matches.

Bradman's innings of 270 at number seven was an extraordinary performance by a player who was the established number three batsman and captaining his country for only the third time. Rain had produced a pitch on which 12 wickets fell in about three hours and, for the first time in Test cricket, each side had declared its first innings closed. The wicket was still a 'gluepot' when Australia had to begin their second innings but Bradman countered these conditions by sending his tailend batsmen in first. Australia were 97 for 5

when Bradman went to the wicket at 2.50 pm on the following day to join his opening batsman, Jack Fingleton, who had been saved until number six. By the time 'The Don' was out two days later at 1.02 pm, Australia were 549 for 9 and their lead 673. He had batted 7 hours 38 minutes, hit 22 fours, shared in what remains **the world record sixth-wicket partnership in Test cricket** of 346 with Fingleton, and recorded his highest innings against England in Australia. Throughout his innings Bradman was suffering from a severe chill. Two matches down in the series, Australia won this Test by 365 runs and went on to win the rubber 3-2.

The most runs added during one batsman's innings is 770 in 797 minutes by England against Australia at The Oval in August 1938 during Hutton's innings of 364. England eventually declared at 903 for 7.

The highest individual contribution to a completed Test match innings is 67 per cent by Charles Bannerman who on 15 and 16 March 1877 in the very first innings in Test cricket, scored

HIGHEST INNINGS FOR EACH TEAM

For			Opponents	Venue	Series
England	364	L. Hutton	Australia	The Oval	1938
Australia	334	D.G. Bradman	England	Leeds	1930
South Africa	274	R.G. Pollock	Australia	Durban	1969-70
West Indies	365*	G. St A. Sobers	Pakistan	Kingston	1957-58
New Zealand	259	G.M. Turner	West Indies	Georgetown	1971-72
India	236*	S.M. Gavaskar	West Indies	Madras	1983-84
Pakistan	337	Hanif Mohammad	West Indies	Bridgetown	1957-58
Sri Lanka	190	S. Wettimuny	England	Lord's	1984

HIGHEST INNINGS FOR EACH BATTING POSITION

No.	Score	Batsman	Match	Venue	Series
1	364	L. Hutton	E v A	The Oval	1938
2	325	A. Sandham	E v WI	Kingston	1929-30
3	365*	G. St A. Sobers	WI v P	Kingston	1957-58
4	307	R.M. Cowper	A v E	Melbourne	1965-66
5	304	D.G. Bradman	A v E	Leeds	1934
6	250	K.D. Walters	A v NZ	Christchurch	1976-77
7	270	D.G. Bradman	A v E	Melbourne	1936-37
8	209	Imtiaz Ahmed	P v NZ	Lahore	1955-56
9	160	C. Hill	A v E	Adelaide	1907-08
10	117	W.W. Read	E v A	The Oval	1884
11	68*	R.O. Collinge	NZ v P	Auckland	1972-73

165 out of Australia's total of 245. As eight of those runs were extras, Bannerman actually scored 69 per cent of the runs scored from the bat. Originally an Englishman, born in Woolwich 25 years earlier, he was playing his tenth first-class innings and seventh match. Having reached his only first-class hundred in 160 minutes, he was forced to retire hurt when a rising ball from George Ulyett split the second finger of his right hand through a damaged glove. He had batted chancelessly for 285 minutes, struck 15 fours, and established what is still **the highest score by an Australian in his first Test against England.**

The only batsman to contribute over half his team's completed innings totals in a Test match is Jimmy Sinclair of South Africa. Playing against England at Newlands, Cape Town in April 1899, he scored 106 and 4 as South Africa were dismissed for 177 and 35-51 per cent of his side's match aggregate. Massively-built, and a prodigious hitter who once struck a ball from Wilfred Rhodes so violently that it separated a cabby parked outside the Harrogate ground from his cab, Sinclair followed his century by taking six wickets in the first innings and three in the second. He was responsible for his county's first fifty (in the previous match) and first hundred, and was **the first player to score a century and take six wickets in an innings of the same Test.**

The longest individual innings in all first-class cricket lasted 970 minutes (16 hours 10 minutes) and was compiled by Hanif Mohammad for Pakistan against West Indies at Bridgetown, Barbados, on 20, 21, 22, 23 January 1958. Opening the innings an hour before tea on the third day, as Pakistan followed on 473 runs behind with three and a half days play left, Hanif had scored 61 out of

Hanif Mohammad – little master of the 16-hour innings. (Sport & General)

LONGEST INNINGS FOR EACH TEAM

	Minutes	Batsman (score)	Opponents	Venue	Series
England	797	L. Hutton (364)	Australia	The Oval	1938
Australia	762	R.B. Simpson (311)	England	Manchester	1964
South Africa	575	D.J. McGlew (105)	Australia	Durban	1957-58
West Indies	682	F.M.M. Worrell (197*)	England	Bridgetown	1959-60
New Zealand	704	G.M. Turner (259)	West Indies	Georgetown	1971-72
India	708	S.M. Gavaskar (172)	England	Bangalore	1981-82
Pakistan	970	Hanif Mohammad (337)	West Indies	Bridgetown	1957-58
Sri Lanka	636	S. Wettimuny (190)	England	Lord's	1984

161 for 1 at stumps. At the close of the fourth five-hour day he had made 161 out of 339 for 2, and he had progressed to 270 out of 525 for 3 by the end of the fifth. At tea on the sixth and final day he was 334 not out and just 30 runs short of the world record then held by Len Hutton (Sobers was to beat it two Tests later). Soon after the interval, Hanif tried to steer a single wide of slip to keep the strike and edged an outswinger from Denis Atkinson and was caught behind the wicket. He had scored 337 out of 626 for 6 when he was dismissed, 32 of that total being extras. The pitch was described by Hanif as a 'batsman's paradise' but by the last day it had begun to break up, causing the ball to keep very low and to turn sharply for the spinners. Pakistan's eventual total of 657 for 8 declared remains their highest and it is also **the record second innings total in all Test cricket – and the highest by any side after being asked to follow on.**

The most hundreds scored by one batsman in Test cricket is 32 in 201 innings by Sunil Gavaskar during 115 matches for India between 1971 and 1986.

MOST HUNDREDS FOR EACH TEAM

	100s	Batsman (innings)
England	22	W.R. Hammond (140), M.C. Cowdrey (188), G. Boycott (193)
Australia	29	D.G. Bradman (80)
South Africa	9	A.D. Nourse (62)
West Indies	26	G. St A. Sobers (160)
New Zealand	7	G.M. Turner (70), B.E. Congdon (114)
India	32	S.M. Gavaskar (201)
Pakistan	14	Javed Miandad (115)
Sri Lanka	4	L.R.D. Mendis (35)

The most hundreds in one series is five by Clyde Walcott for West Indies during their five-match home series against Australia between March and June 1955. He scored 108, 39, 126, 110, 8, 73, 15, 83, 155 and 110 to total 827 runs, average 82.70.

Another of the 'Three Ws', Everton Weekes, holds the Test record for scoring **most hundreds in consecutive innings** with five between March 1948 and January 1949. Starting his sequence with 141 against England at Kingston, Jamaica, he had to wait until November and the West Indies tour of

India for his next innings – 128 at Delhi, one of four centuries in a total of 631. Weekes followed this with 194 at Bombay, 162 and 101 at Calcutta, and 90 (run out from a magnificent piece of fielding by Nirode Chowdhury at point in the first of only two Test appearances) at Madras.

The first batsman to score a hundred in each innings of a Test match was Warren Bardsley when he scored 136 and 130 for Australia at The Oval in August 1909.

The record for scoring a hundred in each innings of a Test on most occasions is held by Sunil Gavaskar who has achieved this feat three times:

Scores		Opponents	Venue	Series
124	220	West Indies	Port-of-Spain	1970-71
111	137	Pakistan	Karachi	1978-79
107	182*	West Indies	Calcutta	1978-79

Lawrence Rowe of Jamaica is **the only batsman to score centuries in both innings of his first Test match.** Playing for West Indies against New Zealand on his home ground at Sabina Park, Kingston, in February 1972, the 23-year-old right-hander scored 214 and 100 not out. **His aggregate of 314 is a record for any player in his first Test.** The only other batsman to exceed 300 on debut is R.E. 'Tip' Foster who scored 287 and 19 for England against Australia at Sydney in December 1903.

The only batsman to score separate hundreds on successive days of a Test match is Vijay Hazare of India. Playing against Australia at Adelaide in 1948, he scored 108 of his first innings 116 on 26 January and 102 of his second innings 145 on 27 January.

Geoffrey Boycott achieved **the only instance in Test cricket of a batsman scoring 99 and a century.** In the Fifth Test between England and West Indies, played at Port-of-Spain, Trinidad, from 30 March to 5 April 1974, he scored 112 after being brilliantly caught off a leg glance in the first innings when the wicket-keeper, Deryck Murray, threw himself far to his left.

Bradman, who holds the record for **the most double centuries in a rubber** (three against England in 1930), is **the only batsman to score**

hundreds in six successive Test matches. In terms of matches in which he actually batted, the sequence extended to eight. Commencing against England in January 1937, he scored 270 at Melbourne, 212 at Adelaide, and 169 at Melbourne – the last three Tests of a series that attracted 943 000 spectators, **an attendance aggregate that is still the largest for any rubber.** Continuing in England in 1938, Bradman scored 144 not out at Nottingham, 102 not out at Lord's, 130 at Leeds, but was unable to bat at The Oval after severely injuring his ankle while bowling during England's record innings of 903-7 declared. Resuming his war-interrupted career eight years later in November 1946, the world's greatest run machine proved his appetite for large scores to be as rapacious as ever with innings of 187 at Brisbane and 234 at Sydney. In the Third Test at Melbourne Bradman failed at last, scoring a mere 79 and 49, dismissed by Norman Yardley on both occasions during the first drawn Test in Australia since March 1882.

The only batsman to score hundreds in each of his first three Tests is Mohammed Azharuddin for India against England in 1984-85. After celebrating his debut with 110 in the Third Test at Calcutta, he scored 48 and 105 at Madras followed by 122 and 54 not out at Kanpur.

The youngest player to score a hundred and the only one to score two centuries before his nineteenth birthday (allowing for the fact that it is impossible to confirm the ages claimed by Pakistani cricketers), is Mushtaq Mohammad. The third of the Mohammad brethren to represent Pakistan was 17 years 82 days old when he scored 101 against India at Delhi on 12 February 1961. **The youngest to score a century for England** is Denis Compton; playing against Australia for the first time, he was 20 years 19 days old when he completed his innings of 102 at Nottingham on 11 June 1938.

Jack Hobbs, **the oldest man to score a hundred at Test level,** was 46 years 82 days old when he scored 142 on 8 March 1929 at Melbourne in his last Test in Australia.

The youngest to score a double century is Javed Miandad; he was 19 years 141 days old (unconfirmed) when he completed his innings of 206 for Pakistan against New Zealand at Karachi on 31 October 1976.

Gary Sobers was only 21 years 216 days old when he reached 300 during his world record 365 not out for West Indies against Pakistan at Kingston, Jamaica, on 1 March 1958, and established himself as **the youngest triple century-maker in Test cricket.** It was his first three-figure score for West Indies.

The first player to be dismissed for 99 in a Test was Clem Hill of Australia. Having been out at that score on 2 January 1902, he was out for 98 and 97 in the next match at Adelaide, and so became **the only player to be dismissed for three successive nineties in Tests.**

The fastest hundred in Test cricket was scored in 70 minutes by Jack Gregory for Australia against South Africa in Johannesburg on 12 November 1921. A right-arm fast bowler and spectacular left-handed batsman, Gregory was at his peak immediately after World War I. His introduction to Test cricket coincided with Australia gaining a record eight successive victories against England, Gregory's contribution being 40 wickets, 512 runs and 22 catches. In the 1921 rubber, his fearsome opening partnership with Ted McDonald had accounted for 46 wickets. Normally a late or middle-order batsman who seldom wore batting gloves, Gregory had opened the batting and scored 51 in the first Test of this three-match rubber played by Armstrong's team on their way home from England. He batted number four in this Second Test, joining Herbie Collins, his new captain, with the Old Wanderers scoreboard showing a total of 128 for 2. He reached his half-century in 35 minutes and maintained exactly the same rate for his second fifty. Surviving three dropped catches, he was eventually stumped off the slow left-arm bowling of Claude Carter for 119 — the higher of his two Test hundreds. The third-wicket partnership had added 209 runs in only 97 minutes. Although forced to follow on 207 runs in arrears, South Africa were able to draw the four-day match when Charlie Frank, in the middle of a three-match Test career, thwarted the efforts of Gregory, McDonald, Mailey and Hendry for 8 hours 38 minutes in an epic innings of 152.

The fastest recorded hundred in terms of balls received was scored off 56 balls (81 minutes) by Viv Richards on 15 April 1986. Captaining West Indies against England at St John's in his native Antigua, Richards reached his fifty off 33 balls in 46 minutes and declared after scoring 110 not out off 58 balls. His 20th Test hundred included 41 scoring strokes, 18 of them singles: 003612614102110 (28 at tea) 41201112021 11000101624441120066461200210 4. This sensational display of controlled hitting enabled Richards to declare at 246 for 2, with a lead of 410 and with seven hours in which to dismiss England. West Indies duly concluded their task with 13.5 overs to spare, their 240-run victory completing their second consecutive series 'blackwash'.

The fastest hundred by an England batsman in Tests in terms of both minutes batted and balls faced is Gilbert Jessop's 75-minute, 75-ball onslaught against Australia at The Oval on 13 August 1902. Set 263 to win, England had lost five wickets for 48 on a rain-damaged pitch when 'The Croucher' began his innings at 1.10 pm. Attacking the bowling from the start, he scored 22 off his first 12 balls, survived two chances, and was 29 not out at lunch after 20 minutes batting. After the interval he completed his fifty out of 70 added with the Hon F.S. Jackson in 43 minutes, and added four consecutive boundaries off the left-arm spin of Jack Saunders. At 3.02 pm Jackson was out for 49, the partnership having added 109 in 67 minutes with Jessop's share being 83. Eight minutes later Jessop reached his hundred out of 135, having hit an all-run five, 16 fours, 2 threes, 4 twos and 17 singles off the bowling of Trumble (who bowled 33.5 overs unchanged throughout the innings from the pavilion end), Saunders, Noble and Armstrong. After hitting one more boundary, Jessop was out two minutes later having made 104 out of 139 in 77 minutes. England went on to snatch an historic

victory in a 'crescendo of excitement' (*Wisden*) with their last pair of George Hirst (58 not out) and Wilfred Rhodes (6 not out) scoring the last 15 runs.

The most runs scored by a batsman for England before lunch on the first day is 98 by Charlie Barnett against Australia at Trent Bridge, Nottingham, on 10 June 1938. He reached 98 in the penultimate over before lunch but Hutton failed to score from the last six balls before the interval. The Gloucestershire right-hander off-drove the first ball of the afternoon session to the boundary, reaching his second Test hundred in two hours.

The most runs scored before lunch on any day of a Test match is 123 by Leslie Ames for England against South Africa at The Oval on 20 August 1935. Resuming his innings at 11 am, on the last day of this three-day match, with his score 25, the Kent wicket-keeper was 148 not out when the innings was declared at lunch 2½ hours later.

Greg Chappell scored **the most recent century before lunch in Test cricket** when he took his overnight score from 76 to 176 in 96 minutes on the second day (20 March 1982) of Australia's Third Test against New Zealand at Christchurch.

The slowest Test hundred in terms of both minutes and balls faced took 9 hours 17 minutes and involved 420 balls, a dual record achieved by Mudassar Nazar for Pakistan against England at the Gaddafi Stadium, Lahore, on 14-15 December 1977. Opening the innings on a dead, mud pitch, he scored 52 in 330 minutes on the first day. Ten minutes after tea on the second day (25 minutes of play having been lost to a minor riot when he reached 99), he took his score to 100 out of 306 for 3. It was **the slowest hundred in all first-class cricket.** His complete innings of 114 lasted 591 minutes.

The fastest double century in Tests was recorded by Don Bradman during his 334 for Australia

HUNDRED BEFORE LUNCH ON THE FIRST DAY

Batsman (final score)	Lunch Score	Match	Venue	Series
V.T. Trumper (104)	103*	A v E	Manchester	1902
C.G. Macartney (151)	112*	A v E	Leeds	1926
D.G. Bradman (334)	105*	A v E	Leeds	1930
Majid Khan (112)	108*	P v NZ	Karachi	1976-77

against England at Headingley, Leeds, on 11 July 1930. He reached his 200 in 214 minutes, his century having taken 99 minutes.

Ian Botham reached his double century off only 220 balls (268 minutes) during his innings of 208 for England against India at The Oval on 8 and 9 July 1982 – **the fastest recorded 200 in Test cricket measured by balls faced.**

Wally Hammond scored **the fastest triple century in Test cricket** when he reached 300 in 288 minutes for England against New Zealand at Auckland on 31 March-1 April 1933. His complete innings of 336 not out took 318 minutes and inclu-

ded **ten sixes – the most in any Test innings. Three of them were struck off successive balls** from the left-arm medium pace bowling of Jack Newman – **another Test record,** subsequently equalled by Sylvester Clarke (West Indies) against the off-spin bowling of Pakistan's Mohammad Nazir at Faisalabad on 11 December 1980 (Clarke's 26th birthday).

The fastest fifty in Test cricket took only 28 minutes and was scored by Jack Brown for England during his 140 against Australia at Melbourne on 6 March 1895. A short, strongly-built

Ian Botham about to be spectacularly dropped by Tony Blain off Derek Stirling. He went on to reach 50 off 32 balls. (Adrian Murrell/All Sport)

SLOWEST 50, 100, 200 AND 300 IN TESTS

Score	Minutes	Batsman (final score)	Match	Venue	Series
50:	357	T.E. Bailey (68)	E v A	Brisbane	1958-59
100:	557	Mudassar Nazar (114)	P v E	Lahore	1977-78
200:	652	A.D. Gaekwad (201)	I v P	Jullundur	1983-84
300:	858	Hanif Mohammad (337)	P v WI	Bridgetown	1957-58

Yorkshireman, Brown went on to reach his hundred in 95 minutes – the fastest in Test matches at that time. His third-wicket partnership of 210 with Albert Ward set a new Test record for any wicket and saw England within sight of victory in the last and decisive match of the series.

The fastest recorded fifty in terms of balls faced took 32 balls and was struck by Ian Botham for England against New Zealand at The Oval on 25 August 1986: 00100000041204210410101412414 646.

The highest partnership in Test cricket added 451 runs for Australia's second wicket against England at The Oval on 18 August 1934. Bill Ponsford (266) and Don Bradman (244) began their record stand at noon on the first day and, in 316 minutes, took the score from 21 to 472 before Bradman was out at 6.16 pm. Attempting to hook a high bouncer from Bill Bowes he could only top-edge it to wicket-keeper Ames. In Australia's previous innings, at Leeds, Ponsford (181) and Bradman (304) had added 388 runs for the fourth innings. Thus, in successive Test innings, these two batsmen scored 839 runs together in 10 hours 57 minutes at a rate of 76 runs per hour.

This record was equalled on 14-15 January 1983 by Pakistan's third-wicket pair, Mudassar Nazar (231) and Javed Miandad (280*), against India at Hyderabad. Their partnership of 451 lasted 533 minutes – 217 minutes longer than that of Ponsford and Bradman – and took the score from 60 to 511.

The Test records for the fifth and seventh wickets are the highest partnerships for those wickets in all first-class cricket. Although 415 runs were added for India's third wicket against England at Madras in January 1982, two separate partnerships were involved: Dilip Vengsarkar retired hurt after a stand of 99 (unbroken) with Gundappa Viswanath, before the latter added a further 316 runs with Yashpal Sharma.

The most boundaries in an individual Test innings – and the only instance of over 50 being struck – is 57 by John Edrich during his 310 not out for England against New Zealand at Headingley, Leeds, on 8-9 July 1965. He hit 5 sixes and 52 fours during an innings lasting 532 minutes. It remains England's only triple century since 1938 and the highest first-class score by an Englishman at Headingley.

The most boundaries off one over in Test cricket is six by Sandeep Patil for India in the

HIGHEST PARTNERSHIPS FOR EACH WICKET

Wkt	Runs	Batsmen (scores)	Match	Venue	Series
1st	413	M.H. Mankad (231), Pankaj Roy (173)	I v NZ	Madras	1955-56
2nd	451	W.H. Ponsford (266), D.G. Bradman (244)	A v E	The Oval	1934
3rd	451	Mudassar Nazar (231), Javed Miandad (280*)	P v I	Hyderabad	1982-83
4th	411	P.B.H. May (285*), M.C. Cowdrey (154)	E v WI	Birmingham	1957
5th	405	S.G. Barnes (234), D.G. Bradman (234)	A v E	Sydney	1946-47
6th	346	J.H.W. Fingleton (136), D.G. Bradman (270)	A v E	Melbourne	1936-37
7th	347	D. St E. Atkinson (219), C.C. Depeiza (122)	WI v A	Bridgetown	1954-55
8th	246	L.E.G. Ames (137), G.O.B. Allen (122)	E v NZ	Lord's	1931
9th	190	Asif Iqbal (146), Intikhab Alam (51)	P v E	The Oval	1967
10th	151	B.F. Hastings (110), R.O. Collinge (68*)	NZ v P	Auckland	1972-73

Second Test against England at Manchester on 27 June 1982. Facing the bowling of Bob Willis, England's captain, Patil began the over with three successive fours, the third delivery being a no-ball. He failed to score off the next ball, a yorker, but hit fours off each of the last three balls. Patil thus equalled **the Test record for the most runs by one batsman off an over** (24), set by Andy Roberts for West Indies at Port-of-Spain, Trinidad, on 15 February 1981. Roberts, the first Antiguan to represent West Indies, struck 4, 6, 2, 6, 6 off the bowling of another England captain, Ian Botham, before taking a leg-bye off the last ball.

Botham subsequently exacted his revenge by equalling this record during his innings of 59 not out for England against New Zealand at The Oval on 25 August 1986. He savaged the medium-fast bowling of Derek Stirling for 4, 6, 4, 6, 0, 4.

Only five players have batted on each day of a five-day Test match, Kim Hughes doing so during the 1980 Centenary Test:

Batsman	Scores	Match	Venue	Series
M.L. Jaisimha	20*	74 I v A	Calcutta	1959-60
G. Boycott	107	80* E v A	Nottingham	1977
K.J. Hughes	117	84 A v E	Lord's	1980
A.J. Lamb	23	110 E v WI	Lord's	1984
R.J. Shastri	111	7* I v E	Calcutta	1984-85

The fewest runs scored by a batsman in an uninterrupted day of Test cricket is 49 by M.L. Jaisimha on 18 December 1960. Playing for India against Pakistan at Green Park, Kanpur, the Hyderabad all-rounder took his score from 5 to 54 in 330 minutes. After batting for 8 hours 20 minutes and spending nearly an hour in the nineties, he attempted to run a single from a push back to the

Richard Collinge and Brian Hastings – Test cricket's record last-wicket partners. (Patrick Eagar)

bowler and was run out for 99.

The longest any batsman has taken to score his first run in a first-class innings is 97 minutes. Playing against Australia at Adelaide on 5-6 February 1947, Godfrey Evans joined Denis Compton (40*) with England's second innings total 255 for 8. He survived 20 balls that evening while Compton scored 19 runs off 60 deliveries. Next day Evans scored his first run off his 61st ball and enabled Compton to reach his second century

HIGHEST PARTNERSHIPS FOR EACH COUNTRY

	Runs	Wkt	Batsmen (scores)	Opponents	Venue	Series
England	411	4th	P.B.H. May (285*), M.C. Cowdrey (154)	West Indies	Birmingham	1957
Australia	451	2nd	W.H. Ponsford (266), D.G. Bradman (244)	England	The Oval	1934
South Africa	341	3rd	E.J. Barlow (201), R.G. Pollock (175)	Australia	Adelaide	1963-64
West Indies	446	2nd	C.C. Hunte (260), G. St A. Sobers (365*)	Pakistan	Kingston	1957-58
New Zealand	387	1st	G.M. Turner (259), T.W. Jarvis (182)	West Indies	Georgetown	1971-72
India	413	1st	M.H. Mankad (231), Pankaj Roy (173)	New Zealand	Madras	1955-56
Pakistan	451	3rd	Mudassar Nazar (231), Javed Miandad (280*)	India	Hyderabad	1982-83
Sri Lanka	240*	4th	A.P. Gurusinha (116*), A. Ranatunga (135*)	Pakistan	Colombo (SO)	1985-86

The first Test in England – Lord Harris fielding at The Oval in September 1880. (Mary Evans Picture Library)

of the match. When England were safe from defeat and Hammond declared, Evans had scored 10 not out off 98 balls, and Compton 63 of his 103 not out off 179 balls in a partnership of 85 in 133 minutes. Five years later Evans amassed 98 runs before lunch off India's bowlers in a Test at Lord's.

The record for being not out most times in a Test career is held, perhaps not surprisingly, by a late-order batsman, Bob Willis. In 128 innings between January 1971 and July 1984, the England fast bowler was not out 55 times.

Equally predictably, another tail-ender, Bhagwat Chandrasekhar, achieved **the most pairs of ducks in Test cricket.** The Indian spin bowler was dismissed twice in a match without scoring on four occasions: by New Zealand at Wellington in February 1976, by England at Delhi in December 1976, and by Australia at Brisbane and Melbourne in the 1977-78 rubber.

The fastest pair in Test cricket was inflicted

upon 'Ebbu' Ghazali of Pakistan by England at Old Trafford, Manchester, on 24 July 1954. Exactly two hours elapsed between the start of his first innings at 4.14 pm and his second dismissal at 6.14. pm.

Ken Barrington holds the record for **the most consecutive Test innings without a duck.** Although he was out for just one run on five occasions between July 1962 and April 1968, he enjoyed a run of 78 innings in that period without being dismissed for nought.

The most innings before a first duck in Test cricket is 58 by Clive Lloyd for West Indies from December 1966 until February 1974.

Clyde Walcott was out for nought only once during his Test career. He played 74 innings for West Indies between January 1948 and March 1960, scoring 3798 runs (average 56.68) and making 15 centuries. His solitary duck occurred at Brisbane on 9 November 1951 when Ray Lindwall had him lbw in his first Test innings in Australia.

3000 Runs in Tests

ENGLAND	M	I	Runs	Average	100	A	SA	Opponents WI	NZ	I	P	SL
G. Boycott	108	193	8114	47.72	22	2945	373	2205	916	1084	591	·
M.C. Cowdrey	114	188	7624	44.06	22	2433	1021	1751	1133	653	633	·
W.R. Hammond	85	140	7249	58.45	22	2852	2188	639	1015	555	·	·
L. Hutton	79	138	6971	56.67	19	2428	1564	1661	777	522	19	·
K.F. Barrington	82	131	6806	58.67	20	2111	989	1042	594	1355	715	·
D.I. Gower	86	148	6149	44.88	13	2075	·	938	1051	1100	799	186
D.C.S. Compton	78	131	5807	50.06	17	1842	2205	592	510	205	453	·
J.B. Hobbs	61	102	5410	56.94	15	3636	1562	212			·	·
J.H. Edrich	77	127	5138	43.54	12	2644	7	792	840	494	361	·
T.W. Graveney	79	123	4882	44.38	11	1075	234	1532	293	805	943	·

	M	I	Runs	Average	100	A	SA	WI	NZ	I	P	SL
I.T. Botham	85	136	**4636**	35.12	13	1422	.	757	830	1201	407	19
H. Sutcliffe	54	84	**4555**	60.73	16	2741	1336	206	250	22	.	.
P.B.H. May	66	106	**4537**	46.77	13	1566	906	986	603	356	120	.
E.R. Dexter	62	102	**4502**	47.89	9	1358	585	866	477	467	749	.
A.P.E. Knott	95	149	**4389**	32.75	5	1682	.	994	352	685	676	.
G.A. Gooch	59	105	**3746**	37.08	7	1105	.	1130	458	926	74	53
D.L. Amiss	50	88	**3612**	46.30	11	305	.	1130	433	965	779	.
A.W. Greig	58	93	**3599**	40.43	8	1303	.	795	267	883	351	.
E.H. Hendren	51	83	**3525**	47.63	7	1740	876	909	.	.	.	.
F.E. Woolley	64	98	**3283**	36.07	5	1664	1354	.	235	30	.	.
K.W.R. Fletcher	59	96	**3272**	39.90	7	661	.	528	578	874	586	45

								Opponents				
AUSTRALIA	M	I	Runs	Average	100	E	SA	WI	NZ	I	P	SL
G.S. Chappell	87	151	**7110**	53.86	24	2619	.	1400	1076	368	1581	66
D.G. Bradman	52	80	**6996**	99.94	29	5028	806	447	.	715	.	.
A.R. Border	81	143	**6199**	52.09	18	1869	.	1221	713	1047	1302	47
R.N. Harvey	79	137	**6149**	48.41	21	2416	1625	1054	.	775	279	.
K.D. Walters	74	125	**5357**	48.26	15	1981	258	1196	901	756	265	.
I.M. Chappell	75	136	**5345**	42.42	14	2138	288	1545	486	536	352	.
W.M. Lawry	67	123	**5234**	47.15	13	2233	985	1035	.	892	89	.
R.B. Simpson	62	111	**4869**	46.81	10	1405	980	1043	.	1125	316	.
I.R. Redpath	66	120	**4737**	43.45	8	1512	791	1247	413	475	299	.
K.J. Hughes	70	124	**4415**	37.41	9	1499	.	774	138	988	1016	.
R.W. Marsh	96	150	**3633**	26.51	3	1633	.	707	486	83	724	.
A.R. Morris	46	79	**3533**	46.48	12	2080	792	452	.	209	.	.
C. Hill	49	89	**3412**	39.21	7	2660	752	.	.	.	.	.
V.T. Trumper	48	89	**3163**	39.04	8	2263	900	.	.	.	.	.
G.M. Wood	53	101	**3109**	32.38	8	1063	.	899	393	287	463	4
C.C. McDonald	47	83	**3107**	39.32	5	1043	786	880	.	224	174	.
A.L. Hassett	43	69	**3073**	46.56	10	1572	748	402	19	332	.	

SOUTH AFRICA	M	I	Runs	Average	100	E	A	NZ
B. Mitchell	42	80	**3471**	48.88	8	2732	573	166

							Opponents		
WEST INDIES	M	I	Runs	Average	100	E	A	NZ	I	P
G. St A. Sobers	93	160	**8032**	57.78	26	3214	1510	404	1920	984
C.H. Lloyd	110	175	**7515**	46.67	19	2120	2211	234	2344	606
R.B. Kanhai	79	137	**6227**	47.53	15	2267	1694	.	1693	573
I.V.A. Richards	82	122	**6220**	54.56	20	2129	1646	310	1497	638
C.G. Greenidge	71	117	**5033**	48.39	12	1728	1056	538	1175	536
E. de C. Weekes	48	81	**4455**	58.61	15	1313	714	478	1495	455
A.I. Kallicharran	66	109	**4399**	44.43	12	891	1325	365	1229	589
R.C. Fredericks	59	109	**4334**	42.49	8	1369	1069	537	767	592
F.M.M. Worrell	51	87	**3860**	49.48	9	1979	918	233	730	.
C.L. Walcott	44	74	**3798**	56.68	15	1391	914	199	909	385
D.L. Haynes	59	97	**3703**	42.56	8	1246	1161	683	509	104
C.C. Hunte	44	78	**3245**	45.06	8	1005	927	.	670	643
B.F. Butcher	44	78	**3104**	43.11	7	1373	810	216	572	133
H.A. Gomes	54	81	**3032**	42.70	9	801	1122	158	806	145

NEW ZEALAND	M	I	Runs	Average	100	E	A	Opponents SA	WI	I	P
B.E. Congdon	61	114	**3448**	32.22	7	1143	456	·	764	713	372
J.R. Reid	58	108	**3428**	33.28	6	953	·	914	212	691	658

INDIA	M	I	Runs	Average	100	E	A	Opponents WI	NZ	P	SL
S.M. Gavaskar	115	201	**9367**	50.63	32	2483	1345	2749	651	1794	345
G.R. Viswanath	91	155	**6080**	41.93	14	1880	1538	1455	585	611	11
D.B. Vengsarkar	85	140	**4985**	40.20	11	1431	960	1181	261	880	272
M. Amarnath	56	95	**3852**	44.79	10	656	686	1020	407	867	216
P.R. Umrigar	59	94	**3631**	42.22	12	770	227	1372	351	911	·
V.L. Manjrekar	55	92	**3208**	39.12	7	1181	377	569	507	574	·
Kapil Dev	77	115	**3132**	29.82	3	1034	402	767	27	713	189
C.G. Borde	55	97	**3061**	35.59	5	746	502	870	613	330	·

PAKISTAN	M	I	Runs	Average	100	E	A	WI	NZ	I	SL
Javed Miandad	74	115	**5413**	55.23	14	517	1195	233	1276	1647	545
Zaheer Abbas	78	124	**5062**	44.79	12	1086	1411	259	428	1740	138
Majid Khan	63	106	**3931**	38.92	8	751	915	821	936	445	63
Hanif Mohammad	55	97	**3915**	43.98	12	1039	548	736	622	970	·
Mushtaq Mohammad	57	100	**3643**	39.17	10	1554	409	488	779	413	·
Asif Iqbal	58	99	**3575**	38.85	11	822	758	416	1113	466	·
Mudassar Nazar	58	90	**3445**	41.50	8	496	781	·	354	1431	383

SRI LANKA
The leading scorer is A. Ranatunga with 1191 runs, average 38.41.

Bowling Records

At 12.28 pm on 21 August 1986, Ian Botham's inswing gained an lbw decision against Jeff Crowe. In the twelfth over of The Oval Test against New Zealand he had overhauled the world record of 355 wickets held by Dennis Lillee since 27 December 1981. It was only Botham's twelfth delivery for England since missing five Tests because of a TCCB suspension for smoking cannabis.

During that final Test of the season Botham extended his **world record for the most Test wickets** to 357 between 28 July 1977 and 26 August 1986.

The first bowler to take 100 wickets in Test matches was the Lancashire and England left-arm slow bowler, Johnny Briggs. He reached the landmark just before tea on the first day of the Fourth Test against Australia at Sydney on 1 February 1895 in his 25th match. Three days later, on the next day of actual play in the same match, the New South Wales fast-medium bowler, Charlie Turner, claimed his hundredth wicket in his 17th and last Test.

Johnny Briggs – first to take 100 Test wickets.

The fastest first hundred Test wickets in the terms of fewest matches played in and balls bowled was achieved by the Surrey and England medium-pace bowler, George Lohmann. He reached that aggregate at the Old Wanderers, Johannesburg, on 4 March 1896 in his 16th Test. At the end of that innings Lohmann had career totals of 3421 balls bowled and 1066 runs conceded; the next lowest in both categories was achieved by Briggs with 3514 and 1350 respectively. If measured by the least number of innings, then the fastest hundred wickets was achieved by 'Terror' Turner in only 30 innings. In that respect he was two innings quicker than Lohmann although one match slower.

Measured in terms of time there is no such confusion. **The shortest period in which a bowler has attained an aggregate of 100 Test wickets** is one year 105 days. This record was achieved by Kapil Dev at Eden Gardens, Calcutta, in the Sixth Test against Pakistan on 31 January 1980. He had made his debut on 18 October 1978. In that short period India had played 25 Test matches, an extraordinary proliferation considering that their first 25 occupied a period of twenty years. Kapil Dev is also **the youngest bowler to take 100 wickets** at this level: 21 years 25 days. Two days later he established similar records by completing 1000 runs and the Test 'Double'.

All the preceding hundred wickets records refer to the first hundred dismissals of a bowler's Test career. **The fastest hundred wickets of all** was achieved by Sydney Barnes of Warwickshire, Staffordshire, Lancashire and England. Assessed by most of his contemporaries as the best bowler ever, Barnes took the last hundred of his 189 wickets in only eleven Tests (21 innings).

The first bowler to take 200 Test wickets was Australia's New Zealand-born leg-break bowler, Clarrie Grimmett. He reached that total on 17 February 1936 at the Old Wanderers, Johannesburg, in the penultimate Test of his career. **The first to take 200 wickets for England** was Alec Bedser on 26 June 1953 against Australia at Lord's.

The fastest first 200 wickets in terms of fewest matches and innings is that of Grimmett; he took 35 matches during which he bowled in 65 innings. Ian Botham holds **the record for taking 200 wickets with fewest balls** (9672); he reached that milestone in fewer innings (71) than anyone except Grimmett. The Somerset and England all-rounder also recorded that feat in the shortest period, only 4 years 43 days elapsing between his debut on 28 July 1977 and his 200th dismissal (Marsh) on 31 August 1981 at The Oval.

The youngest bowler to take 200 wickets is Kapil Dev; he was aged 24 years 68 days on 15 March 1983 when he celebrated his 50th Test by completing the 'double double' (v West Indies at Port-of-Spain).

Fred Trueman was **the first bowler to take 300 wickets in Test cricket.** He reached that total at The Oval in his 65th Test on 15 August 1964 when he had Neil Hawke of Australia caught at slip by Colin Cowdrey.

The fastest 300 wickets was achieved by Dennis Lillee in 56 Tests (108 innings), although Trueman completed his in 340 fewer balls. Lillee needed only 10 years 302 days to claim his 300th victim (Wasim Raja of Pakistan at Brisbane on 27 November 1981), whereas Trueman took 13 years 17 days and Gibbs 17 years 310 days.

Lillee also holds the record for **the most wickets against one country** with 167 wickets (average 21.00) in 29 Tests against England.

300 WICKETS IN TEST CRICKET

		Wkts	Tests	Runs/Wkt	Balls	Balls/Wkts	5wI	10wM
I.T. Botham	England	357	85	27.06	19356	54.2	26	4
D.K. Lillee	Australia	355	70	23.92	18467	52.0	23	7
R.J. Hadlee	New Zealand	334	66	22.51	17179	51.4	27	7
R.G.D. Willis	England	325	90	25.20	17357	53.4	16	·
L.R. Gibbs	West Indies	309	79	29.09	27115	87.7	18	2
F.S. Trueman	England	307	67	21.57	15178	49.4	17	3

The most wickets taken by one bowler in a calendar year is 85 (average 20.95)) by Dennis Lillee in 13 Tests during 1981.

The lowest career bowling average by a bowler taking 25 or more Test wickets is 10.75 by George Lohmann, who took 112 wickets in 18 Tests for England between July 1886 and June 1896. The lowest in modern times is 15.02 by Mike Procter who, between January 1967 and March 1970, took 41 wickets in the last seven Tests played by South Africa.

The highest career bowling average is 284.00 by Roger Wijesuriya in four matches for Sri Lanka between 1982 and 1985. He bowled 586 balls – the most by any bowler taking only one wicket in Tests.

The highest wicket-taking rate in Test cricket was achieved by George Lohmann with a wicket every 34 balls (112 wickets in 3821 balls).

William Attewell of Nottinghamshire and England recorded **the most economical career figures in Test matches** by a bowler delivering at least 2000 balls. A medium pace bowler of exceptional accuracy, Attewell conceded just under 22 runs per 100 balls in taking 27 wickets in ten Tests between December 1884 and March 1892.

The highest number of wickets taken by one bowler in a series is 49 by Sydney Barnes for England in four Tests during the 1913-14 series on matting wickets in South Africa. Barnes took ten wickets in the First Test, established a Test record which stood until 1956 by taking 17 in the Second, claimed eight in the Third, and finished with 14 in the Fourth Test. That proved to be his final appearance for England. He declined to play in the Fifth Test following a difference of opinion concerning his wife's accommodation – much to the relief of the South Africans. His full figures were 222 overs (six-ball), 56 maidens, 536 runs, 49 wickets, average 10.93. In seven Tests against South Africa (the 1912 Triangular Tournament and the 1913-14 rubber), Barnes took 83 wickets (average 9.85), **the record against South Africa by a bowler from any country.** That tally included six instances of ten or more wickets in a match, and twelve of five or more in an innings.

The most wickets by one bowler in a series in England, and the only other instance of a bowler taking 45 or more wickets in one rubber, is 46 (average 9.60) by Jim Laker for England against Australia in the five-match series of 1956.

The lowest average recorded by any bowler taking 25 or more wickets in a series is 5.80 by George Lohmann when he claimed 35 South African wickets in the three-match rubber of 1895-96.

The record number of wickets to fall to one bowler in any first-class match is 19 taken by Jim Laker for England against Australia at Old Trafford, Manchester, on 27, 28, 30 and 31 July 1956. The Yorkshire-born, Surrey off-break bowler took 9 for 37 in 16.4 overs in the first innings and 10 for 53 in 51.2 overs in the second. Ten of his wickets were caught (including five by Alan Oakman at short leg), five were bowled, three lbw and one stumped. All 19 wickets were taken from the Stretford End although Laker frequently switched

MOST WICKETS FOR EACH TEAM IN A SERIES

	Wickets	Bowler	Opponents	Venue	Tests	Series
England	49	S.F. Barnes	South Africa	SA	4	1913-14
Australia	44	C.V. Grimmett	South Africa	SA	5	1935-36
South Africa	37	H.J. Tayfield	England	SA	5	1956-57
West Indies	33	A.L. Valentine	England	E	4	1950
	33	C.E.H. Croft	Pakistan	WI	5	1976-77
	33	M.D. Marshall	India	I	6	1983-84
New Zealand	33	R.J. Hadlee	Australia	A	3	1985-86
India	35	B.S. Chandrasekhar	England	I	5	1972-73
Pakistan	40	Imran Khan	India	P	6	1982-83
Sri Lanka	20	R.J. Ratnayake	India	SL	3	1985-86

ends with Tony Lock. Perhaps the most astounding match statistic was Lock's bowling analysis. In 69 overs on a pitch favouring spin bowlers the Surrey left-arm bowler, then in his heyday, took only one wicket for 106 runs.

No other bowler has taken more than 17 wickets in any first-class match.

The most runs conceded by one bowler in a Test match is 374 by 'Tommy' Scott for West Indies against England at Kingston, Jamaica, in April 1930. Scott bowled 105.2 overs and took nine wickets with his leg-breaks as England scored 849 and 272 for 9 declared in this Timeless Test. Arthur Mailey, the only other bowler to concede 300 runs in a Test match, was also a leg-spinner. Playing for Australia against England, he twice suffered this fate, taking 10 for 302 at Adelaide in January 1921 and 7 for 308 at Sydney in December 1924.

The highest number of balls bowled by one player in a Test is 774 by Sonny Ramadhin for West Indies against England at Edgbaston, Birmingham, in 1957 (30 May-4 June). Having taken 7 for 49 in the first innings as England were dismissed for 186, he was thwarted in the second by a record fourth-wicket stand of 411 by May and Cowdrey. England totalled 583 for 4 declared as Ramadhin bowled a record 98 overs to take 2 for 179. A finger spinner who mesmerized batsmen by turning the ball either way without any obvious change of action, Ramadhin found himself treated as a straightforward off-break bowler and, after this traumatic experience, was never again so effective at Test level.

The best innings analysis in Test cricket — and the only instance of a bowler taking all ten wickets at that level – was recorded by Jim Laker at Old Trafford, Manchester, in 1956 when he took ten Australian second innings wickets for 53 runs. This historic performance was spread over five days including the rest day. Following on 375 behind, after Laker had devastated their first innings with a spell of eight wickets for seven runs in 22 balls to return a final analysis of 9 for 53, Australia lost their first wicket before stumps on the second day. Rain on the third day permitted only 45 minutes cricket during which Laker took his second wicket. Heavy rain fell on the Sunday rest day and allowed just an hour's play in two

S.F. Barnes displays the action that claimed 189 wickets in only 27 Tests.

spells on the fourth day. Fierce winds compelled the use of heavy bails made from lignum vitae. They were not disturbed and Australia had still

Supported by Godfrey Evans, umpire Frank Lee signals the downfall of Ian Craig – one of Jim Laker's 19 wickets in the 1956 Old Trafford Test. (Sport & General)

BEST MATCH ANALYSIS FOR EACH TEAM

For	Analysis	Bowler	Opponents	Venue	Series
England	19-90	J.C. Laker	Australia	Manchester	1956
Australia	16-137	R.A.L. Massie	England	Lord's	1972
South Africa	13-165	H.J. Tayfield	Australia	Melbourne	1952-53
West Indies	14-149	M.A. Holding	England	The Oval	1976
New Zealand	15-123	R.J. Hadlee	Australia	Brisbane	1985-86
India	14-124	J.M. Patel	Australia	Kanpur	1959-60
Pakistan	14-116	Imran Khan	Sri Lanka	Lahore	1981-82
Sri Lanka	9-125	R.J. Ratnayake	India	Colombo (SO)	1985-86

eight wickets intact when play began ten minutes late on the last day (31 July). They were still intact at lunch. Then the sun appeared, the ball began to turn more quickly and four wickets fell to Laker's off-spin before tea. England had 115 minutes in which to take the last four wickets and ensure retention of the Ashes. When Colin McDonald (89) was out to the second ball after tea, Australia's hopes of a draw vanished. He had batted on four different days for the only Australian score above 38 in the match. At 5.27 pm Laker trapped wicket-keeper Len Maddocks lbw and England had won by an innings and 170 runs – or by 33 minutes. All Laker's wickets in both innings fell from the Stretford End. That night the heavy rain returned to cause the abandonment of the entire county cricket programme on the following day.

The most runs conceded by a bowler in one Test innings is 298 by 'Chuck' Fleetwood-Smith of Australia during England's record total of 903 for 7 declared at The Oval in August 1938. A left-arm, back-of-the-hand spin bowler whose natural ball was an off-break, Fleetwood-Smith sent down 87 overs in that innings for just one wicket. Only one England bowler has conceded over 200 runs in a Test innings and he was a Scotsman; fortunately Ian Peebles was also an extremely humorous man. He had the compensation of taking six wickets in the course of his 71 overs, while contributing 204 runs towards Australia's total of 695 (Bradman 232) at The Oval in August 1930.

The highest number of balls bowled in any first-class innings is 588 by Sonny Ramadhin for West Indies during England's second innings at Edgbaston, Birmingham, in June 1957. The 5ft 4in wrist-spinner took 2 for 179 in 98 overs as Peter May (285 not out) and Colin Cowdrey (154) batted England to safety, adding 411 in England's highest-ever partnership. His total of 774 balls bowled in that match remains the Test record.

The most wickets taken by one bowler in a single day of Test cricket is 15 by Johnny Briggs for England against South Africa at Newlands, Cape Town, on 26 March 1889. The first English team to visit South Africa played only two eleven-a-side fixtures; this was the second, and both have come to be rated as full Test matches. South Africa, replying to England's total of 292, were bowled out by Briggs (left-arm slow) for 47 and 43. They were literally bowled out: six of his seven first innings wickets and all of his eight in the second were bowled. He gained all 15 wickets without the aid of a fieldsman, the other one being lbw. In the second innings **nine batsmen were bowled – the most in any Test innings.**

The most wickets to fall to one bowler in a day's Test cricket in England is 14 on 25 June 1934 at Lord's. Australia were caught on a drying pitch and bowled to their first defeat at Lord's since 1896 by the Yorkshire left-arm spinner, Hedley Verity.

DISMISSING ALL ELEVEN BATSMEN IN A MATCH

J.C. Laker	19-90	England v Australia	Manchester	1956
S. Venkataraghavan	12-152	India v New Zealand	Delhi	1964-65
G. Dymock	12-166	Australia v India	Kanpur	1979-80

BEST INNINGS ANALYSIS FOR EACH TEAM

For	Analysis	Bowler	Opponents	Venue	Series
England	10-53	J.C. Laker	Australia	Manchester	1956
Australia	9-121	A.A. Mailey	England	Melbourne	1920-21
South Africa	9-113	H.J. Tayfield	England	Johannesburg	1956-57
West Indies	9-95	J.M. Noreiga	India	Port-of-Spain	1970-71
New Zealand	9-52	R.J. Hadlee	Australia	Brisbane	1985-86
India	9-69	J.M. Patel	Australia	Kanpur	1959-60
Pakistan	9-86	Sarfraz Nawaz	Australia	Melbourne	1978-79
Sri Lanka	8-83	J.R. Ratnayeke	Pakistan	Sialkot	1985-86

There have been 17 hat-tricks in Test cricket, the first being achieved by 'The Demon' Spofforth for Australia against England at Melbourne on 2 January 1879 in only the third Test match played.

Two bowlers, both Australians, took two Test match hat-tricks. Hugh Trumble, a medium-pace off-spinner, took both of his against England at Melbourne, the first in January 1902 and the second in March 1904 in his final first-class match. Jimmy Matthews achieved **the unique feat of taking two hat-tricks in the same Test** – against South Africa at Old Trafford, Manchester, during the opening match of the 1912 Triangular Tournament. A right-arm leg-break bowler, he gained a hat-trick in each innings on the afternoon of 28 May, his only six wickets of the match and all taken without assistance from fieldsmen.

The most recent Test hat-trick was performed by Peter Petherick, an off-break bowler making his debut for New Zealand, against Pakistan at Lahore's Gaddafi Stadium on the first day – 9 October 1976.

The only other bowler to take a hat-trick in his first Test was the Surrey fast-medium bowler, Maurice Allom, who took four wickets in five balls (W-WWW) during his eighth over for England, against New Zealand at Christchurch on his first day of Test cricket – 10 January 1930. There has been only one subsequent instance of a bowler taking four Test wickets in five balls, Chris Old, an exponent similar to Allom, achieving this feat in his 19th over, for England against Pakistan at Edgbaston, Birmingham, on 1 June 1978. He took four wickets with successive legitimate balls but delivered a no-ball in the middle of the sequence, his over reading: – WWnbWW1.

Only two bowlers have taken three wickets in a sequence of four balls on more than one occasion; both were Australians and in every instance their victims were England batsmen. On 29 August 1882, Spofforth became the first

WICKET WITH FIRST BALL IN TEST CRICKET

Bowler	Batsman	Match	Venue	Series
A. Coningham	A.C. MacLaren	A v E	Melbourne	1894-95
W.M. Bradley	F. Laver	E v A	Manchester	1899
E.G. Arnold	V.T. Trumper	E v A	Sydney	1903-04
G.G. Macaulay	G.A.L. Hearne	E v SA	Cape Town	1922-23
M.W. Tate	M.J. Susskind	E v SA	Birmingham	1924
M. Henderson	E.W. Dawson	NZ v E	Christchurch	1929-30
H.D. Smith	E. Paynter	NZ v E	Christchurch	1932-33
T.F. Johnson	W.W. Keeton	WI v E	The Oval	1939
R. Howorth	D.V. Dyer	E v SA	The Oval	1947
Intikhab Alam	C.C. McDonald	P v A	Karachi	1959-60

More than 570 matches have been played since Intikhab Alam achieved the last instance on a matting pitch on 5 December 1959 in the 481st Test.

Geoff Howarth dives to catch his Surrey colleague Intikhab Alam and complete Peter Petherick's hat-trick on Test debut at Lahore in October 1976. Fielders L-R: Warren Lees, Glenn Turner *captain*, **Howarth, Petherick and John Parker. Asif Iqbal is the non-striker.** (Don Neely)

bowler to achieve this feat in the course of taking 7 for 44 at The Oval. His performance brought about England's first home defeat and led to the creation of the Ashes through a mock obituary notice in *The Times.* He repeated the feat at Sydney on 21 February 1885. The second Australian bowler was Dennis Lillee who took three wickets in four balls in the Manchester and Oval Tests of 1972.

100 Wickets in Tests

ENGLAND	M	Wickets	Average	BB	A	SA	Opponents WI	NZ	I	P	SL
I.T. Botham	85	**357**	27.06	8-34	136	·	58	61	59	33	10
R.G.D. Willis	90	**325**	25.20	8-43	128	·	38	60	62	34	3
F.S. Trueman	67	**307**	21.57	8-31	79	27	86	40	53	22	·
D.L. Underwood	86	**297**	25.83	8-51	105	·	38	48	62	36	8
J.B. Statham	70	**252**	24.84	7-39	69	69	42	20	25	27	·
A.V. Bedser	51	**236**	24.89	7-34	104	54	11	13	44	10	·
J.A. Snow	49	**202**	26.66	7-40	83	4	72	20	16	7	·
J.C. Laker	46	**193**	21.24	10-53	79	32	51	21	8	2	·
S.F. Barnes	27	**189**	16.43	9-103	106	83	·	·	·	·	·
G.A.R. Lock	49	**174**	25.58	7-35	31	15	39	47	26	16	·
M.W.Tate	39	**155**	26.16	6-42	83	53	13	6	·	·	·
F.J. Titmus	53	**153**	32.22	7-79	47	27	15	28	27	9	·
H. Verity	40	**144**	24.37	8-43	59	31	9	7	38	·	·
C.M. Old	46	**143**	28.11	7-50	40	·	18	21	43	21	·
A.W. Greig	58	**141**	32.20	8-86	44	·	36	20	27	14	·
T.E. Bailey	61	**132**	29.21	7-34	42	28	29	32	·	1	·
W. Rhodes	58	**127**	26.96	8-68	109	8	10	·	·	·	·
D.A. Allen	39	**122**	30.97	5-30	28	21	15	13	21	24	·
R. Illingworth	61	**122**	31.20	6-29	34	6	19	22	31	10	·
J. Briggs	33	**118**	17.74	8-11	97	21	·	·	·	·	·
G.G.Arnold	34	**115**	28.29	6-45	30	·	17	20	27	21	·
G.A.Lohmann	18	**112**	10.75	9-28	77	35	·	·	·	·	·
D.V.P. Wright	34	**108**	39.11	7-105	48	37	11	8	4	·	·
P.H. Edmonds	41	**106**	33.16	7-66	21	·	3	31	33	18	·
R. Peel	20	**102**	16.81	7-31	102	·	·	·	·	·	·
J.H. Wardle	28	**102**	20.39	7-36	24	46	7	5	·	20	·
C. Blythe	19	**100**	18.63	8-59	41	59	·	·	·	·	·

AUSTRALIA	M	Wickets	Average	BB	E	SA	Opponents WI	NZ	I	P	SL
D.K. Lillee	70	**355**	23.92	7-83	167	·	55	38	21	71	3
R. Benaud	63	**248**	27.03	7-72	83	52	42	·	52	19	·
G.D. McKenzie	60	**246**	29.78	8-71	96	41	47	·	47	15	·
R.R. Lindwall	61	**228**	23.03	7-38	114	31	41	2	36	4	·
C.V. Grimmett	37	**216**	24.21	7-40	106	77	33	·	·	·	·
J.R. Thomson	51	**200**	28.00	6-46	100	·	62	6	22	10	·
A.K. Davidson	44	**186**	20.53	7-93	84	25	33	·	30	14	·
K.R. Miller	55	**170**	22.97	7-60	87	30	40	2	9	2	·
W.A. Johnston	40	**160**	23.91	6-44	75	44	25	·	16	·	·
G.F. Lawson	36	**145**	29.31	8-112	68	·	36	8	·	33	·
W.J. O'Reilly	27	**144**	22.59	7-54	102	34	·	8	·	·	·
H. Trumble	32	**141**	21.78	8-65	141	·	·	·	·	·	·
M.H.N. Walker	34	**138**	27.47	8-143	56	·	37	28	·	17	·
A.A. Mallett	38	**132**	29.84	8-59	50	6	16	19	28	13	·
B. Yardley	33	**126**	31.63	7-98	29	·	35	13	21	21	7
R.M. Hogg	38	**123**	28.47	6-74	56	·	22	10	15	19	1
M.A. Noble	42	**121**	25.00	7-17	115	6	·	·	·	·	·
I.W. Johnson	45	**109**	29.19	7-44	42	22	22	·	19	4	·
G. Giffen	31	**103**	27.09	7-117	103	·	·	·	·	·	·
A.N. Connolly	29	**102**	29.22	6-47	25	26	20	·	31	·	·
C.T.B. Turner	17	**101**	16.53	7-43	101	·	·	·	·	·	·

SOUTH AFRICA	M	Wickets	Average	BB	Opponents E	A	NZ		
H.J. Tayfield	37	170	25.91	9-113	75	64	31		
T.L. Goddard	41	123	26.22	6-53	63	53	7		
P.M. Pollock	28	116	24.18	6-38	32	52	32		
N.A.T. Adcock	26	104	21.10	6-43	57	14	33		

WEST INDIES	M	Wickets	Average	BB	E	A	NZ	I	P
L.R. Gibbs	79	309	29.09	8-38	100	103	11	63	32
M.A. Holding	59	249	23.28	8-92	96	76	16	61	·
J. Garner	56	247	21.16	6-56	92	89	24	7	35
G. St A. Sobers	93	235	34.03	6-73	102	51	19	59	4
M.D. Marshall	45	215	21.57	7-53	69	49	27	57	13
A.M.E. Roberts	47	202	25.61	7-54	50	51	3	67	31
W.W. Hall	48	192	26.38	7-69	65	45	1	65	16
S. Ramadhin	43	158	28.98	7-49	80	22	32	15	9
A.L. Valentine	36	139	30.32	8-104	40	43	23	30	3
C.E.H. Croft	27	125	23.30	8-29	33	32	·	10	50
V.A. Holder	40	109	33.27	6-28	33	28	12	31	5

NEW ZEALAND	M	Wickets	Average	BB	Opponents E	A	SA	WI	I	I•	SL
R.J. Hadlee	66	334	22.51	9-52	81	105	34	35	46	·	33
B.L. Cairns	43	130	32.92	7-74	32	23	17	22	21	·	15
R.O. Collinge	35	116	29.24	6-63	48	17	·	·	23	28	·
B.R. Taylor	30	111	26.60	7-74	28	·	·	32	29	22	·
R.C. Motz	32	100	31.48	6-63	28	·	21	17	22	12	·

INDIA	M	Wickets	Average	BB	Opponents E	A	WI	NZ	P	SL
Kapil Dev	77	291	28.72	9-83	71	54	63	8	76	19
B.S. Bedi	67	266	28.71	7-98	85	56	62	57	6	·
B.S. Chandrasekhar	58	242	29.74	8-79	95	38	65	36	8	·
E.A.S. Prasanna	49	189	30.38	8-76	41	57	34	55	2	·
M.H. Mankad	44	162	32.32	8-52	54	23	36	12	37	·
S. Venkataraghavan	57	156	36.11	8-72	23	20	68	44	1	·
S.P. Gupte	36	149	29.55	9-102	24	8	49	34	34	·
D.R. Doshi	33	114	30.71	6-102	36	38	·	5	27	8
K.D. Ghavri	39	109	33.54	5-33	19	32	36	5	17	·

PAKISTAN	M	Wickets	Average	BB	Opponents E	A	WI	NZ	P	SL
Imran Khan	57	264	22.18	8-58	26	60	35	24	73	46
Sarfraz Nawaz	55	177	32.75	9-86	37	52	26	26	36	·
Fazal Mahmood	34	139	24.70	7-42	25	24	41	5	44	·
Iqbal Qasim	41	137	29.15	7-49	14	45	19	22	22	15
Abdul Qadir	38	128	34.80	7-142	41	34	8	14	17	14
Intikhab Alam	47	125	35.95	7-52	49	9	8	54	5	·

SRI LANKA
The leading wicket-taker is A.L.F. De Mel with 58 wickets, average 35.53.

Wicket-Keeping records

The most dismissals by a wicket-keeper in Test cricket is 355 by Rodney Marsh, who, between 27 November 1970 and 6 January 1984, held a record 343 catches and made 12 stumpings in 96 matches for Australia. Marsh gained the record on 18 July 1981 when he caught Botham in England's first innings of the Third Test at Headingley, Leeds, to overtake Alan Knott's total of 263 dismissals. Although Knott was recalled for the last two Tests of that series and held six more catches, he was unable to regain the record.

Marsh also holds the record for taking most catches off one bowler, 95 of his victims being caught off his fellow West Australian Dennis Lillee.

The highest aggregate of stumpings in a Test career was achieved by Bert Oldfield who made 52 stumpings in 54 matches for Australia between December 1920 and March 1937.

Oldfield became **the first to make 100 wicket-keeping dismissals at Test level** when he stumped Verity off Grimmett at Lord's on 23 June 1934 in his 41st match. His 28 stumpings off Grimmett's leg-breaks, googlies and top-spinners constitute the record off one bowler.

The first wicket-keeper to make 200 dismissals was Godfrey Evans when he caught 'Collie' Smith in West Indies' second innings at Headingley, Leeds on 27 July 1957 in his 80th Test.

The youngest player to keep wicket in a Test match was Hanif Mohammad. He was 17 years 300 days old when he played in Pakistan's first official Test, against India at Feroz Shah Kotla, Delhi, on 16 October 1952. A specialist opening batsman who later established the current record first-class score of 499, Hanif conceded 28 byes in India's only innings and kept wicket in only the first three of his 55 Tests.

Another specialist batsman, Frank Woolley, became **the oldest player to keep wicket in a Test** when he deputized for the injured Ames in the Fifth Test against Australia at The Oval on 22 August 1934. Recalled after a break of two years to make the last international appearance by a pre-First World War Test player, Woolley was 47 years 87 days old when he conceded 37 byes – still **the record for a Test innings.**

The most dismissals in a Test series is 28 – all caught – by Rodney Marsh in five Tests against England in Australia in 1982-83. At Brisbane in the Second Test he set one Ashes record (six catches in an innings), equalled another (nine in a match),

100 DISMISSALS IN TESTS

		M	Dis	Ct	St	E	A	SA	Opponents WI	NZ	I	P	SL
R.W. Marsh	A	96	**355**	343	12	148	·	·	65	58	16	68	·
A.P.E. Knott	E	95	**269**	250	19	·	105	·	43	26	54	41	·
Wasim Bari	P	81	**228**	201	27	54	66	·	21	32	55	·	·
T.G. Evans	E	91	**219**	173	46	·	76	59	37	28	12	7	·
S.M.H. Kirmani	I	88	**198**	160	38	42	41	·	36	28	·	50	1
D.L. Murray	WI	62	**189**	181	8	94	40	·	·	7	27	21	·
A.T.W. Grout	A	51	**187**	163	24	76	·	33	41	·	20	17	·
R.W. Taylor	E	57	**174**	167	7	·	57	·	·	45	40	29	3
J.H.B. Waite	SA	50	**141**	124	17	56	28	·	·	57	·	·	·
W.A.S. Oldfield	A	54	**130**	78	52	90	·	27	13	·	·	·	·
P.J.L. Dujon	WI	37	**126**	124‡	2	16	64	·	·	11	35	·	·
J.M. Parks	E	46	**114**	103†	11	·	21	30	31	22	9	1	·
Highest for other countries:													
I.D.S. Smith	NZ	33	**98**	92	6	26	27	·	8	·	13	16	8
S.A.R. Silva	SL	8	**31**	30	1	3	·	·	·	2	22	4	·

†Including 2 catches in 3 Tests when not keeping wicket.
‡Including 2 catches in 2 Tests when not keeping wicket.

Rodney Marsh appeals unsuccessfully against Mike Brearley at Perth in December 1979. Only 12 of his record 355 dismissals were stumped. (Adrian Murrell/All-Sport)

and became the first to hold 300 catches in Tests.

The most stumpings in a Test series is nine by Percy Sherwell in South Africa's five-match series in Australia in 1910-11, seven of them off the googly bowling of Reggie Schwarz.

The match record for wicket-keeping dismissals and catches is ten by Bob Taylor (including eight off Ian Botham's bowling), for England in the Golden Jubilee Test against India at the Wankhede Stadium, Bombay, in February 1980. In the first innings of that match, Taylor equalled **the Test record for dismissals in an innings —** seven (all caught) by Wasim Bari for Pakistan against New Zealand at Auckland on 23 Feb 1979.

The most dismissals in two successive Tests is 18 by Amal Silva for Sri Lanka against India in Colombo in August-September 1985. In the second match, at the Saravanamuttu Stadium, he became **the first wicket-keeper to score a hundred and make nine dismissals in the same Test.**

The highest innings total in which no byes were conceded is Australia's 659 for 8 declared at Sydney in December 1946 when Godfrey Evans was England's wicket-keeper.

The highest total without byes in which all ten wickets fell is 652 by Pakistan against India at Iqbal Stadium, Faisalabad, on 4-7 January 1983. India's wicket-keeper was Syed Kirmani.

The record for conceding no byes in most consecutive Test matches is held by Denis Lindsay of South Africa. He accomplished this by not allowing a bye during four successive appearances against Australia in South Africa in February 1967 and February/March 1970. Australia totalled 1580 runs in the eight innings concerned. During those matches Lindsay held 17 catches and scored a century in a post-tea session.

W.G. Grace is believed to be **the only player to make a dismissal off his first ball as a wicket-keeper in Test cricket.** At The Oval on 12 August 1884, he deputized for the Hon Alfred Lyttelton and held a good legside catch off the latter's first lob of that spell. Lyttelton, the tenth of eleven England bowlers called upon by Lord Harris in Australia's innings of 551 (declarations were not permitted until 1889), took the last four wickets while still wearing his pads. He finished with 4 for 19 – **the best analysis in Test cricket by a player who began the innings as a wicket-keeper.**

The highest score by an appointed wicket-keeper in a Test match is 210 not out by Taslim Arif for Pakistan at the Iqbal Stadium, Faisalabad, on 10 and 11 March 1980. Opening the innings on the fourth day in reply to Australia's 617 all out, Taslim, playing in only his third Test, batted for 7¼ hours, hit 20 fours, and was on the field throughout the match.

Fielding records

The most catches taken by a non-wicket-keeper in a Test career is 122 by Greg Chappell in 87 matches for Australia between December 1970 and January 1984. He gained the record in his final Test, against Pakistan at Sydney on 5 January 1984, when he held his 121st catch (Mohsin Khan at second slip) to overtake the total which Colin Cowdrey had achieved in 114 matches for England between 1954 and 1975.

The first fielder to hold 100 catches was Wally Hammond of England. He reached that landmark on 25 July 1939 against West Indies at Old Trafford, Manchester in his 76th match.

The fewest Tests to reach an aggregate of 100 catches is 54 by Bob Simpson of Australia between December 1957 and December 1977.

Both Chappell brothers, Ian and Greg, took their hundredth catch in their 69th Test.

The record number of catches taken by a fielder in one series is 15 by Jack Gregory in the five-match home series of 1920-21 against England. Like Cowdrey, Hammond, Simpson and the Chappells, Gregory was primarily a slip fieldsman.

The most catches held by a fielder in one Test match is seven by Greg Chappell for Australia against England at Perth in December 1974, and by Yajurvindra Singh for India against England at Bangalore in January and February 1977.

right, **Comrades in arms: Rodney Marsh and Greg Chappell, Test cricket's most prolific wicket-keeper and fielder.** (Adrian Murrell/All-Sport)

Sydney Copley, about to become Test cricket's famous match-winning substitute, takes the field with K.S Duleepsinhji.

Yajurvindra Singh, playing in his first Test match, also equalled the record for **the most catches in an innings** set on 3 March 1936 at Kingsmead, Durban, by Vic Richardson of Australia. The Chappells' grandfather caught five of the last six South African wickets to fall for 21 runs in his final Test.

One of the most famous and decisive catches in Test cricket was held by a substitute fielder, Sydney Copley, in the First Test between England and Australia at Trent Bridge, Nottingham, on 17 June 1930. Australia were 200 runs away from victory on that final afternoon of a four-day match. They had seven wickets in hand, including those of Bradman and McCabe who had added 77, when Stan McCabe slightly mistimed an on-drive.

100 CATCHES IN TESTS

		M	Ct		E	A	Opponents SA	WI	NZ	I	P	SL
G.S. Chappell	A	87	**122**		61	·	·	16	18	5	22	·
M.C. Cowdrey	E	114	**120**		·	40	22	21	15	11	11	·
R.B. Simpson	A	62	**110**		30	·	27	29	·	21	3	·
W.R. Hammond	E	85	**110**		·	43	30	22	9	6	·	·
G. St A. Sobers	WI	93	**109**		40	27	·	·	11	27	4	·
I.M. Chappell	A	75	**105**		31	·	11	24	16	17	6	·
S.M. Gavaskar	I	115	**100**		35	16	·	17	11	·	16	5

Highest for other countries

		M	Ct		E	A	Opponents SA	WI	NZ	I	P	SL
South Africa	B. Mitchell	42	**56**		43	10	·	·	3	·	·	·
New Zealand	J.V. Coney	49	**59**		12	24	·	3	·	1	10	9
Pakistan	Majid Khan	63	**70**		14	13	·	14	19	9	·	1
Sri Lanka	A.L.F. De Mel	16	**9**		·	·	·	·	·	4	5	·
	S. Wettimuny	20	**9**		·	·	·	·	2	3	4	·

The above figures include catches taken when deputizing as wicket-keeper.

Copley, a 24-year-old member of the Nottingham-shire groundstaff who was fielding as substitute for Larwood, 'Made a lot of ground, took the ball at full-length and, although rolling over, retained possession' (*Wisden*). That catch turned the course of the innings and England went on to gain (by 93 runs) their only victory of the series. Eight days later Copley made the only first-class appearance of his career, against Oxford University; batting at number four he was dismissed for 4 and 3 by Ian Peebles.

Record all-round performances

Test cricket's 'Double' – the scoring of 1 000 runs allied to the taking of 100 wickets – has been achieved by 22 cricketers, the earliest instance being recorded in 1896. Not until 1963 did the first of six of those players achieve the 'Double Double' of 2 000 runs and 200 wickets. 21 years later the first – and only – instance of the 'Treble Double' (3 000 runs and 300 wickets) was completed by Ian Botham.

The fewest Test matches in which a player has completed the 'double' is 21 by Ian Botham for England between 28 July 1977 and 30

THE TEST 'DOUBLE'

ENGLAND	Tests	Runs	Wkts	Tests for 'double'
T.E. Bailey	61	2290	132	47
I.T. Botham	85	4636	357	21
A.W. Greig	58	3599	141	37
R. Illingworth	61	1836	122	47
W. Rhodes	58	2325	127	44
M.W. Tate	39	1198	155	33
F.J. Titmus	53	1449	153	40
AUSTRALIA				
R. Benaud	63	2201	248	32
A.K. Davidson	44	1328	186	34
G. Giffen	31	1238	103	30
I.W. Johnson	45	1000	109	45
R.R. Lindwall	61	1502	228	38
K.R. Miller	55	2958	170	33
M.A. Noble	42	1997	121	27
SOUTH AFRICA				
T.L. Goddard	41	2516	123	36
WEST INDIES				
G. St A. Sobers	93	8032	235	48
NEW ZEALAND				
R.J. Hadlee	66	2397	334	28

INDIA

Kapil Dev	77	3132	291	25
M.H. Mankad	44	2109	162	23

PAKISTAN

Imran Khan	57	2140	264	30
Intikhab Alam	47	1493	125	41
Sarfraz Nawaz	55	1045	177	55

August 1979. Botham holds similar records for the doubles of 1500 runs and 150 wickets (30 Tests) and 2000 runs and 200 wickets (42 Tests).

The fastest 'double' in terms of time was achieved by Kapil Dev for Indian one year 107 days between 18 October 1978 and 2 February 1980. At 21 years 27 days, Kapil Dev is **the youngest to score 1000 runs and take 100 wickets in a Test career.**

The first player to complete the 'double' was George Giffen, the first South Australian to gain an Australian cap. Known as 'The W.G. Grace of Australia', he achieved this feat when he took his 100th wicket on 18 July 1896 against England at Old Trafford, Manchester, in his 30th match. No Englishman did the 'double' until 26 December 1913 when Wilfred Rhodes claimed his 100th wicket, at the Old Wanderers, Johannesburg.

Gary Sobers is **the only player to score 1000 runs, take 100 wickets and hold 100 catches in Test cricket.** In 93 matches between 30 March 1954 and 5 April 1974, he scored 8032 runs, took 235 wickets and held 109 catches. Ian Botham needed just four catches to equal this feat when he began the 1986–87 Ashes series in Australia.

The only player to scored 500 runs and take 25 wickets in a series is Aubrey Faulkner of South Africa. In five matches against England, between 1 January and 14 March 1910, he scored 545 runs (average 60.55) and took 29 wickets (average 21.89) with his variations of flight, pace and spin.

One of the earliest exponents of the googly, Faulkner was dependable right-handed batsman and versatile fieldsman whom many rate as South Africa's greatest all-rounder. One of the games's keenest analysts, he later settled in England and opened the first indoor cricket school (near Richmond-upon-Thames).

The first player to complete the 'double double' was Richie Benaud. He scored his 2000th run on 6 December 1963 against South Africa at Brisbane — in the last of his 28 matches as Australia's captain.

The first player to complete the 'treble double' was Ian Botham when he took his 300th wicket — against West Indies at The Oval on 9 August 1984 in his 72nd Test.

The first player to score a century and take ten or more wickets in the same Test match was Ian Botham. In the Golden Jubilee Test on 15–19 February 1980 at Bombay's newest Test arena, the Wankhede Stadium, Botham took 6 for 58, scored 114 and then routed India's second innings by taking 7 for 48. No other batsman scored fifty in the match. His unique performance hurried the game to a premature end, England winning by ten wickets a day and a half ahead of schedule. Botham's feat was emulated by Imran Khan at the Iqbal Stadium, Faisalabad, on 3–8 January 1983 when Pakistan's captain scored 117 and returned match figures of 11 for 180.

Alan Davidson is the only other cricketer to take ten wickets and score a total of 100 runs in a Test. In the famous tie with West Indies at Brisbane's 'Gabba' on 9–14 December 1960, the Australian left-hander scored 44 and 80, and recorded analyses of 5 for 135 and 6 for 87.

The only player to score a century and take five wickets in an innings of the same Test on more than two occasions is Ian Botham of Somerset and England. He achieved this feat five times during a span of 61 Tests within a six-year

300 RUNS AND 30 WICKETS IN A SERIES

	Tests	Runs	Wickets	Series	Venue	Season
G. Giffen	5	475	34	A v E	Australia	1894-95
R. Benaud	5	329	30	A v SA	South Africa	1957-58
I.T. Botham	6	399	34	E v A	England	1981

period of his Test career:

103	5-73	v New Zealand	Christchurch	1977-78
108	8-34	v Pakistan	Lord's	1978
114	6-58 7-48	v India	Bombay	1979-80
149*	6-95	v Australia	Leeds	1981
138	5-59	v New Zealand	Wellington	1983-84

The only wicket-keeper to score 3000 runs and make 300 dismissals in Test cricket is Rodney Marsh of Western Australia. He completed this treble on 20 March 1982 against New Zealand at Christchurch.

The following have achieved the wicket-keeper's career 'double' of 1000 runs and 100 dismissals:

England	Tests	Runs	Dismissals	Tests for 'Double'
T.G. Evans	91	2439	219	42
A.P.E. Knott	95	4389	269	30
J.M. Parks	46	1962	114	41
R.W. Taylor	57	1156	174	47
Australia				
R.W. Marsh	96	3633	355	25
W.A.S. Oldfield	54	1427	130	41
South Africa				
J.H.B. Waite	50	2405	141	36
West Indies				
P.J.L. Dujon	37	1849	126	30
D.L. Murray	62	1993	189	33
India				
S.M.H. Kirmani	88	2759	198	42
Pakistan				
Wasim Bari	81	1366	228	53

The first wicket-keeper to score 1000 runs and make 100 dismissals was Bert Oldfield of Australia. He achieved that record on 23 June 1934 while playing against England at Lord's in his 41st Test.

The fewest Tests in which a wicket-keeper has reached this double landmark is 25 by Rodney Marsh of Australia, during the period from 27 November 1970 to 24 March 1974.

The youngest to complete the wicket-keeper's Test 'double' is Alan Knott. He was 25 years 120 days old when he made his 100th dis-missal for England on 7 August 1971 during the Manchester Test against India.

The only wicket-keeper to make 25 dismissals and score 250 runs in a series is John Waite of South Africa. In five matches against New Zealand in South Africa during the 1961–62 season, he scored 263 runs and set a new series record (since beaten) by making 26 dismissals.

The most runs in a series by a wicket-keeper is 606, average 86.57, by Waite's successor, Denis Lindsay. Playing in five Tests against Australia in South Africa during the 1966–67 season, Lindsay scored 69, 182, 5, 81, 137, 131 and 1. In the first Test, his contribution to South Africa's first home victory against Australia was 251 runs and eight catches.

The only other wicket-keeper to score 500 runs in a series in 'Budhi' Kunderan of India, who achieved an aggregate of 525 at home against England in the 1963–64 season.

The first wicket-keeper to score a century and make five dismissals in an innings of the same Test is Denis Lindsay. Playing for South Africa against Australia at the New Wanderers in Johannesburg on 23–28 December 1966, he held six catches in the first innings and scored 182 runs in the second.

His achievement has been emulated twice: Ian Smith scored 113 not out and claimed five dismissals for New Zealand against England at Eden Park, Auckland, on 10–15 February 1984; and Amal Silva scored 111 and held five catches for Sri Lanka against India at Colombo's Saravanamuttu Stadium on 6–11 September 1985.

Captaincy records

The youngest Test captain was the Nawab of Pataudi, jr (later Mansur Ali Khan). He was 21 years 77 days old when he first led India against West Indies at Bridgetown, Barbados, on 23 March 1962. He replaced Nari Contractor, whose skull had been fractured in the tourists' previous match, and went on to lead his country in 40 Tests.

The youngest England captain was Monty Bowden of Surrey. On the first tour of South Africa he led England in the Second Test at Newlands,

Cape Town, in the absence of C. Aubrey Smith. Bowden, who was 23 years 144 days old when the match began on 25 March 1889, remained in South Africa and played for Transvaal in the inaugural Currie Cup Challenge Match. Later he travelled to Rhodesia with the Pioneer Column of Cecil Rhodes. After three years there he died in the glorified mud hut which served as Umtali Hospital. His body had to be protected from marauding lions by an armed guard before it was interred in a coffin made out of whisky cases.

The oldest Test captain was W.G. Grace who was 50 years 320 days of age at the end of his 13th match as captain of England. That Test, the first ever played at Trent Bridge, Nottingham, ended on 3 June 1899 and marked the end of Grace's international career. By coincidence, it also marked the England debut of Wilfred Rhodes who was destined to become the oldest man to play in a Test match.

The second-oldest Test captain, and the oldest of modern times, 'Gubby' Allen, was 45 years 245 days old when England's Fourth Test against West Indies ended at Kingston, Jamaica, on 1 April 1948.

The record number of Test matches as captain is 74 by Clive Lloyd who led West Indies from 22 November 1974 until January 1985.

The most successive matches as captain is 39 by Garfield Sobers who led West Indies from March 1965 until April 1972.

The most successful captains in terms of the highest number of wins gained under their leadership, have been Clive Lloyd of West Indies (36 wins in 74 Tests), Greg Chappell of Australia (21 wins in 48 Tests), and Peter May of England (20 wins in 41 matches). Mike Brearley (18 wins in 31 matches) led England in 19 home Tests without a defeat (12 wins, 7 draws).

The most defeats suffered by one captain is 19 by the Nawab of Pataudi, jr (later Mansur Ali Khan) who led India in 40 matches between March 1962 and January 1975.

The highest number of drawn matches under one captain is 30 by Sunil Gavaskar who led India in 47 matches between January 1976 and

W.G. Grace (63) and A.E. Stoddart (71) return for lunch after scoring 134 on the first day of The Oval Test against Australia in 1893. (Mary Evans Picture Library)

February 1985. His leadership inspired nine of India's 38 victories and only eight defeats.

The most tosses won by one captain is 35 (out of 74) by Clive Lloyd for West Indies.

The record for winning the toss most matches in succession is nine by Colin Cowdrey for England (two v West Indies in (1959–60, all five v South Africa in 1960, and two v Australia in 1961).

The following captains have won every toss in a five-match series:

Captain	Series	Venue	Season
Hon F.S. Jackson	E v A	England	1905
M.A. Noble	A v E	England	1909
H.G. Deane	SA v E	South Africa	1927-28
J.D.C. Goddard	WI v I	India	1948-49
A.L. Hassett	A v E	England	1953
M.C. Cowdrey	E v SA	England	1960
Nawab of Pataudi, jr	I v E	India	1963-64
G. St A. Sobers	WI v E	England	1966
G. St A. Sobers	WI v NZ	West Indies	1971-72
C.H. Lloyd	WI v I	West Indies	1982-83

No captain has won every toss in a six-match series but four captains have won five out of six:

Captain	Series	Venue	Season
I.M. Chappell	A v E	Australia	1974-75
G.S. Chappell	A v WI	Australia	1975-76
G.N. Yallop	A v E	Australia	1978-79
K.W.R. Fletcher	E v I	India	1981-82

The first captain to elect to field first on winning the toss in a Test match was Percy McDonnell, the only Greek scholar to lead Australia. He was actually responsible for the first two instances of 'insertion', both were against England at Sydney (January 1887 and February 1888), and both gambles resulted in defeats for Australia.

Other individual records

The records for playing in the most Test matches and **most consecutive** appearances are held by Sunil Gavaskar for India. At the end of the 1986 series in England his records stood at 115 and 99 Tests respectively. Although he made his debut against West Indies at Port-of-Spain on 6 March 1971, his unbroken sequence of caps extends only from 23 January 1975.

The youngest cricketer to play in a Test match is Mushtaq Mohammad, who was 15 years 124 days of age (unconfirmed) when he appeared for Pakistan against West Indies at Bagi-i-Jinnah, Lahore, on 26 March 1959. The youngest whose date of birth has been confirmed is Derek Sealy who was aged 17 years 122 days when he made his debut for West Indies against England at Bridgetown, Barbados, on 11 January 1930. **The youngest Englishman to play Test cricket** is Brian Close, who was 18 years 149 days old when he played against New Zealand at Old Trafford, Manchester, on 23 July 1949.

The oldest man to play in a Test match was Wilfred Rhodes of Yorkshire and England. When he ended the last of his 58 appearances on 12 April 1930, he was 52 years 165 days old.

The oldest man to make his first appearance at Test level was James Southerton, who was 49 years 119 days of age when he played for England against Australia on 15 March 1877 in the first Test of all.

Wilfred Rhodes also holds the record for **the longest Test career,** a period of 30 years 315 days elapsing between his debut at Trent Bridge, Nottingham, on 1 June 1899 and the end of his final match for England at Kingston, Jamaica, on 12 April 1930.

The longest interval between Test match appearances is 17 years 316 days by George Gunn of Nottinghamshire and England. After playing against Australia at Sydney in a match ending on 1 March 1912, he was not recalled until 11 January 1930 at the start of a four-match series in the West Indies during his 51st year.

The longest-lived Test cricketer was The Mackinnon of Mackinnon whose sole Test match appearance was for Lord Harris's team at Melbourne in January 1879. Francis Mackinnon, 35th Chief of the Clan, died at his Morayshire home (Drumduan in Forres) in 1947 at the age of 98 years 324 days. He played in 78 matches for Kent (1875–85) and was the Club's president in 1889.

Twelve cricketers have represented more than one team at Test level. The first to do so, and the only player to appear both for and against Australia, was Billy Midwinter. Born at St Briavels

Wilfred Rhodes – longest Test career, oldest Test cricketer and most first-class appearances.

MOST APPEARANCES FOR EACH TEAM

	Total		E	A	SA	WI	NZ	I	P	SL
						Opponents				
England	114	M.C. Cowdrey	·	43	14	21	18	8	10	·
Australia	96	R.W. Marsh	42	·	·	17	14	3	20	·
South Africa	50	J.H.B. Waite	21	14	·	·	15	·	·	·
West Indies	110	C.H. Lloyd	34	29	·	·	8	28	11	·
New Zealand	66	R.J. Hadlee	17	19	·	7	·	8	10	5
India	115	S.M. Gavaskar	38	17	·	27	9	·	20	4
Pakistan	78	Zaheer Abbas	14	20	·	8	14	19	·	3

in the Forest of Dean, he emigrated to Australia, became a professional in Melbourne and played against England in the first-ever Test, taking 5 for 78 in the first innings. The first of cricket's international commuters, he played for Gloucestershire from 1877 until 1882, as well as appearing for Victoria. Touring Australia with Alfred Shaw's team, he opened the bowling for England in two of his four appearances in 1881–82 before resuming his Test career for Australia.

The record number of Test match appearances as an umpire is 48 by Frank Chester in England between 1924 and 1955.

Ground records

Official Test matches have been played on 59 different grounds, in 48 towns and cities, and within 13 countries (if one includes Bangladesh, seven Tests being staged at Dacca when it was within Pakistan).

The only city to have three grounds in regular current use for Test cricket is Colombo. The Saravanamuttu Stadium (formerly the Colombo Oval), the Singhalese Sports Club and the Colombo Cricket Club have collectively staged seven of Sri Lanka's eleven home Tests and both victories. Seven other centres have staged Test matches on more than one ground; Johannesburg and Bombay have used three, while London, Brisbane, Durban, Madras and Lahore have each employed two grounds.

The first Test match venue was the Melbourne Cricket Ground (MCG), frequently described as 'the paddock that grew'. Largely rebuilt as the main stadium for the 1956 Olympic Games, it is **the largest cricket ground in the world** with a capacity of 130 000. Crowds of over 120 000 are commonplace there for the grand finals of the Australian (Rules) football season. **The largest recorded attendance at any ground for a day of cricket** assembled at the MCG on 11 February 1961; numbering 90 800, it watched the second day's play in the Fifth Test between Australia and West Indies. The receipts for that day amounted to £A13 132 (£10 484 sterling).

PLAYERS WHO HAVE REPRESENTED TWO COUNTRIES

Amir Elahi	India (1) 1947-48	Pakistan (5) 1952-53
J.J. Ferris	Australia (8) 1886-87 to 1890	England (1) 1891-92
S.C. Guillen	West Indies (5) 1951-52	New Zealand (3) 1955-56
Gul Mahomed	India (8) 1946 to 1952-53	Pakistan (1) 1956-57
F. Hearne	England (2) 1888-89	South Africa (4) 1891-92 to 1895-96
A.H. Kardar	India (3) 1946	Pakistan (23) 1952-53 to 1957-58
W.E. Midwinter	Australia (8) 1876-77 to 1886-87	England (4) 1881-82
F. Mitchell	England (2) 1898-99	South Africa (3) 1912
W.L. Murdoch	Australia (18) 1876-77 to 1890	England (1) 1891-92
Nawab of Pataudi, sr	England (3) 1932-33 to 1934	India (3) 1946
A.E. Trott	Australia (3) 1894-95	England (2) 1898-99
S.M.J. Woods	Australia (3) 1888	England (3) 1895-96

The Colombo Cricket Club Ground – most picturesque of Colombo's three Test match arenas. (Author)

The most Test matches staged on one ground is 80 by Lord's Cricket Ground in London which celebrates the Bicentenary of its first Great Match in 1987.

The most recent addition to the list of Test arenas is Jinnah Park in Sialkot where Pakistan defeated Sri Lanka on 27-31 October 1985.

The greatest attendance at any cricket match is the estimated 394 000 for the Fourth Test between India and England at Eden Gardens, Calcutta, on 1-6 January 1982. **The largest recorded attendance** is 350 534 (receipts £30 124) for the Third Test between Australia and England at Melbourne on 1-7 January 1937. **The largest match attendance in England** is 159 000 for the Fourth Test between England and Australia at Headingley, Leeds, on 22-27 July 1948.

The record attendance for a Test series is 933 513 (receipts £87 963) for the five matches between Australia and England during the 1936-37 Australian season. The English record is 549 650 (receipts £200 428) for the series against Australia in 1953.

The world record for receipts from a cricket match is £668 312 from an attendance of 93 329 at the Second Test between England and Australia at Lord's on 27 June-2 July 1985.

The Test series record for receipts is £2 467 030 from the six matches between England and Australia in 1985. Played between 13 June and 3 September, they attracted a total attendance of 370 283.

Test Match Centre	First Test Day	Tests		Ground
England (313)				
Birmingham	29. 5.1902	24		Edgbaston
Leeds	29. 6.1899	49		Headingley
London – Lord's	21. 7.1884	80		Lord's Cricket Ground
– Oval	6. 9.1880	69		Kennington Oval
Manchester	10. 7.1884	54		Old Trafford
Nottingham	1. 6.1899	36		Trent Bridge
Sheffield	3. 7.1902	1		Bramall Lane
Australia (237)				
Adelaide	12.12.1884	4		Adelaide Oval
Brisbane	30.11.1928	30	2	Exhibition Ground (1928-29 to 1930-31)
	27.11.1931		28	Woolloongabba (1931-32 to date)
Melbourne	15. 3.1877	8		Melbourne Cricket Ground
Perth	11.12.1970	13		W. Australia Cricket Ass (WACA) Ground
Sydney	17. 2.1882	72		Sydney Cricket Ground (No. 1)
South Africa (98)				
Cape Town	25. 3.1889	24		Newlands
Durban	21. 1.1910	23	4	Lord's (1909-10 to 1921-22)
	18. 1.1923		19	Kingsmead (1922-23 to 1969-70)
Johannesburg	2. 3.1896		22	Old Wanderers (1895-96 to 1938-39)
	27.12.1948	39	6	Ellis Park (1948-49 to 1953-54)
	24.12.1956		11	Wanderers Stadium (1956-57 to 1969-70)
Port Elizabeth	12. 3.1889	12		St George's Park
West Indies (109)				
Bridgetown, Barbados	11. 1.1930	23		Kensington Oval
Georgetown, Guyana	21. 2.1930	9		Bourda
Kingston, Jamaica	3. 4.1930	6		Sabina Park
Port-of-Spain, Trinidad	1. 2.1930	7		Queen's Park Oval
St John's Antigua	27. 3.1981	4		Recreation Ground
New Zealand (84)				
Auckland	14. 2.1930†	8		Eden Park
Christchurch	10. 1.1930	6		Lancaster Park
Dunedin	11. 3.1955	8		Carisbrook
Napier	16. 2.1979	1		McLean Park
Wellington	24. 1.1930	21		Basin Reserve

The 1890 and 1938 Tests at Manchester, the 1970-71 Third Test at Melbourne, and the 1980-81 Test at Georgetown, all abandoned without a ball being bowled, are excluded from these figures.

† *Rain prevented play until 11.7.1884 at Manchester and until 17.2.1930 at Auckland.*

Test Match Centre	First Test Day	Tests		Ground
India (127)				
Ahmedabad	12.11.1983	1		Gujarat Stadium
Bangalore	22.11.1974	7		Karnataka Cricket Association Stadium
Bombay	15.12.1933	28	1	Gymkhana (1933-34 only)
	9.12.1948		17	Brabourne Stadium (1948-49 to 1972-73)
	23. 1.1975		10	Wankhede Stadium (1974-75 to date)
Calcutta	5. 1.1934	4		Eden Gardens
Delhi	10.11.1948	20		Feroz Shah Kotla
Hyderabad (Deccan)	19.11.1955	2		Fateh Maidan (Lal Bahadur Stadium)
Jullundur	24. 9.1983	1		Burlton Park
Kanpur	12. 1.1952	5		Green Park (Modi Stadium)
Lucknow	23.10.1952	1		University Ground
Madras	10. 2.1934	26	17	Chepauk (Chidambaram Stadium) (1933-34 to 1952-53, 1966-67 to date)
	6. 1.1956		9	Corporation (Nehru) Stadium (1955-56 to 1964-65)
Nagpur	3.10.1969	2		Vidarbha Cricket Association Ground
Pakistan (72)				
Bahawalpur	15. 1.1955	1		Dring Stadium
Dacca	1. 1.1955	7		Dacca Stadium (1954-55 to 1969-70‡)
Faisalabad	16.10.1978	9		Iqbal Stadium
Hyderabad (Sind)	16. 3.1973	5		Niaz Stadium
Karachi	26. 2.1955	24		National Stadium
Lahore	29. 1.1955	22	3	Lawrence Gardens (Bagh-i-Jinnah) (1954-55 to 1958-59)
	21.11.1959		19	Lahore (Gaddafi) Stadium (1959-60 to date)
Multan	30.12.1980	1		Ibn-e-Qasim Bagh Stadium
Peshawar	13. 2.1955	1		Peshawar Club Ground
Rawalpindi	27. 3.1965	1		Pindi Club Ground
Sialkot	27.10.1985	1		Jinnah Park
Sri Lanka (11)				
Colombo	17. 2.1982	7	3	P. Saravanamuttu Stadium (Colombo Oval)
	16. 3.1984		2	Singhalese Sports Club Ground
	24. 3.1984		2	Colombo Cricket Club Ground
Kandy	22. 4.1983	4		Asgiriya Stadium

‡ *East Pakistan became the People's Republic of Bangladesh on 16 December 1971.*

RECORD TOTALS FOR EACH TEST MATCH CENTRE

England

Centre	Highest Total			Lowest Total (Completed Innings)		
Birmingham	633-5d	England v India	1979	30	South Africa v England	1924
Leeds	584	Australia v England	1934	67	New Zealand v England	1958
London – Lord's	729-6d	Australia v England	1930	42	India v England	1974
– Oval	903-7d	England v Australia	1938	44	Australia v England	1896
Manchester	656-8d	Australia v England	1964	58	India v England	1952
Nottingham	658-8d	England v Australia	1938	88	South Africa v England	1960
Sheffield	289	Australia v England	1902	145	England v Australia	1902

Australia

Adelaide	674	Australia v India	1947-48	82	Australia v West Indies	1951-52
			1946-47	58	Australia v England	1936-37
Brisbane	645	Australia v England	1946-47	58	India v Australia	1947-48
Melbourne	604	Australia v England	1936-37	36	South Africa v Australia	1931-32
Perth	585	West Indies v Australia	1975-76	62	Pakistan v Australia	1981-82
Sydney	659-8d	Australia v England	1946-47	42	Australia v England	1887-88

South Africa

Cape Town	559-9d	England v South Africa	1938-39	35	South Africa v England	1898-99
Durban	654-5	England v South Africa	1938-39	75	Australia v South Africa	1949-50
Johannesburg	620	South Africa v Australia	1966-67	72	South Africa v England	1956-57
Port Elizabeth	549-7d	Australia v South Africa	1949-50	30	South Africa v England	1895-96

West Indies

Bridgetown	668	Australia v West Indies	1954-55	94	New Zealand v West Indies	1984-85
Georgetown	543-3d	New Zealand v West Indies	1971-72	109	West Indies v Australia	1972-73
Kingston	849	England v West Indies	1929-30	97†	India v West Indies	1975-76
Port-of-Spain	681-8d	West Indies v England	1953-54	90	Australia v West Indies	1977-78
St John's	550	West Indies v India	1982-83	170	England v West Indies	1985-86

New Zealand

Auckland	593-6d	England v New Zealand	1974-75	26	New Zealand v England	1954-55
Christchurch	560-8d	England v New Zealand	1932-33	65	New Zealand v England	1970-71
Dunedin	507-6d	Pakistan v New Zealand	1972-73	74	New Zealand v West Indies	1955-56
Napier	402	New Zealand v Pakistan	1978-79	360	Pakistan v New Zealand	1978-79
Wellington	537	New Zealand v England	1983-84	42	New Zealand v Australia	1945-46

India

Ahmedabad	281	West Indies v India	1983-84	103	India v West Indies	1983-84
Bangalore	457-5d	India v Australia	1979-80	118	India v West Indies	1974-75
Bombay	629-6d	West Indies v India	1948-49	88	India v New Zealand	1964-65
Calcutta	614-5d	West Indies v India	1958-59	90	India v West Indies	1983-84
Delhi	644-8d	West Indies v India	1958-59	107	Australia v India	1969-70
Hyderabad	498-4d	India v New Zealand	1955-56	89	India v New Zealand	1969-70
Jullundur	374	India v Pakistan	1983-84	337	Pakistan v India	1983-84
Kanpur	644-7d	India v West Indies	1978-79	105	Australia v India	1959-60
Lucknow	331	Pakistan v India	1952-53	106	India v Pakistan	1952-53
Madras	652-7d	England v India	1984-85	83	India v England	1976-77
Nagpur	322	Pakistan v India	1983-84	109	India v New Zealand	1969-70

Pakistan

Bahawalpur	312-9d	Pakistan v India	1954-55	235	India v Pakistan	1954-55
Dacca	439	England v Pakistan	1961-62	70	New Zealand v Pakistan	1955-56
Faisalabad	674-6	Pakistan v India	1984-85	145	Pakistan v West Indies	1980-81
Hyderabad	581-3d	Pakistan v India	1982-83	189	India v Pakistan	1982-83
				189	New Zealand v Pakistan	1984-85
Karachi	565-9d	Pakistan v New Zealand	1976-77	80	Australia v Pakistan	1956-57
Lahore	561	Pakistan v New Zealand	1955-56	104	Pakistan v West Indies	1958-59
Multan	249	West Indies v Pakistan	1980-81	166	Pakistan v West Indies	1980-81
Peshawar	245	India v Pakistan	1954-55	182	Pakistan v India	1954-55
Rawalpindi	318	Pakistan v New Zealand	1964-65	79	New Zealand v Pakistan	1964-65
Sialkot	259	Pakistan v Sri Lanka	1985-86	157	Sri Lanka v Pakistan	1985-86

Sri Lanka

Colombo	459	New Zealand v Sri Lanka	1983-84	132	Pakistan v Sri Lanka	1985-86
Kandy	514-4d	Australia v Sri Lanka	1982-83	97	Sri Lanka v New Zealand	1983-84

† Five men were absent hurt. The second lowest total at Kingston is 103 by England in 1934-35.

HIGHEST INDIVIDUAL SCORE FOR EACH TEST CENTRE

England

Birmingham	285*	P.B.H. May	England v West Indies	1957
Leeds	334	D.G. Bradman	Australia v England	1930
London – Lord's	254	D.G. Bradman	Australia v England	1930
– Oval	364	L. Hutton	England v Australia	1938
Manchester	311	R.B. Simpson	Australia v England	1964
Nottingham	278	D.C.S. Compton	England v Pakistan	1954
Sheffield	119	C. Hill	Australia v England	1902

Australia

Adelaide	299*	D.G. Bradman	Australia v South Africa	1931-32
Brisbane	226	D.G. Bradman	Australia v South Africa	1931-32
Melbourne	307	R.M. Cowper	Australia v England	1965-66
Perth	176	R.B. Simpson	Australia v India	1977-78
Sydney	287	R.E. Foster	England v Australia	1903-04

South Africa

Cape Town	209	R.G. Pollock	South Africa v Australia	1966-67
Durban	274	R.G. Pollock	South Africa v Australia	1969-70
Johannesburg	231	A.D. Nourse	South Africa v Australia	1935-36
Port Elizabeth	167	A.L. Hassett	Australia v South Africa	1949-50

West Indies

Bridgetown	337	Hanif Mohammad	Pakistan v West Indies	1957-58
Georgetown	259	G.M. Turner	New Zealand v West Indies	1971-72
Kingston	365*	G. St A. Sobers	West Indies v Pakistan	1957-58
Port-of-Spain	220	S.M. Gavaskar	India v West Indies	1970-71
St John's	178	I.V.A. Richards	West Indies v Australia	1983-84

New Zealand

Auckland	336*	W.R. Hammond	England v New Zealand	1932-33
Christchurch	258	S.M. Nurse	West Indies v New Zealand	1968-69
Dunedin	201	Mushtaq Mohammad	Pakistan v New Zealand	1972-73
Napier	119*	Majid Khan	Pakistan v New Zealand	1978-79
Wellington	255*	D.J. McGlew	South Africa v New Zealand	1952-53

India

Ahmedabad	98	P.J.L. Dujon	West Indies v India	1983-84
Bangalore	172	S.M. Gavaskar	India v England	1981-82
Bombay	242*	C.H. Lloyd	West Indies v India	1974-75
Calcutta	256	R.B. Kanhai	West Indies v India	1958-59
Delhi	230*	B. Sutcliffe	New Zealand v India	1955-56
Hyderabad	223	P.R. Umrigar	India v New Zealand	1955-56
Jullundur	201	A.D. Gaekwad	India v Pakistan	1983-84
Kanpur	250	S.F.A.F. Bacchus	West Indies v India	1978-79
Lucknow	124*	Nazar Mohammad	Pakistan v India	1952-53
Madras	236*	S.M. Gavaskar	India v West Indies	1983-84
Nagpur	89	M.G. Burgess	New Zealand v India	1969-70

Pakistan

Bahawalpur	142	Hanif Mohammad	Pakistan v India	1954-55
Dacca	165	G. Pullar	England v Pakistan	1961-62
Faisalabad	235	G.S. Chappell	Australia v Pakistan	1979-80
Hyderabad	280*	Javed Miandad	Pakistan v India	1982-83
Karachi	206	Javed Miandad	Pakistan v New Zealand	1976-77
Lahore	235*	Zaheer Abbas	Pakistan v India	1978-79
Multan	120*	I.V.A. Richards	West Indies v Pakistan	1980-81
Peshawar	108	P.R. Umrigar	India v Pakistan	1954-55
Rawalpindi	76	B.R. Taylor	New Zealand v Pakistan	1964-65
Sialkot	78	Mudassar Nazar	Pakistan v Sri Lanka	1985-86

Sri Lanka

Colombo	180	J.F. Reid	New Zealand v Sri Lanka	1983-84
Kandy	143*	D.W. Hookes	Australia v Sri Lanka	1982-83

BEST INNINGS BOWLING ANALYSIS FOR EACH TEST CENTRE

England

Birmingham	7-17	W. Rhodes	England v Australia	1902
Leeds	8-43	R.G.D. Willis	England v Australia	1981
London – Lord's	8-34	I.T. Botham	England v Pakistan	1978
– Oval	8-29	S.F. Barnes	England v South Africa	1912
Manchester	10-53	J.C. Laker	England v Australia	1956
Nottingham	8-107	B.J.T. Bosanquet	England v Australia	1905
Sheffield	6-49	S.F. Barnes	England v Australia	1902

Australia

Adelaide	8-43	A.E. Trott	Australia v England	1894-95
Brisbane	9-52	R.J. Hadlee	New Zealand v Australia	1985-86
Melbourne	9-86	Sarfraz Nawaz	Pakistan v Australia	1978-79
Perth	7-54	A.M.E. Roberts	West Indies v Australia	1975-76
Sydney	8-35	G.A. Lohmann	England v Australia	1886-87

South Africa

Cape Town	8-11	J. Briggs	England v South Africa	1888-89
Durban	8-69	H.J. Tayfield	South Africa v England	1956-57
Johannesburg	9-28	G.A. Lohmann	England v South Africa	1895-96
Port Elizabeth	8-7	G.A. Lohmann	England v South Africa	1895-96

West Indies

Bridgetown	8-38	L.R. Gibbs	West Indies v India	1961-62
Georgetown	7-44	I.W. Johnson	Australia v West Indies	1954-55
Kingston	7-34	T.E. Bailey	England v West Indies	1953-54
Port-of-Spain	9-95	J.M. Noreiga	West Indies v India	1970-71
St John's	6-74	C.E.H. Croft	West Indies v England	1980-81

New Zealand

Auckland	8-76	E.A.S. Prasanna	India v New Zealand	1975-76
Christchurch	7-75	F.S. Trueman	England v New Zealand	1962-63
Dunedin	7-52	Intikhab Alam	Pakistan v New Zealand	1972-73
Napier	5-106	Imran Khan	Pakistan v New Zealand	1978-79
Wellington	7-23	R.J. Hadlee	New Zealand v India	1975-76

India

Ahmedabad	9-83	Kapil Dev	India v West Indies	1983-84
Bangalore	6-53	R.G.D. Willis	England v India	1976-77
Bombay	7-48	I.T. Botham	England v India	1979-80
Calcutta	7-49	Ghulam Ahmed	India v Australia	1956-57
Delhi	8-52	M.H. Mankad	India v Pakistan	1952-53
Hyderabad	7-128	S.P. Gupte	India v New Zealand	1955-56
Jullundur	4-50	Wasim Raja	Pakistan v India	1983-84
Kanpur	9-69	J.M. Patel	India v Australia	1959-60
Lucknow	7-42	Fazal Mahmood	Pakistan v India	1952-53
Madras	8-55	M.H. Mankad	India v England	1951-52
Nagpur	6-74	S. Venkataraghavan	India v New Zealand	1969-70

Pakistan

Bahawalpur	6-74	P.R. Umrigar	India v Pakistan	1954-55
Dacca	6-21	Khan Mohammad	Pakistan v New Zealand	1955-56
Faisalabad	7-142	Abdul Qadir	Pakistan v Australia	1982-83
Hyderabad	7-87	S.L. Boock	New Zealand v Pakistan	1984-85
Karachi	8-60	Imran Khan	Pakistan v India	1982-83
Lahore	8-58	Imran Khan	Pakistan v Sri Lanka	1981-82
Multan	5-62	Imran Khan	Pakistan v West Indies	1980-81
Peshawar	5-63	S.P. Gupte	India v Pakistan	1954-55
Rawalpindi	4-5	Pervez Sajjad	Pakistan v New Zealand	1964-65
Sialkot	8-83	J.R. Ratnayeke	Sri Lanka v Pakistan	1985-86

Sri Lanka

Colombo	6-33	J.E. Emburey	England v Sri Lanka	1981-82
Kandy	6-45	Tausif Ahmed	Pakistan v Sri Lanka	1985-86

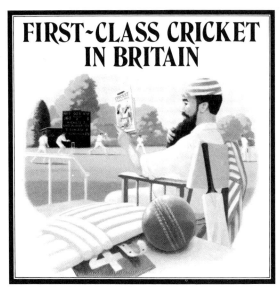

FIRST-CLASS CRICKET IN BRITAIN

The term 'first-class match' was not officially defined until 19 May 1947 when the Imperial Cricket Conference agreed that 'a match of three or more days duration between two sides of eleven players officially adjudged first-class, shall be regarded as a first-class fixture. Matches in which either team has more than eleven players or which are scheduled for less than three days shall not be regarded as first-class. The governing body in each country shall decide the status of teams.'

This ICC definition did not have retrospective effect. Although the MCC had controlled the status of the counties since 1895, the classification of matches outside the County Championship had rested largely with the Cricket Reporting Agency. This agency compiled the first-class averages for the leading publications of the day but only occasionally consulted the MCC about the status of non-Championship fixtures. Prior to 1895 the ranking of matches had been virtually a lottery, with scant agreement even on the status of certain counties.

In 1973 cricket statisticians founded an association which now boasts a world-wide membership of over 1000. The most important of their many publications is *The Guide to First-Class Matches Played in the British Isles 1864-1946.* Until the Association of Cricket Statisticians published that guide in 1976, all compilers of cricket records had to decide on their own list of first-class matches.

In compiling this section, I have accepted the *Guide's* classification of matches and have also only included matches played since the start of the 1864 season. Although 'Great Matches' can be traced back until 1709 when Kent played Surrey, no detailed score survives before that of the 1744 match between All-England and Kent and it was not until 1864 that **over-arm bowling was legalized** (10 June). That year also marked the first appearance of W.G. Grace in important matches (he scored 170 and 56 not out for the South Wales club against the Gentlemen of Sussex shortly before his sixteenth birthday), and the first publication by John Wisden & Co of *The Cricketer's Almanack.*

Team records

The highest innings total in any first-class match in Britain is 903 for 7 declared by England against Australia at The Oval in 1938. Full details appear in the Test Cricket section.

The highest innings total in County cricket – and the second-highest in all first-class matches in the British Isles – is 887 by Yorkshire against Warwickshire at Edgbaston, Birmingham, on 7-8 May 1896. It occupied the whole of the first two days (10 hours 50 minutes) and is **the longest innings in County matches.** It was **the first time in any first-class match that four batsmen had scored hundreds in the same innings:** F.S. Jackson 117, E. Wainwright 126, R. Peel 210 not out, and Lord Hawke 166.

The highest second innings total in Britain is 703 for 9 declared by Cambridge University against Sussex at Hove on 20-21 June 1890. Cambridge began their second innings 91 runs behind at 12.25 pm on the second day and declared after 90 minutes batting on the last morning, once the previous record first-class score (698 by Surrey in 1888) had been passed. The main contributors were F.G.J. Ford (191), C.P. Foley (117) and G. MacGregor (131), and the runs were scored at the rate of 74 per 100 balls.

Cambridge University also achieved **the highest fourth innings total in English first-class cricket** when they scored 507 for 7 on 26-27 June 1896 against MCC at Lord's. It remains **the world record total by a winning side in the fourth innings.** The main scorers were H.H.

Marriott (146*) and N.F. Druce (146).

The highest fourth innings total in Britain without the loss of a wicket is 270 by Surrey against Kent at The Oval on 25 July 1900. With Surrey needing 346 runs for victory in only 170 minutes, Bobby Abel (120*) and William Brockwell (132*) made a remarkable attempt at the virtually impossible target.

The highest match aggregate in Britain is 1723 runs by England and Australia at Headingley, Leeds, in 1948. Test matches apart, the highest is 1502 by MCC and the New Zealanders at Lord's in 1927. **The highest aggregate in a County Championship match** is 1475 by Northamptonshire and Surrey at Northampton in 1920.

The lowest innings total in all first-class cricket is 12, the two instances being by Oxford University (batting one short) against the MCC at Cowley Marsh, Oxford, on 24 May 1877, and by Northamptonshire against Gloucestershire at Gloucester on 11 June 1907.

Played on a poor wicket during a memorably wet season, the Oxford match was completed in one day (12.35 to 6.30 pm). Taking first innings and without their captain and future England cap, A.J. Webbe, Oxford were dismissed for just seven scoring strokes off 174 balls in two hours. Fred Morley's immaculate left-handed swing bowling claimed seven wickets for six runs. With another six wickets for eight runs in Oxford's second innings of 35, Morley returned, **in terms of runs per wicket the best match analysis in all first-class cricket:** 13 wickets for 14 runs.

Northamptonshire were victims of some brilliant left-arm slow bowling on a drying pitch, George Dennett being virtually unplayable and taking eight wickets for only nine runs, including the hat-trick. After dismissing Gloucestershire for 88, Northants needed 136 to win and had lost seven wickets (all to Dennett, who took 15 for 21 in the day) for 40 runs when rain washed out the final day's play.

The lowest first-class match aggregate by one team in Britain is 42 by Northamptonshire who, with one man absent ill, were dismissed for 27 and 15 by Yorkshire at Northampton in 2 hours 15 minutes on 8 May 1908.

The lowest aggregate of runs by both sides in any completed first-class match is 105 by the MCC (33-F.R. Spofforth 6 for 4 including the hat-trick – and 19) and the Australians (41 and 12 for 1) at Lord's on 27 May 1878. Starting at 12.03 pm, the match was all over at 6.20 pm.

The most wickets to fall in a single day's play in a first-class match is 39. This record was established at the Old Magdalen Ground in Oxford on 28 May 1880 when the MCC beat the University by one wicket. Because of rain the match did not begin until 11.30 am on the second day. By the time it ended at 7 pm, Oxford had been dismissed for 53 and 75 by the Nottinghamshire opening bowlers, Alfred Shaw (12 for 53) and Fred Morley (8 for 62), who operated unchanged throughout both innings. In September they were to contribute towards England's victory against Australia in the first Test match to be played in England. The MCC made 89 and 41 for 9, scraping home through an epic last-wicket partnership of 20 by their two successful bowlers.

The largest margin of victory in English first-class cricket is the innings and 579 runs by which England beat Australia at The Oval in August 1938. Excluding Test matches, the record is an innings and 517 runs by the Australians against Nottinghamshire at Trent Bridge, Nottingham, in June 1921. After amassing 675 (C.G. Macartney 345 in 235 minutes), the touring team bowled out Nottinghamshire for 58 and 100.

The largest margin of victory in a County Championship match is an innings and 485 runs by Surrey (698) against Sussex (114 and 99) at The Oval in August 1888.

The largest victory by a runs margin in English first-class cricket is 562 runs by Australia (701 and 327) against England at The Oval in August 1934.

The only instance of a side winning a first-class match in England without losing a wicket occurred at Old Trafford, Manchester, in July 1956 when Lancashire scored 166 for 0 declared and 66 for 0, beating Leicestershire (108 and 122) by ten wickets. Alan Wharton (87* and 33*) and Jack Dyson (75* and 31*) were **the first pair of batsman in all first-class cricket to**

monopolize totally their team's victory.

The most recent tied first-class match in England there have been 30 such results since 1864 – occurred on 17 July 1984 and was the first tie in 745 Championship matches on the County Ground at Northampton. Kent declared twice (250 for 6 and 204 for 5) and set Northamptonshire a target of 331 in 80 overs. A maiden hundred by Duncan Wild left the last-wicket pair of Alan Walker and Jim Griffiths with the task of scoring 17 runs for victory. Although they levelled the scores with four balls to spare, Walker could not make contact with any of them and his partner was run out attempting a scrambled bye off the final delivery. Exactly two weeks earlier Kent had tied against Sussex at Hastings.

The last first-class match to end on the first day was between Kent (187) and Worcestershire (25 and 61) at the Nevill Ground, Tunbridge Wells on 15 June 1960.

The fewest runs in a full day's play in first-class matches in Britain since 1864 is 134 by Glamorgan (134 for 3) against Hampshire at the United Services Officer's Ground, Portsmouth, on 5 June 1964. Glamorgan, 175 runs behind on first innings, batted throughout the final day – the second day had been lost to rain – scoring only 134 for 3 wickets off 95 overs.

The most runs in any day of first-class cricket is 721 by the Australians against Essex at Southchurch Park, Southend-on-Sea, in 5 hours 48 minutes on 15 May 1948. Sid Barnes (79), Bill Brown (153), Don Bradman (187 in 125 minutes), Ron Hamence (46), Sam Loxton (120), and Ron Saggers (104*) took full advantage of a fast pitch and small ground to delight a packed Whit Saturday crowd. The total was scored at a rate of 120 runs per hour and 93 runs per 100 balls.

The fastest innings by any team in all first-class cricket is Kent's 219 for 2 against Gloucestershire at the Crabble Ground, Dover, on 20 August 1937. Needing to score 218 runs for victory in under two hours, Bill Ashdown (62*), Frank Woolley (44), Les Ames (70) and Alan Watt (39*) hit off the runs in 71 minutes at the record rate of

156 runs per 100 balls.

The most hundreds in an innings of a first-class match in Britain is four. There have been 15 instances, the most recent being on 3-4 May 1982 when the first four Kent batsmen – Bob Woolmer (126), Neil Taylor (127), Chris Tavaré (125) and Mark Benson (120) – all reached three figures against Oxford University in The Parks. The last instance in a County Championship match was by Surrey (David Fletcher, Stan Squires, Jack Parker and Errol Holmes) against Nottinghamshire at Trent Bridge, Nottingham, in May 1947.

The highest number of fifties in any first-class innings is eight by the Australians against Oxford and Cambridge Universities Past and Present at the United Services Ground, Portsmouth on 31 July, 1 and 2 August 1893. The main contributors to a total of 843 were, in batting order, J.J. Lyons (51), A.C. Bannerman (133), G.H.S. Trott (61) H. Graham (83), W. Bruce (191), H. Trumble (105), C.T.B. Turner (66) and W.F. Giffen (62). The innings, which lasted ten hours and was compiled at a rate of 69 runs per 100 balls, was then the highest in all first-class matches and remains the highest by any representative Australian team.

The only instance in all first-class cricket of all 22 players bowling in a match occurred at the Central Ground, Hastings, in September 1964 during a light-hearted festival match between A.E.R. Gilligan's XI and the Australians.

The only instance of ten different fielders holding catches during a first-class innings happened at Grace Road, Leicester, on 31 August 1967. The only Leicestershire player not to take a catch during Northamptonshire's first innings of 211, Jack Birkenshaw, compensated by capturing three wickets with his off-breaks.

Although there are now ten ways in which a batsman can lose his wicket, three of them occur very rarely and the tenth one ('timed out') was introduced in 1980 and has yet to claim its first victim at first-class level. The three unusual dismissals are: handled the ball, hit the ball twice, and obstructing the field; the most recent instances of each of them in English first-class cricket are:

Handled the Ball

A. Rees	Glamorgan v Middlesex	Lord's	1965

Hit the Ball Twice

J.H. King	Leicestershire v Surrey	The Oval	1906

Obstructing the Field

Khalid Ibadulla	Warwickshire v Hampshire	Coventry	1963

The most extras conceded in an innings of a first-class match in Britain is 73 (48 byes, 23 leg byes and 2 wides) by Kent during Northamptonshire's innings of 374 at Northampton in August 1955. Most of the byes came from the bowling of Doug Wright; his sharply-spun, lifting leg-breaks and googlies eluded Tony Catt, whose wicket-keeping was seriously impeded by severe sunburn.

Batting records

The highest individual score in first-class cricket in Britain is 424 by Archie MacLaren for Lancashire against Somerset at Taunton on 15-16 July 1895. Opening the innings, he was seventh out at 792 after giving only two chances – the first when he was 262 – and batting for 470 minutes. MacLaren hit a six, 62 fours, 11 threes, 37 twos and 63 singles. His score passed the previous highest of 344 by W.G. Grace and remained the world first-class record until Bill Ponsford scored 429 in 479 minutes in February 1923.

The highest score by a batsman in Britain making his first appearance in first-class cricket is 215 not out by Hubert Doggart for Cambridge University against Lancashire at Fenner's on 3 May 1948.

The highest score by a batsman appearing only once in English first-class cricket is 156 by 2nd Lt Michael Harbottle for the Army against Oxford University at the Royal Military College (Sandhurst) Ground, Camberley, on 25 June 1938. A 21-year-old left-handed opening batsman from the Oxfordshire and Buckinghamshire Light Infantry, he scored another century (before lunch) a month later against the Royal Navy at Lord's but never played again at first-class level. His playing

Mike Harbottle scored 156 in his only first-class innings.

career with Dorset spanned 21 seasons (1936-56). Brigadier Harbottle became director of the Centre for Peacebuilding Studies and one of the 'Generals for Peace'.

The most runs added during a batsman's innings in all first-class matches is 811 during Bobby Abel's 357 not out for Surrey against Somerset at The Oval on 29-30 May 1899. His score, **the highest by anyone carrying their bat through a completed innings,** was made in just over 8½ hours and contained 1 six, 7 fives, 38 fours, 11 threes, 23 twos and 85 singles. Surrey's total remains their highest in all first-class matches and the highest through which any batsman has carried his bat.

The highest score by a number eleven batsman in all first-class cricket is 163 by Peter Smith for Essex against Derbyshire at Queen's Park, Chesterfield on 7 August 1947. Beginning his innings when Essex were 24 runs behind Derbyshire's first innings total of 223, he added 218 with Frank Vigar in what remains the record Essex partnership for the tenth wicket. Smith hit 3 sixes and 22 fours in an historic innings which paved the way for his team's victory by five wickets. The next highest score by a 'last man' is 126.

The record score in all first-class cricket by a batsman compelled by injury to bat with the aid of a runner is 181 by Gerald Crutchley. Playing for the Free Foresters against Cambridge University at Fenner's on 6-7 June 1919 he made the highest score of his career while 'suffering from lameness' *(Wisden)*.

The only batsman to score hundreds in each innings of a first-class match with the aid of a runner is Graeme Fowler of Lancashire at Southport on 28-30 July 1982. He strained a thigh muscle while fielding during Warwickshire's record fourth-wicket stand of 470 on the first day. Opening Lancashire's reply, he managed to score 26 before adding a further 100 runs with a runner. His scores of 126 and 128 not out enabled Lancashire to win an amazing match by ten wickets. When Fowler completed his second hundred, his runner had his hand shaken by a fielder and waved his bat to acknowledge the applause. A month later Fowler marked his Test debut with a fine innings of 86 which gained his selection for the imminent England tour of Australasia.

The only batsman to score double centuries in both innings of a first-class match is Arthur Fagg of Kent. Playing against Essex at Castle Park, Colchester, on 13-15 July 1938, the right-handed opener scored 244 in five hours and 202 not out in only 170 minutes. His second innings opening partnership of 283 with Peter Sunnucks remains the county record.

The only batsman to score two first-class hundreds on the same day is K.S. Ranjitsinhji who scored 100 and 125 not out on 22 August 1896. Playing for Sussex against Yorkshire at Hove, he began the day with his first innings overnight score at 0 not out.

The record for the most hundreds in consecutive first-class innings was set in 1901 by Charles Fry when he ended the season with six succession. After scoring 106, 209, 149, 105 and 140 for Sussex, he hit 105 for the Rest of England against Yorkshire at Lord's. His final century was his thirteenth of the season, setting a record which stood until 1925. Don Bradman and Mike Procter subsequently equalled Fry's record run of six hundreds during seasons overseas.

The only batsman to score hundreds in each innings of successive first-class matches in Britain is Tom Hayward of Surrey. Within a period of six days during the first week of June 1906, he opened the innings with scores of 144 not out and 100 against Nottinghamshire at Trent Bridge, Nottingham, and 143 and 125 against Leicestershire at Aylestone Road, Leicester.

The only instance of a father and son each scoring hundreds in the same first-class innings occurred at Edgbaston, Birmingham, on 23-24 July 1931 when George Gunn and his son George Vernon Gunn scored 183 and 100 not out respectively for Nottinghamshire against Warwickshire. George Gunn, then aged 52, made only one more hundred before retiring from the first-class scene the following year. For his 26-year-old son it was the first of eleven hundreds during a career which ended in 1950 with an isolated emergency recall, eleven years after his retirement from the county game.

The most occasions that any batsman has scored a double century and a century in the same match is four by Zaheer Abbas for Gloucestershire. All eight innings were not out:

Scores		Opponents	Venue	Season
216*	156*	Surrey	The Oval	1976
230*	104*	Kent	Canterbury	1976
205*	108*	Sussex	Cheltenham	1977
215*	150*	Somerset	Bath	1981

Zaheer's match aggregate of 372 against Surrey at The Oval in 1976 is **the highest without dismissal by any batsman in English first-class cricket.**

The only batsman to carry his bat through both innings of a first-class match and to score centuries on each occasion is Cecil Wood of Leicestershire. Playing against Yorkshire at Park Avenue, Bradford, in June 1911, he contributed 107 not out and 117 not out towards Leicestershire's totals of 309 and 296. He batted in all for 8 hours 40 minutes and in neither innings did he give a chance.

The record for the most fifties in consecutive first-class innings was set by Ernest Tyldesley with ten in succession between 26 June and 27 July 1926. It was equalled by Don Bradman during the 1947-48 Australian season and the 1948 tour of England.

His sequence of scores was as follows:

144	Lancashire v Warwickshire	Birmingham
69	Lancashire v Kent	Dover
144*	Lancashire v Kent	Dover
226	Lancashire v Sussex	Manchester
51	Lancashire v Surrey	The Oval
131	Lancashire v Surrey	The Oval
131	Players v Gentlemen	Lord's
106	Lancashire v Essex	Nelson
126	Lancashire v Somerset	Taunton
81	England v Australia	Manchester

The most runs by a batsman during a first-class match in England is 446 by Arthur Fagg of Kent. Playing against Essex at Castle Park, Colchester, in July 1938 he achieved the unique feat of scoring two double centuries in a match (244 and 202*).

The highest sequence of runs scored by any batsman before being dismissed in first-class matches in Britain is 575 by Everton Weekes for West Indies during July 1950. He scored 246 not out against Hampshire at Southampton and 200 not out against Leicestershire at Grace Road, before being dismissed for 129 in the Third Test against England at Nottingham.

The fastest fifty in all first-class cricket took only 8 minutes (1.22 to 1.30 pm), and was scored off 13 balls by Clive Inman for Leicestershire against Nottinghamshire at Trent Bridge, Nottingham, on 20 August 1965. With the home county giving away cheap runs to encourage an early declaration on the final day, the 29-year-old left-hander from Colombo was fed slow full tosses by Norman Hill, who was very much a non-bowler. After getting off the mark with a single from the last ball of an over from Brian Bolus, another very occasional bowler, Inman struck Hill's two overs for 50 runs (440064 and 466664) with pulls to and over the mid-wicket boundary.

The fastest first-class hundred was scored in 35 minutes by Percy Fender for Surrey against Northamptonshire at Northampton on 26 August 1920. Surrey were 448 for 5 in reply to the home county's 306, when Fender joined Alan Peach with 29 minutes to go before tea on the second day. Dropped after making his first run, Fender scored 93 in the 29 minutes before tea and added his next ten runs in 6 minutes afterwards, reaching his century with a six. His first 50 took 19 minutes. The declaration came at 619 for 5 when Peach completed his 200, Fender having scored 113 not out during an unfinished partnership of 171 in 42 minutes. This represents a rate of 244 runs per hour and is the fastest partnership on record of more than 30 minutes duration. Fender's time would almost certainly have been even faster but for the tea interval occurring during his innings. After tea Peach had most of the strike so that he could reach his 200 before the closure. It was his maiden three-figure innings at first-class level.

Although it is generally acknowledged that the only fair and accurate method of assessing the scoring rate of an innings is by comparing the number of balls received, very few first-class innings have been recorded in this way. The 'vertical' scoring system, which is believed to have been the brainchild of the renowned and much-travelled Australian scorer, Bill Ferguson, is still not used by the majority of scorers at first-class matches. Recording the number of balls faced by an individual batsman under the standard system of scoring is very much a hit and miss affair. From the official scorebook it is impossible to calculate the number of balls which Fender received during those 35 minutes. Scorebook research shows that it is likely to have been between 40 and 46.

Fender's world record was equalled in bizarre circumstances 63 years later by Steve O'Shaughnessy. An uncapped 22-year-old all-rounder, he

Steve O'Shaughnessy receives the 1983 Walter Lawrence Trophy from director Brian Thornton. (Author)

opened Lancashire's second innings with Graeme Fowler at Old Trafford shortly before 3.00pm on 13 September, the final afternoon of the 1983 season. The first half of their championship match with Leicestershire had been lost to rain. After scoring 150 to gain the batting point they required to secure fourth place and its prize-money (£1750), the visitors declared 86 runs behind in the hope of being set a target for a victory chase after tea. To induce such an equation two non-bowlers purveyed a succession of long-hops and full-tosses. These were first blocked in protest before the batsmen began an assault which produced 190 runs and O'Shaughnessy's second first-class hundred in 35 minutes before tea. Scored off 54 balls (at least eight more than Fender required), it included 5 sixes and 17 fours. His partnership of 201 in 43 minutes with Fowler is the fastest double-century stand on record. All Leicestershire's efforts were in vain. There was no declaration and, as *Wisden* records sadly, 'the season ended in travesty.'

The fastest 150 in all first-class matches took Gilbert Jessop just 63 minutes. Playing for the Gentlemen of the South against the Players of the South in the Hastings Festival on 3 September 1907, 'The Croucher' scored 191 out of 234 in 90 minutes, taking only 42 minutes to reach his century after being bowled for a duck in the first innings.

The fastest time for scoring a first-class double-century in Britain is exactly 2 hours

and two instances have been recorded. Gilbert Jessop was responsible for the first. Playing for Gloucestershire against Sussex at Hove on 1 June 1903, he made 286 – his highest score – out of 355 in under three hours and with the aid of 41 fours. Jessop's record time was equalled 73 years later by Clive Lloyd when he scored 201 not out against Glamorgan at St Helen's, Swansea. On 9 August 1976, while captaining the West Indians, the Guyanese left-hander hit 7 sixes and 27 fours reached his hundred in 80 minutes (including a break for drinks), and raced to his share of the record just 40 minutes later.

The fastest triple-century in first-class cricket in Britain was scored by Charles Macartney for the Australians against Nottinghamshire at Trent Bridge, Nottingham, on 25 June 1921. After reaching his 300 in 205 minutes, he added another 45 in half an hour before falling lbw after hitting 4 sixes and 47 fours. His innings of 345 remains the highest for the Australians in all matches. It is also the world record for **the most runs in any day of first-class cricket.**

The first batsman to score a century before lunch on the first day of what was then described as an 'important' match was W.G. Grace. On 11 August 1869 at the St Lawrence Ground, Canterbury, he opened the MCC's innings against Kent and was 116 not out at lunch. His innings of 127 founded a total of 449 and victory by an innings.

The only batsman to score a pre-lunch hundred in both innings of any first-class match is Gilbert Jessop. Playing for Gloucestershire against Yorkshire at Park Avenue, Bradford, he scored 104 before lunch on the second day (24 July 1900), and 139, including 7 sixes off Wilfred Rhodes, during the same session on the third. Both his innings were begun and completed before lunch. Jessop was the most prolific scorer of hundreds in an hour or less with eleven instances between 1897 and 1913.

The highest number of runs scored in a pre-lunch session in English first-class cricket is 180 by K.S. Ranjitsinhji for Sussex against Surrey. At Hastings on 15 July 1902, the second day of a match which was to set a new record English aggregate of 1427 runs, 'Ranji' took his overnight score from 54 to 234 not out in 150 minutes. It was a chanceless piece of batting which included 39 fours.

The most runs scored from a single hit in any first-class match is ten. The record was set at The Oval on 14 July 1873 when opening batsman A.N. Hornby, whose score of 20 was the highest of Lancashire's total of 100, made half his runs off a single delivery from James Street of Surrey. It was equalled at Lord's on 26 May 1900 when Samuel Wood (later Hill-Wood) of Derbyshire scored ten off a ball from C.J. Burnup (MCC) in the second innings. This second instance was recorded under the experimental 'net' system of scoring which the

Gilbert Jessop scored two pre-lunch hundreds in one match.

MCC tried out in their own club matches during the early part of that season. The boundary was enclosed with a net of between two and three feet in height with the object of making batsmen run all their hits. Three runs were scored if the ball went over the net and two runs were added to any completed if the net stopped the ball. The system put a premium on hits that just reached the netting but discounted full-blooded strokes, and the whole idea was abandoned after a few trials.

The most runs off any over in all first-class cricket is 36, a record set by Garfield Sobers when he was batting for Nottinghamshire against Glamorgan at St Helen's, Swansea, on 31 August 1968. Coming to the wicket ten minutes before tea on the first day with the scoreboard showing 308 for 5, the Nottinghamshire and West Indies captain had scored 40 in 30 minutes when Malcolm Nash began his historic over. Normally a medium-fast swing bowler, the 23-year-old left-hander was experimenting with a slower style of delivery. Sobers struck the first four balls for giant sixes. His next stroke sent the ball soaring towards long-off but it was caught by Roger Davis just inside the boundary. After completing the catch, Davis fell and his shoulders crossed the line. Sobers was saved by an experimental clause added to Law 35 which decreed that: 'The Fieldsman must have no part of his body grounded outside the playing area in the act of making the catch and afterwards.' The umpires conferred with Davis before awarding a six and Sobers celebrated by striking the last delivery into the garden of The Cricketers pub. The ball was lost until a schoolboy recovered it the next day and it was duly presented to Sobers. As the crowd stood cheering, he closed the innings at 394 for 5. He had scored 76 not out in 35 minutes. As Tony Lewis, captain of Glamorgan, commented: 'It wasn't sheer slogging through strength, but scientific hitting with every movement working in harmony.'

Ravi Shastri equalled this world record in 1985 – see *'First-class cricket in India'.*

Mike Procter is the only other batsman to hit 6 successive sixes in first-class cricket. Captaining Gloucestershire against Somerset at Taunton on 27 August 1979, he struck sixes off the last two balls of Dennis Breakwell's second over. Procter's partner, Andy Stovold, then played out a maiden over from Ian Botham, before the South African all-rounder hit sixes off the first four balls of the left-arm slow bowler's third over.

Until the law was amended in 1910, the ball usually had to be hit right out of the ground and not just over the boundary for six runs to be scored. Before that change the record was held by Charles Thornton with 9 sixes. Batting for Kent on the Common at Tunbridge Wells against Sussex on 13 July 1869, he had to strike the ball over the canvas surrounding the ground to gain six runs. In the words of one of the Sussex team, 'At least three of the hits would have gone away for eights (*if they had been run out).*'

The most sixes in any first-class match is 17 by Jim Stewart for Warwickshire against Lancashire at Stanley Park, Blackpool, in July 1959. A powerfully-built right-handed opening batsman, who had been given rugby football trials for Wales, Stewart hit 10 sixes in his first innings of 155 and 7 in his second of 125.

The highest number of runs in any first-class innings from strokes worth four or more is 272. The record was set by Percy Perrin of Essex against Derbyshire at Queen's Park, Chesterfield, on 18-19 July 1904. Batting first wicket down, he hit 68 fours in his score of 343 not out, made in 5¾ hours. **Besides containing the most boundaries on record in any first-class innings, his score is the highest for Essex, the highest by any Englishman who was never selected for England, and the highest by any player on the losing side.**

The slowest fifty in English first-class cricket was recorded at Lord's on 15-16 August 1982 when Chris Tavaré, playing for England in the

The most sixes hit in a first-class innings in Britain is 13. There have been four such instances, only the most recent being by a home-born batsman:

Second Test against Pakistan, took 350 minutes to reach his half-century. In that time he faced 236 balls, scoring off only 25 (3 fours, 5 threes, 7 twos and 10 singles), and playing out no fewer than 17 maiden overs. He batted 67 minutes before scoring and spent exactly an hour on 24, thus recording **the only first-class innings to include two runless periods of an hour or more.**

The slowest first-class hundred in Britain took Keith Fletcher 7 hours 38 minutes. Playing for England in the Third Test against Pakistan at The Oval in August 1974, he reached his fifth Test century off his 329th ball after hitting 7 fours, 5 threes, 10 twos and 39 singles.

The slowest double and triple centuries in first-class matches in Britain were recorded by Bob Simpson during his innings of 311 for Australia against England in the Fourth Test at Old Trafford, Manchester, in July 1964. He took 10 hours 8 minutes to reach 200, and 12 hours 33 minutes for his triple century. It was his maiden Test hundred and his 52nd innings for Australia. **His innings was the longest ever played against England (762 minutes), and the highest by any Test captain.**

The first batsman to score a century in first-class cricket without hitting a single boundary was Roger Iddison. Captaining Yorkshire against Cambridgeshire at Woodhouse Hill, Hunslet, he batted nearly five and a half hours for 112 on 12 and 13 July 1869. His highest scoring strokes were 15 threes. It remains **the highest innings without a boundary hit,** earned him a presentation of £5, and was sufficient to defeat Cambridgeshire (40 and 46) on its own. Iddison, who also played for Lancashire and Cheshire, was principal organiser of the United North of England Eleven.

The longest time any batsman has waited to score his first run during a first-class innings in Britain is 81 minutes. This bizarre record

Batsman	Score	For	Opponents	Venue	Season
Majid Khan	147*	Pakistanis	Glamorgan	Swansea	1967
C.G. Greenidge	273*	D.H. Robins' XI	Pakistanis	Eastbourne	1974
C.G. Greenidge	259	Hampshire	Sussex	Southampton	1975
G.W. Humpage	254	Warwickshire	Lancashire	Southport	1982

fell to a 19-year-old Law student from Pembroke College, Cambridge, at Lord's in July 1974 during the 130th University Match. Cambridge were 136 runs ahead of Oxford with three second innings wickets in hand, when Edward Jackson began his remarkable innings 66 minutes before the end of the second day's play. Next morning he battled on for a further 15 minutes before getting off the mark with a pull to the mid-wicket boundary off his 72nd ball. In the next over, after that one scoring stroke, he was caught at the wicket off the new ball. The match ended in a disappointing draw.

The longest period without adding to an individual score in a first-class match in Britain is 79 minutes by Trevor Bailey for England against South Africa in the Fourth Test at Heading-ley, Leeds, on 26 July 1955. Bailey, who had opened the batting in the first innings, came to the wicket shortly after lunch on the last (fifth) day with the score 204 for 4. Needing a further 277 runs in four hours, England soon lost two more wickets and decided to try to draw the Test and retain their 2-1 lead in the five-match series. Bailey's masterly display of a full range of defensive strokes could only extend the contest by two hours and he was eventually last out at 256. England won the final Test.

The longest individual innings in English first-class cricket lasted 13 hours 17 minutes and was played by Len Hutton for England against Australia at The Oval on 20, 22 and 23 August 1938. He scored 160 in 355 minutes on the first day, and 140 in 307 minutes on the second, both days being interrupted by rain. Sixth out at 2.30 pm on the third day after helping to add a world record 770 runs, Hutton had amassed the (then) record Test score of 364 by hitting 35 fours, 15 threes, 18 twos and 143 singles.

The world record for the highest percentage of runs by one batsman in any completed first-class innings was set by Glenn

Glenn Turner demonstrates the style and timing that brought him 141 of Worcestershire's 169. (Ken Kelly)

Turner on 30 June 1977. Opening the batting for Worcestershire against Glamorgan at St Helen's, Swansea, he carried his bat throughout the innings of 169 and took his overnight score of 39 to 141 not out. He thus contributed over 83 per cent of the total. The other batsmen managed only 14 scoring strokes between them and none reached double figures. Turner batted for 220 minutes and hit a six and 18 fours.

The lowest completed innings total to include an innings of 50 in first-class cricket is 66 by the Indians against Yorkshire at St George's Road, Harrogate, in July 1932. While his ten colleagues managed nine runs between them, Nazir Ali rattled up 52 in an hour, hitting 3 sixes and 5 fours.

The lowest total to include a first-class century is 143 by Nottinghamshire against Hampshire at Dean Park, Bournemouth, on 4 July 1981. Clive Rice, their captain, scored 105 not out on a well-grassed pitch and under heavy cloud. Coming to the wicket at 19 for 2, he struck a six, a five and 16 fours.

The lowest completed innings total to include a double century is 298 by Gloucestershire against Glamorgan at Newport on 8 August 1956. Starting his innings with the score 9 for 2, Tom Graveney scored 200 in 340 minutes, struck 3 sixes and 20 fours, and, unlike the batsmen monopolizing the previous two records, he finished on the winning side.

The highest number of runs scored in any season of first-class cricket is 3816 by Denis Compton of Middlesex and England in 1947. He averaged 90.85 runs per completed innings and set another world record by making 18 hundreds. He scored 2033 runs in Championship matches, 753 in five Tests against South Africa, and 1030 in other matches; altogether 1187 'of his runs came off the South African attack. In addition the 29-year-old Compton took 73 first-class wickets, 57 of them in the County Championship. That same summer his 'terrible twin' Bill Edrich scored 3539 runs and took 67 wickets. Perhaps not surprisingly Middlesex were County Champions and England were comfortable winners of the rubber against South Africa.

The first batsman to score 2000 runs in first-class matches in a single season was W.G. Grace when he amassed 2739 runs in 1871. War years excepted, at least one batsman scored 2000 runs in every season from 1895 until 1973 inclusive, but no one attained that total in 1974, 1975, 1979 or 1980. The first to score 3000 runs in a season was K.S. Ranjitsinhji with 3159 in 1899.

The record for scoring 2000 runs in a season most times is 17 by Jack Hobbs of Surrey and England between 1907 and 1931.

The youngest batsman to score 2000 runs in a season is Graeme Hick of Worcestershire who was 20 years 112 days old when he reached that milestone during his final innings of the 1986 season.

The only batsman to score 2000 runs in a season without hitting a century is David Green. Playing for Lancashire in 1965, he scored 2037 runs (average 32.85). Although he reached 40 on 20 occasions, his highest score was only 85.

The record for scoring 1000 runs in an English first-class season most times is 28. It is shared by W.G. Grace of Gloucestershire and London County, between 1869 and 1902, and Frank Woolley of Kent who achieved the feat in 28 consecutive seasons from 1907 to 1938 inclusive.

The first batsman to score ten first-class hundreds in a season was W.G. Grace in 1871, and the record has progressed as follows: 12 – R. Abel (1900); 13 – C.B. Fry (1901); 16 – J.B. Hobbs (1925); 18 – D.C.S. Compton (1947). Not until 1978-79 did any batsman score ten centuries in an overseas season.

The first player to average over 100 runs per completed innings in an English season was Don Bradman (115.66 in 1938). On each of his four tours of Britain (1930, 1934, 1938 and 1948) he averaged over 80 (98.66, 84.16, 115.66 and 89.92), and on each tour he exceeded the average of the leading home batsman of that season.

The only English batsman to average over 100 in a home season and the only player to do

right, Graeme Hick threatens to be the master batsman of the Nineties. (Adrian Murrell/All-Sport)

Glenn Turner, off-duty with TVNZ, was seldom caught napping at the crease. (Author)

so on more than one occasion is Geoffrey Boycott.

The highest aggregate of runs scored by a batsman in the season in which he made his initial appearance in first-class cricket is 1839 by Herbert Sutcliffe in 1919. Because of the First World War, he made his debut at the comparatively late age of 24.

The highest partnerships for each wicket by English teams in first-class cricket in Britain have all been recorded in County Championship matches:

The youngest player to score 1000 runs in his first season is Denis Compton who was 18 years 7 days old when he made his first-class debut, scoring 14 at number eleven against Sussex at Lord's in May 1936.

Only three batsmen have scored 1000 runs in May, although four others have reached that aggregate before June with the aid of innings in April. W.G. Grace was the first to do so (1895); he was also the oldest (46 years 10 months), and he did so in the fewest innings (10: 13, 103, 18, 25, 288, 52, 257, 73*, 18, 169). Wally Hammond achieved the highest May aggregate with 1042 in 1927, while Charles Hallows was the last to do so in 1928 and achieved the highest average for 1000 runs in May (125.00).

The four batsmen who scored 1000 runs before June were Tom Hayward (1900), Don Bradman (1930 and 1938), Bill Edrich (1938 – all scored at Lord's), and Glenn Turner (1973).

The earliest date for scoring 1000 runs in a first-class season in Britain is 27 May and was recorded in 1938 by Don Bradman, captain of the Australian touring team.

The earliest dates for reaching both 2000 and 3000 runs in a season were achieved by Tom Hayward of Surrey in 1906. He scored his 2000th run on 5 July and completed his 3000 on 20 August. In 1937 Wally Hammond of Gloucestershire equalled the latter record.

The highest sixth-wicket partnership in Britain is 428 between M.A. Noble (284) and W.W. Armstrong (172*) for the Australians against Sussex at Hove in 1902.

Wkt	Runs	Batsmen (scores)	Match	Venue	Season
1st	555	P. Holmes (224*), H. Sutcliffe (313)	Yorkshire v Essex	Leyton	1932
2nd	465*	J.A. Jameson (240*), R.B. Kanhai (213*)	Warwicks v Gloucs	Birmingham	1974
3rd	424*	W.J. Edrich (168*), D.C.S. Compton (252*)	Middlesex v Somerset	Lord's	1948
4th	470	A.I. Kallicharran (230*), G.W. Humpage (254)	Warwicks v Lancs	Southport	1982
5th	393	E.G. Arnold (200*), W.B. Burns (196)	Worcs v Warwicks	Birmingham	1909
6th	411	R.M. Poore (304), E.G. Wynyard (225)	Hampshire v Somerset	Taunton	1899
7th	344	K.S. Ranjitsinhji (230), W. Newham (153)	Sussex v Essex	Leyton	1902
8th	292	R. Peel (210*), Lord Hawke (166)	Yorkshire v Warwicks	Birmingham	1896
9th	283	J. Chapman (165), A. Warren (123)	Derbyshire v Warwicks	Blackwell	1910
10th	235	F.E. Woolley (185), A. Fielder (112*)	Kent v Worcestershire	Stourbridge	1909

HIGHEST BATTING AVERAGES IN AN ENGLISH SEASON

		Season	I	NO	Runs	Average
D.G. Bradman	Australians	1938	26	5	2429	**115.66**
G. Boycott	Yorkshire	1979	20	5	1538	**102.53**
W.A. Johnston	Australians	1953	17	16	102	**102.00**
G. Boycott	Yorkshire	1971	30	5	2503	**100.12**
D.G. Bradman	Australians	1930	36	6	2960	**98.66**
H. Sutcliffe	Yorkshire	1931	42	11	3006	**96.96**
R.M. Poore	Hampshire	1899	21	4	1551	**91.23**
D.R. Jardine	Surrey	1927	14	3	1002	**91.09**
D.C.S. Compton	Middlesex	1947	50	8	3816	**90.85**
G.M. Turner	Worcestershire	1982	16	3	1171	**90.07**

Jack Hobbs and Herbert Sutcliffe shared eleven century opening partnerships against Australia.

With the exception of the sixth and tenth wickets, the English team records have not been improved upon by visiting teams from overseas.

The record tenth-wicket partnership is 249 between C.T. Sarwate (124*) and S.N. Banerjee (121) for the Indians against Surrey at The Oval in 1946. This stand provided **the only instance of the last two batsmen in the order scoring centuries in the same innings.**

The world record for the most consecutive runless innings in first-class matches is ten by Jim Griffiths, the Northamptonshire opening bowler. After scoring 6 in his debut match, he failed to improve on that aggregate in his next eight games spread over the 1974, 1976 and 1977 seasons. His 'scores' during that barren period were 0,0*,0*,0,0,0,0,0*,0 and 0.

Paul Garlick, a first-year Engineering undergraduate at Jesus College, scored only one run in 12 innings for Cambridge University in 1984. His full record for that season, which encompassed his entire first-class career, included a sequence of nine innings without scoring: 2,0,0,0,0,0,0*,0,0,0,1*, 0,0* and, in the 'Varsity Match, 4*.

Bowling records

The only bowler to take all ten wickets in a first-class innings on three occasions is A.P. 'Tich' Freeman of Kent:

O	M	R	W	Opponents	Venue	Season
42	9	131	10	Lancashire	Maidstone	1929
30.4	8	53	10	Essex	Southend	1930
36.1	9	79	10	Lancashire	Manchester	1931

The only bowler to take all ten wickets in a first-class innings twice in the same season is Jim Laker in 1956. Both instances were achieved against the Australians: 10 for 88 for Surrey at The Oval on 16 May, in 46 overs bowled in 4¼ hours interrupted only by the lunch and tea intervals; and 10 for 53 for England in the Fourth Test at Old Trafford, Manchester, on 28, 30 and 31 July, in 51.2 overs. Only one other bowler, Edward Barratt for the Players in 1878, has taken all ten Australian wickets in an innings.

The least expensive ten wickets analysis in first-class cricket and the only instance to include a hat-trick, was achieved by Hedley Verity for Yorkshire at Headingley, Leeds, on 12 July 1932. At lunch on that last day, Nottinghamshire had scored 38 without loss after gaining a first innings lead of 71. After the interval they lost all ten wickets for the addition of only 29 runs, Verity ending the innings with a spell of seven wickets in 15 balls, including four in six balls. His full analysis read: 19.4-16-10-10.

The last bowler to take all ten wickets in a first-class innings in Britain was Ian Thomson. Playing for Sussex against Warwickshire at the Manor Ground, Worthing, on 6 and 8 June 1964, he exploited a rain-affected pitch to take 10 for 49. Although his medium-fast seam bowling accounted for 15 wickets, Thomson finished on the losing side when Sussex were routed for 23 in the second innings.

The only bowler to take 19 wickets in any first-class match is Jim Laker who took 9 for 37 and 10 for 53 for England against Australia in the Fourth Test at Manchester in July 1956. His incredible performance is fully described in the Test match section.

The most outstanding match analysis in Country cricket (and, Laker's 19 for 90 excepted, the most wickets for least runs in all first-class cricket), is 17 for 48 by Colin Blythe for Kent against Northampton at Northampton on 1 June 1907. Rain had restricted play on the first two days to just three hours. Kent, 212 for 4 overnight, hastily took their total to 254 all out. 'Northamptonshire gave a deplorable display', according to *Wisden*, and lost their first seven wickets for four runs, two of them extras, with six of their first seven batsmen failing to score. Shortly after lunch they were all out for 60, Blythe taking all ten for 30 in 16 overs. Following on, they fared even worse and were dismissed in 75 minutes for 39, Blythe's left-arm spin claiming 7 for 18 in 15.1 overs. He bowled unchanged throughout both innings and became **the first player to take 17 wickets in a day.** Heavy rain fell almost immediately after Kent had completed this remarkable victory.

The most dramatic spell of wicket-taking in post-war first-class cricket was achieved by Pat Pocock's off-breaks on 15 August 1972 in the closing minutes of the match between Sussex and Surrey at The Saffrons, Eastbourne. Sussex, attempting to score 205 for victory, were 187 for 1 with three of the 20 overs compulsory in the last hour still to be bowled. Geoffrey Greenidge (68*) and Roger Prideaux (92*) had so far added 160 runs in 107 minutes for the second wicket and a Sussex victory seemed assured. Pocock's analysis at this stage was 14-1-63-0. Then, at exactly six o'clock, he began his historic spell:

Ball	Striker	Result	Total	Runs required	Balls remaining
1	Greenidge	bowled	187-2	18	17
2	M.A. Buss	no run	187-2	18	16
3	M.A. Buss	bowled	187-3	18	15
4	J.M. Parks	2 runs	189-3	16	14
5	J.M. Parks	no run	189-3	16	13
6	J.M. Parks	ct by bowler	189-4	16	12

Prideaux (4,1) and Mike Griffith (0,0,6,0) took eleven runs off the penultimate over, bowled by Robin Jackman, and five runs were needed for victory when Pocock began the final over:

Ball	Striker	Result	Total	Runs required	Balls remaining
1	Prideaux	caught	200-5	5	5
2a	Griffith	caught	200-6	5	4
3b,c	J.D. Morley	stumped	200-7	5	3
4	J. Spencer	1 run	201-7	4	2
5d,e	A. Buss	bowled	201-8	4	1
6	U.C. Joshi	run out going for 2nd run	202-9	3	–

And so the match was left drawn. Five wickets fell in the final over – **a world record for any over in first-class cricket** – and eight wickets were lost in 18 balls for 15 runs in 20 minutes. The historic final over took ten minutes to bowl. At the end of it Pocock's analysis read 16-1-67-7 and he had equalled or broken three world records. The highlights of his performance were:

a Hat-trick – his second in first-class matches.
b Four wickets in four balls – only the third instance by a Surrey bowler.
c **Six wickets in nine balls – world record.**
d **Seven wickets in eleven balls – world record.**
e **Five wickets in six balls – equalling world record.**

The only other bowler to take five wickets in six balls in English first-class cricket is Bill Copson who achieved this feat for Derbyshire against Warwickshire at Derby on 17 July 1937. Returning after a month's absence through injury, 'he maintained great speed and made the ball swing dis-

concertingly either way' *(Wisden)*. Warwickshire were bowled out for 28, Copson returning figures of 8 for 11 in 8.2 overs – the best analysis of a first-class career which began sensationally in 1932 when he took the wicket of Andy Sandham with his very first ball.

The most outstanding spell of wicket-taking in first-class cricket was recorded by Alonzo Drake for Yorkshire against Somerset at Weston-super-Mare on 28 August 1914. Bowling unchanged throughout both innings of the match with Major Booth for the second time in that week, he took all ten second innings wickets in the space of 42 balls. A left-arm bowler of slow to medium pace, he took full advantage of a rain-affected newly-laid pitch to become the first Yorkshire bowler to take all ten wickets in a first-class innings.

The first recorded instance of a hat being given to a bowler for taking three wickets with consecutive balls occurred on 8 September 1858. Playing for the All-England Eleven against 22 of Hallam and Staveley at the Hyde Park Ground, Sheffield, H.H. Stephenson accomplished this feat in the second innings and was presented with a white hat. The terms 'to do a hat-trick' and 'to get a hat' evolved from this practice.

The only bowler to have hit the stumps with five successive balls in a first-class match is Charlie Parker of Gloucestershire. Bowling against County champions Yorkshire at Bristol in his own benefit match on 10 August 1922, he suffered the mortification of having the second dismissal nullified by a call of 'no ball'.

The only bowler to take two hat-tricks in the same innings of a first-class match in England is Albert Trott. He achieved this unique performance for Middlesex in his benefit match against Somerset at Lord's on 22 May 1907. After taking four wickets with four balls (one lbw and three bowled), he completed his county's victory by 166 runs with his second hat-trick (two caught and one bowled), finishing with figures of 7 for 20 in eight overs.

The only bowler to achieve a hat-trick with three stumpings in all first-class cricket is Charles Townsend of Gloucestershire. A 16-year-old leg-spinner, he was playing against Somerset at Cheltenham on 15 August 1893, when he fi   ed off their second innings with the aid of   ee successive stumpings by William Brain.

The only bowler to take a hat-trick entirely through lbw decisions on more than one occasion in first-class cricket is Mike Proctor. Playing for Gloucestershire, he first achieved this unusual feat against Essex at Westcliff in 1972, and repeated it against Yorkshire at Cheltenham seven years later.

The record number of hat-tricks achieved by a bowler in first-class matches in Britain

Charlie Parker – slow left-arm hat-trick specialist.

is six. Charlie Parker (left-arm spin) was the first to reach this total; all his instances were for Gloucestershire between 1922 and 1930, and, in 1924, he established another record by taking three hat-tricks in the same season. The only other bowler to take six hat-tricks in Britain is Doug Wright; he claimed all his for Kent between 1937 and 1949 with his unique assortment of leg-breaks and googlies delivered at a bounding medium pace. Wright's last instance established the world record as it was his seventh in all first-class matches, the extra hat-trick being achieved for the MCC against Border at East London in January 1939.

TWO HAT-TRICKS IN THE SAME MATCH

Bowler	For	Opponents	Venue	Season
†A. Shaw	Nottinghamshire	Gloucestershire	Nottingham	1884
T.J. Matthews	Australia	South Africa	Manchester	1912
C.W.L. Parker	Gloucestershire	Middlesex	Bristol	1924
R.O. Jenkins	Worcestershire	Surrey	Worcester	1949

† *Alfred Shaw also took three wickets in four balls, a combination of bowling feats never equalled within a single first-class match.*

The only bowler to take a wicket with his first ball in BOTH innings of his maiden first-class match is Rudi Webster. A Barbadian fast bowler who was later to represent Warwickshire and Otago as well as his home Island, Webster played for Scotland against the MCC at Glenpark, Greenock, on 14-16 June 1961 while studying medicine at Edinburgh University. He bowled T.C. 'Dickie' Dodds of Essex with his first ball in the first innings, and repeated the feat against Arthur Phebey of Kent in the second. His first match analysis was 11 for 100.

The highest number of runs conceded by a bowler in a first-class innings in Britain is 298 by L.O. ('Chuck') Fleetwood-Smith of Australia, during 87 overs bowled in England's world record Test total of 903 for 7 declared at The Oval in August 1938. The most expensive analysis in County Championship matches is 6 for 231 by Charlie Parker for Gloucestershire against Somerset at Bristol in August 1923. He bowled 63 overs in the innings which was closed at 532 for 9.

The most runs conceded by a bowler in a first-class match in Britain is 331 by A.P. 'Tich' Freeman of Kent. Playing against the MCC at Folkestone in September 1934, he bowled 68 overs in the match, taking 6 for 199 and 2 for 132. The most runs conceded in a County Championship match is 306 by Johnny Briggs of Lancashire. In July 1897 he bowled 126 five-ball overs against Sussex at Old Trafford, Manchester, taking 2 for 174 and 2 for 132.

The most balls bowled in a first-class innings in Britain is 588 by Sonny Ramadhin for West Indies at Edgbaston in June 1957. After taking 7 for 49 in England's first innings, he was unable to break a partnership of 411 between May and Cowdrey and had figures of 2 for 179 from his record 98 overs. The most sent down by one bowler in a Championship match is 501 by Alfred Shaw for Sussex at Trent Bridge, Nottingham, in May 1895. Eighteen years after bowling the first ball in Test cricket, he contributed 100.1 five-ball overs and took 4 for 168 in Nottinghamshire's (then) record total of 726 all out.

The most balls bowled in a first-class match in Britain is 774 by Sonny Ramadhin for West Indies against England at Edgbaston, Birmingham, in 1957. The record for a County Championship match is held by Johnny Briggs of Lancashire. He bowled 630 balls in taking 4 for 306 against Sussex at Old Trafford, Manchester, in July 1897.

The last instance of a pair of bowlers operating throughout both completed innings of a first-class match anywhere occurred in June 1967. Brian Crump (5 for 45 and 7 for 29) and Ray Bailey (5 for 64 and 3 for 31) bowled Northamptonshire to victory over Glamorgan by 132 runs in the first-class match at Sophia Gardens, Cardiff.

The most recent instance of a bowler taking a wicket with his first ball in first-class cricket occurred on 6 May 1981, at Edgbaston, Birmingham, when Chris Lethbridge of Warwickshire dismissed Geoffrey Boycott of Yorkshire.

The last player to bowl eight batsmen in an innings of a first-class match in Britain was G.O.B. 'Gubby' Allen. Playing for Middlesex against Lancashire at Lord's on 15 June 1929, he took all ten wickets for 40, hitting the stumps eight times and getting his remaining victims caught at the wicket and stumped respectively.

The only bowler to take 300 wickets in a first-class season is A.P. 'Tich' Freeman of Kent. One of the finest leg-break bowlers of all time, he took over 200 wickets in each of eight consecutive seasons from 1928 until 1935 inclusive. It was in the first year of that unique run that he took 304 wickets. Many of his victims were stumped by Les Ames and the two players formed a highly efficient partnership; Ames made over 100 dismissals in 1928, 1929 and 1932, and 47 per cent of his aggregate for those three seasons were stumpings.

The last bowler to take 200 wickets in a first-class season was Tony Lock of Surrey in 1957 (212 wickets at 12.02 runs apiece.

The last bowler to take 150 wickets in a first-class season was another left-arm slow-medium bowler, Derek Underwood of Kent. In 1966 he captured 157 wickets at an average of 13.80 runs each.

The highest aggregate of first-class wickets in any season since 1966 is 134 by Malcolm Marshall in 22 matches for Hampshire in 1982.

MOST FIRST-CLASS WICKETS IN A SEASON

Bowler	Season	Balls	Runs	Wickets	Average
A.P. Freeman	1928	11857	5489	304	18.05
A.P. Freeman	1933	12234	4549	298	15.26
T. Richardson	1895	8451	4170	290	14.37
C.T.B. Turner	1888	9710	3307	283	11.68
A.P. Freeman	1931	9708	4307	276	15.60
A.P. Freeman	1930	11487	4632	275	16.84
T. Richardson	1897	8019	3945	273	14.45
A.P. Freeman	1929	10025	4879	267	18.27
W. Rhodes	1900	9318	3606	261	13.81
J.T. Hearne	1896	10016	3670	257	14.28
A.P. Freeman	1932	9395	4149	253	16.39
W. Rhodes	1901	9390	3797	251	15.12

The feat of taking 100 first-class wickets was achieved in every season from 1864 until 1971 inclusive, war years excepted. In 1972 the County Championship programme was reduced to 20 matches for each county and no bowler took 100 wickets in 1972 or 1976. Order was restored with the addition of two matches from 1977 until 1982 inclusive, and a further two from 1983 onwards. These extra fixtures have helped to produce 14 instances of this feat in the last ten seasons.

Until 1982 no award was made to the first bowler to take 100 wickets in a first-class season. The Swanton Trophy, a handsome silver stump, survived for only four years, Malcolm Marshall becoming its first holder on 25 August 1982. He was succeeded by John Emburey, John Lever and Neal Radford.

The only instance in important matches of a player bowling ten batsmen in an innings was achieved by John Wisden at Lord's on 15 July 1850. Playing for the North against the South, the founder of the most famous *Cricketers' Almanack* bowled unchanged from the Pavilion End for the second time in the match. 'Without exaggeration, his balls turned in a yard from the off' *(Haygarth).*

The record for taking 100 first-class wickets in a season most times is held by Wilfred Rhodes of Yorkshire. The greatest wicket-taker of all time (4184), this left-arm slow bowler, who played Test cricket at later age than any other man, captured 100 or more wickets in a season 23 times between 1898 and 1929.

The highest number of consecutive seasons in which any bowler has taken 100 first-

John Wisden.

Tony Lock. (Sport & General)

Derek Underwood. (Sport & General)

class wickets is 20. This incredible record of consistency was achieved by Derek Shackleton of Hampshire between 1949 and 1968 inclusive. Such was 'Shack's' skill and accuracy that his career average dropped as the years progressed.

The lowest recorded average by a bowler taking 100 wickets in a season is 8.54 runs per wicket by Alfred Shaw of Nottinghamshire when he took 186 wickets for 1589 runs in 1880.

The two most expensive instances of taking 100 first-class wickets in a season were recorded by Ray Smith of Essex. An all-rounder who could bowl either right-arm medium-pace or slow off-spin, he took 125 wickets (average 37.26) in 1947 and 102 (average 34.77) in 1950.

The records for the most runs conceded and most balls bowled in a first-class season were, perhaps not surprisingly, set by the man who took most wickets: A.P. 'Tich' Freeman. In 1928 when he achieved his record haul of 304 wickets, he conceded 5489 runs – the only instance of any bowler conceding 5000 runs in a single summer. Five years later, when he took 298 wickets, he bowled 12 234 balls – the only instance of one man sending down 12 000 balls in one season.

Only eleven bowlers have taken 100 wickets in the season in which they made their debut in first-class cricket. Wilfred Rhodes took most wickets in his first year (154). Derek Underwood was the last to do so and the youngest.

The earliest date for taking 100 first-class

E.W. Swanton presents the trophy bearing his name to John Emburey. (Author)

wickets in a season is 12 June. Jack Hearne of Middlesex set the record in 1896, and Charlie Parker of Gloucestershire equalled it in 1931.

The earliest date for taking 200 first-class wickets in a season is 27 July, a record established by A.P. 'Tich' Freeman of Kent in 1928.

The only instance of a bowler taking 300 first-class wickets in a season was achieved

100 WICKETS IN DEBUT SEASON

Bowler	County	Age	Season	Wickets	Average
G.P. Harrison	Yorkshire	21	1883	100	13.26
A.W. Mold	Lancashire	25	1889	102	11.83
C.H.G. Bland	Sussex	24	1897	129	21.68
W. Rhodes	Yorkshire	20	1898	154	14.60
F. Barratt	Nottinghamshire	20	1914	115	21.80
A. Waddington	Yorkshire	26	1919	100	18.74
J.M. Gregory	Australians	23	1919	131	18.19
G.W. Brook	Worcestershire	41	1930	132	21.88
C. Cook	Gloucestershire	24	1946	133	18.62
D.B. Close	Yorkshire	18	1949	113	27.87
D.L. Underwood	Kent	17	1963	101	21.12

Jack Gregory did not play first-class cricket in Australia until the 1919-20 season.

Jack Hearne – 100 wickets before mid-June.
(Mary Evans Picture Library)

by Freeman in 1928, that unique total being reached on 15 September.

The longest recorded distance for a bail to travel from the stumps after a batsman has been bowled is 67 yards 6 inches. This record occurred at Old Trafford, Manchester, on 29 June 1911 when Robert Burrows of Worcestershire bowled William Huddleston of Lancashire and one of the bails flew as far as the boundary.

Record all-round performances

The only cricketer to score a century and take all ten wickets in an innings in a first-class match in Britain since 1864 is W.G. Grace. Playing for the MCC against Oxford University in the Oxford Parks on 21 and 22 June 1886, 'The Champion' scored 104 in his only innings,

before taking all ten Oxford second innings wickets for 49 runs in 36.2 four-ball overs.

The only player to score a hundred in each innings and take five wickets twice in any first-class match is George Hirst of Yorkshire. At Bath on 27, 28 and 29 August 1906, he scored 111 and 117 not out (during which he completed his 2000 runs for the season), and took 6 for 70 and 5 for 45.

The only player besides Hirst to score hundreds in each innings and take ten wickets in a first-class match is Bernard Bosanquet, orginator of the googly (or 'bosie' as Australians call it). Playing for Middlesex against Sussex at Lord's in May 1905, he scored 103 in 105 minutes, took 3 for 75, hit 100 not out in 75 minutes, and then applied the *coup de grâce* which secured victory by 324 runs when he bowled unchanged through the last innings to return figures of 8 for 53.

Seven cricketers have scored a century and taken a hat-trick in the same first-class match in Britain, Mike Procter being the only one to do so twice. William Roller achieved a unique version of this record when he scored a double century and did the hat-trick for Surrey against Sussex in June 1885.

The double of 1000 runs and 100 wickets in a first-class season was first achieved in 1874 by W.G. Grace when he scored 1664 runs and took 140 wickets. 'The Champion' repeated this performance in each of the next four seasons, but it was not until 1882 that another player, C.T. Studd, emulated him.

From 1895 until 1967 inclusive and war years excepted, the double of 1000 runs and 100 wickets was achieved at least once each season apart from 1951 and 1958. Only one player has completed the double since the Championship was reduced by four matches per county in 1969.

The last player to do the double was Richard Hadlee in 1984. In 24 matches for Nottinghamshire, New Zealand's most talented all-round cricketer scored 1179 runs and took 117 wickets, completing the first double for 17 years on 27 August in his 21st match.

CENTURY AND HAT-TRICK IN THE SAME MATCH

Batsman	Score	For	Opponents	Venue	Season
G. Giffen	113	Australians	Lancashire	Manchester	1884
W.E. Roller	204	Surrey	Sussex	The Oval	1885
W.B. Burns	102*	Worcestershire	Gloucestershire	Worcester	1913
V.W.C. Jupp	102	Sussex	Essex	Colchester	1921
L.N. Constantine	107	West Indians	Northamptonshire	Northampton	1928
D.E. Davies	139	Glamorgan	Leicestershire	Leicester	1937
M.J. Procter	102	Gloucestershire	Essex	Westcliff	1972
M.J. Procter	122	Gloucestershire	Leicestershire	Bristol	1979

The fastest double was completed on 28 June 1906 by George Hirst of Yorkshire after 16 matches.

The youngest player to achieve the double, and the only one to do so in his first season of first-class cricket, was Brian Close of Yorkshire in 1949 at the age of 18.

Two players did this double for two counties: Vallance Jupp for Sussex (1920 and 1921) and Northamptonshire (eight times between 1925 and 1933); and Freddie Brown for Surrey (1932) and Northamptonshire (1949).

The record for scoring 1000 runs and taking 100 wickets in a season most times is held by

George Hirst and Wilfred Rhodes, Yorkshire's most prolific all-rounders, achieved a combined total of 30 doubles.
(Nottinghamshire CCC)

Wilfred Rhodes of Yorkshire; he achieved this double 16 times between 1903 and 1926 inclusive.

The most consecutive seasons in which a player has done the double is eleven by George Hirst of Yorkshire from 1903 until 1913 inclusive. He achieved the double 14 times in all, a total second only to that of Rhodes.

The only player to do the double double of 2000 runs and 200 wickets in a first-class season is also George Hirst. In 1906, at the age of 35, he scored 2385 runs and took 208 wickets in 35 matches.

The only player to score 3000 runs and take 100 wickets in a season of first-class cricket is J.H. Parks (Jim Parks sr). In 1937, at the age of 34, he scored 3003 runs and took 101 wickets in 35 matches.

Only three cricketers have scored 1000 runs and taken 200 wickets in a first-class season, Maurice Tate achieving this unusual feat in three consecutive years:

	Season	Matches	Runs	Wickets
A.E. Trott	1899	32	1175	239
A.E. Trott	1900	36	1337	211
A.S. Kennedy	1922	34	1129	205
M.W. Tate	1923	36	1168	219
M.W. Tate	1924	36	1419	205
M.W. Tate	1925	35	1290	228

Only two wicket-keepers have scored 1000 runs and made 100 dismissals in first-class matches during a season, Leslie Ames achieving the feat on three occasions:

	Season	Matches	Runs	Dismissals
L.E.G. Ames	1928	37	1919	122
L.E.G. Ames	1929	34	1795	128
L.E.G. Ames	1932	36	2482	104
J.T. Murray	1957	33	1025	104

The first all-rounder to complete the treble of 1000 runs, 100 wickets and 50 catches was Percy Fender of Surrey in 1921, when he did the first of his six doubles. In 34 matches he scored 1152 runs, took 134 wickets and held 52 catches. Forty years later Peter Walker of Glamorgan equalled this feat with 1347 runs, 101 wickets and 73 catches in 35 matches.

Wicket-Keeping records

The record number of wicket-keeping dismissals in any first-class innings in Britain is eight by David East of Essex on 27 July 1985 against Somerset at Taunton. He celebrated his 26th birthday by equalling Wally Grout's world record (set at Brisbane in 1960). East established a world record of his own by **catching the first eight batsmen dismissed in the innings.** The ninth wicket fell to a run out before Ian Botham closed the Somerset innings.

The world record for the most stumpings in any first-class innings is six by Hugo Yarnold for Worcestershire against Scotland at Broughty Ferry, near Dundee, on 2 July 1951. His stumpings, made off the leg-breaks and googlies of 'Roley' Jenkins and the slow left-arm deliveries of Michael Bradley, were preceded by a catch to equal the current world record for most dismissals (then seven, set by E.J. 'Tiger' Smith in 1926).

The only wicket-keeper to accomplish a hat-trick of stumpings in a first-class match is William Brain of Gloucestershire. Keeping to the leg-breaks of Charles Townsend, then aged 16, at Cheltenham on 15 August 1893, he stumped Somerset's last three batsmen off successive balls in the second innings.

The only wicket-keepers to complete a hat-trick of catches in first-class cricket are George Dawkes of Derbyshire (off Les Jackson against Worcestershire at Kidderminster on 16 June 1958), and R.C. 'Jack' Russell of Gloucestershire (one off Courtney Walsh and two off David Lawrence, against Surrey at The Oval on 4 September 1986).

The most dismissals by a wicket-keeper in any first-class match is 12 by Ted Pooley for Surrey against Sussex at The Oval on 6-7 July 1868. His aggregate, comprising six dismissals in each innings and including one stumping in the first innings and three in the second, has been equalled twice in Australian Sheffield Shield matches.

The highest number of catches held in any first-class match is eleven, a world record established by Arnold Long, also for Surrey against

MOST DISMISSALS IN AN INNINGS

Dis	Ct		St	For	Opponents	Venue		Season
8	**D.E. East**		8	0	Essex	Somerset	Taunton	1985
7	**E.J. Smith**		4	3	Warwickshire	Derbyshire	Birmingham	1926
7	**W. Farrimond**		6	1	Lancashire	Kent	Manchester	1930
7	**W.F.F. Price**		7	0	Middlesex	Yorkshire	Lord's	1937
7	**H. Yarnold**		1	6	Worcestershire	Scotland	Broughty Ferry	1951
7	**J. Brown**		4	3	Scotland	Ireland	†Dublin	1957
7	**K.V. Andrew**		7	0	Northamptonshire	Lancashire	Manchester	1962
7	**A. Long**		7	0	Surrey	Sussex	Hove	1964
7	**R.W. Taylor**		7	0	Derbyshire	Glamorgan	Derby	1966
7	**E.W. Jones**		6	1	Glamorgan	Cambridge U.	Cambridge	1970
7	**R.W. Taylor**		7	0	Derbyshire	Yorkshire	Chesterfield	1975
7	**D.L. Bairstow**		7	0	Yorkshire	Derbyshire	Scarborough	1982

† Although this instance occurred outside Britain it has been included as the annual fixture between Scotland and Ireland has long been part of the British Isles first-class programme.

Clem Driver's scoresheet records David East's world record.

Sussex, at Hove on 18-21 July 1964. His performance, which involved catching seven batsmen in the first innings (equalling the English record) and four in the second, has been emulated by Rodney Marsh (in Australia), and by David Bairstow for Yorkshire against Derbyshire at Scarborough on 8-10 September 1982.

The record number of stumpings for any first-class match is nine by Fred Huish for Kent against Surrey at The Oval on 21-23 August 1911 during the benefit match for his oppisite number in the Surrey team, Herbert Strudwick. In the first innings, he made four stumpings off the leg-breaks of Douglas Carr, and in the second added another to three off Frank Woolley and one off Colin Blythe (both left-arm leg-spinners). He also held a second innings catch off Woolley, but even his unique performance could not deny Surrey victory by nine runs.

The most wicket-keeping dismissals in a first-class season is 128 (79 catches and 49 stumpings) by Leslie Ames of Kent in 34 matches in 1929 – a summer in which he also scored 1795 runs.

Only seven wicket-keepers have made 100 dismissals in a first-class season, Leslie Ames accomplishing this feat three times:

		Year	Dis	Ct	St
F.H. Huish	Kent (2)	1911	**101**	62	39
		1913	**102**	69	33
G. Duckworth	Lancashire	1928	**107**	77	30
L.E.G. Ames	Kent (3)	1928	**122**	70	52
		1929	**128**	79	49
		1932	**104**	40	64
H. Yarnold	Worcestershire	1949	**110**	63	47
J.T. Murray	Middlesex (2)	1957	**104**	82	22
		1960	**102**	95	7
J.G. Binks	Yorkshire	1960	**107**	96	11
R. Booth	Worcestershire (2)	1960	**101**	85	16
		1964	**100**	91	9

The highest number of catches in any first-class season is 96 by Jimmy Binks of Yorkshire in 38 matches in 1960.

The most stumpings in a season is 64 by Leslie Ames in 1932, a summer in which he stumped almost twice as many batsmen as he caught. Ames, who also made 52 stumpings in 1928, is alone in making 50 stumpings in a season.

The highest innings in all first-class cricket in which no byes were conceded is 672 for 7 declared by Hampshire at Taunton on 20-21 July

1899. Equally remarkable is the fact that Somerset's wicket-keeper during this marathon was the 43-year-old Vicar of Martock, Rev Prebendary Archdale Palmer Wickham.

Fielding records

All records in this section exclude performances by Wicket-keepers.

The highest number of catches by one fielder in any first-class innings is seven. The record was set by Micky Stewart of Surrey during Northamptonshire's second innings, on 7 June 1957. Rain had enlivened the Northampton pitch. Fielding very close to the wicket, Stewart held six catches at backward short-leg and one in the gully; three were off the bowling of Tony Lock, two off Jim Laker, and two off Alec Bedser.

Stewart's record was equalled at Trent Bridge, Nottingham, on 26 July 1966, when Tony Brown of Gloucestershire held seven catches during Nottinghamshire's second innings on another rain-affected pitch. After diving low to his right to intercept a drive off his own bowling, he caught three batsmen at backward short-leg, two at gully and one at second slip. Four catches came from lifting off-breaks bowled by David Allen. Before Brown made the first of his catches he could have claimed a simple skier that was left to the wicket-keeper.

Four other fielders – Bill Voce, Brian Sellers, Arthur Milton and Stuart Surridge – have taken seven catches in a single day of a first-class match but have done so in the course of both innings (see table).

Playing for Kent at Folkestone on 6-7 July 1966, Alan Ealham caught five Gloucestershire batsmen off Derek Underwood's bowling whilst fielding in the same position topographically; four right-

MOST CATCHES IN A DAY

Fielder	For	Opponents	Venue	Season
W. Voce	Nottinghamshire	Glamorgan	Pontypridd	1929
A.B. Sellers	Yorkshire	Essex	Leyton	1933
C.A. Milton	Gloucestershire	Sussex	Hove	1952
W.S. Surridge	South	North	Kingston upon Thames	1952
M.J. Stewart	Surrey	Northamptonshire	Northampton	1957
A.S. Brown	Gloucestershire	Nottinghamshire	Nottingham	1966

handers were caught at long-off and one left-hander was taken at long-on.

The record number of catches taken by a fielder in any first-class match is ten by Wally Hammond for Gloucestershire. Playing against Surrey at Cheltenham College on 16-17 August 1928, he held four catches in the first innings and six in the second. Eight were held at slip off the left-arm bowling of Charlie Parker. No other fielder has held more than eight catches in a first-class match. Hammond made his performance even more exceptional by scoring a century in each innings.

The highest number of catches by a fielder in a first-class season is 78 by Wally Hammond of Gloucestershire in 1928. Ten of them were held in one match.

Only six fielders have held more than 65 catches in a first-class season, John Tunnicliffe and Peter Walker exceeding this total twice:

		Year	Ct
J. Tunnicliffe	Yorkshire	1895	**66**
		1901	**70**
W.R. Hammond	Gloucestershire	1928	**78**
J.G. Langridge	Sussex	1955	**69**
M.J. Stewart	Surrey	1957	**77**
P.M. Walker	Glamorgan	1960	**69**
		1961	**73**
P.J. Sharpe	Yorkshire	1962	**71**

Other individual records

The most first-class match appearances is 1107 by Wilfred Rhodes of Yorkshire and England between 1898 and 1930.

The oldest man to play in a first-class match in England was George Robert Canning, the 4th Lord Harris (1851-1932). When he ended his final appearance for Kent on 4 July 1911, against All India at Catford, he had reached the age of 60 years 151 days. In his final first-class innings his lordship scored 36, the second-highest contribution in Kent's first innings total of 318, and shared in the highest partnership of the match, adding 98 runs for the sixth wicket in under an hour. His last act at first-class level was to abet the tourists' defeat by taking 1 for 34 in ten overs in the second innings. Thirty-one years earlier Lord Harris had led England against Australia at The Oval in the first Test match to be staged in England.

The youngest to appear in English first-class cricket was Charles Robertson Young (b 1852) when he played for Hampshire against Kent at Gravesend on 13 June 1867 at the age of 15 years 131 days. Batting at number nine, he scored 20 not out and was promoted to open the second innings. Although he was out for 8, he later had the satisfaction of taking 1 for 12 in eight overs in his first

Lord Harris – sexagenarian first-class cricketer.

spell at first-class level. Young was born in India at Dharwar near Bombay and his date of birth has been confirmed at the India Office as 2 February 1852. His father, David Young, was an Assistant Superintendent Revenue Surveyor for Southern Marathee County. No record of C.R. Young's death has so far been traced. His last appearance for Hampshire occurred in 1890 but to date no further mention of him has been found. He is not included in the death registers at St Catherine's House nor is there any record of him in the Probate Registry. Possibly he died abroad during or after a coaching assignment.

The second-youngest first-class cricketer was George Frederick Grace. A younger brother of Dr W.G. Grace, 'G.F.' made his first-class debut on 21 May 1866 for the Gentlemen of England against Oxford University, at Oxford, when aged 15 years 159 days.

The second-youngest player to appear for a first-class county was Charles Edgar Winter who was 15 years 288 days old when he appeared for Somerset against Hampshire at Southampton on 24 July 1882. By coincidence, Charles Young was playing for the opposition.

The longest-lived English first-class cricketer on record was Edward Apsey English who played in 18 matches for Hampshire from 1898 to 1901 inclusive. Born at Dorking in Surrey on 1 January 1864, he died at Tiverton in Devon on 8 September 1966 at the age of 102 years 250 days. He held the world record for longevity amongst first-class cricketers from April 1966 (when he outlived the 102 years 102 days of John Wheatley, an Australian who moved to Christchurch and represented Canterbury for many seasons) until August 1986 when Rupert de Smidt (Western Province) died after extending the record by a mere four days.

The only other British Isles first-class cricketer known to have reached his century of years was George Richard Uniake Harman (101 years 191 days). Born at Crosshaven, Co. Cork on 6 June 1874, he died at Torpoint, Cornwall, on 14 December 1975. Although his only first-class appearance was for Dublin University in 1895, he did represent Ireland at rugby union. His brother, William

Ronayne Harman, played first-class cricket for Ireland and lived to the age of 93.

The County Championship

Inter-county cricket has existed since the early 18th century. The earliest match on record took place on 29 June 1709 when Kent played Surrey at Darford Brent. The origins of the County Championship, and the identity of the champions prior to the competition being officially constituted in 1890, are subjects which have provoked considerable argument and controversy.

The concept of a county championship seems to have resulted from a sports journalist or wealthy patron of the game attempting to promote interest in certain inter-county matches in the same way that bare-knuckle prize-fights were publicized. Although it is possible to prepare a list of champions from 1826 by researching contemporary publications, it would be ludicrous to include them with the winners of the modern championship. In several of those early and pre-Victorian seasons only two county matches were played, and only four of the 17 county clubs of today were founded before 1863. References to county champions were very scattered and most usually found in newspapers local to the county claiming the title.

After 1864, the year in which overarm bowling was legalized and as many as 24 county matches were staged, references to a champion county become more frequent. There was still scant agreement among contemporary cricket publications concerning the title-holders. Frequently the title was left undecided as there was no generally accepted method of determining the holder. Although the 'least matches lost' method existed, it was not consistently applied. The playing quality of a team seems to have been as important as its results. Although rules governing playing qualifications were agreed by the counties in 1873, it was not until 1888 that an unofficial points system was introduced.

On 10 December 1889 a private meeting of the representatives of Gloucestershire, Kent, Lancashire, Middlesex, Nottinghamshire, Surrey, Sussex and Yorkshire took place at Lord's and agreed a method of deciding the championship. Only from 1890 was the competition officially constituted and the title awarded by the counties themselves. Only from that date can any authorized list of county champions commence.

The County Championship Final Positions since 1890

	Derbyshire	Essex	Glamorgan	Gloucestershire	Hampshire	Kent	Lancashire	Leicestershire	Middlesex	Northamptonshire	Nottinghamshire	Somerset	Surrey	Sussex	Warwickshire	Worcestershire	Yorkshire
1890	·	·	·	6	·	3	2	·	7	·	5	·	1	8	·	·	3
1891	·	·	·	9	·	5	2	·	3	·	4	5	1	7	·	·	8
1892	·	·	·	7	·	7	4	·	5	·	2	3	1	9	·	·	6
1893	·	·	·	9	·	4	2	·	3	·	6	8	5	7	·	·	1
1894	·	·	·	9	·	4	4	·	3	·	7	6	1	8	·	·	2
1895	5	9	·	4	10	14	2	12	6	·	12	8	1	11	6	·	3
1896	7	5	·	10	8	9	2	13	3	·	6	11	4	14	12	·	1
1897	14	3	·	5	9	12	1	13	8	·	10	11	2	6	7	·	4
1898	9	5	·	3	12	7	6	13	2	·	8	13	4	9	9	·	1
1899	15	6	·	9	10	8	4	13	2	·	10	13	1	5	7	12	3
1900	13	10	·	7	15	3	2	14	7	·	5	11	7	3	6	12	1
1901	15	10	·	14	7	7	3	12	2	·	9	12	6	4	5	11	1
1902	10	13	·	14	15	7	5	11	12	·	3	7	4	2	6	9	1
1903	12	8	·	13	14	8	4	14	1	·	5	10	11	2	7	6	3
1904	10	14	·	9	15	3	1	7	4	·	5	12	11	6	7	13	2
1905	14	12	·	8	16	6	2	5	11	13	10	15	4	3	7	8	1
1906	16	7	·	9	8	1	4	15	11	11	5	11	3	10	6	14	2
1907	16	7	·	10	12	8	6	11	5	15	1	14	4	13	9	2	2
1908	14	11	·	10	9	2	7	13	4	15	8	16	3	5	12	6	1
1909	15	14	·	16	8	1	2	13	6	7	10	11	5	4	12	8	3
1910	15	11	·	12	6	1	4	10	3	9	5	16	2	7	14	13	8
1911	14	6	·	12	11	2	4	15	3	10	8	16	5	13	1	9	7
1912	12	15	·	11	6	3	4	13	5	2	8	14	7	10	9	16	1
1913	13	15	·	9	10	1	8	14	6	4	5	16	3	7	11	12	2
1914	12	8	·	16	5	3	11	13	2	9	10	15	1	6	7	14	4
1919	9	14	·	8	7	2	5	9	13	12	3	5	4	11	15	·	1
1920	16	9	·	8	11	5	2	13	1	14	7	10	3	6	12	15	4
1921	12	15	17	7	6	4	5	11	1	13	8	10	2	9	16	14	3
1922	11	8	16	13	6	4	5	14	7	15	2	10	3	9	12	17	1
1923	10	13	16	11	7	5	3	14	8	17	2	9	4	6	12	15	1
1924	17	15	13	6	12	5	4	11	2	16	6	8	3	10	9	14	1
1925	14	7	17	10	9	5	3	12	6	11	4	15	2	13	8	16	1
1926	11	9	8	15	7	3	1	13	6	16	4	14	5	10	12	17	2
1927	5	8	15	12	13	4	1	7	9	16	2	14	6	10	11	17	3
1928	10	16	15	5	12	2	1	9	8	13	3	14	6	7	11	17	4
1929	7	12	17	4	11	8	2	9	6	13	1	15	10	4	14	16	2
1930	9	6	11	2	13	5	1	12	16	17	4	13	8	7	15	10	3

	D	E	Gm	Gs	H	K	La	Le	M	Nh	Nt	Sm	Sy	Sx	Wa	Wo	Y
1931	7	10	15	2	12	3	6	16	11	17	5	13	8	4	9	14	1
1932	10	14	15	13	8	3	6	12	10	16	4	7	5	2	9	17	1
1933	6	4	16	10	14	3	5	17	12	13	8	11	9	2	7	15	1
1934	3	8	13	7	14	5	1	12	10	17	9	15	11	2	4	16	5
1935	2	9	13	15	16	10	4	6	3	17	5	14	11	7	8	12	1
1936	1	9	16	4	10	8	11	15	2	17	5	7	6	14	13	12	3
1937	3	6	7	4	14	12	9	16	2	17	10	13	8	5	11	15	1
1938	5	6	16	10	14	9	4	15	2	17	12	7	3	8	13	11	1
1939	9	4	13	3	15	5	6	17	2	16	12	14	8	10	11	7	1
1946	15	8	6	5	10	6	3	11	2	16	13	4	11	17	14	8	1
1947	5	11	9	2	16	4	3	14	1	17	11	11	6	9	15	7	7
1948	6	13	1	8	9	15	5	11	3	17	14	12	2	16	7	10	4
1949	15	9	8	7	16	13	11	17	1	6	11	9	5	13	4	3	1
1950	5	17	11	7	12	9	1	16	14	10	15	7	1	13	4	6	3
1951	11	8	5	12	9	16	3	15	7	13	17	14	6	10	1	4	2
1952	4	10	7	9	12	15	3	6	5	8	16	17	1	13	10	14	2
1953	6	12	10	6	14	16	3	3	5	11	8	17	1	2	9	15	12
1954	3	15	4	13	14	11	10	16	7	7	5	17	1	9	6	11	2
1955	8	14	16	12	3	13	9	6	5	7	11	17	1	4	9	15	2
1956	12	11	13	3	6	16	2	17	5	4	8	15	1	9	14	9	7
1957	4	5	9	12	13	14	6	17	7	2	15	8	1	9	11	16	3
1958	5	6	15	14	2	8	7	12	10	4	17	3	1	13	16	9	11
1959	7	9	6	2	8	13	5	16	10	11	17	12	3	15	4	14	1
1960	5	6	11	8	12	10	2	17	3	9	16	14	7	4	15	13	1
1961	7	6	14	5	1	11	13	9	3	16	17	10	15	8	12	4	2
1962	7	9	14	4	10	11	16	17	13	8	15	6	5	12	3	2	1
1963	17	12	2	8	10	13	15	16	6	7	9	3	11	4	4	14	1
1964	12	10	11	17	12	7	14	16	6	3	15	8	4	9	2	1	5
1965	9	15	3	10	12	5	13	14	6	2	17	7	8	16	11	1	4
1966	9	16	14	15	11	4	12	8	12	5	17	3	7	10	6	2	1
1967	6	15	14	17	12	2	11	3	7	9	16	8	4	13	10	5	1
1968	8	14	3	16	5	2	6	9	10	13	4	12	15	17	11	7	1
1969	16	6	1	2	5	10	15	14	11	9	8	17	3	7	4	12	13
1970	7	12	2	17	10	1	3	15	16	14	11	13	5	9	7	6	4
1971	17	10	16	8	9	4	3	5	6	14	12	7	1	11	2	15	13
1972	17	5	13	3	9	2	15	6	8	4	14	11	12	16	1	7	10
1973	16	8	11	5	1	4	12	9	13	3	17	10	2	15	7	6	14
1974	17	12	16	14	2	10	8	4	6	3	15	5	7	13	9	1	11
1975	15	7	9	16	3	5	4	1	11	8	13	12	6	17	14	10	2
1976	15	6	17	3	12	14	16	4	1	2	13	7	9	10	5	11	8
1977	7	6	14	3	11	1	16	5	1	9	17	4	14	8	10	13	12
1978	14	2	13	10	8	1	12	6	3	17	7	5	16	9	11	15	4
1979	16	1	17	10	12	5	13	6	14	11	9	8	3	4	15	2	7
1980	9	8	13	7	17	16	15	9	1	12	3	5	2	4	14	11	6
1981	12	5	14	13	7	9	16	8	4	15	1	3	6	2	17	11	10
1982	11	7	16	15	3	13	12	2	1	9	4	6	5	8	17	14	10
1983	9	1	15	12	3	7	12	4	2	6	14	10	8	11	5	16	17
1984	12	1	13	17	15	5	16	4	3	11	2	7	8	6	9	10	14
1985	13	4	12	3	2	9	14	16	1	10	8	17	6	7	15	5	11
1986	11	1	17	2	6	8	15	7	12	9	4	16	3	14	12	5	10

NO DRAWN MATCHES IN A SEASON

	Season	Played	Won	Lost	Tied	Position
Sussex	1890	12	1	11		8th
Surrey	1894	16	13	2	1	1st
Leicestershire	1910	17	6	11	·	10th
Northamptonshire	1911	17	8	9	·	10th
Somerset	1914	19	3	16	·	15th
Derbyshire	1920	17	·	17	·	16th
Gloucestershire	1921	24	12	12	·	7th
Surrey	1955	28	23	5	·	1st

The earliest date for winning the title is 12 August (1912) – by Kent, when they beat Gloucestershire by an innings in two days at Cheltenham.

The record number of successive titles is seven by Surrey from 1952 to 1958 inclusive. Their playing record during that period was: played 195, won 121, lost 28, drew 46.

The highest number of victories in a season is 25 by Yorkshire in 1923. They lost only one of their 32 matches, Nottinghamshire winning by three runs at Headingley, gained first innings lead in four of their six drawn games, and obtained 133 points out of a possible maximum of 155.

The longest unbeaten run in Championship matches was achieved by Yorkshire when, after losing to Surrey at The Oval on 26 August 1924, they avoided defeat until Warwickshire beat them at Hull on 24 May 1927. During that period they played 70 matches, winning 41, drawing 28 and having one abandoned.

The most defeats in a season is 20, an unfortunate record set by Glamorgan in 1925, when they won only one of their 26 matches, and equalled by Nottinghamshire in 1961 when they won four of their 28 games.

The longest run of Championship matches without a victory was endured by Northamptonshire. It lasted from their win against Somerset at Taunton on 14 May 1935 until 29 May 1939, when they inflicted an innings defeat upon a startled Leicestershire in two days at Northampton. During that barren period they lost 61 of their 99 matches. Northamptonshire supporters had to wait until 16 July 1946 for their next victory, a lengthy innings from the Third Reich intervening, and thus were able to celebrate just one solitary success in a period of more than eleven years.

Six counties have remained unbeaten throughout a season of County Championship cricket, Yorkshire achieving this feat on five occasions:

NO DEFEATS IN A SEASON

	Season	Played	Won	Drew	Position
Yorkshire	1900	28	16	12	1st
Lancashire	1904	26	16	10	1st
Nottinghamshire	1907	19	15	4	1st
Yorkshire	1908	28	16	12	1st
Yorkshire	1925	32	21	11	1st
Yorkshire	1926	31	14	17	2nd
Lancashire	1928	30	15	15	1st
Yorkshire	1928	26	8	18	4th
Lancashire	1930	28	10	18	1st
Glamorgan	1969	24	11	13	1st
Warwickshire	1972	20	9	11	1st
Hampshire	1973	20	10	10	1st
Lancashire	1974	20	5	15	8th

There have been only eight instances of a side gaining an outright result in every match during a season. The outstanding instance was achieved by Surrey under the captaincy of Stuart Surridge in 1955. Leicestershire's record in 1910 excludes their match against Yorkshire which, restricted to two days because of the funeral of King Edward VII, was not counted (along with five others) in the Championship. In 1911 matches in which no result on first innings was achieved were not counted, Northamptonshire's fixture against Yorkshire at Dewsbury being the lone instance.

Eight counties have failed to win a single match during an entire season, Derbyshire suffering this misfortune on four occasions. With the exception of Nottinghamshire, who finished in 16th place in 1967, all the counties concerned finished last in the Championship table.

NO VICTORIES IN A SEASON

	Season	Played	Drew	Lost
Derbyshire	1897	16	7	9
Hampshire	1900	22	6	16
Derbyshire	1901	20	7	13
Somerset	1910	18	3	15
Derbyshire	1920	17	·	17
Derbyshire	1924	24	11	13
Worcestershire	1928	30	11	19
Northamptonshire	1936	24	15	9
Northamptonshire	1937	24	8	16
Northamptonshire	1938	24	7	17
Nottinghamshire	1967	28	24	4
Glamorgan	1979	21	11	10
Warwickshire	1982	22	14	8

The highest number of drawn matches involving one county during a Championship season is 24 by Nottinghamshire in 1967 when they failed to win any of their 28 fixtures.

The most appearances in County Championship matches is 763 by Wilfred Rhodes for Yorkshire from 1898 until 1930 inclusive.

The highest number of consecutive appearances is 423 by Ken Suttle for Sussex between 18 August 1954 and 28 July 1969, including one match abandoned without a ball being bowled.

The oldest player to appear in a Championship match is the Rev Reginald Moss, who was 57 years 89 days old when he made his only appearance for Worcestershire on 23-26 May 1925 against Gloucestershire at Worcester. He had previously represented Oxford University and Lancashire.

The leading run-scorer in Championship matches is Philip Mead of Hampshire, who made 665 appearances in the period 1906-36. He holds the records for the most runs in a career (46 268), most runs in a season (2843 in 1928), most hundreds (132), most times 1000 runs in a season (26), and most times 2000 runs in a season (9). Wally Hammond holds the records for the most double centuries (22) and the most hundreds in a season (13 in 1938).

The leading wicket-taker in Championship matches is A.P. 'Tich' Freeman of Kent. He established the records for most wickets in a career (3151 during the period 1914-36), most wickets in a season (252 in 1933), most instances of ten or more wickets in a match (123), most times ten or more wickets in a season (15 – equalling the record set by Tom Richardson of Surrey), and most times 200 wickets in a season (6). Until 1968, when Derek Shackleton surpassed it with his 18th and final instance, Freeman also shared (with Wilfred Rhodes) the record for taking 100 wickets in a season most times.

The two most successful all-rounders in the history of the County Championship are Yorkshire's 'great twin brethren' from the Golden Age of cricket, George Herbert Hirst and Wilfred Rhodes. Both batted right-handed and bowled left, and both scored over 20 000 runs and took more than 2000 wickets in Championship matches – a double achieved by no other player. Hirst, who played from 1891 until 1921 inclusive, scored 27 318 runs and took 2096 wickets, achieving the double of 1000 runs and 100 wickets in a season eight times. Rhodes (1898-1930) scored 26 874 runs, took 3118 wickets and did the double seven times.

The wicket-keeping records are more widely distributed. Until 1980, Herbert Strudwick (1902-27) held the career record for most catches (964) and until 1982, that for most dismissals (1132). In

Three Kent and England stalwarts: Percy Chapman, 'Tich' Freeman and Frank Woolley. (John Reader)

those seasons Bob Taylor established new records, having started his career with Derbyshire in 1961. When he retired at the end of the 1984 season, Taylor had made 1222 dismissals, including 1087 catches, in 480 Championship matches.

The only instances of 100 dismissals in a season were achieved by Leslie Ames, who made 102 in 1929 and 100 in 1928. Ames is also alone in making 50 stumpings in a season of Championship cricket – 52 in 1932. His career total of stumpings fell just two short of the record of 315 established by his Kent predecessor, Fred Huish (1895-1914).

The most catches in a season is 88 by Roy Booth for Worcestershire in 1964.

The highest career aggregate of catches in Championship matches by a fielder other than a wicket-keeper is 710 by Frank Woolley for Kent in 707 matches between 1906 and 1938 inclusive.

The most catches by a non-wicket-keeper during a season of Championship matches is 66 by John Langridge for Sussex in 1959. Like Woolley, Langridge was an outstanding slip fielder.

County First-class records

DERBYSHIRE

Badge	Rose and Crown
Colours	Chocolate, Amber and Pale Blue
Foundation	4 November 1870 at The Guildhall, Derby
Headquarters	County Cricket Ground, Nottingham Road, Derby, DE2 6DA
Champions	(1) 1936

DERBYSHIRE RECORDS IN ALL FIRST-CLASS CRICKET

MATCH RECORDS

For Derbyshire	Record	Holder(s)	Opponents	Venue	Season
Highest Total	645		Hampshire	Derby	1898
Lowest Total	16		Nottinghamshire	Nottingham	1879
Highest Score	274	G.A. Davidson	Lancashire	Manchester	1896
Highest Partnership	349	C.S. Elliott, J.D. Eggar	Nottinghamshire	Nottingham	1947
Best Bowling–Innings	10-40	W. Bestwick	Glamorgan	Cardiff	1921
–Match	17-103	W. Mycroft	Hampshire	Southampton	1876
Most Dismissals–Innings	7	R.W. Taylor (7c)	Glamorgan	Derby	1966
	7	R.W. Taylor (7c)	Yorkshire	Chesterfield	1975
–Match	10	H. Elliott (8c, 2s)	Lancashire	Manchester	1935
	10	R.W. Taylor (10c)	Hampshire	Chesterfield	1963

Against Derbyshire	Record	Holder(s)	Opponents	Venue	Season
Highest Total	662		Yorkshire	Chesterfield	1898
Lowest Total	23		Hampshire	Burton upon Trent	1959
Highest Score	343*	P.A. Perrin	Essex	Chesterfield	1904
Highest Partnership	554	J.T. Brown, J. Tunnicliffe	Yorkshire	Chesterfield	1898
Best Bowling–Innings	10-47	T.F. Smailes	Yorkshire	Sheffield	1939
–Match	16-101	G. Giffen	Australians	Derby	1886

far left, Alan Ward – had genuine pace but was plagued by injuries. (Bill Smith) **left, Mike Hendrick – an international-class fast-medium bowler of great accuracy.** (Bill Smith)

Derbyshire 1962. STANDING: I.W. Hall, R.W. Taylor, I.R. Buxton, H.J. Rhodes, W.F. Oates, E. Smith. SEATED: C. Lee, H.L. Jackson, D.B. Carr *captain*, D.C. Morgan, H.L. Johnson. (Central Press)

SEASON RECORDS

Most Runs	2165	D.B. Carr	1959
Most Hundreds	8	P.N. Kirsten	1982
Most Wickets	168	T.B. Mitchell	1935
Most Wicket-Keeping Dismissals	90	H. Elliott (69c, 21s)	1935
Most Catches (non WK)	49	M.H. Page	1967

CAREER RECORDS

Most Appearances	540	D.C. Morgan	1950-69
Most Runs	20516	D. Smith	1927-52
Most Hundreds	30	D. Smith	1927-52
Most Times 1000 Runs in a Season	12	D. Smith (1931-50)	1927-52
Most Wickets	1670	H.L. Jackson	1947-63
Most Hat-Tricks	4	A.E.G. Rhodes (1947-51)	1937-54
Most Times 100 Wickets in a Season	12	C. Gladwin (1946-58)	1939-58
Most Wicket-Keeping Dismissals	1304	R.W. Taylor (1157c, 147s)	1961-84
Most Catches (non WK)	563	D.C. Morgan	1950-69

ESSEX

Badge	Three Seaxes above Scroll bearing 'Essex'
Colours	Blue, Gold and Red
Foundation	14 January 1876 at The Shire Hall, Chelmsford
Headquarters	County Ground, New Writtle Street, Chelmsford, CM2 0PG
Champions	(4) 1979, 1983, 1984, 1986

ESSEX RECORDS IN ALL FIRST-CLASS CRICKET

MATCH RECORDS

For Essex	Record	Holder(s)	Opponents	Venue	Season
Highest Total	692		Somerset	Taunton	1895
Lowest Total	30		Yorkshire	Leyton	1901
Highest Score	343*	P.A. Perrin	Derbyshire	Chesterfield	1904
Highest Partnership	343	P.A. Gibb, R. Horsfall	Kent	Blackheath	1951
Best Bowling–Innings	10-32	H. Pickett	Leicestershire	Leyton	1895
–Match	17-119	W. Mead	Hampshire	Southampton	1895
Most Dismissals–Innings	8	D.E. East (8c)	Somerset	Taunton	1985
–Match	9	K.L. Gibson (7c, 2s)	Derbyshire	Leyton	1911
	9	D.E. East (9c)	Sussex	Hove	1983

Against Essex	Record	Holder(s)	Opponents	Venue	Season
Highest Total	803-4d		Kent	Brentwood	1934
Lowest Total	14		Surrey	Chelmsford	1983
Highest Score	332	W.H. Ashdown	Kent	Brentwood	1934
Highest Partnership	555	P. Holmes, H. Sutcliffe	Yorkshire	Leyton	1932
Best Bowling–Innings	10-40	E.G. Dennett	Gloucestershire	Bristol	1906
–Match	17-56	C.W.L. Parker	Gloucestershire	Gloucester	1925

far left, Percy Perrin – record number of boundaries in an innings but finished on the losing side. (Illustrated London News)

left, Brian 'Tonker' Taylor – forthright and enthusiastic captain, batsman and wicket-keeper. (Central Press)

Essex 1985. STANDING: **K.S. McEwan, D.E. East, A.W. Lilley, D.R. Pringle, N.A. Foster, C. Gladwin, P.J. Prichard.** SEATED: **B.R. Hardie, S. Turner, G.A. Gooch, K.W.R. Fletcher** *captain*, **J.K. Lever, D.L. Acfield, K.R. Pont.** (Bill Smith)

SEASON RECORDS

Most Runs	2559	G.A. Gooch	1984
Most Hundreds	9	J. O'Connor	1934
	9	D.J. Insole	1955
Most Wickets	172	T.P.B. Smith	1947
Most Wicket-Keeping Dismissals	89	B. Taylor (79c, 10s)	1962
Most Catches (non WK)	40	K.W.R. Fletcher	1966

CAREER RECORDS

Most Appearances	539	B. Taylor	1949-73
Most Runs	29172	P.A. Perrin	1896-1928
Most Hundreds	71	J. O'Connor	1921-39
Most Times 1000 Runs in a Season	19	K.W.R. Fletcher (1963-84)	1962-86
Most Wickets	1610	T.P.B. Smith	1929-51
Most Hat-Tricks	2	J.W.H.T. Douglas (1905-23)	1901-28
Most Times 100 Wickets in a Season	11	M.S. Nichols (1926-39)	1924-39
Most Wicket-Keeping Dismissals	1205	B. Taylor (1013c, 192s)	1949-73
Most Catches (non WK)	498	K.W.R. Fletcher	1962-86

GLAMORGAN

Badge	Gold Daffodil
Colours	Blue and Gold
Foundation	6 July 1888 at Cardiff
Headquarters	Sophia Gardens, Cardiff, CF1 9XR
Champions	(2) 1948, 1969

GLAMORGAN RECORDS IN ALL FIRST-CLASS CRICKET

MATCH RECORDS

For Glamorgan	Record	Holder(s)	Opponents	Venue	Season
Highest Total	587-8d		Derbyshire	Cardiff	1951
Lowest Total	22		Lancashire	Liverpool	1924
Highest Score	287*	D.E. Davies	Gloucestershire	Newport	1939
Highest Partnership	330	A. Jones, R.C. Fredericks	Northamptonshire	Swansea	1972
Best Bowling–Innings	10-51	J. Mercer	Worcestershire	Worcester	1936
–Match	17-212	J.C. Clay	Worcestershire	Swansea	1937
Most Dismissals–Innings	7	E.W. Jones (6c, 1s)	Cambridge U.	Cambridge	1970
–Match	8	H.G. Davies (6c, 2s)	South Africans	Swansea	1955
	8	E.W. Jones (8c)	Warwickshire	Birmingham	1970
	8	E.W. Jones (8c)	Essex	Cardiff	1982

Against Glamorgan	Record	Holder(s)	Opponents	Venue	Season
Highest Total	653-6d		Gloucestershire	Bristol	1928
Lowest Total	33		Leicestershire	Ebbw Vale	1965
Highest Score	302*	W.R. Hammond	Gloucestershire	Bristol	1934
	302	W.R. Hammond	Gloucestershire	Newport	1939
Highest Partnership	344	A. Sandham, R.J. Gregory	Surrey	The Oval	1937
Best Bowling–Innings	10-18	G. Geary	Leicestershire	Pontypridd	1929
–Match	16-96	G. Geary	Leicestershire	Pontypridd	1929

far left, Alan Rees – last batsman to be given out 'handled the ball' in England. (Central Press)
left, Rodney Ontong – all-rounder who changed from seam to off-spin in mid-career. (Bill Smith)

Glamorgan – 1969 Champions. STANDING: E.W. Jones, B.A. Davis, M.A. Nash, D.L. Williams, R.C. Davis, Majid Khan. SEATED: A.E. Cordle, P.M. Walker, A.R. Lewis *captain*, D.J. Shepherd, A. Jones. (Central Press)

SEASON RECORDS

Most Runs	2083	Javed Miandad	1981
Most Hundreds	8	Javed Miandad	1981
Most Wickets	176	J.C. Clay	1937
Most Wicket-Keeping Dismissals	94	E.W. Jones (85c, 9s)	1970
Most Catches (non WK)	67	P.M. Walker	1961

CAREER RECORDS

Most Appearances	647	D.J. Shepherd	1950-72
Most Runs	34056	A. Jones	1957-83
Most Hundreds	52	A. Jones	1957-83
Most Times 1000 Runs in a Season	23	A. Jones (1961-83)	1957-83
Most Wickets	2174	D.J. Shepherd	1950-72
Most Hat-Tricks	1	(8 bowlers)	1926-69
Most Times 100 Wickets in a Season	12	D.J. Shepherd (1952-70)	1950-72
Most Wicket-Keeping Dismissals	933†	E.W. Jones (840c, 93s)	1961-83
Most Catches (non WK)	656	P.M. Walker	1955-72

† Including 21 catches as a fielder

GLOUCESTERSHIRE

Badge	Coat of Arms of the City and County of Bristol
Colours	Blue, Gold, Brown, Silver, Green and Red
Foundation	1871 (between 14 March and mid-May)
Headquarters	Phoenix County Ground, Nevil Road, Bristol, BS7 9EJ
Champions	No instance since 1890

GLOUCESTERSHIRE RECORDS IN ALL FIRST-CLASS CRICKET

MATCH RECORDS

For Gloucestershire	Record	Holder(s)	Opponents	Venue	Season
Highest Total	653-6d		Glamorgan	Bristol	1928
Lowest Total	17		Australians	Cheltenham	1896
Highest Score	318*	W.G. Grace	Yorkshire	Cheltenham	1876
Highest Partnership	395	D.M. Young, R.B. Nicholls	Oxford U.	Oxford	1962
Best Bowling–Innings	10-40	E.G. Dennett	Essex	Bristol	1906
–Match	17-56	C.W.L. Parker	Essex	Gloucester	1925
Most Dismissals–Innings	6	H. Smith (3c, 3s)	Sussex	Bristol	1923
	6	A.E. Wilson (6c)	Hampshire	Portsmouth	1953
	6	B.J. Meyer (6c)	Somerset	Taunton	1962
–Match	10	A.E. Wilson (10c)	Hampshire	Portsmouth	1953

Against Gloucestershire	Record	Holder(s)	Opponents	Venue	Season
Highest Total	774-7d		Australians	Bristol	1948
Lowest Total	12		Northamptonshire	Gloucester	1907
Highest Score	296	A.O. Jones	Nottinghamshire	Nottingham	1903
Highest Partnership	465*	J.A. Jameson, R.B. Kanhai	Warwickshire	Birmingham	1974
Best Bowling–Innings	10-66	A.A. Mailey	Australians	Cheltenham	1921
	10-66	K. Smales	Nottinghamshire	Stroud	1956
–Match	15-87	A.J. Conway	Worcestershire	Moreton-in-Marsh	1914

SEASON RECORDS

Most Runs	2860	W.R. Hammond	1933
Most Hundreds	13	W.R. Hammond	1938
Most Wickets	222	T.W.J. Goddard	1937
	222	T.W.J. Goddard	1947
Most Wicket-Keeping Dismissals	75	J.H. Board (52c, 23s)	1895
	75	B.J. Meyer (59c, 16s)	1964
Most Catches (non WK)	62	W.R. Hammond	1928

CAREER RECORDS

Most Appearances	602	C.W.L. Parker	1903-35
Most Runs	33664	W.R. Hammond	1920-51
Most Hundreds	113	W.R. Hammond	1920-51
Most Times 1000 Runs in a Season	17	W.R. Hammond (1923-46)	1920-51
Most Wickets	3170	C.W.L. Parker	1903-35
Most Hat-Tricks	6†	C.W.L. Parker (1922-30)	1903-35
Most Times 100 Wickets in a Season	16	C.W.L. Parker (1920-35)	1903-35
	16	T.W.J. Goddard (1929-50)	1922-52
Most Wicket-Keeping Dismissals	1016	J.H. Board (699c, 317s)	1891-1914
Most Catches (non WK)	719	C.A. Milton	1948-74

† Including two hat-tricks in the same match.

Wally Hammond – all-rounder supreme. (Adrian Murrell/All-Sport)

HAMPSHIRE

Badge	Tudor Rose and Crown
Colours	Blue, Gold and White
Foundation	12 August 1863 in Southampton
Headquarters	County Cricket Ground, Northlands Road, Southampton, SO9 2TY
Champions	(2) 1961, 1973

HAMPSHIRE RECORDS IN ALL FIRST-CLASS CRICKET

MATCH RECORDS

For Hampshire	Record	Holder(s)	Opponents	Venue	Season
Highest Total	672-7d		Somerset	Taunton	1899
Lowest Total	15		Warwickshire	Birmingham	1922
Highest Score	316	R H. Moore	Warwickshire	Bournemouth	1937
Highest Partnership	411	R.M.Poore, E.G.Wynyard	Somerset	Taunton	1899
Best Bowling–Innings	9-25	R.M.H. Cottam	Lancashire	Manchester	1965
–Match	16-88	J.A. Newman	Somerset	Weston-s-Mare	1927
Most Dismissals–Innings	6	Six instances by G. Ubsdell, B.S.V. Timms, G.R. Stephenson and R.J. Parks (3).			
–Match	10	R.J. Parks (10c)	Derbyshire	Portsmouth	1981

Against Hampshire	Record	Holder(s)	Opponents	Venue	Season
Highest Total	742		Surrey	The Oval	1909
Lowest Total	23		Yorkshire	Middlesbrough	1965
Highest Score	302*	P. Holmes	Yorkshire	Portsmouth	1920
Highest Partnership	379	R. Abel, W. Brockwell	Surrey	The Oval	1897
Best Bowling–Innings	10-46	W. Hickton	Lancashire	Manchester	1870
–Match	17-103	W. Mycroft	Derbyshire	Southampton	1876

far left, Philip Mead – his 48 892 remains the record aggregate for any county.

left, Gordon Greenidge – scored four hundreds in successive championship innings in 1986. (Bill Smith)

Hampshire – 1961 Champions. STANDING: **D.A. Livingstone, D.W. White, H. Horton, M. Heath, H.M. Barnard, M.D. Burden, P.J. Sainsbury.** SEATED: **D. Shackleton, L. Harrison, A.C.D. Ingleby-Mackenzie** *captain*, **R.E. Marshall, J.R. Gray.** (Central Press)

SEASON RECORDS

Most Runs	2854	C.P. Mead	1928
Most Hundreds	12	C.P. Mead	1928
Most Wickets	190	A.S. Kennedy	1922
Most Wicket-Keeping Dismissals	83	L. Harrison (76c, 7s)	1959
Most Catches (non WK)	56	P.J. Sainsbury	1957

CAREER RECORDS

Most Appearances	700	C.P. Mead	1905-36
Most Runs	48892	C.P. Mead	1905-36
Most Hundreds	138	C.P. Mead	1905-36
Most Times 1000 Runs in a Season	27	C.P. Mead (1906-36)	1905-36
Most Wickets	2669	D. Shackleton	1948-69
Most Hat-Tricks	3	A.S. Kennedy (1920-24)	1907-36
Most Times 100 Wickets in a Season	19	D. Shackleton (1949-68)	1948-69
Most Wicket-Keeping Dismissals	688	N.T. McCorkell (512c, 176s)	1932-51
Most Catches (non WK)	629	C.P. Mead	1905-36

KENT

Badge	White Horse on a Red Ground
Colours	Maroon and White
Foundation	1 March 1859 in Maidstone
	(substantially reorganized 6 December 1870)
Headquarters	St Lawrence Ground, Canterbury, CT1 3NZ
Champions	(6) 1906, 1909, 1910, 1913, 1970, 1978
Joint Champions	(1) 1977

KENT RECORDS IN ALL FIRST-CLASS CRICKET

MATCH RECORDS

For Kent	Record	Holder(s)	Opponents	Venue	Season
Highest Total	803-4d		Essex	Brentwood	1934
Lowest Total	18		Sussex	Gravesend	1867
Highest Score	332	W.H. Ashdown	Essex	Brentwood	1934
Highest Partnership	352	W.H.Ashdown,F.E.Woolley	Essex	Brentwood	1934
Best Bowling–Innings	10-30	C. Blythe	Northamptonshire	Northampton	1907
–Match	17-48	C. Blythe	Northamptonshire	Northampton	1907
Most Dismissals–Innings	6	14 instances by F.H. Huish, J.C. Hubble, L.E.G. Ames (2), W.H.V. Levett (2), A.P.E. Knott (6), D. Nicholls and S.A. Marsh.			
–Match	10	F.H. Huish (1c, 9s)	Surrey	The Oval	1911
	10	J.C. Hubble (9c, 1s)	Gloucestershire	Cheltenham	1923

Against Kent	Record	Holder(s)	Opponents	Venue	Season
Highest Total	676		Australians	Canterbury	1921
Lowest Total	16		Warwickshire	Tonbridge	1913
Highest Score	344	W.G. Grace	MCC	Canterbury	1876
Highest Partnership	367*	G.D.Barlow,W.N.Slack	Middlesex	Lord's	1981
Best Bowling–Innings	10-48	C.H.G. Bland	Sussex	Tonbridge	1899
–Match	17-106	T.W.J. Goddard	Gloucestershire	Bristol	1939

SEASON RECORDS

Most Runs	2894	F.E. Woolley	1928
Most Hundreds	10	F.E. Woolley	1928
	10	F.E. Woolley	1934
Most Wickets	262	A.P. Freeman	1933
Most Wicket-Keeping Dismissals	116	L.E.G. Ames (71c, 45s)	1929
Most Catches (non WK)	48	C.J. Tavaré	1978

CAREER RECORDS

Most Appearances	764	F.E. Woolley	1906-38
Most Runs	47868	F.E. Woolley	1906-38
Most Hundreds	122	F.E. Woolley	1906-38
Most Times 1000 Runs in a Season	27	F.E. Woolley (1907-38)	1906-38
Most Wickets	3340	A.P. Freeman	1914-36
Most Hat-Tricks	6	D.V.P. Wright (1937-49)	1932-57
Most Times 100 Wickets in a Season	17	A.P. Freeman (1920-36)	1914-36
Most Wicket-Keeping Dismissals	1253	F.H. Huish (901c, 352s)	1895-1914
Most Catches (non WK)	773	F.E. Woolley	1906-38

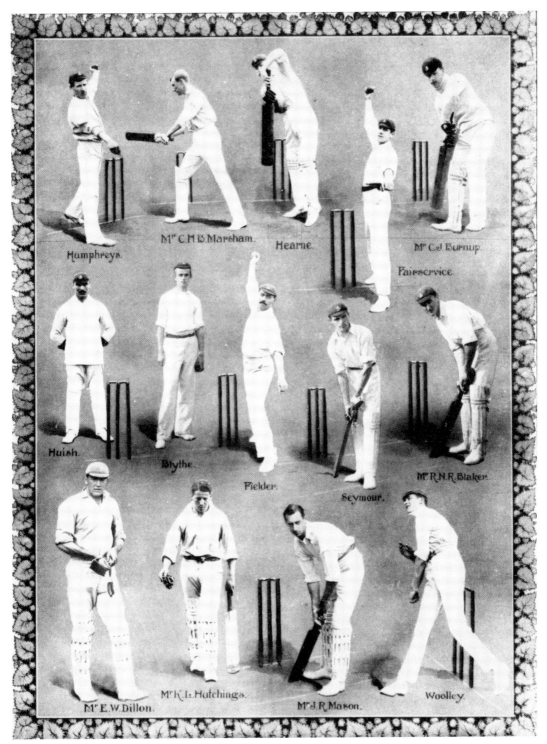

Humphreys.

Mr C. H. B. Marsham.

Hearne.

Mr C. J. Burnup.

Fairservice.

Huish.

Blythe.

Fielder.

Seymour.

Mr R. N. R. Blaker.

Mr E. W. Dillon.

Mr K. L. Hutchings.

Mr J. R. Mason.

Woolley.

Kent – 1906 Champions. (Illustrated London News)

LANCASHIRE

Badge	Red Rose
Colours	Red, Green and Blue
Foundation	12 January 1864 in Manchester
Headquarters	Old Trafford, Manchester, M16 0PX
Champions	(7) 1897, 1904, 1926, 1927, 1928, 1930, 1934
Joint Champions	(1) 1950

LANCASHIRE RECORDS IN ALL FIRST-CLASS CRICKET

MATCH RECORDS

For Lancashire	Record	Holder(s)	Opponents	Venue	Season
Highest Total	801		Somerset	Taunton	1895
Lowest Total	25		Derbyshire	Manchester	1871
Highest Score	424	A.C. MacLaren	Somerset	Taunton	1895
Highest Partnership	371	F.Watson,G.E.Tyldesley	Surrey	Manchester	1928
Best Bowling–Innings	10-46	W. Hickton	Hampshire	Manchester	1870
–Match	17-91	H. Dean	Yorkshire	Liverpool	1913
Most Dismissals–Innings	7	W. Farrimond (6c, 1s)	Kent	Manchester	1930
–Match	9	G. Clayton (8c, 1s)	Gloucestershire	Gloucester	1959
	9	C. Maynard (8c, 1s)	Somerset	Taunton	1982

Against Lancashire	Record	Holder(s)	Opponents	Venue	Season
Highest Total	634		Surrey	The Oval	1898
Lowest Total	22		Glamorgan	Liverpool	1924
Highest Score	315*	T.W. Hayward	Surrey	The Oval	1898
Highest Partnership	470	A.I. Kallicharran, G.W.Humpage	Lancashire	Southport	1982
Best Bowling–Innings	10-40	G.O.B. Allen	Middlesex	Lord's	1929
–Match	16-65	G. Giffen	Australians	Manchester	1886

far left, A.C. MacLaren – made the highest first-class score in England. **left, Brian Statham –** supremely accurate fast bowler. (Central Press)

Lancashire – 1934 Champions. STANDING: C. Washbrook, J.L. Hopwood, J. Iddon, F.S. Booth, R. Pollard, L.W. Parkinson, N. Oldfield. SEATED: E. Paynter, G.E. Tyldesley, P.T. Eckersley *captain*, W.H.L. Lister, G. Duckworth.

SEASON RECORDS

Most Runs	2633	J.T. Tyldesley	1901
Most Hundreds	11	C. Hallows	1928
Most Wickets	198	E.A. McDonald	1925
Most Wicket-Keeping Dismissals	97	G. Duckworth (69c, 28s)	1928
Most Catches (non WK)	63	K.J. Grieves	1950

CAREER RECORDS

Most Appearances	573	G.E. Tyldesley	1909-36
Most Runs	34222	G.E. Tyldesley	1909-36
Most Hundreds	90	G.E. Tyldesley	1909-36
Most Times 1000 Runs in a Season	19	J.T. Tyldesley (1897-1919)	1895-1923
Most Wickets	1816	J.B. Statham	1950-68
Most Hat-Tricks	3	R.G. Barlow (1879-86)	1871-91
	3	E.A. McDonald (1925-30)	1924-31
Most Times 100 Wickets in a Season	11	J. Briggs (1887-1900)	1879-1900
Most Wicket-Keeping Dismissals	922	G. Duckworth (634c, 288s)	1923-38
Most Catches (non WK)	555	K.J. Grieves	1949-64

LEICESTERSHIRE

Badge	Gold Running Fox on Green Ground
Colours	Dark Green and Scarlet
Foundation	25 March 1879 at Leicester
Headquarters	County Ground, Grace Road, Leicester, LE2 8AD
Champions	(1) 1975

LEICESTERSHIRE RECORDS IN ALL FIRST-CLASS CRICKET

MATCH RECORDS

For Leicestershire	Record	Holder(s)	Opponents	Venue	Season
Highest Total	701-4d		Worcestershire	Worcester	1906
Lowest Total	25		Kent	Leicester	1912
Highest Score	252*	S. Coe	Northamptonshire	Leicester	1914
Highest Partnership	390	B.Dudleston, J.F.Steele	Derbyshire	Leicester	1979
Best Bowling–Innings	10-18	G. Geary	Glamorgan	Pontypridd	1929
–Match	16-96	G. Geary	Glamorgan	Pontypridd	1929
Most Dismissals–Innings	6	P. Corrall (4c, 2s)	Sussex	Hove	1936
	6	P. Corrall (3c, 3s)	Middlesex	Leicester	1949
	6	R.W. Tolchard (6c)	Yorkshire	Leeds	1973
	6	R.W. Tolchard (6c)	Hampshire	Southampton	1980
–Match	10	P. Corrall (7c, 3s)	Sussex	Hove	1936

Against Leicestershire	Record	Holder(s)	Opponents	Venue	Season
Highest Total	739-7d		Nottinghamshire	Nottingham	1903
Lowest Total	24		Glamorgan	Leicester	1971
	24		Oxford U.	Oxford	1985
Highest Score	341	G.H. Hirst	Yorkshire	Leicester	1905
Highest Partnership	369	W. Gunn, J.R. Gunn	Nottinghamshire	Nottingham	1903
Best Bowling–Innings	10-32	H. Pickett	Essex	Leyton	1958
–Match	16-102	C. Blythe	Kent	Leicester	1909

**far left, Clive Inman –
scored 50 in eight
minutes.**
(Sport & General)

**left, Phillip DeFreitas –
a Test all-rounder at 20.**
(Bill Smith)

Leicestershire – 1975 Champions. STANDING: **R.W. Tolchard, B. Dudleston, D.I. Gower, J.C. Balderstone, B.F. Davison, J.F. Steele.** SEATED: **J. Birkenshaw, K. Higgs, R. Illingworth** *captain*, **G.D. McKenzie, N.M. McVicker.** (Bill Smith)

SEASON RECORDS

Most Runs	2446	G.L. Berry	1937
Most Hundreds	7	G.L. Berry	1937
	7	W. Watson	1959
	7	B.F. Davison	1982
Most Wickets	170	J.E. Walsh	1948
Most Wicket-Keeping Dismissals	85	J. Firth (60c, 25s)	1952
Most Catches (non WK)	56	M.R. Hallam	1961

CAREER RECORDS

Most Appearances	628	W.E. Astill	1906-39
Most Runs	30143	G.L. Berry	1924-51
Most Hundreds	45	G.L. Berry	1924-51
Most Times 1000 Runs in a Season	18	G.L. Berry (1925-50)	1924-51
Most Wickets	2130	W.E. Astill	1906-39
Most Hat-Tricks	2	T. Jayes, J.H. King, V.E. Jackson, J. Birkenshaw, P.B. Clift	
Most Times 100 Wickets in a Season	9	G. Geary (1914-36)	1912-38
Most Wicket-Keeping Dismissals	903†	R.W. Tolchard (794c, 109s)	1965-83
Most Catches (non WK)	427	M.R. Hallam	1950-70

† Including 16 catches taken as a fielder

117

MIDDLESEX

Badge	Three Seaxes
Colours	Blue
Foundation	2 February 1864 at the London Tavern, Bishopsgate
Headquarters	Lord's Cricket Ground, London, NW8 8QN
Champions	(8) 1903, 1920, 1921, 1947, 1976, 1980, 1982, 1985
Joint Champions	(2) 1949, 1977

MIDDLESEX RECORDS IN ALL FIRST-CLASS CRICKET

MATCH RECORDS

For Middlesex	Record	Holder(s)	Opponents	Venue	Season
Highest Total	642-3d		Hampshire	Southampton	1923
Lowest Total	20		MCC	Lord's	1864
Highest Score	331*	J.D.B. Robertson	Worcestershire	Worcester	1949
Highest Partnership	424*	W.J. Edrich, D.C.S. Compton	Somerset	Lord's	1948
Best Bowling–Innings	10-40	G.O.B. Allen	Lancashire	Lord's	1929
–Match	16-114	G. Burton	Yorkshire	Sheffield	1888
	16-114	J.T. Hearne	Lancashire	Manchester	1898
Most Dismissals–Innings	7	W.F.F. Price (7c)	Yorkshire	Lord's	1937
–Match	9	M. Turner (6c, 3s)	Nottinghamshire	Prince's	1875
	9	J.T. Murray (8c, 1s)	Hampshire	Lord's	1965

Against Middlesex	Record	Holder(s)	Opponents	Venue	Season
Highest Total	665		West Indians	Lord's	1939
Lowest Total	31		Gloucestershire	Bristol	1924
Highest Score	316*	J.B. Hobbs	Surrey	Lord's	1926
Highest Partnership	490	E.H. Bowley, J.G. Langridge	Sussex	Hove	1933
Best Bowling–Innings	9-38	R.C. Robertson-Glasgow	Somerset	Lord's	1924
–Match	16-109	C.W.L. Parker	Gloucestershire	Cheltenham	1930

far left, The inimitable Denis Compton.

left, Mike Gatting – captain courageous.

(Adrian Murrell/All-Sport)

118

Middlesex – 1903 Champions. BACK: **J.T. Hearne, R.W. Nicholls, B.J.T. Bosanquet, J.T. Rawlin.** CENTRE: **L.J. Moon, C.M. Wells, G. MacGregor** *captain*, **P.F. Warner, G.W. Beldam.** FRONT: **J. Douglas, A.E. Trott, E.A. Beldam.**
(Illustrated London News)

SEASON RECORDS

Most Runs	2669	E.H. Hendren	1923
Most Hundreds	13	D.C.S. Compton	1947
Most Wickets	158	F.J. Titmus	1955
Most Wicket-Keeping Dismissals	99	J.T. Murray (92c, 7s)	1960
Most Catches (non WK)	46	P.H. Parfitt	1960
	46	P.H. Parfitt	1966

CAREER RECORDS

Most Appearances	642	F.J. Titmus	1949-82
Most Runs	40302	E.H. Hendren	1907-37
Most Hundreds	119	E.H. Hendren	1907-37
Most Times 1000 Runs in a Season	20	E.H. Hendren (1913-37)	1907-37
Most Wickets	2361	F.J. Titmus	1949-82
Most Hat-Tricks	4	F.A. Tarrant (1907-11)	1904-14
Most Times 100 Wickets in a Season	11	F.J. Titmus (1953-71)	1949-82
Most Wicket-Keeping Dismissals	1223	J.T. Murray (1024c, 199s)	1952-75
Most Catches (non WK)	562	E.H. Hendren	1907-37

NORTHAMPTONSHIRE

Badge	Tudor Rose
Colours	Maroon
Foundation	1820 (substantially reorganized 31 July 1878)
Headquarters	County Cricket Ground, Wantage Road, Northampton, NN1 4TJ
Champions	No instance

NORTHAMPTONSHIRE RECORDS IN ALL FIRST-CLASS CRICKET

MATCH RECORDS

For Northamptonshire	Record	Holder(s)	Opponents	Venue	Season
Highest Total	557-6d		Sussex	Hove	1914
Lowest total	12		Gloucestershire	Gloucester	1907
Highest Score	300	R. Subba Row	Surrey	The Oval	1958
Highest Partnership	376	R. Subba Row, A. Lightfoot	Surrey	The Oval	1958
Best Bowling–Innings	10-127	V.W.C. Jupp	Kent	Tunbridge Wells	1932
–Match	15-31	G.E. Tribe	Yorkshire	Northampton	1958
Most Dismissals–Innings	7	K.V. Andrew (7c)	Lancashire	Manchester	1962
–Match	10	L.A. Johnson (10c)	Sussex	Worthing	1963
	10	L.A. Johnson (8c, 2s)	Warwickshire	Birmingham	1965

Against Northamptonshire	Record	Holder(s)	Opponents	Venue	Season
Highest Total	670-9d		Sussex	Hove	1921
Lowest Total	33		Lancashire	Northampton	1977
Highest Score	333	K.S. Duleepsinhji	Sussex	Hove	1930
Highest Partnership	385	E.H. Bowley, M.W. Tate	Sussex	Hove	1921
Best Bowling–Innings	10-30	C. Blythe	Kent	Northampton	1907
–Match	17-48	C. Blythe	Kent	Northampton	1907

SEASON RECORDS

Most Runs	2198	D. Brookes	1952
Most Hundreds	8	R.A. Haywood	1921
Most Wickets	175	G.E. Tribe	1955
Most Wicket-Keeping Dismissals	90	K.V. Andrew (84c, 6s)	1962
Most Catches (non WK)	43	C. Milburn	1964

CAREER RECORDS

Most Appearances	492	D. Brookes	1934-59
Most Runs	28980	D. Brookes	1934-59
Most Hundreds	67	D. Brookes	1934-59
Most Times 1000 Runs in a Season	17	D. Brookes (1937-59)	1934-59
Most Wickets	1097	E.W. Clark	1922-47
Most Hat-Tricks	2	S.G. Smith, V.W.C. Jupp, M.R. Dilley	
Most Times 100 Wickets in a Season	8	G.E. Tribe (1952-59)	1951-59
Most Wicket-Keeping Dismissals	810	K.V. Andrew (653c, 157s)	1953-66
Most Catches (non WK)	469	D.S. Steele	1963-84

David Steele – England's folk-hero of the mid-Seventies. (Bill Smith)

NOTTINGHAMSHIRE

Badge	County Badge of Nottinghamshire
Colours	Green and Gold
Foundation	March/April 1841
Headquarters	Trent Bridge, Nottingham, NG2 6AG
Champions	(3) 1907, 1929, 1981

NOTTINGHAMSHIRE RECORDS IN ALL FIRST-CLASS CRICKET

MATCH RECORDS

For Nottinghamshire	Record	Holder(s)	Opponents	Venue	Season
Highest Total	739-7d		Leicestershire	Nottingham	1903
Lowest Total	13		Yorkshire	Nottingham	1901
Highest Score	312*	W.W. Keeton	Middlesex	The Oval	1939
Highest Partnership	398	W. Gunn, A. Shrewsbury	Sussex	Nottingham	1890
Best Bowling–Innings	10-66	K. Smales	Gloucestershire	Stroud	1956
–Match	17-89	F.C. Matthews	Northamptonshire	Nottingham	1923
Most Dismissals–Innings	6	Nine instances by T.W. Oates (2), B. Lilley, E.A. Meads (2), G. Millman and B.N. French (3).			
–Match	10	T.W. Oates (9c, 1s)	Middlesex	Nottingham	1906
	10	B.N. French (7c, 3s)	Oxford U.	Oxford	1984

Against Nottinghamshire	Record	Holder(s)	Opponents	Venue	Season
Highest Total	706-4d		Surrey	Nottingham	1947
Lowest Total	16		Derbyshire	Nottingham	1879
	16		Surrey	The Oval	1880
Highest Score	345	C.G. Macartney	Australians	Nottingham	1921
Highest Partnership	402	R.B. Kanhai, K. Ibadulla	Warwickshire	Nottingham	1968
Best Bowling–Innings	10-10	H. Verity	Yorkshire	Leeds	1932
–Match	17-89	W.G. Grace	Gloucestershire	Cheltenham	1877

Nottinghamshire take on All England at William Clarke's Trent Bridge Cricket Ground in August 1842.
(Mary Evans Picture Library)

Walter Keeton – played Nottinghamshire's highest innings against Middlesex at The Oval while Lord's staged the Eton v Harrow match.

Harold Larwood – legendary and exceptionally fast bowler who spearheaded Douglas Jardine's Bodyline campaign.

SEASON RECORDS

Most Runs	2620	W.W. Whysall	1929
Most Hundreds	9	W.W. Whysall	1928
	9	M.J. Harris	1971
Most Wickets	181	B. Dooland	1954
Most Wicket-Keeping Dismissals	87	B.N. French (76c, 11s)	1984
Most Catches (non WK)	44	W.W. Whysall	1929

CAREER RECORDS

Most Appearances	583	G. Gunn	1902-32
Most Runs	31592	G. Gunn	1902-32
Most Hundreds	65	J. Hardstaff, jr	1930-55
Most Times 1000 Runs in a Season	20	G. Gunn (1905-31)	1902-32
Most Wickets	1653	T.G. Wass	1896-1920
Most Hat-Tricks	3†	A. Shaw (1875-84)	1864-97
	3	H.J. Butler (1937-39)	1933-54
Most Times 100 Wickets in a Season	10	T.G. Wass (1900-12)	1896-1920
Most Wicket-Keeping Dismissals	958	T.W. Oates (734c, 224s)	1897-1925
Most Catches (non WK)	466	A.O. Jones	1892-1914

† Including two in the same match

SOMERSET

Badge	Wessex Wyvern
Colours	Black, White and Maroon
Foundation	18 August 1875 at Sidmouth, Devon
Headquarters	County Ground, St James Street, Taunton, TA1 1JT
Champions	No instance

SOMERSET RECORDS IN ALL FIRST-CLASS CRICKET

MATCH RECORDS

For Somerset	Record	Holder(s)	Opponents	Venue	Season
Highest Total	675-9d		Hampshire	Bath	1924
Lowest Total	25		Gloucestershire	Bristol	1947
Highest Score	322	I.V.A. Richards	Warwickshire	Taunton	1985
Highest Partnership	346	H.T.Hewett,L.C.H.Palairet	Yorkshire	Taunton	1892
Best Bowling–Innings	10-49	E.J. Tyler	Surrey	Taunton	1895
–Match	16-83	J.C. White	Worcestershire	Bath	1919
Most Dismissals–Innings	6	H.W. Stephenson (5c, 1s)	Glamorgan	Bath	1962
	6	G. Clayton (6c)	Worcestershire	Kidderminster	1965
	6	D.J.S. Taylor (6c)	Sussex	Taunton	1981
	6	D.J.S. Taylor (6c)	Hampshire	Bath	1982
–Match	9	A.E. Newton (6c, 3s)	Middlesex	Lord's	1901
	9	H.W. Stephenson (8c, 1s)	Yorkshire	Taunton	1963

Against Somerset	Record	Holder(s)	Opponents	Venue	Season
Highest Total	811		Surrey	The Oval	1899
Lowest Total	22		Gloucestershire	Bristol	1920
Highest Score	424	A.C. MacLaren	Lancashire	Taunton	1895
Highest Partnership	424*	W.J.Edrich,D.C.S.Compton	Middlesex	Lord's	1948
Best Bowling–Innings	10-35	A. Drake	Yorkshire	Weston-s-Mare	1914
–Match	17-137	W. Brearley	Lancashire	Manchester	1905

far left, Arthur Wellard – first to hit 50 first-class sixes in a season. left, Harold Gimblett – scored a 63-minute hundred on debut.
(Press Association)

Somerset 1965. STANDING: T. Tout *scorer*, R.T. Virgin, K.E. Palmer, G.H. Hall, C.H.M. Greetham, G. Clayton, P.J. Robinson. SEATED: P.B. Wight, B.A. Langford, C.R.M. Atkinson, W.E. Alley, G. Atkinson. (Sport & General)

SEASON RECORDS

Most Runs	2761	W.E. Alley	1961
Most Hundreds	10	W.E. Alley	1961
Most Wickets	169	A.W. Wellard	1938
Most Wicket-Keeping Dismissals	86	H.W. Stephenson (50c, 36s)	1954
Most Catches (non WK)	42	R.T. Virgin	1966

CAREER RECORDS

Most Appearances	504	B.A. Langford	1953-74
Most Runs	21142	H. Gimblett	1935-54
Most Hundreds	49	H. Gimblett	1935-54
Most Times 1000 Runs in a Season	12	H. Gimblett (1936-53)	1935-54
Most Wickets	2166	J.C. White	1909-37
Most Hat-Tricks	2	E.Robson (1898-1902)	1895-1923
Most Times 100 Wickets in a Season	14	J.C. White (1919-32)	1909-37
Most Wicket-Keeping Dismissals	1007	H.W. Stephenson (698c, 309s)	1948-64
Most Catches (non WK)	381	J.C. White	1909-37

SURREY

Badge	Prince of Wales' Feathers
Colours	Chocolate
Foundation	22 August 1845 at The Horns, Kennington
Headquarters	The Oval, Kennington, London, SE11 5SS
Champions	(15) 1890, 1891, 1892, 1894, 1895, 1899, 1914, 1952, 1953, 1954, 1955, 1956, 1957, 1958, 1971
Joint Champions	(1) 1950

SURREY RECORDS IN ALL FIRST-CLASS CRICKET

MATCH RECORDS

For Surrey	Record	Holder(s)	Opponents	Venue	Season
Highest Total	811		Somerset	The Oval	1899
Lowest Total	14		Essex	Chelmsford	1983
Highest Score	357*	R. Abel	Somerset	The Oval	1899
Highest Partnership	448	R. Abel, T.W. Hayward	Yorkshire	The Oval	1899
Best Bowling–Innings	10-43	T. Rushby	Somerset	Taunton	1921
–Match	16-83	G.A.R. Lock	Kent	Blackheath	1956
Most Dismissals–Innings	7	A. Long (7c)	Sussex	Hove	1964
–Match	12	E. Pooley (8c, 4s)	Sussex	The Oval	1868

Against Surrey	Record	Holder(s)	Opponents	Venue	Season
Highest Total	705-8d		Sussex	Hastings	1902
Lowest Total	16		MCC	Lord's	1872
Highest Score	300*	F. Watson	Lancashire	Manchester	1928
	300	R. Subba Row	Northamptonshire	The Oval	1958
Highest Partnership	377*	N.F. Horner, K. Ibadulla	Warwickshire	The Oval	1960
Best Bowling–Innings	10-28	W.P. Howell	Australians	The Oval	1899
–Match	15-57	W.P. Howell	Australians	The Oval	1899

far left, George Lohmann – Test cricket's most frequent wicket-taker.
left, Jack Hobbs – the most skilful batsman of all time?
(Mary Evans Picture Library)

Surrey – 1894 Champions. BACK: J.M. Read, T. Richardson, G.W. Ayres, F.E. Smith. CENTRE: H. Wood, W. Lockwood, K.J. Key *captain*, W.Brockwell, W.W. Read. FRONT: T.W. Hayward, R. Abel, A. Street.

SEASON RECORDS

Most Runs	3246	T.W. Hayward	1906
Most Hundreds	13	T.W. Hayward	1906
	13	J.B. Hobbs	1925
Most Wickets	252	T. Richardson	1895
Most Wicket-Keeping Dismissals	90	A. Long (73c, 17s)	1962
Most Catches (non WK)	77	M.J. Stewart	1957

CAREER RECORDS

Most Appearances	598	J.B. Hobbs	1905-34
Most Runs	43554	J.B. Hobbs	1905-34
Most Hundreds	144	J.B. Hobbs	1905-34
Most Times 1000 Runs in a Season	24	J.B. Hobbs (1905-33)	1905-34
Most Wickets	1775	T. Richardson	1892-1904
Most Hat-Tricks	4	T. Richardson (1893-98)	1892-1904
Most Times 100 Wickets in a Season	10	T. Richardson (1893-1903)	1892-1904
Most Wicket-Keeping Dismissals	1223	H. Strudwick (1040c, 183s)	1902-27
Most Catches (non WK)	604	M.J. Stewart	1954-72

SUSSEX

Badge	County Arms of Six Martlets
Colours	Dark Blue, Light Blue and Gold
Foundation	1 March 1839
Headquarters	County Ground, Eaton Road, Hove, BN3 3AN
Champions	No instance

SUSSEX RECORDS IN ALL FIRST-CLASS CRICKET

MATCH RECORDS

For Sussex	Record	Holder(s)	Opponents	Venue	Season
Highest Total	705-8d		Surrey	Hastings	1902
Lowest Total	19		Nottinghamshire	Hove	1873
Highest Score	333	K.S. Duleepsinhji	Northamptonshire	Hove	1930
Highest Partnership	490	E.H.Bowley, J.G.Langridge	Middlesex	Hove	1933
Best Bowling–Innings	10-48	C.H.G. Bland	Kent	Tonbridge	1899
–Match	17-106	G.R. Cox	Warwickshire	Horsham	1926
Most Dismissals–Innings	6	Nine instances by H.R. Butt (3), A.A. Shaw, R.T. Webb (2), J.M. Parks, M.G. Griffith and H. Phillips.			
–Match	10	H. Phillips (5c, 5s)	Surrey	The Oval	1872

Against Sussex	Record	Holder(s)	Opponents	Venue	Season
Highest Total	726		Nottinghamshire	Nottingham	1895
Lowest Total	18		Kent	Gravesend	1867
Highest Score	322	E. Paynter	Lancashire	Hove	1937
Highest Partnership	428	W.W.Armstrong, M.A.Noble	Australians	Hove	1902
Best Bowling–Innings	9-11	A.P. Freeman	Kent	Hove	1922
–Match	17-67	A.P. Freeman	Kent	Hove	1922

far left, Maurice Tate – three major bowling records for Sussex from an eight-pace run-up.
left, Mike Griffith – the only man to play first-class cricket and international hockey at Lord's. (Bill Smith)

Sussex 1962. STANDING: **K.G. Suttle, A. Buss, N.I. Thomson, D.L.Bates, R.J. Langridge, R.V. Bell.**
SEATED: **A.S.M. Oakman, D.V. Smith, E.R. Dexter** *captain*, **Rev D.S. Sheppard, J.M. Parks.** (Central Press)

SEASON RECORDS

Most Runs	2850	J.G. Langridge	1949
Most Hundreds	12	J.G. Langridge	1949
Most Wickets	198	M.W. Tate	1925
Most Wicket-Keeping Dismissals	95	G.B. Street (69c, 26s)	1923
Most Catches (non WK)	69	J.G. Langridge	1959

CAREER RECORDS

Most Appearances	622	J. Langridge	1924-53
Most Runs	34152	J.G. Langridge	1928-55
Most Hundreds	76	J.G. Langridge	1928-55
Most Times 1000 Runs in a Season	20	J. Langridge (1927-52)	1924-53
Most Wickets	2211	M.W. Tate	1912-37
Most Hat-Tricks	3	W.A. Humphreys, sr (1880-85)	1871-96
	3	V.W.C. Jupp (1911-21)	1909-21
Most Times 100 Wickets in a Season	13	M.W. Tate (1922-35)	1912-37
Most Wicket-Keeping Dismissals	1176	H.R. Butt (911c, 265s)	1890-1912
Most Catches (non WK)	779	J.G. Langridge	1928-55

WARWICKSHIRE

Badge	Bear and Ragged Staff
Colours	Dark Blue, Gold and Silver
Foundation	8 April 1882 at the Queen's Hotel, Coventry (substantially reorganized 19 January 1884)
Headquarters	County Ground, Edgbaston, Birmingham, B5 7QU
Champions	(3) 1911, 1951, 1972

WARWICKSHIRE RECORDS IN ALL FIRST-CLASS CRICKET

MATCH RECORDS

For Warwickshire	Record	Holder(s)	Opponents	Venue	Season
Highest Total	657-6d		Hampshire	Birmingham	1899
Lowest Total	16		Kent	Tonbridge	1913
Highest Score	305*	F.R. Foster	Worcestershire	Dudley	1914
Highest Partnership	470	A.I. Kallicharran, G.W. Humpage	Lancashire	Southport	1982
Best Bowling–Innings	10-41	J.D. Bannister	Comb Services	Birmingham	1959
–Match	15-76	S. Hargreave	Surrey	The Oval	1903
Most Dismissals–Innings	7	E.J. Smith (4c, 3s)	Derbyshire	Birmingham	1926
–Match	9	E.B. Lewis (8c, 1s)	Oxford U.	Birmingham	1949

Against Warwickshire	Record	Holder(s)	Opponents	Venue	Season
Highest Total	887		Yorkshire	Birmingham	1896
Lowest Total	15		Hampshire	Birmingham	1922
Highest Score	322	I.V.A. Richards	Somerset	Taunton	1985
Highest Partnership	393	E.G. Arnold, W.B. Burns	Worcestershire	Birmingham	1909
Best Bowling–Innings	10-36	H. Verity	Yorkshire	Leeds	1931
–Match	17-92	A.P. Freeman	Kent	Folkestone	1932

Warwickshire – 1972 Champions. STANDING: B. Thomas *physiotherapist*, W Blenkiron, N.M. McVicker, J. Whitehouse, D.L. Murray, J.A. Jameson, R.G.D. Willis, D.L. Amiss, S.J. Rouse, A.I. Kallicharran, W.N. Tidy, P. Pike *scorer*. SEATED: R.B. Kanhai, L.T. Deakins *secretary*, M.J.K. Smith, Lt-Gen Sir Oliver Leese *president*, A.C. Smith *captain*, C.C. Goodway *chairman*, D.J. Brown, A.S.M. Oakman *coach*, L.R. Gibbs. (Ken Kelly)

John Jameson and Rohan Kanhai display their world record second-wicket partnership. (Ken Kelly)

Jim Stewart – set world record with 17 sixes in a first-class match. (Ken Kelly)

SEASON RECORDS

Most Runs	2417	M.J.K. Smith	1959
Most Hundreds	9	A.I. Kallicharran	1984
Most Wickets	180	W.E. Hollies	1946
Most Wicket-Keeping Dismissals	80	G.W. Humpage (76c, 4s)	1985
Most Catches (non WK)	52	M.J.K. Smith	1961

CAREER RECORDS

Most Appearances	665	W.G. Quaife	1894-1928
Most Runs	33862	W.G. Quaife	1894-1928
Most Hundreds	76	D.L. Amiss	1960-86
Most Times 1000 Runs in a Season	20	W.G. Quaife (1898-1926)	1894-1928
Most Wickets	2201	W.E. Hollies	1932-57
Most Hat-Tricks	3	T.L. Pritchard (1948-51)	1946-55
Most Times 100 Wickets in a Season	14	W.E. Hollies (1935-57)	1932-57
Most Wicket-Keeping Dismissals	800	E.J. Smith (662c, 138s)	1904-30
Most Catches (non WK)	422	M.J.K. Smith	1956-75

WORCESTERSHIRE

Badge	Shield Argent bearing Fess between Three Pears Sable
Colours	Dark Green and Black
Foundation	11 March 1865 at the Star Hotel, Worcester
Headquarters	County Ground, New Road, Worcester, WR2 4QQ.
Champions	(3) 1964, 1965, 1974

WORCESTERSHIRE RECORDS IN ALL FIRST-CLASS CRICKET

MATCH RECORDS

For Worcestershire	Record	Holder(s)	Opponents	Venue	Season
Highest Total	633		Warwickshire	Worcester	1906
Lowest Total	24		Yorkshire	Huddersfield	1903
Highest Score	311*	G.M. Turner	Warwickshire	Worcester	1982
Highest Partnership	393	E.G. Arnold, W.B. Burns	Warwickshire	Birmingham	1909
Best Bowling–Innings	9-23	C.F. Root	Lancashire	Worcester	1931
–Match	15-87	A.J. Conway	Gloucestershire	Moreton-in-M	1914
Most Dismissals–Innings	7	H. Yarnold (1c, 6s)	Scotland	Dundee	1951
–Match	9	H. Yarnold (5c, 4s)	Hampshire	Worcester	1949

Against Worcestershire	Record	Holder(s)	Opponents	Venue	Season
Highest Total	701-4d		Leicestershire	Worcester	1906
Lowest Total	30		Hampshire	Worcester	1903
Highest Score	331*	J.D.B. Robertson	Middlesex	Worcester	1949
Highest Partnership	380	C.J.B. Wood, H. Whitehead	Leicestershire	Worcester	1906
Best Bowling–Innings	10-51	J. Mercer	Glamorgan	Worcester	1936
–Match	17-212	J.C. Clay	Glamorgan	Swansea	1937

far left, Tom Graveney – grace and elegance personified.
(Sport & General)

left, Steven Rhodes – England's next wicket-keeper?
(Bill Smith)

Worcestershire – 1964 Champions. STANDING: **J.A. Ormrod, N. Gifford, B.L. D'Oliveira, L.J. Coldwell, R.G.A. Headley, D.N.F. Slade.** SEATED: **T.W. Graveney, J.A. Flavell, D. Kenyon** *captain*, **M.J. Horton, D.W. Richardson, R. Booth.** (Sport & General)

SEASON RECORDS

Most Runs	2654	H.H.I. Gibbons	1934
Most Hundreds	10	G.M. Turner	1970
Most Wickets	207	C.F. Root	1925
Most Wicket-Keeping Dismissals	110	H. Yarnold (63c, 47s)	1949
Most Catches (non WK)	65	D.W. Richardson	1958

CAREER RECORDS

Most Appearances	589	D. Kenyon	1946-67
Most Runs	34490	D. Kenyon	1946-67
Most Hundreds	72	G.M. Turner	1967-82
Most Times 1000 Runs in a Season	19	D. Kenyon (1947-67)	1946-67
Most Wickets	2143	R.T.D. Perks	1930-55
Most Hat-Tricks	3	G.A. Wilson (1900-05)	1899-1906
	3†	R.O. Jenkins (1948-49)	1938-58
	3	J.A. Flavell (1951-63)	1949-67
Most Times 100 Wickets in a Season	15	R.T.D. Perks (1934-55)	1930-55
Most Wicket-Keeping Dismissals	1015	R. Booth (868c, 147s)	1946-70
Most Catches (non WK)	412	D.W. Richardson	1952-67

† including two in one match

YORKSHIRE

Badge	White Rose
Colours	Dark Blue, Light Blue and Gold
Foundation	8 January 1863 at the Adelphi Hotel, Sheffield
Headquarters	Headingley Cricket Ground, Leeds, LS6 3BU
Champions	(29) 1893, 1896, 1898, 1900, 1901, 1902, 1905, 1908, 1912, 1919, 1922, 1923, 1924, 1925, 1931, 1932, 1933, 1935, 1937, 1938, 1939, 194◼ 1959, 1960, 1962, 1963, 1966, 1967, 1968
Joint Champions	(1) 1949

YORKSHIRE RECORDS IN ALL FIRST-CLASS CRICKET

MATCH RECORDS

For Yorkshire	Record	Holder(s)	Opponents	Venue	Season
Highest Total	887		Warwickshire	Birmingham	1896
Lowest Total	23		Hampshire	Middlesbrough	1965
Highest Score	341	G.H. Hirst	Leicestershire	Leicester	1905
Highest Partnership	555	P. Holmes, H. Sutcliffe	Essex	Leyton	1932
Best Bowling–Innings	10-10	H. Verity	Nottinghamshire	Leeds	1932
–Match	17-91	H. Verity	Essex	Leyton	1933
Most Dismissals–Innings	7	D.L. Bairstow (7c)	Derbyshire	Scarborough	1982
–Match	11	D.L. Bairstow (11c)	Derbyshire	Scarborough	1982

Against Yorkshire	Record	Holder(s)	Opponents	Venue	Season
Highest Total	630		Somerset	Leeds	1901
Lowest Total	13		Nottinghamshire	Nottingham	1901
Highest Score	318*	W.G. Grace	Gloucestershire	Cheltenham	1876
Highest Partnership	448	R. Abel, T.W. Hayward	Surrey	The Oval	1899
Best Bowling–Innings	10-37	C.V. Grimmett	Australians	Sheffield	1930
–Match	17-91	H. Dean	Lancashire	Liverpool	1913

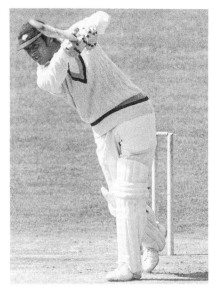

far left, Geoffrey Boycott – the arch perfectionist. (Bill Smith)
left, Fiery Fred Trueman in his pomp. (Sport & General)

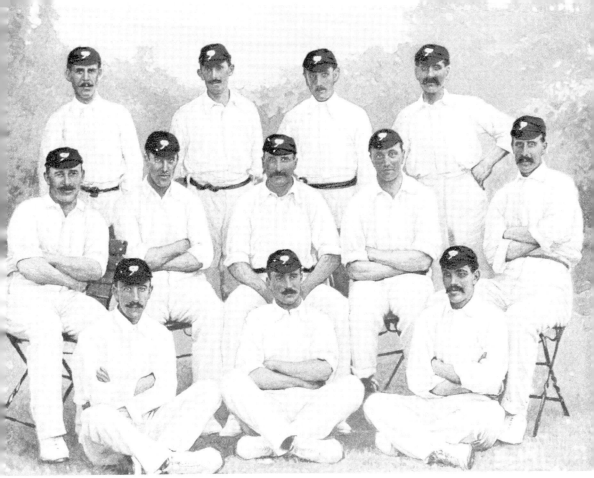

Yorkshire – 1901 Champions. BACK: E. Wainwright, L. Whitehead, W. Rhodes, D. Hunter. CENTRE: G.H. Hirst, E. Smith, Lord Hawke *captain*, F. Mitchell, J. Tunnicliffe, D. Denton, T.L. Taylor, J.T. Brown.

SEASON RECORDS

Most Runs	2883	H. Sutcliffe	1932
Most Hundreds	12	H. Sutcliffe	1932
Most Wickets	240	W. Rhodes	1900
Most Wicket-Keeping Dismissals	107	J.G. Binks (96c, 11s)	1960
Most Catches (non WK)	70	J. Tunnicliffe	1901
	70	P.J. Sharpe	1962

CAREER RECORDS

Most Appearances	881	W. Rhodes	1898-1930
Most Runs	38561	H. Sutcliffe	1919-45
Most Hundreds	112	H. Sutcliffe	1919-45
Most Times 1000 Runs in a Season	21	H. Sutcliffe (1919-39)	1919-45
Most Wickets	3608	W. Rhodes	1898-1930
Most Hat-Tricks	4	G.G. Macaulay (1923-33)	1920-35
	4	F.S. Trueman (1951-63)	1949-68
Most Times 100 Wickets in a Season	22	W. Rhodes (1898-1929)	1898-1930
Most Wicket-Keeping Dismissals	1189	D. Hunter (861c, 328s)	1888-1909
Most Catches (non WK)	665	J. Tunnicliffe	1891-1907

Gentlemen v Players matches

This series of matches between amateurs and professionals began in 1806 and ended when amateur status in first-class cricket was abol-, ished after the 1962 season.

The Lord's match between these two sides was the high point of the English season before Test matches became annual events. Teams for that fixture were selected by the MCC and an invitation to play was regarded as one of the games's highest honours, with the match itself effectively assuming the status of a Test trial. Until 1952, when Len Hutton was appointed as England's first professional captain of modern times, the captaincy of the Players was the greatest honour available to a professional cricketer. It was bestowed upon Jack Hobbs a record 22 times.

The first two matches were played at Thomas Lord's first ground in Dorset Fields (now Dorset Square) and both were won by the Gentlemen. Before the next encounter in 1819, Lord had moved his turf twice and it had come to rest in its present home in St John's Wood. The matches became very popular and additional fixtures at The Oval (1857-1934) and at the Scarborough Festival (1885-1962) became annual events. In 1919 Jack Hobbs scored a hundred in each of the three fixtures. Other matches under this title were occasionally staged at various grounds in Kent and Sussex, as well as at Prince's in London.

The Gentleman 1894. BACK: J. Douglas, J.R. Mason, G.J. Mordaunt, A.C. MacLaren. CENTRE: S.M.J. Woods, H.T. Hewett, W.G. Grace *captain*, H.W. Bainbridge, F.S. Jackson. FRONT: G. MacGregor, A.E. Stoddart.

The Players 1894. BACK: W. Chatterton, W.H. Lockwood, J.T. Hearne, W. Flowers, W. Hearn *umpire*. CENTRE: E. Wainwright, A. Ward, W. Gunn *captain*, F. Martin, W. Brockwell. FRONT: J. Briggs, W. Storer.

After the final match in 1962, the Players had won 68 of the 137 matches played on Lord's grounds, the Gentlemen had won 41, and 28 had been drawn.

The highest total in the fixtures was 651 for 7 declared by the Players at The Oval in 1934. The highest by the Gentlemen was 578 at The Oval in 1934. The best at Lord's was 579 by the Players in 1926.

Jack Hobbs played the highest individual innings in the series when he scored 266 not out for the Players at Scarborough in 1925. The record for the Gentlemen and the highest for either side in matches at Lord's was 232 not out by Charles Fry in 1903. During that innings Fry shared with Archie MacLaren the highest partnership for any wicket by either side in all these matches:

309 unbroken for the third wicket.

The best bowling analysis in these matches was 10 for 37 by Alex Kennedy for the Players at The Oval in 1927. His figures improved upon those of Arthur Fielder, who took 10 for 90 for the Players at Lord's in 1906 – the only other instance of a bowler taking all ten wickets in this series. The best performance for the Gentlemen was 9 for 46 by Jack Stephenson at Lord's in 1936.

There were three instances of the match double of 100 runs and ten wickets in these contests and they were all accomplished by W.G. Grace for the Gentlemen:

134*		6-50	4-31	Lord's	1868
23	110	3-61	7-58	Prince's	1874
7	152	7-64	5-61	Lord's	1875

W.G. Grace dominated these matches from 1865 until he made the last of his record total of 85 appearances in 1906. The next highest number of appearances was 49 by Jack Hobbs for the Players between 1907 and 1934.

Six cricketers appeared for both sides in these matches:

	Gentlemen	Players
R. Daft	1858	1860-1879
E.J. Diver	1884	1886-1899
W.J. Edrich	1947-1957	1938
W.R. Hammond	1938-1946	1923-1937
J.H. Parsons	1929-1931	1914-1927
P.E. Richardson	1955-1958	1959

Wally Hammond achieved a unique double when he captained both sides to victory at Lord's in successive years – the Players in 1937 and the Gentlemen in 1938.

Ian Peebles, who was to play for England before appearing in county cricket, made his first-class debut for the Gentlemen against the Players at The Oval on 6 July 1927. The first of his 923 first-class wickets was Andrew Sandham – the first wicket to fall in the match and clean bowled by the 19-year-old leg-spinner from Aberdeen.

University cricket

□ The University Match between Cambridge and Oxford is the oldest surviving 'important' or 'great' fixture, having first been played in 1827. Apart from wartime intervals it has been staged annually since 1838.

□ Although the first encounter took place at Lord's, the fixture did not become established there until 1851. Five of the early matches were played in the Oxford area: 1829, 1846 and 1848 at Magdalen College; 1843 at Bullingdon Green; and 1850 at Cowley Marsh.

□ After the 1986 match (which Cambridge won by five wickets off the last possible ball), Cambridge had 54 wins, Oxford 46, and 42 of the 142 official contests had been drawn.

□ The most successive victories by either side is five by Cambridge from 1839 to 1843.

□ The most historic finish occurred in 1870 in Cobden's Match. With Oxford needing only three runs for victory and with three wickets in

hand, Frank Cobden took a hat-trick and so snatched an extraordinary win for Cambridge. Although he appeared for Shropshire and Hertfordshire, Cobden, who was born in Nottinghamshire, never played for a first-class county.

□ Oxford holds the records for the highest and lowest totals in this series of matches – 503 in 1900 and 32 in 1878. The respective records for Cambridge are 432 for 9 declared in 1936 and 39 in 1858.

□ The highest of 41 hundreds for Oxford – and the record score in these matches – is 238 not out by the Nawab of Pataudi (sr) in 1931. The highest of 51 Cambridge hundreds is 211 by Gamini Goonesena in 1957, his seventh-wicket partnership of 289 with Geoffrey Cook being the highest for any wicket by either side in University Matches.

□ The only batsman to score a hundred in each innings of the University Match is Robin Boyd-Moss, who scored 139 and 124 in 1983. Having scored 100 the previous year, he also became the only player to score hundreds in three successive innings of this fixture. His aggregate of 489 is a record for these matches.

□ The only other batsman to score three centuries in these matches in M.J.K. (Mike) Smith of Oxford. The eventual captain of Warwickshire and England scored 201 not out in 1954, 104 in 1955 and 117 in 1956.

□ The best innings and match bowling analyses were achieved in the 1871 match by Samuel Butler for Oxford. A tall (6ft 2in), right-handed bowler whose pace was genuinely fast, he took all ten first innings wickets for 38 runs and a further 5 for 57 when Cambridge followed on. Butler, who became a barrister and settled in Somerset, was chosen for the Gentlemen against the Players that season on the strength of his unique performance. The previous year he had been the first of Cobden's hat-trick victims. Ironically the winning hit for Oxford in 1871 was made off Cobden's bowling.

□ The best innings and match analyses for Cambridge were achieved in 1878 by Allan Steel, later to lead England to victory in all three Tests of the 1886 series against Australia. An extremely accurate right-arm slow bowler who could spin the ball either way, he took 8 for 62 and, in Oxford's record and catastrophic total of 32, 5 for 11 in 20.1 four-ball overs. Three weeks later Steel played a major role in his University's historic two-day defeat of the Australians at Lord's.

☐ The first player to do the match double (100 runs and ten wickets) in a University Match was an Australian Rhodes scholar. In 1910 Philip Le Couteur scored 160 of Oxford's total of 315 before taking 6 for 20 and 5 for 46. Cambridge, 76 and 113, lost by an innings and 126 runs – at that time their worst defeat by Oxford. Le Couteur, a right-handed batsman and deceptive leg-break bowler, took 8 for 99 in the second Cambridge innings the following year and made six appearances for the Gentlemen against the Players. After Oxford, he studied psychology at Bonn University before returning home to lecture in philosophy and play a few matches for Victoria.

☐ The only Englishman to achieve the University Match double is Giles Toogood in 1985. Then a trainee doctor at the John Radcliffe Hospital in Headington, Oxford, he scored 149 (emulating M.J.K. Smith's feat of scoring hundreds for Oxford in successive years) and, bowling brisk-medium seamers from a lively run-up, returned match figures of 10 for 93. His first innings analysis of 8 for 52 doubled his aggregate of wickets for the season; three earlier years of off-spin had claimed only three victims at 73.66 runs apiece.

☐ Blues are awarded for appearances in the University Match and, since the 1860s, these have been restricted to four per player. Not until 1976 did anyone gain blues from both universities. After representing Oxford in the 1975 match at the end of the fourth and final year of his Classics course at Worcester College, David Jarrett moved to St Catherine's College for a one-year Certificate of Education course and

Giles Toogood – successive hundreds and a University Match double. (Bill Smith)

appeared for Cambridge in 1976. He remains the only player to represent different universities in successive years at Lord's, although Stephen Wookey appeared for Cambridge in 1975 and 1976 and for Oxford in 1978, and Gajanand Pathmanathan gained four blues for Oxford (1975-76-77-78) before representing Cambridge in 1983.

FIRST-CLASS CRICKET IN AUSTRALIA

The status of matches in Australia was first defined in 1908, when the Associations of New South Wales, South Australia and Victoria agreed that all international matches, all matches between English and other representative and interstate teams, all interstate matches and matches against New Zealand, and all matches of a representative character played on even terms and comprising first-class players, including Australia against The Rest of Australia, should be ranked as first-class.

This definition did not have retrospective effect. The term 'first-class match' was rarely used in Australia until the 1890s, major fixtures being described as 'important', 'representative' or 'inter-colonial'. In 1977, the Association of Cricket Statisticians produced their *Guide to First-Class Matches Played in Australia,* and their decisions regarding the status of doubtful matches played before 1908 have been respected in compiling these records.

The first inter-colonial match (and the first match in Australia to be ranked as first-class by the ACS) was played in February 1851 between Van Diemen's Land (Tasmania) and Port Philip District (Victoria) at Launceston. Its status has always been the subject of much argument but both teams were properly representative of their colonies, with the home team being drawn from clubs throughout the island and the Victorians able to choose from a host of immigrants attracted

initially by the region's farming potential. The discovery of gold in Bathurst on 15 February 1851 was to give Victoria's selectors a considerably wider range of choice.

The first reference to cricket in Australia occurred in 1803 and described the game being played regularly in Sydney, although the first clubs there were not established until 1826.

The first match between two mainland colonies did not take place until March 1856 when New South Wales (76 and 16 for 7) beat Victoria (63 and 28) by three wickets on the Melbourne Cricket Club's new ground at Richmond Paddock – the Paddock that was to grow into the Melbourne Cricket Ground (MCG) of today. There can be no dispute about the status of this match. Traditionalists who disagree with the ACS *Guide,* regard it as the start of first-class cricket in Australia, and it is the first overseas match to have its full scores published in *Scores and Biographies.*

Team records

The world record total in all first-class cricket is 1107 by Victoria against New South Wales at Melbourne on 27-28 December 1926. It was based on a first-wicket partnership of 375 runs (still the record for that wicket in Sheffield Shield matches), made in $3\frac{3}{4}$ hours by Bill Woodfull (133) and Bill Ponsford (352 including 36 fours). H.S.T.L. 'Stork' Hendry (100) and Jack Ryder (295 in just over four hours and including 6 sixes and 33 fours) were the other century-makers in an innings which lasted $10\frac{1}{2}$ hours. It exceeded their previous record of 1059 (the only other four-figure total in first-class cricket), against Tasmania on the same ground in February 1923. A month later New South Wales revenged this massive defeat by dismissing Victoria for 35 and gaining an innings victory.

The highest second innings total in all first-class cricket is 770 by New South Wales against South Australia at the Adelaide Oval in January 1921 (Warren Bardsley 235, Johnny Taylor 180, Charles Kelleway 103 not out). South Australia's bowlers had conceded 724 runs in Victoria's second innings a few weeks earlier, their oppo-

The first Kalgoorlie cricket team (1896). The umpire seems to be expecting trouble.

Kalgoorlie welcomes the 1897 Australians.

nents' scores in Sheffield Shield matches that season being 639, 310, 724, 802, 304 and 770. Declarations were not permitted in that competition until the 1926-27 season and none occurred until the season after that.

The highest fourth innings total in Australia is 572 by New South Wales in December 1907 at Sydney. Even that effort, the highest innings of a match which produced 1716 runs in five days plus three balls, could not save them from a 20-runs defeat by South Australia.

The record match aggregate in Australia is 1929 by New South Wales (642 and 593) and South Australia (475 and 219) at Sydney in January 1926. South Australia, defeated by 541 runs, had to begin this eight-day epic immediately after an overnight rail journey following a six-day match that had ended in Melbourne the previous day.

The lowest innings total in first-class matches Australia is 15 by Victoria against the MCC at Melbourne on 9 February 1904. Batting one man short on a sticky wicket, the State side, unequal to the wiles of Wilfred Rhodes (5 for 6) and Ted Arnold (4 for 8), were dismissed in ¾ hour (12.1 six-ball overs).

The lowest total in a Sheffield Shield match is 27 by South Australia against New South Wales at Sydney on 18 November 1955. Although overnight rain had caused moisture to condense on plastic covers and fall on the pitch, it was the late swing and pace variations of Keith Miller's bowling that produced this dramatic collapse. Supported by Pat Crawford (3 for 14), Miller took 7 for 12 in 7.3 eight-ball overs – the best analysis in the Sheffield Shield in terms of most wickets for least runs.

The two greatest margins of victory in Australian first-class cricket were obtained by Victoria as a result of their two record innings totals

of over 1000 runs at Melbourne. In February 1923 they beat Tasmania by an innings and 666 runs after scoring 1059, and in December 1926 they defeated New South Wales by an innings and 656 runs after amassing 1107.

The largest victory by a runs margin in all first-class cricket occurred in January 1930 when New South Wales (235 and 761 for 8 declared) defeated Queensland (227 and 84) by 685 runs at Sydney. After ending the first innings only eight runs in arrears, the visiting State found themselves faced by Don Bradman in his most brilliant and insatiable form. His gently cameo of 452 not out left them with the task of scoring 770 to win. The fast right-arm bowling of Sam Everett (6 for 23) ensured their record defeat.

No batsmen have been given out in Australian first-class cricket for hitting the ball twice or obstructing the field, there have been four instances of dismissals for handling the ball (see table).

Batting records

The highest individual innings in first-class matches in Australia is 452 not out by Donald George Bradman for New South Wales against Queensland at Sydney on 4 and 6 January 1930. Opening the batting and being dismissed for 3, the lowest score of the NSW first innings of 235, Bradman began his record innings on the second day with his side 22 for 1 and 30 runs ahead. He batted 415 minutes, hit 49 fours and took his score from 205 to 310 before lunch on the third day. 'Displaying a wider range of strokes than usual, Bradman batted without a trace of error during his long stay' *(Wisden)*. His innings exceeded the previous highest first-class score of 437 by Bill Ponsford made two years earlier, and remained the world record until Hanif Mohammad (499) surpassed it

GIVEN OUT FOR HANDLING THE BALL

Batsman	For	Opponents	Venue	Season
W.H. Scotton	Smokers	Non-Smokers	East Melbourne	1886-87
E. Jones	South Australia	Victoria	Melbourne	1894-95
P.J.P. Burge	Queensland	New South Wales	Sydney	1958-59
A.M.J. Hilditch	Australia	Pakistan	Perth	1978-79

Archie Jackson and Donald Bradman – a formidable pairing.

Bill Ponsford – unique scorer of two quadruple hundreds.

in Pakistan almost exactly 29 years later. Bradman's match aggregate of 455 is the record for Australian first-class cricket.

The highest score by a batsman in Australia making his first appearance in first-class cricket is 232 not out by Sam Loxton at Melbourne on 19-20 December 1946. Taking full advantage of an opportunity created by five of his fellow Victorians being absent on Test duty, the 25-year-old right-hander batted for 390 minutes against Queensland's attack, hitting a six and 22 fours. When he had made 183 he concussed himself with the bat when attempting a hook. He managed to complete his innings and to take the first Queensland wicket before seeking medical treatment.

The highest score by any batsman who appeared in only one first-class match is 207 by Norman Callaway for New South Wales, at Sydney on 19-20 February 1915. A 19-year-old right-hander, he went to the wicket with the score 17 for 3. His fifth-wicket with the score 17 for 3. His fifth-wicket partnership of 256 with Charles Macartney, his captain, was the basis of Queens-

land's defeat by an innings in two days. Two years later Callaway was killed in action in France.

The only number eleven batsman to score a century in Australian first-class cricket is Thomas Hastings. A wicket-keeper, he played 15 times for Victoria from 1887 until 1908 and achieved a career batting average of 11.91. Playing against South Australia at Melbourne in January 1903, Hastings came to the wicket when Victoria were 261 for 9. His partnership with Mathew Ellis (118) took the total to 472, fell just 19 runs short of the world record for the tenth wicket at that time, and was largely responsible for his State's victory by 179 runs.

The longest innings played in Australia took Bob Cowper 727 minutes as he scored 307 against England at Melbourne on 12-16 February 1966 during the Fifth Test.

The only batsman to see over 800 runs scored during his innings in Australian first-class cricket is Bill Ponsford. Playing only his fourth first-class innings for Victoria, against Tasmania at Melbourne in February 1923, he scored 429 in 7 hours 57 minutes, hit 42 fours, and saw the total progress from 200 for 3 to 1001 for 8. There has been only one higher aggregate of runs during an individual innings, 811 being added during Bobby Abel's 357 not out for Surrey against Somerset in 1899. Ponsford is alone in making two scores in excess of 400 in first-class cricket, his later one being 437 against Queensland at Melbourne in December 1927; both scores were world records at the time.

The only batsman to score six hundreds in succesive first-class innings in Australia is Don Bradman in the 1938-39 season. After scoring 118 for his own team against K.E. Rigg's XI at Melbourne, he made five consecutive Sheffield Shield centuries for South Australia (143 v New South Wales and 225 v Queensland at Adelaide, 107 v Victoria at Melbourne, 186 v Queensland at Brisbane, and 135 not out v New South Wales at Sydney). This sequence equalled the world record established by C.B. Fry in 1901 and was itself equalled by M.J. Procter in South Africa in 1970-71.

Ken Barrington achieved a unique feat when he exceeded 50 in each of the ten first-class innings he played at the Adelaide Oval for England and the MCC. His scores were 104, 52, 52*, 63 and 132* on the 1962-63 tour, and 69, 51, 63, 60 and 102 in 1965-66.

The first batsman to score a century in each innings of his first first-class match, and the only Australian to do so, was Arthur Morris, playing for New South Wales at Sydney in December 1940. Opening the innings, the 18-year-old left-hander scored 148 and 111 against the Queensland bowling.

The only Australian to score a hundred in each innings of successive first-class matches was another left-hander, David Hookes. Batting on his home ground at Adelaide, he scored 185 and 105 against Queensland on 11-14 February 1977 in a match which ended in a tie, and then made 135 and 156 against New South Wales on 18-21 February.

Archie Jackson was only 18 years 125 days old when he completed the second of his two hundreds (131 and 122) for New South Wales against South Australia at Sydney in January 1928.

David Hookes – thrashed a hundred off only 34 balls.
(Author)

The fastest recorded first-class hundred in terms of fewest balls faced was scored by David Hookes on 25 October 1982. Captaining South Australia against Victoria at the Adelaide Oval, he reached his century off only 34 balls and in 43 minutes **(also the fastest hundred in Australian first-class cricket in terms of time).** Hitting 18 fours and three sixes, Hookes went to 102 (out of 120 for no wicket) in 8.4 overs. Twelve minutes later Hookes was caught for 107 – scored off 40 balls. He had made 137 in the first innings.

The most runs off one over in Australian first-class cricket is 32. Playing for Arthur Morris's XI against Lindsay Hassett's XI in the latter's Testimonial Match at Melbourne in January 1954, Ian Craig (3--66066) and Keith Carmody (-41-----) achieved the record off an eight-ball over from the off-break bowler, Ian Johnson. Together they added 50 in eight minutes, Craig scoring 106 and Carmody 66 before both fell to Johnson (4 for 182 in 18 overs). Hassett celebrated the occasion by scoring a century.

The Australian and Philadelphian Teams of 1894 as pictured in the Boy's Own Paper.
(Mary Evans Picture Library)

above, W.G. Grace
wearing Ranji's turban
during dinner at his
host's Shillinglea Park
residence on 19 May
1903, from a
watercolour by his
friend, Henry Scott
Tuke, RA. (Tom Troman)
right, K.S. Ranjitsinhji,
most princely of
batsmen and alone in
scoring separate first-
class hundreds on the
same day.

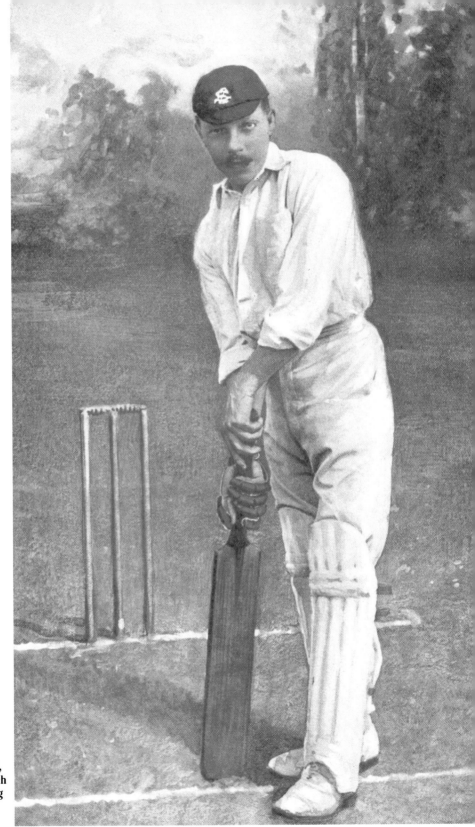

Bobby Abel, 'The
Guv'nor', who, in 1899,
set world records which
still survive by carrying
his bat for 357 in a
Surrey total of 811.

above, The delightful
cathedral setting of the
Worcester Ground
captured by artist Roy
Perry, RI.
left, A helicopter dries
the Worcester pitch
during the rain-
prolonged 1986
NatWest Trophy semi-
final against Sussex,
the eventual
champions.
(NatWest/Adrian Murrell)

Madame Tussauds' waxwork impression of Ian Botham confirms that England's all-rounder really is larger than life.

An incongruous mobile stand at Moratuwa. (Author)

The exotic setting of Kandy's Asgiriya Stadium. (Author)

Palms shelter spectators from the midday sun at the Colombo Cricket Club Ground. (Author)

The Dimbulla Cricket Club Ground at Radella, resplendent within the tea estates. (Author)

Umpire: "Will you take middle or leg, Sir?"
Batsman: "I think I had better take a GUINNESS!"

"OUT FIRST BALL"

Guinness proves that cricket is good for you. The other card, sent by a youthful Lucy in 1907, asked if her beau (in Leicester) wore the same expression when he made a duck.

Wicket Keeper: "*How's that!*"

The most runs by one batsman off a first-class over in Australia, and the record in Sheffield Shield matches, is 29 by David Hookes of South Australia at Adelaide on 4 February 1977. During his first three-figure innings the left-hander struck 4 sixes, a four, and a single (60660641) from an over of leg-breaks from Victoria's Colin Thwaites. His innings of 163 was made out of a total of 290 all out, to which the next highest contribution was 24.

The highest number of boundaries hit during an individual first-class innings in Australia is 55 by C.W. (Charles) Gregory. Playing for New South Wales against Queensland at Brisbane in November 1906, Gregory opened the innings and scored 383 – then the record score in Australian first-class cricket – in 5¾ hours, 220 of his runs coming from boundaries. 'His play was disfigured by three chances, but when he gave the first of them he had scored 282' *(Wisden)*. This match was played before Queensland were admitted to the Sheffield Shield competition in 1926.

Two notable world records for slow scoring were set in Australia, both during Test matches involving England. At Adelaide on 5-6 February 1947, Godfrey Evans batted for 97 minutes before scoring his first runs from his 61st ball – his innings is described in detail in the Test cricket section. The other record was achieved by Trevor Bailey at Brisbane on 8-9 December 1958, during the first Test match to be televised in Australia, when he took 357 minutes to reach his 50. In spite of several determined attempts in recent Test matches,

'Barnacle's' innings, has survived as the slowest half-century in all first-class cricket. His complete innings of 68 endured for 458 minutes at a rate of under nine runs an hour, and he scored off only 40 of the 425 balls he received: 4 fours, 3 threes, 10 twos and 23 singles. Years later, when confronted by this dismal survey, Bailey commented gleefully: 'Yes, and I ran out Tom Graveney too!'

The only Australian to score a first-class hundred without hitting a boundary is Paul Hibbert of Victoria. A left-handed opening batsman, Hibbert scored exactly 100 out of 233 for 7 against the Indian spinners at Melbourne on 11 November 1977. He batted for 327 minutes without being able to penetrate an astutely-placed field which was aided by damp turf. When India batted, Chetan Chauhan hit only two boundaries in his innings of 157 off 436 balls in 516 minutes.

The highest aggregate of runs by one batsman in an Australian first-class season is 1690, average 93.88, by Don Bradman in 1928-29 – his first full season and the one in which he began his Test career. He exceeded 1000 runs in a home season on 12 occasions, twice as many as any other batsman, and is alone in scoring 1500 runs more than twice. Bradman also scored over 2000 runs on each of his four tours of England.

Only seven Australian batsmen have scored 1000 runs in a home season when there were no matches against a touring team, Bill Ponsford achieving this feat in successive seasons (see table).

1000 RUNS IN A SEASON IN INTER-STATE MATCHES

	For	Season	I	NO	HS	Runs	Average	100
S.G. Barnes	NSW	1940-41	14	0	185	1050	75.00	6
D.G. Bradman	NSW	1933-34	11	2	253	1192	132.44	5
	SA	1939-40	15	3	267	1475	122.91	5
W.A. Brown	Q	1938-39	11	1	215	1057	105.70	3
A.F. Kippax	NSW	1926-27	13	1	217*	1039	86.58	5
A.R. Morris	NSW	1948-49	17	1	177	1069	66.81	6
N.C. O'Neill	NSW	1957-58	14	2	233	1005	83.75	4
W.H. Ponsford	V	1926-27	10	0	352	1229	122.90	6
	V	1927-28	8	0	437	1217	152.12	4

Ponsford's average of 152.12 in 1927-28 is the highest by any batsman scoring 1000 runs in an Australian season.
(NSW–New South Wales;   Q–Queensland;   SA–South Australia;   V–Victoria)

1000 RUNS IN A SEASON AGAINST A TOURING TEAM

	Season	I	NO	HS	Runs	Average	100
D.G. Bradman	1931-32	8	1	299*	1190	170.00	6
I.M. Chappell	1968-69	12	1	188*	1062	96.54	5

Only two batsman have scored 1000 runs in first-class matches against a team touring Australia, Don Bradman accomplishing this feat against H.B. 'Jock' Cameron's South Africans and Ian Chappell doing so against the West Indies team captained by Garfield Sobers.

The record number of first-class centuries by one batsman during an Australian season is eight in only 12 innings by Don Bradman in 1947-48. Six of those hundreds were scored against the Indian team captained by Lala Amarnath, including four in the five-match Test series, one for South Australia in his only Sheffield Shield match of the summer, and one for his Australian team against Western Australia before leaving for the 1948 tour of England.

The highest partnerships in Australia for the fifth and tenth wickets are world records for those wickets in all first-class cricket, the last wicket stand of 307 between Alan Kippax and Hal Hooker being probably the most remarkable in the entire history of cricket. It began at 11.50 on Christmas morning in 1928 at the Melbourne Cricket Ground. New South Wales were 113 for 9 in reply to Victoria's first innings total of 376. Their captain, Kippax, was 22 not out and, having failed in the first two Tests of that summer's series against England, he was

under some pressure from the crowd. He cannot have dreamt that the 6ft 2in number eleven batsman, playing in only his sixth first-class match, about to join him in the middle would still be batting with him 24 hours later. John Edward Halford Hooker, then aged 30, was an extremely accurate, fast-medium, right-arm bowler whose stock ball was the late inswinger. Although he had won batting awards at grade level with the Mosman Club, he was a natural tail-ender by first-class standards. His main assets were a calm temperament and a good defence cultivated by observing Jack Hobbs. Kippax was a year older. Known as 'Mr Elegant', he was an extremely graceful player who had to date made three of his 22 appearances for Australia. Together they took the score to 170 at lunch (Kippax 60*, Hooker 18*). In the next session they managed to negotiate the second new ball and add 100 runs. Of those, Hooker contributed 14 while Kippax made 85. After tea the crowd, which had built up as news of this gallant partnership spread, switched their allegiance and cheered every run. The pair continued to thwart the Victorian attack which included four current or future Test bowlers, and were still there at stumps: New South Wales 367 for 9 (Kippax 221*, Hooker 51*). Just ten runs were needed for the vital first innings lead. Kippax accomplished it in the second over next day. Hooker then hit two successive boun-

HIGHEST PARTNERSHIPS IN AUSTRALIAN FIRST-CLASS CRICKET

Wkt	Runs	Batsmen (scores)	Match	Venue	Season
1st	456	W.H. Ponsford (248), E.R. Mayne (209)	Victoria v Queensland	Melbourne	1923-24
2nd	378	L.A. Marks (185), K.D. Walters (253)	NSW v South Australia	Adelaide	1964-65
3rd	390*	J.M. Wiener (221*), J.K. Moss (200*)	Victoria v W. Australia	Melbourne†	1981-82
4th	424	I.S. Lee (258), S.O. Quin (210)	Victoria v Tasmania	Melbourne	1933-34
5th	405	S.G. Barnes (234), D.G. Bradman (234)	Australia v England	Sydney	1946-47
6th	346	J.H.W. Fingleton (136), D.G. Bradman (270)	Australia v England	Melbourne	1936-37
7th	335	C.W. Andrews (253), E. C. Bensted (155)	Queensland v NSW	Sydney	1934-35
8th	270	V.T. Trumper (138), E.P. Barbour (146)	NSW v Victoria	Sydney	1912-13
9th	232	C. Hill (365*), E. Walkley (53)	South Australia v NSW	Adelaide	1900-01
10th	307	A.F. Kippax (260*), J.E.H. Hooker (62)	NSW v Victoria	Melbourne	1928-29

Alan Kippax and Hal Hooker resume their remarkable tenth-wicket partnership on Christmas Day 1928.

daries off Ted a'Beckett. Attempting a third, he was caught high and one-handed by Jack Ryder at mid-off. It was 12.40 pm on Boxing Day. New South Wales had made 420. Kippax, after a masterly exhibition in which he paraded his full range of strokes including many delightful late-cuts and leg-glances, was left 260 not out (387 minutes, 30 fours) – the last of his six double-centuries in Shield matches. Hooker, close to exhaustion after the longest innings of his life, finished with 62 including 3 fours. For 304 mintes he had resisted an extremely strong attack without giving a chance. His abiding memory though was of a very annoyed Kippax racing down the pitch to repri-mand him: 'You fool! You threw it away! Why didn't you get a hundred?'

Bowling records

The last bowler to take all ten wickets in a first-class innings in Australia was Ian Bray-shaw at Perth on 21-22 October 1967. Swinging the ball at a little above medium pace, he returned figures of 10 for 44 as Victoria were dismissed for 152 in reply to Western Australia's 161. This his-toric performance led to victory by 136 runs. A consistent all-rounder, Brayshaw was unlucky not to gain representative honours. He retired from playing in 1978 and became a much-respected cricket writer and broadcaster.

The only bowler to take 17 wickets in a first-class match in Australia is George Giffen. South

George Giffen, South Australia's first Test cricketer. The only player to score a double century and take 16 wickets in the same first-class match, he was dubbed the 'W.G. Grace of Australia'.

Australia's first Test cricketer, he was a highly talented all-rounder who bowled very accurately at slow-medium pace. Against Victoria at Adelaide in March 1886 he recorded match figures of 17 for 201 in 116.2 four-ball overs. After taking 9 for 91 (278 balls) in Victoria's first innings of 187, he had figures of 8 for 110 (188 balls) as they scored 219 in their second. Giffen completed a notable match double by scoring 20 and 82.

The most outstanding analysis in all first-class cricket in terms of most wickets for fewest runs was returned by Gideon Elliott when he took 9 for 2 against Tasmania. Playing for Victoria at Launceston on 26 February 1858, this 30-year-old right-arm fast bowler achieved these figures in an opening spell lasting 76 balls. Tasmania reached a first innings total of 33 thanks to 14 extras; no batsman contributed more than five runs.

The only Australian to take four wickets with consecutive balls in a first-class match in Australia is Halford Hooker of New South Wales. He performed this feat against Victoria at Sydney in January 1929 – just a month after

sharing in a world record tenth-wicket partnership of 307 against them in Melbourne in his previous first-class match. After ending the Victorian first innings by dismissing their three specialist bowlers in a hat-trick, he bowled their opening batsman with his first ball of the second innings. Three of his victims were clean bowled and he caught the fourth himself. His analyses were 6 for 42 and 2 for 94. Hooker's all-round performances in the two key matches against Victoria made sure that New South Wales regained the Sheffield Shield from them.

The only other instance of a bowler taking four wickets with consecutive balls in Australian first-class cricket was accomplished by George Ulyett for Lord Harris's English XI on 10 February 1879. Rain followed by bright sun made the Association Ground pitch at Sydney absolutely unplayable and New South Wales lost their last five wickets for no runs in the second innings.

No pair of opening bowlers has bowled unchanged throughout both innings of a completed first-class match in Australia since 24-25 February 1888. On that occasion George Lohmann (9 for 67) and Johnny Briggs (11 for 58) accomplished this feat for Arthur Shrewsbury's XI against an Australian XI at Sydney. The last instance in Sheffield Shield cricket occurred on 9-10 February 1883 when Harry Boyle (8 for 46) and G.E. 'Joey' Palmer (9 for 61) bowled unchanged for Victoria during their innings defeat of New South Wales at Sydney.

The world record for the most runs conceded by one bowler during a first-class innings was established at Melbourne in December 1926 by Arthur Mailey. In the course of Victoria'a world record total of 1107, the New South Wales leg-break bowler conceded 362 runs while taking four wickets in the course of 64 eight-ball overs.

The highest number of runs conceded by one bowler during a first-class match in Australia is 394 by Clarrie Grimmett. At Sydney on 8-16 January 1926, in an eight-day match against New South Wales, the South Australian leg-break bowler took 4 for 192 and 6 for 202. He bowled 106 eight-ball overs as the home State contributed totals of 642 and 593 towards the national match aggregate record of 1929 runs.

The most balls bowled during a first-class innings in Australia is 522 by George Giffen for South Australia against A.E. Stoddart's XI at Adelaide on 29 March-1 April 1895. During the English team's first innings of 609, Giffen bowled 87 six-ball overs and took 5 for 309. **The highest number of balls bowled in a match in Australia** is 848 by Clarrie Grimmett for South Australia against New South Wales at Sydney in January 1926 (see previous item).

The most first-class wickets taken by one bowler during an Australian season is 106 by Charlie Turner of New South Wales in 1887-88. Bowling fast-medium right-arm, with a chest-on action, he captured his wickets at a rate of one every 40 balls and at a cost of 13.59 runs apiece. Turner remains the only bowler to take 100

Charles 'The Terror' Turner, the only bowler to take a hundred first-class wickets in an Australian season.

wickets in a season in Australia. His 283 wickets in England in 1888 is comfortably the world record by any bowler on tour.

Record all-round performances

The only player to score a double century and take 16 wickets in any first-class match is George Giffen of South Australia. Known as the 'W.G. Grace of Australia' he accomplished this unique double against Victoria at Adelaide on 7-11 November 1891. Batting at number three, he scored 271 in seven hours to take his aggregate against Victoria in his last seven innings to 921 runs. Giffen then completed the visitor's defeat by an innings and 164 runs when he took 9 for 96 and 7 for 70.

ALL TEN WICKETS IN AN INNINGS

Bowler	O	M	R	W	Match	Venue	Season
G. Giffen	26	10	66	10	Australian XI v Rest	Sydney	1883-84
T.W. Wall	12.4	2	36	10	South Australia v NSW	Sydney	1932-33
P.J. Allan	15.6	3	61	10	Queensland v Victoria	Melbourne	1965-66
I.J. Brayshaw	17.6	4	44	10	Western Australia v Victoria	Perth	1967-68

The last player to score a century and take ten wickets in a first-class match in Australia was Phillip Carlson of Queensland. Against New South Wales at Woolloongabba, Brisbane, on 5-8 January 1979, the right-handed all-rounder scored 24 and took 5 for 46 in the first innings. He then completed Queensland's victory, and the best all-round performance in that State's history, by scoring 102 not out before taking 5 for 27 with his medium-paced swing bowling.

The only player to score 1000 runs and take 50 wickets in an Australian first-class season is Garfield Sobers. The West Indies all-rounder achieved this remarkable feat twice, in 1962-63 and 1963-64 – his second and third seasons with South Australia.

Wicket-Keeping records

The world record for the most dismissals by a wicket-keeper in any first-class innings is eight and was set by A.T.W. 'Wally' Grout of Queensland. Returning from the Australians' long tour of Pakistan and India, Grout achieved his record at Brisbane on 15 February 1960 by catching eight Western Australian batsmen in the first innings. Grout's feat was equalled by David East for Essex at Taunton in 1985.

The world record of 12 dismissals in a first-class match was established in 1868 by Ted Pooley of Surrey. It has been equalled on only two occasions, both of them in Australia. Don Tallon (Queensland) held nine catches and made three stumpings against New South Wales at Sydney on 2-4 January 1939. His performance was emulated exactly by Brian Taber (New South Wales) against South Australia at Adelaide on 13-17 December 1968.

The highest number of catches taken in a first-class match is eleven. The record was set by Arnold Long for Surrey in 1964 and equalled by Rodney Marsh against Victoria at Perth on 15-17

November 1975. Western Australia's captain completed a notable all-round performance by scoring 36 and 76 in leading his team to victory by four wickets. In 1982 David Bairstow became the third share-holder in this record when he held eleven catches in a County Championship match for Yorkshire.

Fielding records

These records exclude performances by wicket-keepers.

The only fielder to hold six catches in an innings of a first-class match in Australia is James Sheppard of Queensland. He accomplished this record at Brisbane's Exhibition Ground on 7 November 1914 during the first innings of New South Wales. Five of his catches were taken off the fast-medium left-arm bowling of Jack McAndrew.

Although the world record number of catches by a fielder in a first-class match is ten (by Wally Hammond in 1928), there has been no instance in Australia of more than seven being held. Three fielders have achieved this total, Greg Chappell setting a world Test record with his performance (see table).

Other individual records

The youngest player to appear in first-class cricket in Australia was Leonard Junor of Victoria. A right-handed batsman, he was 15 years 266 days of age when he made his debut against Western Australia at Melbourne on 18 January 1930.

The oldest player to appear in first-class cricket in Australia whose date of birth has been confirmed was George Moore of New South Wales. A right-handed round-arm bowler, he was born in Ampthill, Bedfordshire, on 8 April 1820 and

SEVEN CATCHES IN A MATCH

Fielder	For	Opponents	Venue	Season
J.A. Atkinson	Tasmania	Victoria	Melbourne	1928-29
E.W. Freeman	South Australia	Western Australia	Adelaide	1971-72
G.S. Chappell	Australia	England	Perth	1974-75

RESULTS SUMMARY 1892-93 TO 1985-86

	First Match	P	W	L	D	T
New South Wales	1892-93	523	244	131	147	1
Victoria	1892-93	517	206	153	157	1
South Australia	1892-93	517	151	240	125	1
Queensland	1926-27	401	95	156	149	1
Western Australia	1947-48	289	93	86	110	–
Tasmania	1977-78	65	5	28	32	–
		2312	794	794	720	4

Matches abandoned without a ball being bowled are excluded.
Wins: 39 – New South Wales. 24 – Victoria. 12 – South Australia. 9 – Western Australia.
0 – Queensland, Tasmania.

ended his three-match career, against Victoria on the Albert Ground at Sydney, on 8 March 1873 when he was 52 years 334 days old. Thirteen years later, his grandson and future captain of Australia, Charles Macartney, was born.

John Marshall of Tasmania, said to have been born in 1795, could have been in his 60th year when he played the last of his three matches in March 1854. Captain of Van Diemen's Land in the first match on Australian soil to be ranked as first-class, his date of birth is unconfirmed.

The Sheffield Shield

Although the first inter-colonial match took place in February 1851 when Tasmania received Victoria at Launceston, no regular competition existed when the Third Earl of Sheffield brought a team captained by W.G. Grace to Australia in 1891-92. This visit was so enthusiastically received that the Earl donated 150 guineas for the advancement of cricket in the colonies. The newly-formed Australian Cricket Council invested the money in a shield measuring 46 inches by 30 inches and bearing the Sheffield and Australian coats of arms.

The annual domestic championship was instituted the following season, with only the three leading cricket colonies, New South Wales, Victoria and South Australia, taking part. Queensland were admitted to the competition in 1926-27, from which season all matches were played on a time basis instead of to a finish. Western Australia were admitted on an experimental basis in 1947-48, playing the other states once only. Although they won the Shield in their first season, they were not admitted to full membership until 1956-57. Tasmania were admitted on a similar experimental basis in 1977-78 and, until 1982-83, played each state only once in a season.

Since 1982-83 the competition has culminated in a final between the first two teams in the Shield table.

SHEFFIELD SHIELD HOLDERS

1892-93 Victoria	1908-09 New South Wales	1928-29 New South Wales	1950-51 Victoria
1893-94 South Australia	1909-10 South Australia	1929-30 Victoria	1951-52 New South Wales
1894-95 Victoria	1910-11 New South Wales	1930-31 Victoria	1952-53 South Australia
1895-96 New South Wales	1911-12 New South Wales	1931-32 New South Wales	1953-54 New South Wales
1896-97 New South Wales	1912-13 South Australia	1932-33 New South Wales	1954-55 New South Wales
1897-98 Victoria	1913-14 New South Wales	1933-34 Victoria	1955-56 New South Wales
1898-99 Victoria	1914-15 Victoria	1934-35 Victoria	1956-57 New South Wales
1899-00 New South Wales	1919-20 New South Wales	1935-36 South Australia	1957-58 New South Wales
1900-01 Victoria	1920-21 New South Wales	1936-37 Victoria	1958-59 New South Wales
1901-02 New South Wales	1921-22 Victoria	1937-38 New South Wales	1959-60 New South Wales
1902-03 New South Wales	1922-23 New South Wales	1938-39 South Australia	1960-61 New South Wales
1903-04 New South Wales	1923-24 Victoria	1939-40 New South Wales	1961-62 New South Wales
1904-05 New South Wales	1924-25 Victoria	1946-47 Victoria	1962-63 Victoria
1905-06 New South Wales	1925-26 New South Wales	1947-48 Western Australia	1963-64 South Australia
1906-07 New South Wales	1926-27 South Australia	1948-49 New South Wales	1964-65 New South Wales
1907-08 Victoria	1927-28 Victoria	1949-50 New South Wales	1965-66 New South Wales

1966-67 Victoria	1971-72 Western Australia	1976-77 Western Australia	1981-82 South Australia
1967-68 Western Australia	1972-73 Western Australia	1977-78 Western Australia	1982-83 New South Wales
1968-69 South Australia	1973-74 Victoria	1978-79 Victoria	1983-84 Western Australia
1969-70 Victoria	1974-75 Western Australia	1979-80 Victoria	1984-85 New South Wales
1970-71 South Australia	1975-76 South Australia	1980-81 Western Australia	1985-86 New South Wales

The 1921 Australians – was their 1948 side superior? BACK: **W. Bardsley, J. Ryder, H.S.T.L. Hendry, J.M. Gregory, E.R. Mayne, T.J.E. Andrews, S. Smith** *manager*. CENTRE: **A.A. Mailey, E.A. McDonald, H.L. Collins, W.W. Armstrong** *captain*, **C.G. Macartney, H. Carter, J.M. Taylor.** FRONT: **C.E. Pellew, W.A.S. Oldfield.**
(Christopher Warne)

FIRST-CLASS CRICKET IN SOUTH AFRICA

British soldiers introduced cricket to South Africa, quite probably during the early period of the Napoleonic Wars when garrison troops first occupied the Cape (1795-1802). The first reference to cricket appeared in 1806, in *The Cape Town Gazette and African Advertiser.*

The first club was founded on 15 January 1843 when the Port Elizabeth Cricket Club was formed. Another 46 years were to pass before their ground

at St George's Park saw the start of first-class and Test cricket in the Union.

The first tour of South Africa by a team of first-class cricketers took place in 1888 and was arranged by Major R.G. Warton. He had been attached to the Army General Staff in Cape Town and was a member of the Western Province Cricket Club, whose ground at Newlands, at the foot of Table Mountain, was opened on 1 January 1888. Captained by C.A. Smith of Sussex ('Round-the-Corner' Smith, so named because of his bowling run-up, who was to become Sir Aubrey Smith and earn fame in Hollywood), and managed by Major Warton, the English team was only of county strength. Nevertheless, it won 13 of its 19 matches, all but two of which were played against sides of more than eleven players. Those two matches marked the start of first-class cricket in South Africa and were subsequently elevated to Test match status.

South African first-class cricket began at St George's Park in Port Elizabeth on 12 March 1889 and ended just before 3.30 pm on the following day with England winning by eight wickets. The match was played on matting which produced an individual highest score of 46 (by Bobby Abel). Aubrey Smith became the only player to captain England on his only appearance in Test cricket.

1929 South Africans in England. BACK: H.O. Frielinghans *manager*, I.J. Siedle, B. Mitchell, N.A. Quinn, A.J. Bell, D.P.B. Morkel, J.A.J. Christy, A.L. Ochse, E.L. Dalton, A.S. Frames *secretary*. CENTRE: C.L. Vincent, H.W. Taylor, H.G. Deane *captain*, R.H. Catterall, H.B. Cameron. FRONT: H.G. Owen-Smith, E.A. van der Merwe, Q. McMillan.

Team records

The highest total in South African first-class cricket is 676 by the MCC against Griqualand West at Kimberley on 19-21 November 1938. Amassed under a 'baking sun', it was based on an opening stand of 263 in 156 minutes by Len Hutton (149) and Bill Edrich (109). Eddie Paynter (158) and Norman Yardley (142) followed up with a fifth-wicket partnership of 107 in only 39 minutes. Hedley Verity was able to exploit a wearing pitch when the home team batted; his analyses of 7 for 22 and 4 for 44 saw the Englishmen to victory by an innings and 289 runs.

The highest total in Currie Cup matches is 664 for 6 declared by Natal against Western Province at Kingsmead, Durban, in March 1937. Its main contributors were I.J. ('Jack') Siedle (207) and Dudley Nourse (240); their partnership of 223 remains Natal's record for the third wicket.

The world record total for the fourth innings of a first-class match is 654 for 5 by England, when they required 696 runs to beat South Africa in the famous timeless Test at Durban in March 1939. That match produced the record aggregate of runs in South Africa with 1981 being scored for the loss of 35 wickets during 43 hours 16 minutes of play spread over a 12-day period.

The two lowest totals in South African first-class cricket and the world record lowest match aggregate by one team occurred at the Jan Smuts Ground, East London, on 19 and 21 December 1959. Border were dismissed by Natal for 16 and 18 in 23 and 26 six-ball overs respectively. Although the pitch was badly affected by rain during their first innings, it had returned to normal for their second. No Border player reached double figures in either innings; Niel During (9) made their highest score and it included their only boundary of the match.

Only one first-class match has been tied in South Africa and that instance would have been regarded as a draw under present-day laws. Before 1948 a match was considered to be tied if the scores were level after the fourth innings, even if the side batting last had wickets in hand. The match at Ramblers, Bloemfontein, on 11-13 March 1926, between Orange Free State (100 and 349) and Eastern Province (225 and 224 for 8 wickets) ended with the scores level but with the last innings unfinished.

The most runs by one side in a single day of first-class cricket in South Africa is 618 for 4 wickets declared by South Africa against The Rest of South Africa at the Wanderers, Johannesburg, on 2 October 1964. The total was scored off 114 six-ball overs and included 7 sixes and 84 fours. Openers Eddie Barlow (33) and Trevor Goddard (71) paved the way for Tony Pithey (110 in 223 minutes) and Graeme Pollock (123 in 105 minutes). The record was broken during an explosive and unbroken partnership of 267 in 99 minutes between Colin Bland (151 not out) and Denis Lindsay (107 not out).

The only instance of all eleven players

UNUSUAL DISMISSALS IN SOUTH AFRICAN FIRST-CLASS CRICKET

Handled the ball

W.R. Endean (3)	South Africa v England	Cape Town	1956-57
(The first instance in Test cricket)			
R.G. Pollock (66)	Eastern Prov v Western Prov	Cape Town	1973-74
C.I. Dey (20)	Northern Transvaal v OFS	Bloemfontein	1973-74
D.K. Pearse (2)	Natal v Western Province	Cape Town	1978-79

Hit the ball twice

P.S. Wimble (0)	Transvaal v Griqualand West	Kimberley	1892-93

Obstructing the field

T. Quirk (10)	Northern Transvaal v Border	East London	1978-79

Christopher Dey's instance is unique as he was the non-striker. Backing up he collided with a fielder, fell with the ball under him and, while lying on the ground, threw the ball away.

bowling during a first-class innings in South Africa occurred at Kimberley on 3-4 January 1890. During Kimberley's innings of 445 the entire Natal team shared 116 overs.

Batting records

The highest individual score in South African first-class cricket is 306 not out by Eric Rowan for Transvaal against Natal at the (Old) Wanderers Ground, Johannesburg, in December 1939. Opening the innings, Rowan scored his runs out of a total of 608 for 6 declared.

The first triple century in South African first-class cricket was scored by A.W. ('Dave') Nourse for Natal against Transvaal at Johannesburg in April 1920. His innings of 304 not out enabled Natal (532 for 8 declared) to win by an innings.

The world record for the fastest first-class triple century was established at Benoni on 3-4 December 1948. Playing for the MCC against North-Eastern Transvaal, Denis Compton produced possibly the most amazing exhibition of sustained brilliance and unorthodoxy ever seen at first-class level. He scored exactly 300 out of a third-wicket partnership of 399 with Reg Simpson (130 not out), his innings and that stand lasting only 181 minutes. He scored 120 in the last 91 minutes of the day and the remaining 180 in the first 90 minutes of the second morning before being caught on the boundary. His three centuries took 66, 78 and 37 minutes respectively. *Wisden* reports: 'Often he walked down the pitch before the bowler released the ball and mixed orthodoxy with a bewildering assortment of unclassified strokes which went from the middle of the bat at lightning speed. He whipped balls pitched outside his off stump to the mid wicket boundary and he stepped away in order to cut leg-breaks pitched outside the wicket.' His hits included 5 sixes and 42 fours – 198 of his runs coming in boundaries. Compton's own description of his innings, given 30 years later, was typically vague but he claimed to have progressed from his century to about 190 whilst enjoying a few experimental strokes, and from 200 to 290 while trying to get out!

Eric Rowan, whose 306 not out remains the highest score in South Africa. (Sport & General)

The highest maiden hundred in South African first-class cricket is 261 not out by Stephen Steyn for Western Province against Border at Cape Town in December 1929. Although he was a member of the South African team which toured Australia in 1930-31, Steyn (nicknamed 'Stodgy') never played in a Test match.

The world record score on debut in first-class cricket is 240 by Eric Marx when he opened the innings for Transvaal against Griqualand West at the (Old) Wanderers, Johannesburg, in December 1920. His innings, which included a six and 30 fours, lasted only 220 minutes.

The record for scoring the most runs before being dismissed in first-class cricket was established by Raymond Watson-Smith of Border in November 1969. After scoring 183 not out in his first match, against Orange Free State at Bloemfontein batting at number seven, he made 125 not out in 145 minutes against Griqualand West at East London. He was stumped for 2 in his next innings and thus scored 310 runs before being dismissed in first-class cricket.

Peter May's first four innings in South Africa were hundreds; captaining the MCC on their 1956-

57 tour, he scored 162 against Western Province at Cape Town, 118 against Eastern Province at Port Elizabeth, 124 not out against Rhodesia at Bulawayo, and 206 against Rhodesia at Salisbury. He scored another hundred two matches later (107 v Natal at Durban) before having the worst Test series of his career (6, 14, 8, 15, 2, 2, 61, 0, 24 and 21).

The youngest player to score a century in South African first-class cricket is Daryll Cullinan. He was 16 years 304 days old and still studying at Queens College, Queenstown, when he scored 106 not out for Border v Natal B at East London on 2 January 1984.

South African first-class cricket's youngest double century-maker is Graeme Pollock. He was 19 years 19 days old when he scored 209 not out for an Eastern Province Invitation XI against the Cavaliers, a touring side composed mainly of England and Australian Test cricketers, at Port Elizabeth on 18 March 1963.

The record for the most consecutive first-class hundreds was equalled in 1970-71 by Mike Procter of Rhodesia. The 24-year-old all-rounder accomplished his record in six different matches played between 21 November 1970 and 7 March 1971. His scores were: 119 against Natal 'B' at Bulawayo, 129 against Transvaal 'B' at Salisbury, 107 against Orange Free State at Bloemfontein, 174 against North-Eastern Transvaal at Pretoria, 106 against Griqualand West at Kimberley, and 254 in a friendly match against Western Province at Salisbury. Playing for the Rest of South Africa against Transvaal at Cape Town in his next innings, he struck his wicket in hitting a boundary and was out for 22. His performance equalled the world record set by Charles Fry in 1901 and emulated by Don Bradman in 1938-39.

The highest aggregate of runs by a South African in a home season is 1285 by Barry Richards of Natal in 1973-74. In 1969-70 Richards established the record number of first-class hundreds in a South African season. His total of six was equalled by Mike Procter in 1970-71 and by Peter Kirsten for Western Province and South African Universities in 1976-77.

The records for the most hundreds in South African first-class cricket and in Currie Cup matches are both held by Graeme Pollock. At the end of the 1985-86 season, the stylish left-hander had scored 41 hundreds in South Africa, 34 of them in Currie Cup matches. In all first-class cricket he had scored 62 centuries, including seven in his 23 Test matches. Pollock is the only South African to score a hundred in each innings of a first-class match on two occasions.

The fastest hundred in South African first-class cricket was scored in 53 minutes by M.G. Francis for Orange Free State against Griqualand West at Bloemfontein on 3 January 1928. His innings of 115 not out in 66 minutes carried his side to victory by seven wickets.

The fastest double century in first-class matches in South Africa was scored by Denis Compton in 144 minutes for the MCC against North-Eastern Transvaal at Benoni in December 1948. He went on to achieve the fastest triple century in all first-class cricket, reaching his 300 in 181 minutes.

The world record number of runs in a pre-lunch session of a first-class match was established at Ellis Park, Johannesburg, on 17 December 1954. Opening the Transvaal innings against Orange Free State on the first morning, Russell Endean scored 197 not out in three hours before the lunch interval. Afterwards he took his total to 235, made in 228 minutes and including 2 sixes and 34 fours. Four days earlier he had taken 88 minutes to score 16 against Natal at Durban.

The only instance of two batsmen scoring hundreds before lunch on the first day of a first-class match occurred in the same Currie Cup season as Endean's record. Playing against Rhodesia at the Jan Smuts Ground, East London, on 1 January 1955, Ossie Dawson and his captain, Keith Kirton, came together at 10.30 am with Border's total 33 for the loss of the opening pair. At lunch Dawson had scored 117 and Kirton 105. Their partnership eventually reached 255 in 208 minutes and remains Border's record for the third wicket. Both batsmen fell at the same total, Dawson scoring 139 in 221 minutes and Kirton 124 in 191 minutes.

Graeme Pollock, a left-handed batsman of infinite grace and power. Political pressures have denied him a full Test career and a Lord's Bicentenary Match finale. Bob Barber is the admiring leg-slip. (Central Press)

The most runs off one over in South African first-class cricket is 32 by Ian Redpath for the Australians against Orange Free State at Ramblers, Bloemfontein, on 19 March 1970. Not associated with aggressive strokeplay, Redpath launched a tremendous onslaught on the medium-pace bowling of Neil Rosendorff after reaching his hundred in 168 minutes. His next 51 runs came from 15 scoring strokes in 12 minutes, including 666644 off one Rosendorff over.

The slowest fifty and hundred in South African first-class cricket were both recorded by D.J. ('Jackie') McGlew during the 1957-58 series against Australia. He took 9 hours 5 minutes to reach his hundred when he scored 105 in the Third Test at Durban. In the second innings of the next Test at Johannesburg McGlew took 5 hours 13 minutes to reach 50, before progressing to 70 in 6 hours.

South Africa's slowest double century took Berry Versfeld 9 hours 19 minutes. Batting for Natal against Transvaal at Kingsmead, Durban, in February 1966, he took 73 minutes to score his first run, reached his century in 350 minutes, and was 201 not out when the innings was declared closed.

The longest 'duck' in South African first-class cricket was recorded at the Pietermaritzburg Oval on 20 January 1980 by Vincent Hogg. Playing for Zimbabwe-Rhodesia 'B' against Natal 'B' in the Castle Bowl competition, he survived for 87 minutes without scoring while his last-wicket partner and captain, Edward Parker (76*), increased the total by 64 runs.

HIGHEST PARTNERSHIPS IN SOUTH AFRICAN FIRST-CLASS CRICKET

Wicket	Runs	Batsmen (scores)	Match	Venue	Season
1st	424	J.F.W. Nicolson (252*), I.J. Siedle (174)	Natal v Orange Free State	Bloemfontein	1926-27
2nd	374	R.B. Simpson (243), R.M. Cowper (171)	Australians v NE Transvaal	Pretoria	1966-67
3rd	399	R.T. Simpson (130*), D.C.S. Compton (300)	MCC v NE Transvaal	Benoni	1948-49
4th	342	E.A.B. Rowan (195), P.J.M. Gibb (203)	Transvaal v NE Transvaal	Johannesburg	1952-53
5th	338	R.G. Pollock (194), A.L. Wilmot (152)	Eastern Province v Natal	Port Elizabeth	1975-76
6th	244*	J.M.M. Commaille (132*), A.W. Palm (106*)	Western Province v GW	Johannesburg	1923-24
7th	299	B. Mitchell (159), A. Melville (153)	Transvaal v GW	Kimberley	1946-47
8th	222	S.S.L. Steyn (261*), D.P.B. Morkel (114)	Western Province v Border	Cape Town	1929-30
9th	221	N.V. Lindsay (160*), G.R.McCubbin (97)	Transvaal v Rhodesia	Bulawayo	1922-23
10th	174	H.R. Lance (168), D. Mackay-Coghill (57*)	Transvaal v Natal	Johannesburg	1965-66

GW – Griqualand West

Bowling records

The only bowler to take all ten wickets in a first-class innings in South Africa is A.E.E. (Bert) Vogler. Playing for Eastern Province at the (Old) Wanderers Ground, Johannesburg, on 28 December 1906, he bowled unchanged throughout both innings and took 16 Griqualand West wickets in the day, including 10 for 26 in 12 six-ball overs in the second innings. A right-arm bowler of leg-breaks, googlies, top-spinners and flighted yorkers, he toured England in 1907 as one of South Africa's 'googly quartet' and was rated by England's captain, R.E. Foster, as 'the best bowler in the world'. Vogler's match analysis of 16 for 38 is the best by a South African in domestic first-class matches.

The two instances of a bowler taking 17 wickets in a first-class match in South Africa were both achieved by overseas players. Bill Howell, a bee farmer from New South Wales, took 17 for 54 against Western Province, including four wickets in five balls for the Australians at Cape Town on matting on 5-6 November 1902. Bowling medium-pace off-breaks throughout both innings, he took 8 for 31 and 9 for 23. On a similar pitch at Johannesburg in December 1913, Sydney Barnes of England took 8 for 56 and 9 for 103 in the Second Test. In four matches he set the world record for any series by taking 49 wickets.

No bowler has taken four wickets with consecutive balls or five wickets in six balls in South Africa since 28 February 1938 when W.A. Henderson accomplished both feats. Playing in a Currie Cup match for North Eastern Transvaal, he took seven Orange Free State second innings wickets and conceded only four runs from 75 balls.

The only player to take three hat-tricks in South African first-class cricket is Bob Crisp. A right-arm fast bowler, he achieved all three instances in Currie Cup matches for Western Province, and established a unique world record by twice taking four wickets with consecutive balls. His first two hat-tricks were taken during the 1931-32 season on the Wanderers' back ground in Johannesburg, against Griqualand West on 24 December 1931 when his analysis of 8 for 31 included four wickets in consecutive balls, and against Transvaal on 1 January 1932 when he took his four wickets in the space of five balls. Crisp's final hat-trick was part of another four-in-four sequence, against Natal at Durban on 3 March 1934 when he recorded the best analysis of his career: 9 for 64. Crisp, who was awarded the DSO and MC during wartime service as a tank commander, is the only Test cricketer to climb Mount Kilimanjaro twice.

The last pair of opening bowlers to operate unchanged throughout both innings of a completed first-class match in South Africa accomplished this feat in March 1938 in the final match of that season's Currie Cup programme. Norman Gordon (4 for 21 and 5 for 29) and F.J. Wickham (5 for 13 and 5 for 31) shared Transvaal's attack as Eastern Province were bowled out for 36 and 62 in a total of 29.7 eight-ball overs on a rain-affected Port Elizabeth pitch.

The world record number of balls by one

Vintcent van der Bijl, (above), was described by John Arlott as being 'a more healthy, exuberant and expansive version of Lord Longford – but not nearly so tolerant'. His exceptional bounce and late movement spearheaded Middlesex to two titles in 1980.

Mike Procter (right) was a world-class all-rounder who inspired Gloucestershire for 14 summers.
(Photos by Bill Smith)

bowler without conceding a run was established in the Third Test at Kingsmead, Durban, on 25-26 January 1957 by Hugh Tayfield. Undoubtedly South Africa's most outstanding off-break bowler, he bowled 16 consecutive maiden eight-ball overs in England's first innings, delivering a total of 137 balls without conceding a run.

Only two bowlers have taken 100 first-class wickets in a season in South Africa – Sydney Barnes took 104 wickets (average 10.74) in only 12 matches on matting during MCC's 1913-14 tour, and Richie Benaud established the national record by taking 106 wickets (average 19.39) in 18 matches on the Australians' 1957-58 tour.

The record number of wickets by a South African bowler in a home season is 75 (average 14.92) by Vintcent van der Bijl in 1981-82. An imposing right-arm fast medium opening bowler, Van der Bijl is 6ft 7in tall and weighs 17½ stone. By the end of the 1981-82 season he had taken more wickets than any other bowler in first-class matches in South Africa.

Record all-round performances

The first to accomplish the match double of 100 runs and ten wickets in a first-class match in South Africa was Albert Trott in

500 RUNS AND 50 WICKETS IN A SOUTH AFRICAN SEASON

		Season	Runs	Wickets
A.E.E. Vogler	Eastern Province	1906-07	505	55
P.N.F. Mansell	Rhodesia	1951-52	571	52
J.R. Reid	New Zealanders	1953-54	1012	51
R. Benaud	Australians	1957-58	817	106
A.K. Davidson	Australians	1957-58	813	72
M.J. Procter	Rhodesia	1971-72	695	52
M.J. Procter	Rhodesia	1972-73	870	60

February 1899. Playing for Lord Hawke's English Team against Transvaal at Johannesburg, he took 7 for 74 and scored 101 not out before completing the tourists' victory by an innings and 203 runs with 4 for 66 in the second innings.

The only player to achieve the match double twice in successive first-class matches is Xenophon Constantine Balaskas. Born in Kimberley of Greek parents, 'Bally' was a right-arm leg-break bowler and middle-order batsman. Both his doubles were inflicted upon Griqualand West's Currie Cup opponents in home matches at Kimberley, and both were major contributions towards innings victories. He scored 132 and had match figures of 11 for 130 against Eastern Province on 14-15 February 1930. A week later, against Western Province, he scored 101 of his team's record total of 603 and took 12 for 235.

The last player to do the match double in South Africa was Ivor Foulkes for Border on 26-28 December 1977. A left-handed all-rounder who bowled leg-breaks, he scored 130 and took 10 wickets for 116 against Eastern Province 'B' in a Castle Bowl match at East London.

Although there have been seven other instances of the match double being accomplished in South African first-class cricket, only Trott, Balaskas and Foulkes have scored a century in the process.

Wicket-Keeping records

The most dismissals in a first-class innings in South Africa is seven, a record shared by three wicket-keepers. In successive Currie Cup matches at the Jan Smuts Ground, East London, in the 1959-60 season, the record was set by Malcolm Smith of Natal and then equalled by Noel Kirsten of Border. Robert East became the record's third shareholder on 28 February 1985 with six catches and a stumping for Orange Free State against Western Province 'B' in a Castle Bowl match at Newlands.

The South African wicket-keeping match record of ten dismissals was set by Ray Jennings for Transvaal against the touring Arosa Sri Lankans at Johannesburg on 4-6 December 1982; he held four catches in the first innings and six in the second. His performance has been equalled on three subsequent occasions in the Union (see table).

The most stumpings in a first-class match in South Africa is seven by W.W. ('Billy') Wade of Natal at Kingsmead, Durban, on 21-24 November 1947. Playing against Griqualand West in a Currie Cup match, Wade scored 71 and made eight dismissals, his seven stumpings all coming off the leg-break bowling of V.I. (Ian) Smith, who had match figures of 11 for 119.

Roland Pearce of Natal enjoyed the most successful debut by a wicket-keeper/batsman in first-class cricket. Playing for Natal against Western Province at Kingsmead, Durban, on 30 November-2 December 1956, he made eight dismissals in the match and scored 95 in his only innings – after sharing in an opening partnership of 163, he was caught on the boundary.

The most wicket-keeping dismissals in a South African season is 65 (57 catches and eight stumpings) by Ray Jennings in 1982-83. No other wicket-keeper has made 50 dismissals in a season, a total which Jennings also surpassed in 1984-85 with 49 matches and six stumpings.

TEN WICKET-KEEPING DISMISSALS IN A MATCH IN SOUTH AFRICA

	Ct	St	Match	Venue	Season
R.V. Jennings	10	0	Transvaal v Arosa Sri Lankans	Johannesburg	1982-83
D.A. Murray	10	0	West Indies XI v South Africa	Port Elizabeth	1983-84
R.J. Ryall	8	2	Western Province v Transvaal	Cape Town	1984-85
S.J. Rixon	10	0	Australian XI v South Africa	Johannesburg	1985-86

Fielding records

The most catches taken in the field in South Africa is five. This tally is shared by six fielders (see table), notably Victor Richardson of Australia who set the current Test match record at Durban on 3 March 1936. Cyril White's performance includes a unique hat-trick of slip catches from successive balls bowled by R. Beesly, and Alan Jordaan's was achieved on his debut in first-class cricket.

FIVE CATCHES IN AN INNINGS

	Match	Venue	Season
A.D. Nourse	Natal v Border	Durban	1933-34
V.Y. Richardson	Australia v South Africa	Durban	1935-36
C. White	Border v Griqualand West	Queenstown	1946-47
P.H. Parfitt	MCC v SA Universities	Pietermaritzburg	1964-65
A.H. Jordaan	N. Transvaal v Border	East London	1972-73
A. Barrow	Transvaal B v N Transvaal B	Pietersburg	1982-83

SEVEN CATCHES IN A MATCH

	Match	Venue	Season
S.P. de Vigne	NE Transvaal v OFS	Benoni	1950-51
A. Barrow	Transvaal B v N Transvaal B	Pietersburg	1982-83

The Currie Cup

South Africa's main domestic first-class competition was created as a direct result of Major R.G. Warton's team making the first English tour of the Union in 1888. Sir Donald Currie, head of the Castle Mail Packets Company whose ship brought Warton's team to South Africa, donated a trophy as a Challenge Cup to be awarded to the team which excelled most against the pioneer tourists.

The Currie Cup was first presented to Kimberley (later to be renamed Griqualand West). In subsequent seasons it was competed for by the the trophy awarded to the winners of a full interprovincial tournament. Transvaal won the first Currie Cup match when they defeated the original holders on 5-8 April 1890, but Kimberley regained it from them the following season. From November 1892 it became the feature of provinces, first on a challenge basis and later as South Africa's main domestic competition, in succession to the 'Champion Bat' tournament which had been held five times between 1876 and 1891.

By 1946-47 the number of teams competing for the trophy had risen to nine, and the tournament was divided into two sections from 1951-52. Until 1966-67 the Currie Cup competition was not held during seasons when an overseas touring team visited the Union, occasional friendly matches being played between the provinces instead.

Since 1972-73 the competition has been sponsored and is currently the Castle Currie Cup, with its B Section playing for the Castle Bowl.

Rhodesia, who joined the competition in March 1905 and played as Zimbabwe-Rhodesia in 1979-80, were withdrawn from all South African cricket by the newly independent Zimbabwe government in 1980.

CURRIE CUP WINNERS

1889-90	Transvaal	1952-53	Western Province
1890-91	Kimberley	1954-55	Natal
1892-93	Western Province	1955-56	Western Province
1893-94	Western Province	1958-59	Transvaal
1894-95	Transvaal	1959-60	Natal
1896-97	Western Province	1960-61	Natal
1897-98	Western Province	1962-63	Natal
1902-03	Transvaal	1963-64	Natal
1903-04	Transvaal	1965-66	Natal/Transvaal
1904-05	Transvaal	1966-67	Natal
1906-07	Transvaal	1967-68	Natal
1908-09	Western Province	1968-69	Transvaal
1910-11	Natal	1969-70	Transvaal
1912-13	Natal		Western Province
1920-21	Western Province	1970-71	Transvaal
1921-22	Natal	1971-72	Transvaal
	Transvaal	1972-73	Transvaal
	Western Province	1973-74	Natal
1923-24	Transvaal	1974-75	Western Province
1925-26	Transvaal	1975-76	Natal
1926-27	Transvaal	1976-77	Natal
1929-30	Transvaal	1977-78	Western Province
1931-32	Western Province	1978-79	Transvaal
1933-34	Natal	1979-80	Transvaal
1934-35	Transvaal	1980-81	Natal
1936-37	Natal	1981-82	Western Province
1937-38	Natal/Transvaal	1982-83	Transvaal
1946-47	Natal	1983-84	Transvaal
1947-48	Natal	1984-85	Transvaal
1950-51	Transvaal	1985-86	Western Province
1951-52	Natal		

SECTION B WINNERS

1951-52	Orange Free State
1952-53	Transvaal
1954-55	Eastern Province
1955-56	Rhodesia
1958-59	Border
1959-60	Eastern Province
	Transvaal B
1962-63	Transvaal B
1963-64	Rhodesia
1965-66	N-Eastern Transvaal
1966-67	N-Eastern Transvaal
1967-68	Rhodesia
1968-69	Western Province
1969-70	Transvaal B
1970-71	Rhodesia
1971-72	Northern Transvaal
1972-73	Transvaal B
1973-74	Natal B
1974-75	Transvaal B
1975-76	Orange Free State
1976-77	Transvaal B
1977-78	Northern Transvaal
1978-79	Northern Transvaal
1979-80	Natal B
1980-81	Western Province B
1981-82	Boland
1982-83	Western Province B
1983-84	Western Province B
1984-85	Transvaal B
1985-86	Boland

Outright wins: 22 – Transvaal. 18 – Natal. 13 – Western Province. 1 – Kimberley (now Griqualand West).
Shared titles: 4 – Transvaal. 3 – Natal. 2 – Western Province.

FIRST-CLASS CRICKET IN THE WEST INDIES

The first inter-colonial match was played between Barbados, the traditional centre of West Indian cricket, and Demerara (now part of Guyana) on 15-16 February 1865 on the Garrison Savannah in Bridgetown.

The first West Indian team to play overseas toured North America in 1886. The 13-match programme was described in the first West Indian cricket book, published the following year in Georgetown.

The first touring team to visit the West Indies arrived from America in 1887. They dismissed West Indies for 19 in the only international match played.

The first inter-colonial tournament was held on 1-10 September 1891 at Wanderers Bay Pasture, Barbados, when the home team successfully challenged Demerara and Trinidad. From 1893 the colonies competed for a cup. Although Jamaica first played against Demerara and Barbados in 1896, it was not until October 1956 that the four colonies contested a quadrangular tournament on the same ground (Bourda in Georgetown, British Guiana). Five years later the tournament became pentangular with the introduction of combined team from the Leeward and Windward Islands.

The first sponsored regional tournament was instituted in January 1966 and resulted in

Barbados becoming the first holders of 'The Shell Shield for Caribbean Regional Cricket'.

SHELL SHIELD HOLDERS

1965-66	Barbados	1976-77	Barbados
1966-67	Barbados	1977-78	Barbados
1968-69	Jamaica	1978-79	Barbados
1969-70	Trinidad	1979-80	Barbados
1970-71	Trinidad	1980-81	Combined Islands
1971-72	Barbados	1981-82	Barbados
1972-73	Guyana	1982-83	Guyana
1973-74	Barbados	1983-84	Barbados
1974-75	Guyana	1984-85	Trinidad
1975-76	Barbados Trinidad	1985-86	Barbados

Shield wins: 11 – Barbados. 3 – Guyana, Trinidad. 1 – Combined Islands, Jamaica. Shared titles: 1 – Barbados, Trinidad.

Team records

The highest innings total in any first-class match in the West Indies is 849 by England against West Indies at Sabina Park, Kingston, Jamaica, on 3-5 April 1930. It remained the highest total in Test cricket until August 1938, when England reached 903 for 8 declared against Australia at The Oval, and included the first triple century at Test level – 325 (out of 720 for 5 in ten hours) by Andrew Sandham. It also included an innings of 8 not out by Wilfred Rhodes who was to be 52 years 165 days of age and the oldest Test cricketer when the nine-day 'timeless' match was declared a draw after rain had prevented play on the last two days.

The highest total in West Indian domestic first-class matches is 753 by Barbados against Jamaica at Kensington Oval, Bridgetown, Barbados, in January 1952.

The lowest total and the lowest match aggregate in West Indies first-class cricket were both inflicted upon colonies visiting Barbados in Bridgetown. Trininidad were dismissed on a rain-affected pitch for 16, in 69 minutes, on 20 July 1942, Derek Sealy taking 8 for 8, including four wickets in seven balls. Only three Trinidad batsmen got off the mark. In the first inter-colonial match ever played, on 15-16 February 1865, Demerara were bowled out for 22 and 33 by a brace of Smiths (F.B. and A.E.) who operated unchanged throughout both innings. Of the 18 wickets which fell to their bowling, 15 were bowled and three were caught – by the two Smiths! Just to ensure that their name would be firmly etched on the records of this match, F.B. Smith, the Barbados captain, became the first player to carry his bat through a first-class innings in the West Indies and the first to score a fifty (50 not out).

The lowest total in Shell Shield matches is 41 by Guyana at Kingston, Jamaica, on 9 January 1986. Just as England were to discover a few weeks later, short-pitched fast bowling on a recently relaid Sabina Park pitch presented insurmountable problems. Guyana were dismissed in 15.1 overs by Patrick Patterson (7 for 24) and Courtney Walsh (3 for 13).

The largest variation in a side's totals in all first-class cricket is 551 runs. This extraordinary margin of difference has occurred on three occasions, the first two at Bridgetown, and the third at Chelmsford:

Barbados	175 & 726-7d	v Trinidad	1926-27
Pakistan	106 & 657-8d	v West Indies	1957-58
Middlesex	83 & 634-7d	v Essex	1983

The only first-class match in the Caribbean to result in a tie took place at Kingston, Jamaica, on 3-5 April 1911. The first official MCC team to tour the West Indies dismissed Jamaica for 173 and 227 after scoring 269 and 131.

The world record for conceding most extras in a first-class innings was set at Bourda, Georgetown, British Guiana, in 1909. William Shepherd's Eleven conceded 74 extras (54 byes, 16 leg-byes, 1 wide and 3 no balls) in Demerara's total of 529 – the highest innings in West Indian first-class cricket at that time.

The only batsman to be dismissed for hitting the ball twice in West Indies first-class cricket is Alfred Binns of Jamaica. This unique instance occurred in the match against British Guiana at Georgetown in October 1956, with the batsman's score on 151 – a slightly rapacious act by a player with that total on the board. The next highest score by any batsman being dismissed for falling foul of the three more obscure laws is 73.

The only batsman to be given out in West Indies first-class cricket for handling the ball is George Linton. Batting for Barbados against the Windward Islands at Kensington Oval, Bridgetown, on 17 January 1986, he played a defensive deadbat stroke to a lifting delivery from Desmond Collymore, and innocently picked up the ball to return it to the bowler.

So far no batsman has been dismissed for obstructing the field in the Caribbean.

Batting records

The highest individual score in West Indies first-class cricket and the world record Test score is 365 not out by Garfield Sobers. Playing for West Indies against Pakistan in the Third Test at

HIGHEST PARTNERSHIPS IN WEST INDIES FIRST-CLASS CRICKET

Wicket	Runs	Batsmen (scores)	Match	Venue	
1st	390	G.L. Wight (262*), G.L. Gibbs (216)	British Guiana v Barbados	Georgetown	1951-52
2nd	446	C.C. Hunte (260), G. St A. Sobers (365*)	West Indies v Pakistan	Kingston	1957-58
3rd	434	J.B. Stollmeyer (324), G.E. Gomez (190)	Trinidad v British Guiana	Port-of-Spain	1946-47
4th	574*	C.L. Walcott (314*), F.M.M. Worrell (255*)	Barbados v Trinidad	Port-of-Spain	1945-46
5th	327	P. Holmes (244), W.E. Astill (156)	MCC v Jamaica	Kingston	1925-26
6th	487*	G.A. Headley (344*), C.C. Passailaigue (261*)	Jamaica v Lord Tennyson's XI	Kingston	1931-32
7th	347	D.St E. Atkinson (219), C.C. Depeiza (122)	West Indies v Australia	Bridgetown	1954-55
8th	255	E.A.V. Williams (131*), E.A. Martindale (134)	Barbados v Trinidad	Bridgetown	1935-36
9th	168	L.G. Crawley (85), F.B. Watson (103*)	MCC v Jamaica	Kingston	1926-27
10th	167	A.W.F. Somerset (53*), W.C. Smith (126)	MCC v Barbados	Bridgetown	1912-13

The partnerships for the sixth and seventh wickets are world first-class records.
William Smith (Surrey and MCC) is **the only player to score a first-class century batting at number eleven in the West Indies.**

Jeff Stollmeyer, manager of the West Indies 1966 tour, enjoys a 'net' at Southend. (Author)

Sabina Park, Kingston, Jamaica on 27 February-1 March 1958, Sobers batted for 10 hours 14 minutes and hit 38 fours. He remains the youngest (21 years 216 days) to score a triple century in Test cricket.

The highest individual innings in West Indies domestic cricket is 324 by Jeffrey Stollmeyer, for Trinidad against British Guiana at Port-of-Spain in March 1947.

The longest innings in all first-class cricket is Hanif Mohammad's 337 which lasted 16 hours 10 minutes on 20-23 January 1958 at Kensington Oval, Bridgetown, Barbados, after Pakistan had been asked to follow on 473 runs behind.

Bowling records

The only bowler to take all ten wickets in a first-class innings in the West Indies is the English off-spinner, Eddie Hemmings. Playing for an International XI against a West Indies Invitation XI at Sabina Park, Kingston, on 26-27 September 1982, he took 10 for 175 in 49.3 overs. It remains the most expensive ten-wickets analysis in all first-class cricket and the Invitation team's total of 419 is the highest in which any bowler has taken all ten wickets.

The best innings analysis in West Indian domestic cricket is 9 for 19 by O.H. Layne in 15.4 overs for Demerara against W.C. Shepherd's XI at Georgetown in 1909.

The best Test match innings analysis by a West Indies bowler is 9 for 95 by Jack Noreiga, against India at Port-of-Spain, Trinidad, in March 1971, in the second of his four international appearances. A 34-year-old off-spin bowler, Noreiga replaced a temporarily out-of-form Lance Gibbs and exploited a helpful pitch on his home ground to become the only West Indian to take nine wickets in a Test innings.

The best match analysis in first-class cricket in the West Indies is 16 for 58 by E.M. ('Toddles') Dowson for R.A. Bennett's XI against Jamaica at Kingston on 8-9 February 1902. No more than five feet tall, Dowson bowled left-arm leg-breaks extremely slowly. Aged 21 when he took part in this all-amateur mission, he was mid-way through his four-year career with Cambridge University and Surrey.

The best match analysis in West Indian domestic cricket is 15 for 101 by Derek Parry for Combined Islands against Jamaica at Sabina Park, Kingston on 21-24 March 1980. An off-break bowler with the ability to turn the ball sharply on good pitches, Parry took 6 for 25 and 9 for 76 to establish innings and match record analyses for Shell Shield matches.

Wicket-Keeping records

SIX WICKET-KEEPING DISMISSALS IN AN INNINGS

	Ct	St	Match	Venue	Season
A.P. Binns	3	3	Jamaica v British Guiana	Georgetown	1952-53
R.A. Pinnock	4	2	Jamaica v Trinidad	Port-of-Spain	1969-70
T.M. Findelay	3	3	Windward Is v Leeward Is	Roseau, Dominica	1971-72
M.C. Worrell	6	0	Barbados v Leeward Is	Bridgetown	1984-85
T.R.O. Payne	5	1	Barbados v England XI	Bridgetown	1985-86

The record number of dismissals in a first-class match in the Caribbean is nine by Michael Findlay for the Combined Islands against Guyana at Rose Hall, Berbice, Guyana, on 28 February-3 March 1974. He held four catches in the first innings and three in the second, as well as stumping one batsman in each innings.

Fielding records

FIVE CATCHES IN AN INNINGS

	Match	Venue	Season
T.N. Pierce	Barbados v Trinidad	Bridgetown	1942-43
O.M. Durity (2)	Trinidad v Guyana	Georgetown	1970-71
	South Trinidad v East Trinidad	Pointe-à-Pierre	1971-72
G.S. Camacho	Demerara v Berbice	Georgetown	1971-72
I.V.A. Richards	Leeward Islands v Barbados	Basseterre	1981-82

The record number of catches taken in the field in a first-class match in the West Indies is seven by Tom Pierce for Barbados against Trinidad at Kensington Oval, Bridgetown, on 18-21 July 1942.

Gascoigne Wildey's impressions of pitch preparation in the West Indies in 1895. (Mary Evans Picture Library)

FIRST-CLASS CRICKET IN NEW ZEALAND

The first fully recorded cricket match in New Zealand took place at Nelson in March 1844 between Nelson and the Surveyors of the Land Company. However, there are references to the game being played before New Zealand became a British crown colony under the Treaty of Waitangi on 6 February 1840.

The first inter-provincial match was a one-day game played between Wellington and Auckland at Wellington in March 1860.

The first match in New Zealand to be recognized as first-class by the Association of Cricket Statisticians was played at South Dunedin Recre-church, on 26-27 December 1952. Opening the inn-and 74) beat Canterbury (34 and 42) by 76 runs after being put in to bat. The highest individual score was 25 not out and the opening bowlers for Otago bowled unchanged throughout the match. This match was arranged as part of a cricket carnival in Dunedin which coincided wih the arrival from Australia of George Parr's All-England XI, **the first overseas team to visit New Zealand.**

The first overseas tour by a team from New Zealand took place in the 1878-79 season when Canterbury visited Victoria and Tasmania.

Team records

The highest innings total in a first-class match in New Zealand is 752 for 8 declared by New South Wales against Otago at Dunedin on 15-18 February 1924.

The highest total in an inter-provincial match is 693 for 9 declared by Auckland against Canterbury at Eden Park, Auckland on 5-9 January 1940.

The lowest total in New Zealand first-class cricket is 13 by Auckland against Canterbury at Eden Park, Auckland on 28-31 December 1877.

The lowest innings total in all Test cricket was also recorded at Eden Park when New Zealand were dismissed for 26 by England on 28 March 1955.

Only two first-class matches in New Zealand have resulted in a tie and over 100 years separated them. The first instance occurred at Basin Reserve, Wellington on 17-18 March 1874 when Wellington, who won the toss, scored 63 and 118, and dismissed Nelson for 111 (!) and 70. A glance at the glossary will explain the exclamation mark. The second tie resulted when England (296 for 6 declared and 104) dismissed Central Districts (139 and 188) with the last possible ball of the match, at Pukekura Park, New Plymouth, on 1-3 February 1978. Hero of the dramatic finish was England's fast bowler Bob Willis, captaining an England XI for the first time. With the scores level, Willis bowled top-scorer Terry Horne (40) leg stump.

Batting records

The highest score by left-handed batsman in all first-class cricket – and the record individual score in New Zealand – is 385 by Bert Sutcliffe for Otago against Canterbury in a Plunket Shield match at Lancaster Park, Christchurch, on 26-27 December 1952. Opening the innings in reply to Canterbury's total of 309, Sutcliffe batted for 461 minutes, hit 46 fours and 3 sixes, and was ninth out when the total reached 500. The last wicket fell without addition to that score. Canter-

Bert Sutcliffe (right), with former Test batsman, John Sparling. His 385 remains the highest first-class innings by a left-hander. (Author)

bury were dismissed for 98 and lost by an innings and 93 runs. His world record is commemorated by a plaque which was unveiled at Lancaster Park on 1 March 1986. Sutcliffe also registered scores of 355, 275 and 264 for Otago and can still claim four of the eight highest innings by New Zealanders in domestic cricket, all of them occurring in Plunket Shield matches. In a career spanning the years 1941 to 1966, Sutcliffe achieved the record total of 26 first-class centuries in New Zealand.

The highest aggregate of runs by a batsman in one season is 1244 by Glenn Turner for Otago and New Zealand in 1975-76. In 20 innings during eight games for Otago and three Test matches against India, Turner recorded 5 hundreds and 5 fifties, and averaged 77.75. He is **the only batsman** to score 1000 runs in a season in first-class matches in New Zealand.

The most sixes hit by one batsman in any first-class innings is 15 by John Reid during his innings of 296 in a Plunket Shield match for Wellington on 14-15 January 1963. Playing against Northern Districts on his home ground at Basin Reserve, the Wellington and New Zealand captain batted for only 220 minutes. Not out without scoring overnight, he raced to 174 in 142 minutes before lunch. His first 50 took 67 minutes and included no sixes. The times in minutes for his subsequent fifties, with the number of six-hits in brackets, were: 32 (3), 35 (3), 33 (0), and 28 (4). His last 46 runs came in 25 minutes and included 5 sixes. He also hit 35 fours and so scored 230 of his runs in boundaries. Reid contributed 70 per cent of his side's total of 422, the next highest contribution being 24.

Bowling records

The only bowler to take all ten wickets in a first-class innings in New Zealand is A.E. Moss of Canterbury. Playing against Wellington at Christchurch on 27-28 December 1889, Moss returned an analysis of 21.3-10-28-10 in a total of 71. **He is the only bowler to take ten wickets in an innings in his first-class match.**

The best match analysis in New Zealand first-class cricket is 15 for 60 by Sydney Callaway for Canterbury against Hawke's Bay at Napier on 14-15 January 1904. His full analyses were 23.3-

HIGHEST PARTNERSHIPS IN NEW ZEALAND FIRST-CLASS CRICKET

Wicket	Runs	Batsmen (scores)	Match	Venue	Season
1st	373	B. Sutcliffe (275), L. Watt (96)	Otago v Auckland	Auckland	1950-51
2nd	317	R.T. Hart (167*), P.S. Briasco (157)	Central Districts v Canterbury	New Plymouth	1983-84
3rd	445	P.E. Whitelaw (195), W.N. Carson (290)	Auckland v Otago	Dunedin	1936-37
4th	350	Mushtaq Mohammad (201), Asif Iqbal (175)	Pakistan v New Zealand	Dunedin	1972-73
5th	266	B. Sutcliffe (355), W.S. Haig (67)	Otago v Auckland	Dunedin	1949-50
6th	269	V.T. Trumper (172), C. Hill (129)	Australians v New Zealand XI	Wellington	1904-05
7th	265	J.L. Powell (164), N. Dorreen (105*)	Canterbury v Otago	Christchurch	1929-30
8th	433	A. Sims (184*), V.T. Trumper (293)	Australians v Canterbury	Christchurch	1913-14
9th	239	H.B. Cave (118), I.B. Leggat (142*)	Central Districts v Otago	Dunedin	1952-53
10th	184	R.C. Blunt (338*), W. Hawksworth (21)	Otago v Canterbury	Christchurch	1931-32

The partnership for the eighth wicket is a world first-class record.

10-33-8 and 17-7-27-7. An Australian who settled and eventually died in Christchurch, Callaway is the only bowler to take 15 wickets in a first-class match in New Zealand on two occasions. He had previously taken 15 for 175 for New South Wales against New Zealand at Christchurch in December 1895.

The only bowler to take four first-class wickets in four balls in New Zealand is A.D. Downes of Otago. He achieved this feat against Auckland at Dunedin in 1893-94.

The record number of wickets by any bowler in a season in New Zealand is 66, average 16.48, in 1977-78 by Stephen Boock in 13 matches for Canterbury (9), South Island (1) and New Zealand (3 v England).

Wicket-Keeping records

SEVEN DISMISSALS IN AN INNINGS

	Ct	St	Match	Venue	Season
R.M. Schofield	7	0	Central Districts v Wellington	Wellington	1964-65
Wasim Bari	7	0	Pakistan v New Zealand	Auckland	1978-79

NINE DISMISSALS IN A MATCH

R.M. Schofield	9	0	Central Districts v Wellington	Wellington	1964-65
R.H. Vance	9	0	Wellington v Otago	Wellington	1977-78
E.B. McSweeney	8	1	Wellington v Otago	Lower Hutt	1983-84

Fielding records

FIVE CATCHES IN AN INNINGS

	Match	Venue	Season
N.T. Williams	Auckland v Hawke's Bay	Napier	1894-95
J.R. Lamason	Wellington v Otago	Dunedin	1937-38
J.R. Lamason	North Island Army v South Island Army	Wellington	1942-43
J.T. Ikin	MCC v Auckland	Auckland	1946-47
J.F.M. Morrison	Wellington v Northern Districts	Wellington	1980-81
G.K. MacDonald	Canterbury v Pakistanis	Christchurch	1984-85

John Morrison's five second-innings catches in the instance above gave him the New Zealand first-class match record of seven.

The Plunket Shield

During the 1906-07 season Lord Plunket, Governor General of New Zealand, gave a shield for a competition among the first-class provinces. The New Zealand Cricket Council, which had been formed in Christchurch on 27 December 1894, awarded the Plunket Shield to Canterbury as the association with the best record in 1906-07.

Until the 1921-22 season the Shield was contested on a challenge basis by the provinces of Auckland, Wellington, Canterbury and Otago, the players being recruited almost entirely from the cities of Auckland, Wellington, Christchurch and Dunedin respectively. There were 32 challenges during the first phase of this competition, Canterbury winning 16, Auckland 14 and Wellington 2.

From 1921 until 1975, when Shell Oil began their sponsorship of New Zealand inter-provincial cricket, the Shield was contested on a league basis.

SHELL TROPHY HOLDERS

1975-76	Canterbury	1981-82	Wellington
1976-77	Otago	1982-83	Wellington
1977-78	Auckland	1983-84	Canterbury
1978-79	Otago	1984-85	Wellington
1979-80	Northern Districts	1985-86	Otago
1980-81	Auckland		

PLUNKET SHIELD HOLDERS UNDER THE LEAGUE SYSTEM

1921-22	Auckland	1934-35	Canterbury	1952-53	Otago	1965-66	Wellington
1922-23	Canterbury	1935-36	Wellington	1953-54	Central Districts	1966-67	Central Districts
1923-24	Wellington	1936-37	Auckland	1954-55	Wellington	1967-68	Central Districts
1924-25	Otago	1937-38	Auckland	1955-56	Canterbury	1968-69	Auckland
1925-26	Wellington	1938-39	Auckland	1956-57	Wellington	1969-70	Otago
1926-27	Auckland	1939-40	Auckland	1957-58	Otago	1970-71	Central Districts
1927-28	Wellington	1945-46	Canterbury	1958-59	Auckland	1971-72	Otago
1928-29	Auckland	1946-47	Auckland	1959-60	Canterbury	1972-73	Wellington
1929-30	Wellington	1947-48	Otago	1960-61	Wellington	1973-74	Wellington
1930-31	Canterbury	1948-49	Canterbury	1961-62	Wellington	1974-75	Otago
1931-32	Wellington	1949-50	Wellington	1962-63	North. Districts		
1932-33	Otago	1950-51	Otago	1963-64	Auckland		
1933-34	Auckland	1951-52	Canterbury	1964-65	Canterbury		

Two new associations were formed in this period: Central Districts (the minor provinces of Taranaki, Wanganui, Hawke's Bay, Manawatu, Wairarapa, Nelson and Marlborough) competed from 1950-51; Northern Districts (Northland Waikato, Bay of Plenty and Poverty Bay) were admitted in 1956-57.

The Shell Trophy

A league-cup competition, sponsored by Shell Oil and with two separate trophies, replaced the Plunket shield in 1975-76. Besides the financial advantages, this change increased the amount of first-class cricket and, in its first four seasons, had the added attraction of culminating in a final. From 1979-80, the two-trophy competition was abandoned and the single league system reintroduced. The Shell Cup, awarded initially to the winners of the first part of the season's programme, was won by Canterbury twice and by Northern Districts and Otago once each.

Cricket on the Auckland Domain circa 1880. Note the doubly-exposed bowler and mid-off.
(Auckland Public Library)

FIRST-CLASS CRICKET IN INDIA

The earliest reference to cricket being played on Indian soil dates back to 1721. This was an impromptu game among sailors from an East India Company trading ship at Cambay in the western region. Cricket matches were soon commonplace in Calcutta, usually between Army teams and the settlers of the East India Company.

The first club to be formed was the Calcutta Cricket Club. Dating from at least 1792 and with its membership restricted to Europeans, it was established on the site of the present Test match stadium at Eden Gardens, where in January 1982 the largest attendance at any cricket match, an estimated 394 000, watched the Fourth Test between India and England.

The first book of cricket scores known outside Britain was published in India in 1854 – *Calcutta Cricket Club Matches 1844-54.*

The Indians, notably the Parsees, began playing cricket in Bombay in the late 18th century, forming the Orient Club in 1848. In 1877 they beat a Europeans team and, in 1886, undertook **the first tour from the subcontinent,** to England.

The first known tour by an English team to India took place in 1889-90. Led by G.F. Vernon of Middlesex and including Lord Hawke, the all-amateur side lost only one match – to the Parsees of Bombay who dismissed them for 97 and 61.

India's first centralized cricket administration, the Board of Control for Cricket in India, was formed in 1928. Four years later came the inaugural Test match against England at Lord's.

Team records

The highest total in first-class cricket in India is 912 for 8 declared by Holkar against Mysore at Indore on 2-4 March 1946. It included seven century partnerships and **the record number of individual hundreds in any first-class innings:** six, by K.V. Bhandarkar (142), C.T. Sarwate (101), M.M. Jagdale (164), C.K. Nayudu (101), B.B. Nimbalkar (172), and R. Pratap Singh (100). In reply, Mysore scored 190 (C.T. Sarwate 9 for 91) and 509 for 6 before declaring and so conceding this Ranji Trophy semi-final by an innings and 213 runs.

The lowest first-class innings total in India is 21 by the Muslims against the Europeans at Poona during the Quadrangular Tournament of 1915-16.

Batting records

The highest individual innings in Indian first-class cricket is 443 not out by B.B. Nimbalkar for Maharashtra against Kathiawar at Poona on 16-18 December 1948. A 29-year-old right-handed batsman, Bhausahib Nambalkar batted for 8 hours 14 minutes, hit a six and 49 fours, and shared in a second wicket partnership of 455 with K.V. Bhandarkar which remained the world record until 1974. He is **the only batsman to score 400 in a first-class innings and not to be selected for Test cricket.** Maharashtra had reached 826 for 4 at lunch on the third day, with Nimbalkar just nine runs short of Bradman's record score (452 not out), when Kathiawar (238) conceded this Ranji Trophy match. His score remains the third-highest in all first-class cricket, Hanif Mohammad establishing the record with his 499 ten years later.

Maharashtra were involved in another record batting feat, also at Poona, in that season's Ranji Trophy championship when they played Bombay in the semi-final on 5-11 March 1949. That match produced **the unique record of three batsmen**

The 1932 All-India team in England. BACK: Lall Singh, P.E. Palia, Jahangir Khan, Mahomed Nissar, Amar Singh, B.E. Kapadia, S.R. Godambe, Ghulam Mahomed, J.G. Navle. CENTRE: Syed Wazir Ali, C.K. Nayudu, HH Maharaja Porbandar *captain*, K.S.G. Limbdi, Syed Nazir Ali, Joginder Singh. FRONT: Naoomal Jeoomal, S.H.M. Colah, N.D. Marshall.

scoring a century in each innings: U.M. Merchant (143 and 156) and D.G. Phadkar (131 and 160) for Bombay, and M.R. Rege (133 and 100) for Maharashtra. Played over seven days, the match established **the world record aggregate of runs for all first-class cricket:** 2376 at an average of 64.2 runs per wicket.

The highest number of runs scored by any batsman in all first-class cricket between one dismissal and the next is 709 by K.C. Ibrahim of Bombay. He achieved this record sequence in 1947-48 with scores of 218*, 36*, 234*, 77* and 144.

The world record partnership for any wicket in all first-class cricket was established in the final of the Vanji Trophy tournament at Baroda played on 7-11 March 1947. Baroda had scored 91 for 3 in reply to Holkar's 337, when Gul Mahomed joined Vijay Hazare in a partnership of 577 made in 533 minutes. It ended with Gul

HIGHEST PARTNERSHIPS IN INDIAN FIRST-CLASS CRICKET

Wicket	Runs	Batsmen (scores)	Match	Venue	Season
1st	451*	S. Desai (218*), R.M.H. Binny (211*)	Karnataka v Kerala	Chikmagalur	1977-78
2nd	455	K.V. Bhandarkar (205), B.B. Nimbalkar (443*)	Maharashtra v Kathiawar	Poona	1948-49
3rd	410	L. Amarnath (262), R.S. Modi (156)	India in England v Rest	Calcutta	1946-47
4th	577	V.S. Hazare (288), Gul Mahomed (319)	Baroda v Holkar	Baroda	1946-47
5th	360	U.M. Merchant (217), M.N. Raiji (170)	Bombay v Hyderabad	Bombay	1947-48
6th	371	V.M. Merchant (359*), R.S. Modi (168)	Bombay v Maharashtra	Bombay	1943-44
7th	274	K.C. Ibrahim (250), K.M. Rangnekar (138)	Bijapur XI v Bengal XI	Bombay	1942-43
8th	236	C.T. Sarwate (235), R.P. Singh (88)	Holkar v Delhi	Delhi	1949-50
9th	245	V.S. Hazare (316*), N.D. Nagarwalla (98)	Maharashtra v Baroda	Poona	1939-40
10th	145	K.S. More (181*), V. Patel (34)	Baroda v Uttar Pradesh	Baroda	1983-84

The fourth-wicket partnership of 577 is the world record for any wicket in first-class cricket.

Mahomed's dismissal for an audacious 319, but Hazare went on to score 288 in 628 minutes. Holkar used nine bowlers during the record stand and, after eventually dismissing Baroda for 784, were themselves bowled out for 173 to lose by an innings and 409 runs.

Bowling records

The best innings analysis in first-class cricket in India is 10 for 20 by P.M. Chatterjee for Bengal against Assam in a Ranji Trophy match at Jorhat in January 1957. Aged 29, Premansu Chatterjee, a versatile left-arm bowler who could swing a new ball at medium pace or spin leg-breaks, was responsible for dismissing Assam for 54. Bengal's handy lead of 451 was soon converted into an innings victory, but they were to lose their 'drawn' semi-final on the spin of a coin. Only two bowlers, Hedley Verity and George Geary, have taken ten wickets more cheaply.

The record match analysis in Indian first-class cricket is 16 for 154 by Pradeep Sunderam at Jodhpur on 17-19 November 1985. Opening the Rajasthan attack against Vidarbha on a matting pitch, he bowled unchanged throughout the first innings to take 10 for 78 in 22 overs. A 25-year-old right-arm medium-fast bowler, he was only the third Indian to take all ten wickets in a first-class innings: he emulated the feats of P.M. Chatterjee (above) and S.P. Gupte (10 for 78 for Bombay v Pakistan Services and Bahawalpur at Bombay in 1954-55). Sunderam, whose father had opened India's bowling in two Tests against New Zealand in 1955-56, added six more wickets from another 22 overs toil in the second innings to gain his team a tense victory by 9 runs.

The world record for the most balls bowled and most runs conceded in any first-class match are held by C.S. Nayudu. Both records were set in the Ranji Trophy Final at Bombay on 4-8 March 1945. Representing Holkar, he bowled 152.5 six-ball overs (917 balls) of leg-breaks and googlies and conceded 428 runs as Bombay amassed scores of 462 and 764 **(the second-highest second innings total in all first-class cricket).** His full analyses were 64.5-10-153-6 and 88-15-275-

5. Holkar replied with 360 and 492, Denis Compton, in India on wartime service, contributing 249 not out. A local businessman had promised Denis 100 rupees (about £7.50) for every run he scored over 100. Exhausted after his marathon innings in extreme heat and humidity, but elated by the handsome reward his score had earned, 'Compo' was dismayed to receive a message from his benefactor. It read simply: 'Very sorry, Mister Compton. I have been called away to Calcutta on very urgent business!'

Wicket-Keeping records

The most dismissals by a wicket-keeper in a first-class innings in India is seven, the record being set by S. Benjamin when he held six catches and made one stumping for the Central Zone against the North in the final of the Duleep Trophy at the Brabourne Stadium, Bombay, in December 1973. This feat was emulated by Bob Taylor for England when he equalled the world Test match record by catching seven Indian batsmen at the Wankhede Stadium, Bombay, on the first day of the Golden Jubilee Test (15 February 1980). By holding another three catches in the second innings, Taylor set **a new world Test record and a new first-class record for matches in India (since equalled).**

Fielding records

The most catches taken in the field in a first-class innings in India is six by L.M. Deas for the Europeans against the Parsees in the Presidency Match at Poona in 1898-99.

The Indian record for the most catches by a non-wicket-keeper in a first-class match is seven and was established by J.G. Greig in the Presidency Match of 1893-94 at Bombay. John Greig was stationed in India on army service. He was to play 77 matches for Hampshire between 1901 and 1920 before being ordained in Rome in 1935.

Greig's performance has been equalled by four other fielders (see table), including two of India's specialist short-leg catchers, Eknath Solkar (Bombay v Rest of India at Brabourne Stadium, Bombay,

SEVEN CATCHES IN A MATCH

	Match	Venue	Season
J.G. Greig	Europeans v Parsees	Bombay	1893-94
L.M. Deas	Europeans v Parsees	Poona	1898-99
E.D. Solkar	Bombay v Rest of India	Bombay	1968-69
Yadurvindra Singh	India v England	Bangalore	1976-77
S. Dukanwala	Baroda v Saurashtra	Bhavnagar	1981-82

26-29 November 1968) and Yajurvindra Singh (India v England at Bangalore, 28 January-2 February 1977). Solkar's performance was for the previous season's Ranji Trophy champions in the annual Irani Trophy match, while that of Yajurvindra equalled the Test record.

The Bombay Pentangular

Until 1946 this annual tournament took pride of place in India's domestic fixture list. Originated in 1892 as the Presidency Match between the Europeans and the Parsees (the earliest Indian cricketers), the ultimate Pentangular Tournament was evolved by the addition of the Hindus (1907), the Mohammedans, or Muslims (1912), and The Rest (1937). Because of political agitation the tournament was abandoned as a major event after the 1945-46 season.

The Ranji Trophy

This championship was instituted in 1934 to commemorate the great Cambridge University, Sussex and England cricketer, 'Ranji' – Prince Kumar Shri Ranjitsinhji, the Jam Sahib of Nawanagar – who had died the previous year. Since 1946 it has been India's premier championship.

Between 1959 and 1973, Bombay established the world record for most consecutive national championship wins by winning the final in 15 successive seasons. Their record run was ended at Bangalore on 18 March 1974 when Karnataka defeated them in the semi-final by virtue of a first innings lead of 78 runs.

The 1982 final, played at the Feroz Shah Kotla Ground, Kelhi, on 24-49 March between Delhi and Karnataka, was the most extraordinary match in the history of the Ranji Trophy. Delhi, confronted by the astronomical total of 705, overhauled their objective with two wickets to spare and thus won the championship on first innings after the contest had been allowed to continue into an extra (sixth) day. The match produced two world records: **the highest first innings aggregate (1412) in all first-class cricket,** and **the first time that a side scoring 700 had been led on first innings.**

The Duleep Trophy

An inter-zonal tournament introduced in 1961 and named after Ranji's nephew, K.S. Duleepsinhji, who also played for Cambridge University, Sussex

RANJI TROPHY CHAMPIONS

1934-35	Bombay	1947-48	Holkar	1960-61	Bombay	1973-74	Karnataka
1935-36	Bombay	1948-49	Bombay	1961-62	Bombay	1974-75	Bombay
1936-37	Nawanagar	1949-50	Baroda	1962-63	Bombay	1975-76	Bombay
1937-38	Hyderabad	1950-51	Holkar	1963-64	Bombay	1976-77	Bombay
1938-39	Bengal	1951-52	Bombay	1964-65	Bombay	1977-78	Karnataka
1939-40	Maharashtra	1952-53	Holkar	1965-66	Bombay	1978-79	Delhi
1940-41	Maharashtra	1953-54	Bombay	1966-67	Bombay	1979-80	Delhi
1941-42	Bombay	1954-55	Madras	1967-68	Bombay	1980-81	Bombay
1942-43	Baroda	1955-56	Bombay	1968-69	Bombay	1981-82	Delhi
1943-44	W.IndiaStates	1956-57	Bombay	1969-70	Bombay	1982-83	Karnataka
1944-45	Bombay	1957-58	Barada	1970-71	Bombay	1983-84	Bombay
1945-46	Holkar	1958-59	Bombay	1971-72	Bombay	1984-85	Bombay
1946-47	Baroda	1959-60	Bombay	1972-73	Bombay	1985-86	Delhi

and England. Played early in the season on a knock-out basis, the Duleep Trophy frequently draws attention to new candidates for Test matches and tours overseas.

Farokh Engineer, whose batting and wicket-keeping provided rich entertainment for followers of Bombay, Lancashire and India. (Bill Smith)

DULEEP TROPHY CHAMPIONS

1961-62	West	1969-70	West	1978-79	North
1962-63	West	1970-71	South	1979-80	North
1963-64	South	1971-72	Central	1980-81	West
	West	1972-73	West	1981-82	West
1964-65	West	1973-74	North	1982-83	North
1965-66	South	1974-75	South	1983-84	North
1966-67	South	1975-76	South	1984-85	South
1967-68	South	1976-77	West	1985-86	West
1968-69	West	1977-78	West		

FIRST-CLASS CRICKET IN PAKISTAN

First-class cricket was played in the various provinces of NW India and Bengal before 1947 when they became partitioned from India to form the two wings of Jinnah's Muslim state of Pakistan. The following cricket associations already existed: Northern India (renamed Punjab), Sind, and the North-West Frontier Province.

Although cricket was not immediately affected by partition and two players, Amir Elahi and Gul Mahomed, who were subsequently to represent Pakistan toured Australia with India in 1947-48, events soon combined to separate cricket as well.

The first Pakistan representative team to take the field drew with West Indies at Lahore on 26-29 November 1948. Three years later the MCC team interrupted their Test series in India to play four first-class matches and one minor game in Pakistan, and lost the second of two unofficial Tests. **Pakistan's first victory against a country of full Test status** was thus gained at Karachi on 2 December 1951.

Pakistan's first official overseas tour was to Ceylon where they won both the unofficial Test matches played at the Colombo Oval in March 1949.

The Board of Control for Cricket in Pakistan (BCCP) was formed on 1 May 1949. Sponsored by India and seconded by the MCC, Pakistan were admitted to full membership of the ICC (and thus awarded full Test status) on 28 July 1952. On 16 October of that year, Pakistan entered the official Test arena against India at Feroz Shah Kotla, Delhi. Although beaten in that match, they gained their first victory ten days later in the Second Test at Lucknow. At The Oval in August 1954, they became **the first country to win a Test match on their first tour of England.**

Although the Karachi Quadrangular Tournament was revived, it was not until 1953 that Pakistan's first national championship, the Qaid-e-Azam Trophy, was inaugurated.

Team records

The highest total in first-class cricket in Pakistan is 951 for 7 declared by Sind against Baluchistan at the National Stadium, Karachi, in a Qaid-e-Azam Trophy match on 18-20 February 1974. The innings, in reply to Baluchistan's 93, was dominated by the Sind captain, Aftab Baloch, who scored 428 in 584 minutes, hitting 25 fours. Sind's eventual margin of victory – an innings and 575 runs – is the sixth largest in all first-class cricket. Their total has been exceeded at first-class level only by Victoria, with scores of 1107 and 1059 in inter-state matches at Melbourne in the 1920s.

The most one-sided cricket match ever played was the Ayub Trophy fixture between Railways and Dera Ismail Khan at Lahore on 2-4 December 1964. After batting until lunch on the third day for 910 for 6 declared, Railways dismissed the visitors for 32 and 27 to win by an innings and 851 runs – **the largest margin of victory in all first-class cricket.** Pervez Akhtar contributed 337 not out to the Railways' total to establish **a world record for the highest maiden hundred in first-class cricket.** Dera Ismail Khan's second **innings total** of 27 and **match aggregate** of 59 **are the lowest in first-class matches in Pakistan.** Their two innings lasted only 28 overs in total and two different pairs of bowlers operated unchanged in the two innings.

Batting records

The highest individual innings in all first-

class cricket is 499 by Hanif Mohammad for Karachi against Bahawalpur at the Parsee Institute Ground, Karachi on 8-11 January 1959. The match, a semi-final of the Qaid-e-Azam Trophy, was played on a coir matting pitch. After the visitors had been dismissed for 185, Hanif, aged 24 and the second of four brothers to represent his country in official Tests, opened the Karachi innings and scored 25 in 40 minutes before stumps. Next day he added another 230 runs in five hours. He batted on throughout the third day, overtook the previous world record score of 452 not out by Bradman, and, according to the scoreboard, had reached 496 with about two minutes of the session left. Off the last ball of the over he attempted a quick single to keep the strike and so complete his 500 off the final over. He was run out and returned to the pavilion to discover that the scoreboard was wrong and that he was only one run short of his unique target. Karachi, captained by Hanif's elder brother Wazir, who had also scored a century, declared at that total (772 for 7), and bowled out Bahawalpur for 108 to win by an innings and 479 runs. They went on to win the final against Services by 279 runs, Hanif scoring 130 in the first innings to total 712 runs in the tournament for an average of 178. His 499 occupied 635 minutes and included 64 fours. His score also represents **the highest aggregate of runs by one batsman in any first-class match.**

Nowadays, the Parsee Institute Ground stages only minor youth matches, with grazing goats its only groundstaff.

Hanif Mohammad – run out off the last ball of the day when going for his 500.

The slowest century in all first-class cricket was scored in 557 minutes by Mudassar Nazar (114) for Pakistan in the First Test against England at the Gaddafi Stadium, Lahore, on 14-15 December 1977. Opening the innings in his second Test match, Mudassar scored 52 in 330 minutes on the first day. A minor riot interrupted his innings when he took his 99th run and confused the less mathematically adept spectators. With tea being taken, 45 minutes elapsed before his innings resumed and he took a further ten minutes to acquire the final single, reaching his hundred out of 306 for 3 in 9 hours 17 minutes. When he was eventually

HIGHEST PARTNERSHIPS IN PAKISTAN FIRST-CLASS CRICKET

Wicket	Runs	Batsmen (scores)	Match	Venue	Season
1st	561	Waheed Mirza (324), Mansoor Akhtar (224*)	Karachi Whites v Quetta	Karachi	1976-77
2nd	426	Arshad Pervez (220), Mohsin Khan (220)	Habib Bank v Income Tax Dept.	Lahore	1977-78
3rd	456	Khalid Irtiza (290), Aslam Ali (236)	United Bank v Multan	Karachi	1975-76
4th	346	Zafar Altaf (268), Majid Khan (241)	Lahore Greens v Bahawalpur	Lahore	1965-66
5th	355	Altaf Shah (276), Tariq Bashir (196)	HBFC v Multan	Multan	1976-77
6th	353	Salahuddin (256), Zaheer Abbas (197)	Karachi v East Pakistan	Karachi	1968-69
7th	308	Waqar Hassan (189), Imtiaz Ahmed (209)	Pakistan v New Zealand	Lahore	1955-56
8th	240	Gulfraz Khan (207), Raja Sarfraz (102)	Railways v Universities	Lahore	1976-77
9th	181	Rashid Israr (350), Abdur Raqib (45)	Habib Bank v National Bank	Lahore	1976-77
10th	196*	Nadim Yousuf (202*), Maqsood Kundi (109*)	MCB v National Bank	Lahore	1981-82

The partnership for the first and third wickets are world first-class records.
HBFC – House Building Finance Corporation; MCB – Muslim Commercial Banks

The 1954 Pakistanis in England. BACK: Wazir Mohammad, Khalid Hassan, Shujauddin, Shakoor Ahmed, Zulfiqar Ahmed. CENTRE: Khalid Wazir, Waqar Hassan, Ikram Elahi, Mohammad Aslam, Mahmood Hussain, Alimuddin, Hanif Mohammad. FRONT: M.E.Z. Ghazali, Fazal Mahmood, A.H. Kardar *captain*, Imtiaz Ahmed, Maqsood Ahmed. (Sport & General)

caught off a hard return drive to the bowler, Mudassar had batted 591 minutes for 114 runs, a marathon which included 12 fours and 42 singles. His father, Nazar Mohammad, had opened the batting in Pakistan's first Test series, and, in the Second Test against India at Lucknow, had carried his bat through the innings and become **the first player to be on the field for an entire Test match.**

Bowling records

The only Pakistani bowler to take all ten wickets in a first-class innings is Shahid Mahmood, a 30-year-old opening batsman and left-arm bowler of medium pace. Playing for Karachi Whites in a home Qaid-e-Azam Trophy

match at the National Stadium against Khairpur on 6 September 1969, Shahid recorded a second innings analysis of 25-5-58-10. Dismissed for 146, Khairpur lost by an innings and 56 runs in two days. It is **the only ten-wicket innings analysis in first-class cricket in Pakistan.** In his only Test appearance, against England at Nottingham seven years earlier, Shahid had failed to take a wicket.

The best match analysis in first-class cricket in Pakistan is 15 for 76 by Fazal Mahmood for Punjab against Services in a semi-final of the Qaid-e-Azam Trophy at Lahore on 7-12 February 1957. He returned figures of 6 for 35 and 9 for 43 as Services (112 and 99) lost by an innings. Punjab went on to defeat Karachi in the final a month later. Now a senior police inspector, Fazal Mahmood is arguably Pakistan's greatest ever bowler. At a fast

Wicket-Keeping records

SEVEN DISMISSALS IN AN INNINGS

	Ct	St	Match	Venue	Season
Shahid Israr	6	1	Karachi Whites v Quetta	Karachi	1976-77
Wasim Bari	4	3	PIA v Sind	Lahore	1977-78
Taslim Arif	5	2	National Bank v Punjab	Lahore	1978-79
Masood Iqbal	4	3	Habib Bank v Lahore	Lahore	1982-83
Arifuddin	3	4	United Bank v PACO	Sahiwal	1983-84

PACO – Pakistan Automobile Company

TEN DISMISSALS IN A MATCH

	Ct	St	Match	Venue	Season
Taslim Arif	6	4	National Bank v Punjab	Lahore	1978-79
Arifuddin	9	1	United Bank v Karachi B	Karachi	1978-79
Kamal Najamuddin	9	1	Karachi v Lahore	Multan	1982-83
Azhar Abbas	7	3	Bahawalpur v Lahore Greens	Bahawalpur	1983-84
Anil Dalpat	8	2	Karachi v United Bank	Lahore	1985-86

medium pace he could swing and cut the ball both ways off a nagging length, and could be virtually unplayable on matting or rain-affected turf pitches.

Fielding records

The most catches taken in the field in a first-class innings in Pakistan is six. The record was set by Gulfraz Khan in a Qaid-e-Azam Trophy match for Railways against the Muslim Commercial Bank at Sialkot in November 1981. His performance was equalled by Masood Anwar in a BCCP Patron's Trophy match for Rawalpindi against Lahore Division at the Pindi Club Ground in October 1983.

The Pakistan match record by a non-wicket-keeper is eight and was set by Javed Miandad in a Patron's Trophy match for Habib Bank against Universities at the Punjab University Ground, Lahore, on 13-16 February 1978. His record was equalled by Masood Anwar in October 1983 (see above).

Qaid-e-Azam Trophy

Pakistan's premier national championship did not come into being until six years after Partition. It was named after Pakistan's first Governor-General, the Qaid-e-Azam ('Great Leader'), Mohammad Ali Jinnah (1876-1948). Head of the All-India Muslim League and the main creator of Pakistan, Jinnah was a great cricket enthusiast.

HOLDERS

1953-54 Bahawalpur	1972-73 Railways
1954-55 Karachi	1973-74 Railways
1956-57 Punjab	1974-75 Punjab A
1957-58 Bahawalpur	1975-76 National Bank
1958-59 Karachi	1976-77 United Bank
1959-60 Karachi	1977-78 Habib Bank
1961-62 Karachi B	1978-79 National Bank
1962-63 Karachi A	1979-80 PIA
1963-64 Karachi Blues	1980-81 United Bank
1964-65 Karachi Blues	1981-82 National Bank
1966-67 Karachi	1982-83 United Bank
1968-69 Lahore	1983-84 National Bank
1969-70 PIA	1984-85 United Bank
1970-71 Karachi Blues	1985-96 Karachi

PIA – Pakistan International Airlines

FIRST-CLASS CRICKET IN SRI LANKA

Cricket was introduced to Ceylon in 1832 by the Rev Brooke Bailey. Arriving from Cambridge as assistant master at the Colombo Academy (now the Royal College), he immediately added cricket coaching to his duties.

Ceylon's first cricket club, the Colombo Cricket Club, was formed in 1832. According to the 'Colombo Journal' of 19 September 1832 the inaugural meeting, attended by between 40 and 50 members, framed rules and appointed a committee.

The first cricket match to be played in Ceylon was reported in the *Colombo Journal* of 3 November 1832. The Colombo C.C. suffered a ten-wicket defeat at the hands of a section of the British Garrison (the 97th Regiment), at the Galle Face Ground.

Until 1873 when the Colts C.C. was formed, units of the British Garrison provided the Colombo C.C.'s sole opposition. From 1880 to 1912 George Vanderspar organized and promoted Ceylon's cricket to international level. A millionaire businessman who played for Somerset and MCC, he captained the Colombo C.C. and scored the Club's first century. His MCC connections enabled him to persuade touring teams to break their journeys to and from Australia with a match in Colombo. These whistle stop tours continued until 1965. Vander-

spar organized **the first tour by a Ceylon team overseas,** the Colombo C.C. visiting Calcutta in 1884-85.

The first overseas side to visit Ceylon was the All England team captained by the Hon I.F.W. Bligh on 13-14 October 1882. The tourists defeated a Colombo C.C. XVIII (all Englishmen) on first innings. Two days later, and 360 miles from Colombo, the tourists' ship *Pershawar* was rammed by a barque *(Glenroy)* and had to return to Ceylon for repairs and an inquiry. This allowed a second match to be played, Ivo Bligh's XI drawing with the Royal Dublin Fusiliers Officers. Both games were played on the Galle Face Ground at Colombo.

The first touring team to play first-class matches in Ceylon was the MCC in January and February 1927. Captained by A.E.R. Gilligan they played four games during an 18-week tour of the Indian sub-continent, during which they remained undefeated after 34 matches.

Ceylon's first centralized cricket administration was the Ceylon Cricket Association and was formed in 1922. The Ceylon Cricket Board of Control (formed 1948) merged with the Ceylon CA in 1965.

Team Records

The highest total in first-class cricket in Sri Lanka is 549 for 8 wickets declared by the West Indians against Ceylon at the Colombo Oval (now the Saravanamuttu Stadium) on 22-23 January 1967. It included hundreds by B.F. Butcher, C.H. Lloyd and the captain, G.St A. Sobers.

The lowest total in first-class cricket in Sri Lanka is 42 by the Ceylon President's XI against J. Lister's International XI at the Colombo Oval on 5-6 March 1968.

Batting Records

The highest individual innings in Sri Lankan first-class cricket is by F.M.M. Worrell for a Commonwealth XI against Ceylon at the Colombo Oval on 16 February 1951. He batted only 274 minutes, hitting 5 sixes and 31 fours.

Sri Lanka's captain, Duleep Mendis (wearing cap), leads his team's celebrations at the conclusion of their first Test victory (against India at the Saravanamuttu Stadium in Colombo on 11 September 1985). (The Hindu)

The highest innings by a Sri Lankan on home soil is 212 in 285 minutes by C.I. Gunasekara for Ceylon against Madras in a Gopalan Trophy match at the Colombo Oval on 7 March 1959.

The first Sri Lankan batsman to score a hundred on first-class debut on home soil was M. Rodrigo. Opening Ceylon's second innings against the West Indians at the Colombo Oval on 20-21 February 1949, he carried his bat, contributing 135 not out towards a total of 318 in 382 minutes.

The first overseas batsman to score a hundred on his first-class debut in Sri Lanka was C.J. Barnett who made 116 in 125 minutes for the MCC against Ceylon at the Colombo Cricket Club Ground on 17 February 1934.

The first batsman to score a hundred in both innings of a first-class match in Sri Lanka was A.V. Mankad who made 105 and 100 not out for the Indians against the President's XI at Katugastota, Kandy, on 1-3 February 1974.

The highest partnership for any wicket in first-class matches in Sri Lanka is 301 by F.M.M. Worrell (285) and W.H.H. Sutcliffe (95) for the fifth wicket for a Commonwealth XI against Ceylon at the Colombo Oval on 16 February 1951.

Bowling Records

The best innings analysis in Sri Lankan first-class cricket is 9 for 18 in 13 overs by R.K. Oxenham for F.A. Tarrant's Australians against All Ceylon at the Singhalese Sports Club Ground, Colombo, on 25 October 1935. The Queensland

Kandapolla play host to Badulla in July 1878. (Illustrated London News)

Dadulla v Kandapolla

Kandapolla Club and Grounds

leg-spin and googly bowler's career-best analysis included four wickets in one over and a hat-trick as the home side were skittled our for 96.

The best match analysis in Sri Lanka first-class cricket is 15 for 43 by D.L. Underwood for J. Lister's International XI against the Ceylon President's XI at the Colombo Oval on 5-7 March 1968. A thunderstorm followed by blazing sun produced conditions ideally suited to the spin and swerve of the Kent and England left-hander. The home side were dismissed for 42 and 98, Underwood's innings analyses being 11.3-6-10-8 and 26.1-13-33-7.

Wicket-Keeping records

The most dismissals in an innings in Sri Lankan first-class cricket is six by K.V. Bhandarkar for Holkar against Ceylon at the Colombo Oval on 17 April 1948. This record was equalled on 30-31 August 1985 by S.A.R. Silva for Sri Lanka against India in the First Test at the Singhalese Sports Club Ground in Colombo.

The most dismissals in a match in Sri Lankan first-class cricket is nine by S.A.R. Silva for Sri Lanka against India in Colombo – twice. He set the record at the Singhalese Sports Club Ground on 30 August-4 September 1985, and then repeated the feat in the Second Test at the Saravanamuttu Stadium on 7-11 September.

S.A.R. Silva set a world record by making 18 dismissals in consecutive Test matches. He compounded the record by also scoring a century (111) in the Second Test.

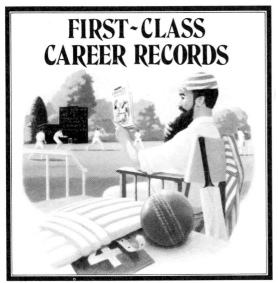

FIRST-CLASS CAREER RECORDS

All records are complete to the end of the 1986 English season (16 September). Dates in italics denote the first half of an overseas season, ie *1971* means 1971-72.

The last column shows the number of seasons in which each batsman scored 1000 or more runs. J.B. Hobbs scored 1000 runs in each of 24 seasons in Britain and on two tours overseas.

Key to the less obvious team abbreviations:

CU	Cambridge University	PIA	Pakistan International
GW	Griqualand West		Airlines
NSW	New South Wales	Q	Queensland
NT	Northern Transvaal	R	Rhodesia
		T	Transvaal
OFS	Orange Free State	WA	Western Australia
OU	Oxford University	WP	Western Province

30 000 Runs in First-Class Matches

		Career	I	NO	HS	Runs	Average	100	1000
J.B. Hobbs	Surrey	1905-1934	1315	106	316*	**61237**	50.65	197	24+2
F.E. Woolley	Kent	1906-1938	1532	85	305*	**58969**	40.75	145	28
E.H. Hendren	Middlesex	1907-1938	1300	166	301*	**57611**	50.80	170	21+4
C.P. Mead	Hampshire	1905-1936	1340	185	280*	**55061**	47.67	153	27
W.G. Grace	Gloucestershire	1865-1908	1493	105	344	**54896**	39.55	126	28
W.R. Hammond	Gloucestershire	1920-1951	1005	104	336*	**50551**	56.10	167	17+5
H. Sutcliffe	Yorkshire	1919-1945	1088	123	313	**50138**	51.95	149	21+3
G. Boycott	Yorkshire/NT	1962-1986	1014	162	261*	**48426**	56.83	151	23+3
T.W. Graveney	Glos/Worcs/Q	1948-*1971*	1223	159	258	**47793**	44.91	122	20+2
T.W. Hayward	Surrey	1893-1914	1138	96	315*	**43551**	41.79	104	20
M.C. Cowdrey	OU/Kent	1950-1976	1130	134	307	**42719**	42.89	107	21+6
D.L. Amiss	Warwickshire	1960-1986	1093	123	262*	**42123**	43.42	100	22+1
A. Sandham	Surrey	1911-*1937*	1000	79	325	**41284**	44.82	107	18+2
L. Hutton	Yorkshire	1934-1960	814	91	364	**40140**	55.51	129	12+5
M.J.K. Smith	OU/Leics/Warwicks	1951-1975	1091	139	204	**39832**	41.84	69	19+1
W. Rhodes	Yorkshire	1898-1930	1528	237	267*	**39802**	30.83	58	20+1
J.H. Edrich	Surrey	1956-1978	979	104	310*	**39790**	45.47	103	19+2
R.E.S. Wyatt	Warwicks/Worcs	1923-1957	1141	157	232	**39405**	40.04	85	17+1
D.C.S. Compton	Middlesex/Holkar	1936-1964	839	88	300	**38942**	51.85	123	14+3
G.E. Tyldesley	Lancashire	1909-1936	961	106	256*	**38874**	45.46	102	18+1
J.T. Tyldesley	Lancashire	1895-1923	994	62	295*	**37897**	40.66	86	19
J.W. Hearne	Middlesex	1909-1936	1025	116	285*	**37252**	40.98	96	19
L.E.G. Ames	Kent	1926-1951	951	95	295	**37248**	43.51	102	17
D. Kenyon	Worcestershire	1946-1967	1159	59	259	**37002**	33.63	74	19
W.J. Edrich	Middlesex	1934-1958	964	92	267*	**36965**	42.39	86	15
J.M. Parks	Sussex/Somerset	1949-1976	1227	172	205*	**36673**	34.76	51	20
D. Denton	Yorkshire	1894-1920	1163	70	221	**36479**	33.37	69	21
K.W.R. Fletcher	Essex	1962-1986	1118	164	228*	**36437**	38.19	62	20

		Career	I	NO	HS	Runs	Average	100	1000
G.H. Hirst	Yorkshire	1891-1929	1215	151	341	**36323**	34.13	60	19
A. Jones	Glamorgan/WA/NT/Natal	1957-1983	1168	72	204*	**36049**	32.89	56	23
W.G. Quaife	Warwickshire/GW	1894-1928	1203	185	255*	**36012**	35.37	72	24
R.E. Marshall	Barbados/Hampshire	*1945*-1972	1053	59	228*	**35725**	35.94	68	18
G. Gunn	Nottinghamshire	1902-1932	1061	82	220	**35208**	35.96	62	20
D.B. Close	Yorkshire/Somerset	1949-1986	1225	173	198	**34994**	33.26	52	20
J.G. Langridge	Sussex	1928-1955	984	66	250*	**34380**	37.45	76	17
G.M. Turner	Otago/Worcestershire	*1964-1982*	792	101	311*	**34346**	49.70	103	15+3
Zaheer Abbas	Karachi/PIA/Glos	*1965-1985*	747	89	274	**34289**	52.11	107	11+6
C. Washbrook	Lancashire	1933-1964	906	107	251*	**34101**	42.67	76	17+3
M. Leyland	Yorkshire	1920-1948	932	101	263	**33659**	40.50	80	17
H.T.W. Hardinge	Kent	1902-1933	1021	103	263*	**33519**	36.51	75	18
R. Abel	Surrey	1881-1904	1007	73	357*	**33124**	35.46	74	14
C.A. Milton	Gloucestershire	1948-1974	1078	125	170	**32150**	33.73	56	16
J.D.B. Robertson	Middlesex	1937-1959	897	46	331*	**31914**	37.50	67	14+1
J. Hardstaff jr	Notts/Auckland	1930-1955	812	94	266	**31847**	44.35	83	13+1
J. Langridge	Sussex	1924-1953	1058	157	167	**31716**	35.20	42	20
K.F. Barrington	Surrey	1953-1968	831	136	256	**31714**	45.63	76	12+3
C.H. Lloyd	Guyana/Lancashire	*1963*-1986	730	96	242*	**31232**	49.26	79	10+4
Mushtaq Mohammad	Karachi/PIA/Northants	*1956*-1985	843	104	303*	**31091**	42.07	72	12+3
C.G. Greenidge	Hampshire/Barbados	1970-1986	743	64	273*	**31074**	45.76	73	15+1
C.B. Fry	OU/Surrey/Sussex/Hants	1892-*1921*	658	43	258*	**30886**	50.22	94	12
D. Brookes	Northamptonshire	1934-1959	925	70	257	**30874**	36.10	71	17
A.I. Kallicharran	Guyana/Warwicks/Q/T	*1966*-1986	762	82	243*	**30775**	45.25	83	12+1
P. Holmes	Yorkshire	1913-1935	810	84	315*	**30574**	42.11	67	14+1
R.T. Simpson	Nottinghamshire/Sind	*1944*-1963	852	55	259	**30546**	38.32	64	13+1
G.L. Berry	Leicestershire	1924-1951	1056	57	232	**30225**	30.25	45	18
K.G. Suttle	Sussex	1949-1971	1064	92	204*	**30225**	31.09	49	17

D.G. Bradman holds the record for the highest career average in first-class cricket with 95.14 runs per innings. K.S. Ranjitsinhji achieved the highest average by any batsman whose career was based in England. Their full details are:

		Career	I	NO	HS	Runs	Average	100	1000
D.G. Bradman	NSW/South Australia	*1927-1948*	338	43	452*	**28067**	95.14	117	4+12
K.S. Ranjitsinhji	CU/Sussex	1893-1920	500	62	285*	**24692**	56.37	72	11+1

100 Hundreds in First-Class Matches

		Career	Innings	100	Innings per 100
J.B. Hobbs	Surrey	1905-1934	1315	**197**	6.6
E.H. Hendren	Middlesex	1907-1938	1300	**170**	7.6
W.R. Hammond	Gloucestershire	1920-1951	1005	**167**	6.0
C.P. Mead	Hampshire	1905-1936	1340	**153**	8.7
G. Boycott	Yorkshire/NT	1962-1986	1014	**151**	6.7
H. Sutcliffe	Yorkshire	1919-1945	1088	**149**	7.3
F.E. Woolley	Kent	1906-1938	1532	**145**	10.5
L. Hutton	Yorkshire	1934-1960	814	**129**	6.3
W.G. Grace	Gloucestershire	1865-1908	1493	**126**	11.8
D.C.S. Compton	Middlesex/Holkar	1936-1964	839	**123**	6.8

T.W. Graveney	Glos/Worcs/Queensland	1948-*1971*	1223	**122**	10.0
D.G. Bradman	NSW/South Australia	*1927-1948*	338	**117**	2.8
Zaheer Abbas	Karachi/PIA/Glos	*1965-1985*	747	**107**	6.9
A. Sandham	Surrey	1911-*1937*	1000	**107**	9.3
M.C. Cowdrey	OU/Kent	1950-1976	1130	**107**	10.5
T.W. Hayward	Surrey	1893-1914	1138	**104**	10.9
G.M. Turner	Otago/Worcestershire	*1964-1982*	792	**103**	7.6
J.H. Edrich	Surrey	1956-1978	979	**103**	9.5
L.E.G. Ames	Kent	1926-1951	951	**102**	9.3
G.E. Tyldesley	Lancashire	1909-1936	961	**102**	9.4
D.L. Amiss	Warwickshire	1960-1986	1093	**100**	10.9

2000 Wickets in First-Class Matches

		Career	Runs	Wickets	Average	100W Season
W. Rhodes	Yorkshire	1898-1930	69993	**4187**	16.71	23
A.P. Freeman	Kent	1914-1936	69577	**3776**	18.42	17
C.W.L. Parker	Gloucestershire	1903-1935	63817	**3278**	19.46	16
J.T. Hearne	Middlesex	1888-1923	54361	**3061**	17.75	15
T.W.J. Goddard	Gloucestershire	1922-1952	59116	**2979**	19.84	16
W.G. Grace	Gloucestershire	1865-1908	51545	**2876**	17.92	10
A.S. Kennedy	Hampshire	1907-1936	61034	**2874**	21.23	15
D. Shackleton	Hampshire	1948-1969	53303	**2857**	18.65	20
G.A.R. Lock	Surrey/Leics/WA	1946-*1970*	54710	**2844**	19.23	14
F.J. Titmus	Middx/Surrey/OFS	1949-1982	63313	**2830**	22.37	16
M.W. Tate	Sussex	1912-1937	50567	**2784**	18.16	14†
G.H. Hirst	Yorkshire	1891-1929	51300	**2739**	18.72	15
C. Blythe	Kent	1899-1914	42136	**2506**	16.81	14
W.E. Astill	Leicestershire	1906-1939	57783	**2431**	23.76	9
D.L. Underwood	Kent	1963-1986	48698	**2420**	20.12	10
J.C. White	Somerset	1909-1937	43759	**2356**	18.57	14
W.E. Hollies	Warwickshire	1932-1957	48656	**2323**	20.94	14
F.S. Trueman	Yorkshire	1949-1969	42154	**2304**	18.29	12
J.B. Statham	Lancashire	1950-1968	36995	**2260**	16.36	13
R.T.D. Perks	Worcestershire	1930-1955	53770	**2233**	24.07	16
J. Briggs	Lancashire	1879-1900	35432	**2221**	15.95	12
D.J. Shepherd	Glamorgan	1950-1972	47298	**2218**	21.32	12
E.G. Dennett	Gloucestershire	1903-1926	42568	**2147**	19.82	12
T. Richardson	Surrey/Somerset	1892-1905	38794	**2105**	18.42	10
T.E. Bailey	CU/Essex	1945-1967	48170	**2082**	23.13	9
R. Illingworth	Yorkshire/Leics	1951-1983	42023	**2072**	20.28	10
F.E. Woolley	Kent	1906-1938	41066	**2068**	19.85	8
G. Geary	Leicestershire	1912-1938	41339	**2063**	20.03	11
D.V.P. Wright	Kent	1932-1957	49305	**2056**	23.98	10
J.A. Newman	Hampshire	1906-1930	51211	**2032**	25.20	9
A. Shaw	Notts/Sussex	1864-1897	24579	**2027**	12.12	9
S. Haigh	Yorkshire	1895-1913	32091	**2012**	15.94	11
N. Gifford	Worcs/Warwicks	1960-1986	46634	**2001**	23.30	4

† Including 116 wickets on MCC tour of India and Ceylon in 1926-1927.

Dennis Amiss, the last batsman to score 100 first-class hundreds. (Ken Kelly)

1000 Wicket-Keeping Dismissals

		Career	Dismissals	Ct	St
R.W. Taylor	Derbyshire	1960-1986	**1648**	1473	175
J.T. Murray	Middlesex	1952-1975	**1527**	1270	257
H. Strudwick	Surrey	1902-1927	**1496**	1242	254
A.P.E. Knott	Kent/Tasmania	1964-1985	**1344**	1211	133
F.H. Huish	Kent	1895-1914	**1310**	933	377
B. Taylor	Essex	1949-1973	**1294**	1082	212
D. Hunter	Yorkshire	1889-1909	**1265**	914	351
H.R. Butt	Sussex	1890-1912	**1228**	953	275
J.H. Board	Gloucestershire	1891-*1914*	**1207**	852	355
H. Elliott	Derbyshire	1920-1947	**1206**	904	302
J.M. Parks	Sussex/Somerset	1949-1976	**1181**	1088	93
R. Booth	Yorkshire/Worcs	1951-1970	**1126**	949	177
L.E.G. Ames	Kent	1926-1951	**1121**	703	418
G. Duckworth	Lancashire	1923-1947	**1090**	751	339
H.W. Stephenson	Somerset	1948-1964	**1082**	748	334
J.G. Binks	Yorkshire	1955-1975	**1071**	895	176
T.G. Evans	Kent	1939-1969	**1066**	816	250
A. Long	Surrey/Sussex	1960-1980	**1046**	922	124
G.O. Dawkes	Leics/Derbyshire	1937-1961	**1043**	895	148
R.W. Tolchard	Leicestershire	1965-1983	**1037**	912	125
W.L. Cornford	Sussex	1921-1947	**1017**	673	344

Catches taken in the field are included.

500 Catches by Non-Wicket Keepers

		Career	Catches
F.E. Woolley	Kent	1906-1938	**1018**
W.G. Grace	Gloucestershire	1865-1908	**874**
G.A.R. Lock	Surrey/Leics/WA	1946-*1970*	**831**
W.R. Hammond	Gloucestershire	1920-1951	**819**
D.B. Close	Yorkshire/Somerset	1949-1986	**813**
J.G. Langridge	Sussex	1928-1955	**786**
W. Rhodes	Yorkshire	1898-1930	**764**
C.A. Milton	Gloucestershire	1948-1974	**758**
E.H. Hendren	Middlesex	1907-1938	**754**
P.M. Walker	Glamorgan/Transvaal/WP	1956-1972	**697**
J. Tunnicliffe	Yorkshire	1891-1907	**695**
J. Seymour	Kent	1900-1926	**675**
C.P. Mead	Hampshire	1905-1936	**671**
M.C. Cowdrey	OU/Kent	1950-1976	**638**
M.J. Stewart	Surrey	1954-1972	**634**
K.W.R. Fletcher	Essex	1962-1986	**623**
P.J. Sainsbury	Hampshire	1954-1976	**617**
P.J. Sharpe	Yorkshire/Derbyshire	1956-1976	**616**
K.J. Grieves	NSW/Lancashire	*1945*-1964	**610**
E.G. Hayes	Surrey/Leics	1896-1926	**609**
G.H. Hirst	Yorkshire	1891-1929	**607**
G.R.J. Roope	Surrey	1964-1986	**602**
P.G.H. Fender	Sussex/Surrey	1910-1936	**600**

A.S.M. Oakman	Sussex	1947-1968	**594**
M.J.K. Smith	OU/Leics/Warwicks	1951-1975	**592**
R.Abel	Surrey	1881-1904	**586**
A.O. Jones	CU/Nottinghamshire	1892-1914	**577**
D.C. Morgan	Derbyshire	1950-1969	**572**
P.H. Parfitt	Middlesex	1956-1974	**564**
G.R. Cox	Sussex	1895-1928	**551**
T.W. Graveney	Glos/Worcs/Q	1948-*1971*	**550**
J.V. Wilson	Yorkshire	1946-1963	**548**
D.S. Steele	Northants/Derbyshire	1963-1984	**546**
L.C. Braund	Surrey/Somerset	1896-1920	**545**
A.E. Relf	Sussex/Auckland	1900-1921	**537**
W.J. Edrich	Middlesex	1934-1958	**529**
A.S. Kennedy	Hampshire	1907-1936	**528**
K.F. Barrington	Surrey	1953-1968	**515**
C.T. Radley	Middlesex	1964-1986	**513**
D.B. Carr	OU/Derbyshire	1945-1968	**501**

Catches taken during occasional wicket-keeping appearances are included.

10 000 Runs and 1000 Wickets in First-Class Matches

		Career	Runs	Wickets	Doubles
Arnold, E.G.	Worcestershire	1899-1913	15853	1069	4
Astill, W.E.	Leicestershire	1906-1939	22731	2431	9
Bailey, T.E	CU/Essex	1945-1967	28642	2082	8
Birkenshaw, J.	Yorkshire/Leics/Worcs	1958-1981	12780	1073	–
Braund, L.C.	Surrey/Somerset	1896-1920	17801	1114	3
Briggs, J.	Lancashire	1879-1900	14092	2221	–
Brown, A.S.	Gloucestershire	1953-1976	12851	1230	–
Brown, F.R.	CU/Surrey/Northants	1930-1961	13327	1221	2
Cartwright, T.W.	Warwicks/Somerset/Glamorgan	1952-1977	13710	1536	1
Close, D.B.	Yorkshire/Somerset	1949-1986	34994	1171	2
Cox, G.R.	Sussex	1895-1928	14643	1843	–
Douglas, J.W.H.T.	Essex	1901-1930	24531	1893	5
Eastman, L.C.	Essex/Otago	1920-1939	13385	1006	–
Fender, P.G.H.	Sussex/Surrey	1910-1936	19034	1894	6
Flowers, W.	Nottinghamshire	1877-1896	12891	1188	1
Geary, G.	Leicestershire	1912-1938	13504	2063	–
Giffen, G.	South Australia	*1877-1903*	11758	1023	3
Grace, W.G.	Gloucestershire	1865-1908	54896	2876	8
Gunn, J.R.	Nottinghamshire	1896-1932	24557	1242	4
Haig, N.E.	Middlesex	1912-1936	15220	1117	3
Haigh, S.	Yorkshire	1895-1913	11715	2012	1
Hearne, A.	Kent	1884-1910	16346	1160	–
Hearne, J.W.	Middlesex	1909-1936	37252	1839	5
Hirst, G.H.	Yorkshire	1891-1929	36323	2739	14
Howorth, R.	Worcestershire	1933-1951	11479	1345	3
Illingworth, R.	Yorkshire/Leicestershire	1951-1983	24134	2072	6
Imran Khan	Lahore/PIAOU/Worcs/Sussex	*1969*-1986	15349	1145	–
Intikhab Alam	Karachi/PIA/Surrey	*1957*-1982	14331	1571	–
Jenkins, R.O.	Worcestershire	1938-1958	10073	1309	2

		Career	Runs	Wickets	Doubles
Jupp, V.W.C.	Sussex/Northamptonshire	1909-1938	23296	1658	10
Kennedy, A.S.	Hampshire	1907-1936	16586	2874	5
King, J.H.	Leicestershire	1895-1925	25122	1204	1
Knight, B.R.	Essex/Leicestershire	1955-1969	13336	1089	4
Langridge, J.	Sussex	1924-1953	31716	1530	6
Llewellyn, C.B.	Natal/Hampshire	1894-1912	11425	1013	3
Lock, G.A.R.	Surrey/Leics/W. Australia	1946-1970	10342	2844	–
Lockwood, W.	Nottinghamshire/Surrey	1886-1904	10673	1376	2
Morgan, D.C.	Derbyshire	1950-1969	18356	1248	–
Mortimore, J.B.	Gloucestershire	1950-1975	15891	1807	3
Newman, J.A.	Hampshire	1906-1930	15333	2032	5
Nichols, M.S.	Essex	1924-1939	17827	1833	8
Peel, R.	Yorkshire	1882-1899	12191	1776	1
Procter, M.J.	Natal/WP/R/Glos	1965-1983	21904	1407	–
Relf, A.E.	Sussex/Auckland	1900-1921	22238	1897	8
Rhodes, W.	Yorkshire	1898-1930	39802	4187	16
Robson, E.	Somerset	1895-1923	12620	1147	–
Sainsbury, P.J.	Hampshire	1954-1976	20176	1316	–
Shepherd, J.N.	Barbados/Kent/Glos/R	1964-1985	13353	1155	–
Sinfield, R.A.	Gloucestershire	1921-1939	15674	1173	2
Smith, R.	Essex	1934-1956	12042	1350	3
Smith, T.P.B.	Essex	1929-1952	10161	1697	1
Sobers, G.St A.	Barbados/S. Aust/Notts	1952-1974	28315	1043	–
Tarrant, F.A.	Victoria/Middlesex	1898-1936	17857	1511	8
Tate, M.W.	Sussex	1912-1937	21717	2784	8
Thompson, G.J.	Northamptonshire	1897-1922	12018	1591	2
Titmus, F.J.	Middlesex/Surrey/OFS	1949-1982	21588	2830	8
Townsend, L.F.	Derbyshire	1922-1939	19555	1088	3
Tribe, G.E.	Victoria/Northants	1945-1959	10177	1378	7
Trott, A.E.	Victoria/Middlesex	1892-1911	10696	1674	2
Wainwright, E.	Yorkshire	1888-1902	12513	1071	1
Wellard, A.W.	Somerset	1927-1950	12515	1614	3
Wensley, A.F.	Sussex/Auckland	1922-1939	10849	1142	1
White, J.C.	Somerset	1909-1937	12202	2356	2
Woods, S.M.J.	CU/Somerset	1886-1910	15345	1040	–
Woolley, F.E.	Kent	1906-1938	58969	2068	8

10000 Runs and 1000 Wicket-Keeping Dismissals

		Career	Runs	Dismissals	W-K Doubles
L.E.G. Ames	Kent	1926-1951	37248	1121	3
J.H. Board	Gloucestershire	1891-*1914*	15674	1207	–
R. Booth	Yorkshire/Worcs	1951-1970	10138	1126	–
G.O. Dawkes	Leics/Derbyshire	1937-1961	11411	1043	–
T.G. Evans	Kent	1939-1969	14882	1066	–
A.P.E. Knott	Kent/Tasmania	1964-1985	18105	1344	–
J.T. Murray	Middlesex	1952-1975	18872	1527	1
J.M. Parks	Sussex/Somerset	1949-1976	36673	1181	–
H.W. Stephenson	Somerset	1948-1964	13195	1082	–
B. Taylor	Essex	1949-1973	19091	1294	–
R.W. Taylor	Derbyshire	1960-1986	12061	1648	–
R.W. Tolchard	Leicestershire	1965-1983	15288	1037	–

10000 Runs and 1000 Catches

		Career	Runs	Catches
F.E.Woolley	Kent	1906-1938	58969	1018

Woolley's career aggregates also include 2068 first-class wickets.

The Rev Prebendary Archdale Palmer Wickham (Somerset), who, in 1899 when Vicar of Martock and in his 44th year, established a world record which still survives by not conceding a bye during Hampshire's innings of 672 for 7 declared.

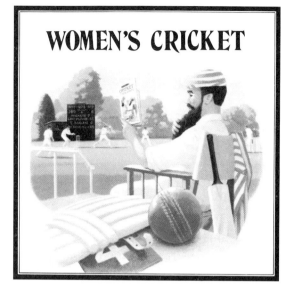

WOMEN'S CRICKET

First Ladies

The first account of a women's match was published in the *Reading Mercury* on 26 July 1745:

'The greatest cricket-match that ever was played in the South part of England was on Friday, the 26th of last month, on Gosden Common, near Guildford, in Surrey, between eleven maids of Bramley and eleven maids of Hambleton, dressed all in white. The Bramley maids had blue ribbons and the Hambleton maids red ribbons on their heads. The Bramley girls got 119 notches and the Hambleton girls 127. There was of both sexes the greatest number that ever was seen on such an occasion. The girls bowled, batted, ran and catched as well as most men could do in that game.'

Village cricket between women's teams had been popular in many parts of Surrey and Sussex before that first report.

The first time that women were invited to play on a major ground was on 13 July 1747 when the 'maids' of Westdean, Chilgrove and Charlton were 'bidden' to play a match on the famous Honourable Artillery Ground in London.

From these inter-village contests, women's cricket spread to the top of the social scale. In 1777 the *Morning Post* reported a match

'played in private between the Countess of Derby and some other Ladies of Quality and Fashion, at the Oaks, in Surrey, the rural and enchanting retreat of her ladyship'.

'The Woman of the Match' award seems to have been given to Elizabeth Ann Burrell, fourth daughter of a notable White Conduit Club player, who

'got more notches in the first and second innings than any lady in the game',

and was then aged 20 and extremely attractive. Her prize was the 8th Duke of Hamilton who married her before the next cricket season.

Not all women's cricket was elegant. The most disgraceful behaviour by female cricketers was reported in the *Nottingham Review* of 4 October 1833:

'Last week, at Sileby feast, the women so far forgot themselves as to enter upon a game of cricket, and by their deportment as well as frequent applications to the tankard, they rendered themselves objects such as no husband, brother, parent, or lover could contemplate with any degree of satisfaction.'

The first woman technically to assist the development of cricket was Christina Willes, later Mrs Hodges. It is generally accepted that she originated round-arm bowling *c* 1807 when she practised with her brother John in the barn of their home at Tonford, near Canterbury. Her full skirt of the period made the legitimate bowling style of the times impossible. John, who was to become a squire and sports patron, found round-arm bowling difficult to play, adopted it himself, was the first to be no-balled for employing it in a major match (see 'First Notches – Bowling'), and had the satisfaction of seeing the style made legal six years later in 1828. It was said that

'Willes, his sister and his dog (a retriever?) *could beat any eleven in England'*.

The first woman to be included in the 'Births and Deaths of Cricketers' section of *Wisden Cricketers' Almanack* was Martha Grace (*née* Pocock):

'Grace, Mrs H.M. (mother of W.G., E.M. and G.F.) b July 18, 1812, d July 25, 1884'.

Martha's husband Dr Henry Mills Grace, was a Somerset man who, in 1831 moved to Downend, a village four miles from Bristol, and took over a large general practice. A tremendous cricket enthusiast, he established the Mangotsfield Cricket Club for cricketers in the neighbouring villages, and prepared a cricket pitch for his seven children on the lawn of Downend House. Martha became as keen on the game as her husband and used to coach her sons. She drove her fourth son, William Gilbert – aged nearly six – in her pony-carriage to watch his first game of cricket when William Clarke's All-England Eleven came to Bristol on 22-24 June 1854 to play 22 of West Gloucestershire. The match was arranged by her husband who captained the home side. 'W.G.' wrote in his *Cricketing Reminiscences and Personal Recollections:*

> 'I was with my mother, who sat in her pony-carriage all day. I don't remember much about the cricket, but I recollect that some of the England team played in top hats. My mother was very enthusiastic, and watched every ball. She preserved cuttings of the newspaper reports of this and most other matches, and took great care of the score books. I have several of her scrapbooks, with the cuttings pasted in, and very useful I find them, because in those days "Wisden's Annual" was not in existence, and no proper record was kept.'

Two years later Martha Grace mentioned to George Parr that 'W.G.' would do better than his brother, 'E.M.', because his back play was superior. She attended all the matches she could, watched all the play and often criticized vociferously. Once, after 'W.G.' returned at the end of his innings, she rebuked him: 'Willie, Willie, haven't I told you over and over again how to play that ball?'.

The first women's cricket club, White Heather, was founded at Nun Appelton, Yorkshire, in the summer of 1887 by eight ladies, the majority of aristocratic birth and independent means. The name was derived from the favourite badge of the founders, who adopted colours of pink, white and green for the same reason.

The club's most celebrated cricketer was Lucy Ridsdale, elder daughter of the Assay Master at the Royal Mint. She married Stanley Baldwin, Prime Minister three times between 1923 and 1937 and a fine batsman who averaged 62 in 1892.

The White Heather Club ceased to function as a playing club after the 1950 season.

In 1890 the English Cricket and Athletic Association Limited organized two teams of women cricketers under the title of **'The Original English Lady Cricketers'.** The two teams, the Red XI and the Blue XI, played each other in exhibition matches on many county grounds around England and were the first to play at Headingley, Leeds. The OELC players were specially selected and coached, bowled overarm, and were forbidden to use their real names. Their uniform consisted of a flannel blouse and skirt, adorned round the hem and collar with striped bands of blue (or red) and white braid. A large blue (or red) bow kept in place the sailor collar, and they wore their colours on sashes around their waists. Caps perched on Victorian hair-styles completed their dress. The OELC was disbanded after two seasons.

'The Original English Lady Cricketers' of 1890 whose blouses and skirts were adorned with bands of blue or red.

The 1934-35 England tourists, eleven of whom featured in the first women's match ever to involve an overseas team.

The first tour by a women's cricket team took place in 1926 when a scratch team played on college grounds in Cheltenham and Malvern.

Following that successful first tour a number of its members called a meeting on 4 October 1926 when **the Women's Cricket Association was formed.** Its arms were simply to enable any woman or girl wishing to play cricket to do so, and to play the game with strict order and decorum. The first uniform regulation stipulated that 'WCA teams must play in white or cream. Hats and knickers must be white. Dresses and tunics must not be shorter than touching the ground when kneeling. Sleeveless dresses and transparent stockings are not permitted'.

Others countries followed England's example and official administrations for women's cricket were formed in Australia (1931), New Zealand (1933), Holland (1934), South Africa and Rhodesia (1952), Jamaica (1966), Trinidad and Tobago (1967), India (1973), Barbados (1973) and Grenada (1974).

In 1958 the International Women's Cricket Council (IWCC) was formed to determine tour schedules between member countries.

The first overseas tour by a women's cricket team left Tilbury on the *SS Cathay* on 19 October 1934 bound for Australia and New Zealand. The 15 English players, captained by Betty Archdale, had been selected from those available after trial matches at Old Trafford and Northampton. **The first women's match involving an overseas team** took place on 24 and 26 November 1934 at Perth between Western Australia and England and was drawn. Molly Hide scored **the first century for a touring women's team.**

The first women's Test match was played between Australia and England at Brisbane on 28-31 December 1934, England winning by nine wickets after Myrtle Maclagan (off-breaks) had exploited a sticky wicket to record the remarkable analysis of 17–11–10–7. It remained the Test record until 1958.

The first Test century by a woman was scored in the Second Test at Sydney on 7 January 1935 by Myrtle Maclagan who, opening the innings, made 119 for England on the second day.

Some fifty years after the event she wrote: 'I have so often realized how lucky I was to make the first century in a Test match – that will always stand.' She represented Surrey and England until 1951, and the Army until 1963 when she was 52.

The first women's cricket tour to England was made by Australia in 1937. They defeated England by 31 runs at the County Ground, Northampton on 12-15 June in **the first women's Test played in England.** The tourists were allowed scant opportunity for social licence during the tour as the rules laid down by the Australian WCA ordained that:

No member shall drink, smoke or gamble while on tour.
No girl may be accompanied by her husband, a relation or a friend.
Writing articles on cricket during the tour is strictly forbidden.
While on board ship, no girl shall visit the top deck of the liner after dinner.
Members of the team must retire to bed by 10 pm during the voyage.
Members will do physical drill on deck at 7.15 am daily except on Sundays.
The team will participate in all deck games.

The first women's cricket cricket world cup competition was held in England in 1973 and won by the host country who were captained by Rachael Heyhoe Flint.

The first women's cricket magazine was first published in England in May 1930, price 6d. *Women's Cricket* was founded by **Marjorie Pollard** who had been a member of the first women's cricket tour in 1926. A hockey international who, in 1935, had been described as one of that game's greatest exponents of all time, she became an institution in herself. In 1929 the WCA decided to publish its own paper and Marjorie Pollard had volunteered to produce and edit it. She remained its editor until 1949 when she handed over to Netta Rheinberg and Nancy Joy. As a player Marjorie Pollard was 'a mighty hitter, fine fielder and a resourceful captain. No year went by between 1929 and 1936 when she did not excel at one or other facet of the game.' (Netta Rheinberg in *Fair Play, the Story of Women's Cricket.*) Apart from being **the first public relations and publicity officer for women's cricket,** she was its **first reporter, first broadcaster** and **first commentator.** In 1965 she was awarded the OBE for services to sport.

The elegant off-drive that enabled Myrtle Maclagan to complete the first hundred in Women's Test matches. (Myrtle Maclagan)

Summary of Official Test Match Results

ENGLAND v AUSTRALIA

Season	Venue	Played	England	Australia	Drawn
1934-35	Australia	3	2	–	1
1937	England	3	1	1	1
1948-49	Australia	3	–	1	2
1951	England	3	1	1	1
1957-58	Australia	3	–	–	3
1963	England	3	1	–	2
1968-69	Australia	3	–	–	3
1976	England	3	–	–	3
1984-85	Australia	5	1	2	2
		29	6	5	18

ENGLAND v NEW ZEALAND

Season	Venue	Played	England	New Zealand	Drawn
1934-35	New Zealand	1	1	–	–
1948-49	New Zealand	1	1	–	–
1954	England	3	1	–	2
1957-58	New Zealand	2	–	–	2
1966	England	3	–	–	3
1968-69	New Zealand	3	2	–	1
1984	England	3	–	–	3
		16	5	–	11

ENGLAND v SOUTH AFRICA

Season	Venue	Played	England	South Africa	Drawn
1960-61	South Africa	4	1	–	3

ENGLAND v WEST INDIES

Season	Venue	Played	England	West Indies	Drawn
1979	England	3	2	–	1

ENGLAND v INDIA

Season	Venue	Played	England	India	Drawn
1986	England	3	–	–	3

AUSTRALIA v NEW ZEALAND

Season	Venue	Played	Australia	New Zealand	Drawn
1947-48	New Zealand	1	1	–	–
1956-57	Australia	1	1	–	–
1960-61	New Zealand	1	–	–	1
1971-72	Australia	1	–	1	–
1974-75	New Zealand	1	–	–	1
1978-79	Australia	3	1	–	2
		8	3	1	4

AUSTRALIA v INDIA

Season	Venue	Played	Australia	India	Drawn
1976-77	Australia	1	1	–	–
1983-84	India	4	–	–	4
		5	1	–	4

NEW ZEALAND v SOUTH AFRICA

Season	Venue	Played	New Zealand	South Africa	Drawn
1971-72	South Africa	3	1	–	2

NEW ZEALAND v INDIA

Season	Venue	Played	New Zealand	India	Drawn
1976-77	New Zealand	1	–	–	1
1984-85	India	3	–	–	3
		4	–	–	4

Netta Rheinberg edited *Women's Cricket* until it failed to win its battle against inflation and appeared for the last time in 1967. She was the correspondent on women's cricket in *The Cricketer* from 1959 to 1970 before handing over to Rachael Heyhoe, the current England captain. Netta Rheinberg captained Middlesex for four post-war seasons, was player/manager of the England team which toured Australasia in 1948-49, playing in the First Test. She also managed the 1957-58 touring team to Australasia, became an umpire and was one of the first women to pass the men's ACU examination, and is currently **The Cricket Society's first female vice-chairman.** She has been women's correspondent to *Wisden Cricketers' Almanack* since 1959 and, in 1984, was awarded the MBE for services to women's cricket.

Rachael Heyhoe, who added her husband's name when she married Derrick Flint in 1971, captained England from 1966 until 1977 and never suffered a defeat. A former England hockey international (goalkeeper) and county squash player, she has been an outstanding public relations and publicity officer for women's cricket since succeeding Netta Rheinberg as *The Cricketer's* cor-

respondent in June 1971. She played a major part in the sponsorship of women's cricket, and in its first World Cup in 1973. She was captain of the England team in the WCA Golden Jubilee Match, on the first appearance of women's teams at Lord's on 4 August 1976 when England beat Australia by eight wickets in a 60-overs match. Commentator, broadcaster, after-dinner speaker (she was honoured with the Guild of Toastmasters' Best After-Dinner Speaker Award in 1973), and organizer of charity cricket matches, she was awarded the MBE in 1973 for services to women's cricket.

Women's Test Match Records

TEAM RECORDS

The highest innings total is 503 for 5 declared by England against New Zealand at Christchurch on 16 and 18 February 1935 in the first match between the two countries. The first day's play produced 474 runs with New Zealand being dismissed for 44 and England replying with 430 for 4 wickets.

The highest total in a Test in England is 426 for 9 wickets by India at Blackpool on 3-4 July 1986.

The lowest innings total is 35 by England against Australia on a rain-affected pitch at St Kilda, Melbourne on 22 February 1958. This was in reply to Australia's total of 38.

The lowest total in a Test in England is 63 by New Zealand at Worcester on 5 July 1954.

BATTING RECORDS

The highest individual innings in women's Test cricket is 190 by Sandhya Aggarwal for India at Worcester on 13-14 July 1986. Opening the innings, she scored her runs out of a total of 374, being

Netta Rheinberg.

last out after batting for 563 minutes and hitting 19 fours.

The highest score for England is 189 by E.A. 'Betty' Snowball for England against New Zealand at Christchurch on 16 February 1935 in 222 minutes.

The highest aggregate of runs in a Test career is 1814, average 49.02, with four centuries, in 25 matches by Rachael Heyhoe Flint for England between December 1960 and July 1979. She also hit **the first six in women's Tests** – over long-on against Australia at The Oval on 20 July 1963 – and recorded England's highest individual score in a home Test: 179 against Australia at The Oval on 27-28 July 1976, when an epic innings, lasting 521 minutes and including 30 fours, earned England a famous draw.

BOWLING RECORDS

The best innings analysis in women's Test Cricket is 7 for 6 by Mary Duggan when she captained England against Australia at St Kilda, Melbourne, on 22 February 1958.

The best match analysis is 11 for 16 by Betty Wilson for Australia in the same match. No play was possible on the first day and both teams were dismissed cheaply on a 'sticky' pitch on the second day: Australia 38 (Mary Duggan 7 for 6). England 35 (Betty Wilson 7 for 7 including **the first hat-trick in women's Test cricket**). They are the two lowest totals and the two best analyses in women's Test matches. In the second innings Betty Wilson scored 100 and Australia declared at 202 for 9. England were 76 for 8 when the game ended. Betty Wilson's analysis of 4 for 9 not only gave her the match bowling record, it also enabled her to become **the first cricketer to complete the match double of 100 runs and ten wickets in a Test match.** The first instance in men's Test cricket occured on 14 December 1960.

The best match analysis in a women's Test in England is 11 for 63 by Julia Greenwood against West Indies at Canterbury on 16-18 June 1979 in the first Test match involving a West Indies team.

The most wickets in a Test career is 77, average 13.49, in 17 matches by Mary Duggan for England between 1949 and 1963.

WICKET-KEEPING RECORDS

The records for the most dismissals in an innings, most in a series and most in a career are held by Shirley Hodges of Sussex and England:

Innings: 5 (twice) v New Zealand at Christchurch and Auckland in 1968-69.

Series: 16 (5ct, 11st) in 3 Tests v New Zealand in 1968-69.

Career: 36 (19ct, 17st) in 11 Tests.

Women's Cricket Records in other matches

The highest innings total in any women's match is 567 by Tarana against Rockley at Rockley in New South Wales, Australia, in October 1896.

The record total in England is 410 for 2 declared by the South against the East at Oakham School, Rutland, on 29 May 1982.

The record individual innings in women's cricket is 224 not out in 135 minutes by Mabel Bryant for the Visitors against the Residents at Eastbourne, Sussex, in August 1901.

The highest scored in a Test trial match was recorded by Jan Southgate when she made 201 not out for the South against the East at Oakham School, Rutland, on 29 May 1982. She shared an unbroken third-wicket partnership of 246 with Jackie Court (105 not out).

The highest score in the three World Cup tournaments held in England (1973), India (1978) and New Zealand (1982) is 138 not out in 60 overs by Janette Brittin for England against the International XI at Hamilton on 14 January 1982

There have been two recorded instances of bowlers taking **all ten wickets in women's cricket without conceding a run.** The first to do so was Rubina Humphries, aged 15, for Dalton Ladies against Woodfield Sports Club on 26 June

1931; she also scored all her side's runs. Her 10 for 0 feat was equalled in July 1962 by Rosemary White for Wallington Ladies against Beaconsfield Ladies.

The first tour double in women' cricket was achieved for England by Enid Bakewell (*née* Turton) on the 1968-69 tour of Australia and New Zealand. In 20 matches (eleven in Australia and nine in New Zealand) she scored 1031 runs (average 39.65) and, bowling slow left-arm, took 118 wickets (average 9.77). Playing against a New South Wales XI at Manly, she took a hat-trick, all her victims falling to catches by June Moorhouse at silly mid-off.

The first English cricketer to achieve the Test match double of a century and ten wickets was Enid Bakewell. At Edgbaston on 1-3 July 1979 she carried England to victory by 24 runs in the Third Test against West Indies, scoring 68 and 112 not out, in addition to taking 3 for 14 and 7 for 61. Seven months later, Ian Botham recorded England's first match double in men's Test cricket during the Golden Jubilee Test against India in Bombay.

Women's World Cup competitions

The first Women's World Cup competition was staged in England in June and July 1973 and was the brainchild of Jack Hayward, an English millionaire based in the Bahamas who was a generous patron of women's cricket.

Subsequent competitions have been staged in India (January 1978) and New Zealand (January and February 1982). The tournaments in England and New Zealand followed the regulations of the Prudential Cup and limited each innings to 60 overs. The Indian tournament of 1978 consisted of 50-overs matches, there being fewer daylight hours available.

1973 WORLD CUP IN ENGLAND

Final table	P	W	L	NR	Points
ENGLAND	6	5	1	0	20
Australia	6	4	1	1	17
International XI	6	3	2	1	13
New Zealand	6	3	2	1	13
Trinidad & Tobago	6	2	4	0	8
Jamaica	6	1	4	1	5
Young England	6	1	5	0	4

1978 WORLD CUP IN INDIA

Final table	P	W	L	Points
AUSTRALIA	3	3	0	12
England	3	2	1	8
New Zealand	3	1	2	4
India	3	0	3	0

1982 WORLD CUP IN NEW ZEALAND

Preliminary matches Results table	P	W	T	L	Points
AUSTRALIA	12	11	1	0	46
ENGLAND	12	7	2	3	32
New Zealand	12	6	1	5	26
India	12	4	0	8	16
International XI	12	0	0	12	0

FINAL
7 February. **AUSTRALIA** beat England by 3 wickets at Lancaster Park, Christchurch. England 151-5 (60 overs). Australia 152-7 (59 overs).

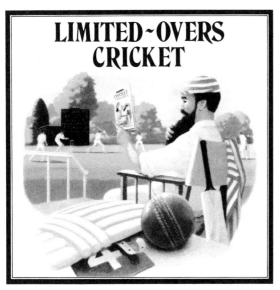

LIMITED-OVERS CRICKET

Arguably the most far-reaching innovation in professional cricket in the last hundred years has been limited-overs one-day cricket.

The reason for its invention was purely financial. Attendances at the only inter-county competition in Britain, the County Championship, had fallen dramatically since the halcyon days immediately after the Hitler War. From two million in 1950 the total attendance at county matches dropped to 700 000 in 1963, the season when the first one-day county competition was introduced. An MCC committee had been set up in 1956 to examine the decline in attendances and the general tempo of the game. It was this committee, under the chairmanship of H.S. Altham, which proposed a one-day knock-out tournament.

The revolutionary concept was certainly not palatable to many adminstrators either at Lord's or around the counties, but the desperate financial position of county cricket dictated urgent action.

The Midlands Knock-Out Cup

In 1962 a pilot scheme, sponsored by Leicestershire at the instigation of their secretary, Michael Turner, and featuring four counties, was held at Leicester and Nottingham in May. Each innings was restricted to 65 overs and no bowler could

deliver more than 15 of them. Three matches were played. Leicestershire beat Derbyshire to reach the final against Northamptonshire who had beaten Nottinghamshire by 31 runs. In the final no limit was placed on the number of overs permitted to each bowler. This led to slow bowlers having scant say in the proceedings and was swiftly remedied when the rules of the knock-out cup proper were drafted. Northamptonshire defeated Leicestershire on their Grace Road Ground to become the first (and last) holders of the Midlands Knock-Out Cup.

Limited-overs cricket had been born. Traditionalists were alarmed – many still are. Sir Neville Cardus wanted it called 'Snicket' or 'Slogget' – anything but Cricket.

The first balls in 'instant cricket' were bowled at Grace Road, Leicester by Les Jackson to Maurice Hallam, and, at Trent Bridge, Nottingham, by John Cotton to Mick Norman, at 11am on 2 May 1962.

The first 50 in limited-overs cricket was scored by the Leicestershire opener, Maurice Hallam. His score of 86 on that first historic morning remained the highest in one-day county cricket until Peter Marner scored **the first limited-overs century:** 121 for Lancashire against Leicestershire at Manchester in the preliminary round of the Gillette Cup on 1 May 1963. Hallam scored the second hundred on the following day. Ironically he had won the toss and elected to field.

The first wicket in limited-overs county cricket was taken by Nottinghamshire's opening bowler, John Cotton. His victim was Mick Norman, then playing for Northamptonshire, who registered **the first duck**. He was caught by wicket-keeper Geoff Millman who thereby made **the first catch.**

The Knock-Out Cup

GILLETTE CUP/NATWEST TROPHY

The Knock-out Competition proper (Wisden Cricketers' Almanack declined to call it the Gillette Cup in its review of that first season) began with a preliminary match between Lancashire and Leicestershire at Old Trafford, Manchester, on 1 May 1963. Rain held up the start of the new competition for three hours, thus ensuring that it was the first one-day match to involve overtime. **The first Man of the Match award** in the Gillette Cup (or in any national competition) was won by Peter Marner who scored 121 and took 3 for 49 in his side's 101 runs victory. Lancashire did not re-engage him after the next season and he moved to Leicestershire.

Lancashire reached the semi-finals only to contribute to **the earliest finish** in these contests. Bowled out for 59 in 95 minutes they lost by ten wickets after just 2 hours 10 minutes of play. That early closing time of 2.20pm was emulated at Westcliff-on-Sea in 1972 when Essex disposed of Middlesex with equal brevity.

The first Lord's Cup Final was held on Saturday, 7 September 1963 on a day of cloud and drizzle, but one which offered much excitement to a capacity crowd of over 25 000. Sussex elected to bat on a soft pitch and were all out for 168 in 60.2 overs. England wicket-keeper Jim Parks, whose son Bobby is now Hampshire's occupant of that post, contributed 57 – **the first half-century in a cup final.** The next highest score was 34. Norman Gifford, currently captain of Warwickshire, took 4 for 33 in 15 overs of left-arm spin and was judged **the first Man of the Match in a Lord's final. The first cup final adjudicators** were Herbert Sutcliffe, Frank Woolley and H.S. Altham (absent ill). When Sutcliffe and Woolley disagreed, the Duke of Norfolk and S.C. Griffith were asked to judge. They also disagreed and the ultimate judgment was made by Gordon Ross who had conceived the idea of a match award for these one-day games. Worcestershire made a valiant effort to acquire 2.5 runs per over as the light deteriorated. When Ted Dexter brought back his fast bowlers four wickets fell for five runs and, at 133 for 9, 36 runs were needed from the last pair. A belligerent innings from Roy Booth (33 not out) caused Dexter to position every available fielder on the boundary and he had taken the total to 154 when his partner was run out, leaving Sussex **the first holders of the Gillette Cup.**

In all subsequent years the length of each side's innings has been restricted to 60 overs, with 12 being the current personal limit for each bowler. The top five minor counties in the previous season's table were first included in 1964. Since

Norman Gifford – first Man of the Match in a Lord's Final. (Sport & General)

1983 the competition, sponsored from 1981 by the National Westminister Bank and played for the NatWest Trophy, has included the top 13 minor counties as well as Ireland and Scotland – 32 teams in all. Apart from a manic experiment in 1982 which involved a 10am start, the only major changes in the oldest limited-overs competition have involved its sponsor and restrictions on field-placing. The latter involve a minimum of six players, including bowler and wicket-keeper, being within a specific area (bounded by two semi-circles centred on each middle stump and with a radius of 30 yards, and joined by a parallel line on each side of the pitch), at the instant of delivery. Under this regulation Alvin Kallicharran recorded **the highest score in any limited-overs match in Britain:** 206 for Warwickshire against Oxfordshire at Edgbaston in 1984.

GILLETTE CUP WINNERS

Season	Champions	Losing Finalists	Victory Margin
1963	SUSSEX	Worcestershire	14 runs
1964	SUSSEX	Warwickshire	8 wickets
1965	YORKSHIRE	Surrey	175 runs
1966	WARWICKSHIRE	Worcestershire	5 wickets
1967	KENT	Somerset	32 runs
1968	WARWICKSHIRE	Sussex	4 wickets
1969	YORKSHIRE	Derbyshire	69 runs
1970	LANCASHIRE	Sussex	6 wickets
1971	LANCASHIRE	Kent	24 runs
1972	LANCASHIRE	Warwickshire	4 wickets
1973	GLOUCESTERSHIRE	Sussex	40 runs
1974	KENT	Lancashire	4 wickets
1975	LANCASHIRE	Middlesex	7 wickets
1976	NORTHAMPTONSHIRE	Lancashire	4 wickets
1977	MIDDLESEX	Glamorgan	5 wickets
1978	SUSSEX	Somerset	5 wickets
1979	SOMERSET	Northamptonshire	45 runs
1980	MIDDLESEX	Surrey	7 wickets

NATWEST TROPHY WINNERS

1981	DERBYSHIRE	Northamptonshire	Tied†
1982	SURREY	Warwickshire	9 wickets
1983	SOMERSET	Kent	24 runs
1984	MIDDLESEX	Kent	4 wickets
1985	ESSEX	Nottinghamshire	1 run
1986	SUSSEX	Lancashire	7 wickets

† *Derbyshire (235-6) beat Northamptonshire (235-9) by losing fewer wickets in a tied match.*
The winners scored the equalizing run off the last possible ball when Geoff Miller sprinted and
dived to complete the leg-bye – arguably the fastest 'extra' ever taken.

HUNDREDS IN KNOCK-OUT CUP FINALS

G. Boycott	146	Yorkshire v Surrey	1965
C.H. Lloyd	126	Lancashire v Warwickshire	1972
I.V.A. Richards	117	Somerset v Northants	1979
G. Cook	111	Northants v Derbyshire	1981
B.R. Hardie	110	Essex v Notts	1985

Geoffrey Boycott's innings of 146 is the highest in any Lord's Final.

FIVE WICKETS IN KNOCK-OUT CUP FINALS

J. Garner	6-29	Somerset v Northants	1979
R. Illingworth	5-29	Yorkshire v Surrey	1965

HIGHEST TOTAL IN A KNOCK-OUT CUP FINAL

317-4	Yorkshire v Surrey	1965

LOWEST TOTAL IN A KNOCK-OUT CUP FINAL

118	Lancashire v Kent	1974

NO CUP FINAL APPEARANCES

Only two counties – Hampshire and Leicestershire – have failed to reach the final of the Knock-Out Cup. Hampshire are alone in not appearing in ANY cup final at Lord's.

The scene at a packed Lord's in September 1963 when Sussex met Worcestershire in the first Cup Final. (Sport & General)

The Sunday League

JOHN PLAYER LEAGUE

A second limited-overs competition was introduced in 1969 and it remains the only one-day county competition which cannot be extended into a second or third day in the case of inclement weather. It is also the only one in which bowlers have the distance of their run-ups restricted and the only one in which a tie stands as an acceptable result.

It came about largely because of the success of a private promotion sponsored by Rothman's. The Rothmans 'Cavaliers', comprising great players of the past and present from all cricketing countries, played against a different professional county side each Sunday afternoon, often in aid of that county's beneficiary. The matches were designed to last for two hours each innings and were an ideal package for BBC2 television. The popularity of these matches grew steadily each season. From their humble beginnings in 1962 when they played untelevised matches on village greens and at small clubs, through their early televised days in 1965 (total attendance 34000; total money collected £4100), the Cavaliers had blossomed to such proportions in 1967 (total attendance 114000; total money collected £13500), that they had attracted a bigger audience during the season than either the county champions (Yorkshire – 83000) or runners-up (Kent – 76000).

After the 1967 season the counties decided to institute a Sunday League of their own and, in the following year, the newly-formed TCCB appointed their secretary, S.C. Griffith, to negotiate contracts with a sponsor and television. Rothmans' rival tobacco firm, John Player and Sons, won the scramble for sponsorship and the BBC won the broadcasting contract. Both had been considerably heartened by seeing the crowd at Edgbaston one June Sunday of 1968 when Tom Cartwright's benefit fund was swelled by the sum of £3295.

The John Player League has become an accepted part of the English season. Each county plays its 16 opponents once in a 40-overs game, less if the weather reduces the time available, the minimum being the farcical 10-overs slog. It has attracted a considerable following of its own, although a private survey carried out during the competi-

John Arlott, OBE.

tion's first eight seasons showed that only a small proportion of the Sunday League following also attended championship or Test matches, and vice versa. No matter. Sunday cricket has brought much benefit to the TCCB's exchequer and given tremendous entertainment value. Sadly it has not been possible since 1981 to watch an entire match on television each summer Sunday afternoon. In the present format, cricket is slotted in with two or three other sports and sometimes omitted altogether. Possibly this change of coverage resulted from John Arlott's retirement from all commentary boxes after the 1980 season. He could always be relied upon for original and witty comments, even if very little action was worthy of description. Once, when Worcestershire were fielding in that most delightful of cathedral settings, John asked the producer to pan a camera on to the only overseas player on view, Ivan Johnson. A brilliant schoolboy allrounder whilst at Malvern, Johnson had just come into the county side. His dusky West Indian complexion was surrounded by a generous crop of hair including a beard and moustache. 'There he is,' captioned Arlott, 'Ivan Johnson. Comes from the Bahamas. You can tell him from the rest. He's got one sleeve rolled higher than the other!'

JOHN PLAYER LEAGUE CHAMPIONS

1969	Lancashire	1978	Hampshire
1970	Lancashire	1979	Somerset
1971	Worcestershire	1980	Warwickshire
1972	Kent	1981	Essex
1973	Kent	1982	Sussex
1974	Leicestershire	1983	Yorkshire
1975	Hampshire	1984	Essex
1976	Kent	1985	Essex
1977	Leicestershire	1986	Hampshire

In 1982 Sussex established new records by winning 14 of their 16 matches and totalling 58 points. They lost to Worcestershire by three wickets with an over to spare and the other match was abandoned without a ball bowled.

Imperial Tobacco ended their sponsorship after the 1986 season and were succeeded by Refuge Assurance.

The League Cup
BENSON AND HEDGES CUP

Britain's third county limited-overs competition was introduced in 1972. The 17 first-class counties, supplemented by two select minor counties sides and Cambridge University, were divided into four regions of five teams. Each played the other four once and the top two qualified for the knock-out stage of the competition, which culminated in a July final at Lord's. The playing conditions were exactly the same as for the (then) Gillette Cup, except that each innings was limited to 55 overs and each individual bowler to eleven overs.

The competition has undergone only superficial changes, whereby the counties have been shuffled around in their mini-leagues or groups and the three extra sides have at times included Oxford University, a full Minor Counties XI, Scotland and Ireland. Since 1980 the three 'extra' teams have been Scotland, Combined Universities and Minor Counties. From 1987 cricketers from all universities, not just Cambridge and Oxford, were eligible for the combined eleven.

The restriction on field-placing was introduced to all limited-overs cricket in 1982 following a trial in the Benson and Hedges Cup in 1981. It stated: 'At the instant of delivery, a minimum of four fieldsmen (plus the bowler and wicket-keeper) must be within an area bounded by two semi-circles centred on each middle stump (each with a radius of 30 yards) and joined by a parallel line on each side of the pitch. In the event of an infringement, the square-leg umpire shall call "No Ball".'

It immediately found favour with players and administrators. Ultra-defensive field-placings, involving nine or even ten men around the boundary in the closing stages of an innings, were no longer possible. Undefended spaces in the outfield prompted intriguing tactical battles between the batsmen and the opposition captain and bowlers.

BENSON AND HEDGES CUP WINNERS

Season	Champions	Losing Finalists	Victory Margin
1972	LEICESTERSHIRE	Yorkshire	5 wickets
1973	KENT	Worcestershire	39 runs
1974	SURREY	Leicestershire	27 runs
1975	LEICESTERSHIRE	Middlesex	5 wickets
1976	KENT	Worcestershire	43 runs
1977	GLOUCESTERSHIRE	Kent	64 runs
1978	KENT	Derbyshire	6 wickets
1979	ESSEX	Surrey	35 runs
1980	NORTHAMPTONSHIRE	Essex	6 runs
1981	SOMERSET	Surrey	7 wickets
1982	SOMERSET	Nottinghamshire	9 wickets
1983	MIDDLESEX	Essex	4 runs
1984	LANCASHIRE	Warwickshire	6 wickets
1985	LEICESTERSHIRE	Essex	5 wickets
1986	MIDDLESEX	Kent	2 runs

HUNDREDS IN LEAGUE CUP FINALS

I.V.A. Richards	132*	Somerset v Surrey	1981
G.A. Gooch	120	Essex v Surrey	1979

FIVE WICKETS IN LEAGUE CUP FINALS

J. Garner	5-14	Somerset v Surrey	1981

HAT-TRICK IN LEAGUE CUP FINALS

K. Higgs	4-10	Leicestershire v Surrey	1974

HIGHEST TOTAL IN LEAGUE CUP FINALS

290-6	Essex v Surrey	1979

LOWEST TOTAL IN LEAGUE CUP FINALS

130	Nottinghamshire v Somerset	1982

NO CUP FINAL APPEARANCES

Three counties – Glamorgan, Hampshire and Sussex – have yet to reach the League Cup final.

Highest aggregates in a season of limited-overs cricket

Matches for those competitions in which only four counties participate (Fenner Trophy, Tilcon Trophy, and Asda Challenge) are excluded. Performances in one-day internationals (Prudential Cup, Prudential Trophy and Texaco Trophy) are included.

1000 RUNS	County	Season	M	I	NO	HS	Runs	Average	100	50
G.A. Gooch	Essex	1985	24	24	4	171	1432	71.60	3	12
C.G. Greenidge	Hampshire	1983	27	27	4	162*	1208	52.52	4	6
I.V.A. Richards	Somerset	1983	29	26	4	119	1177	53.50	2	8
G.A. Gooch	Essex	1979	24	24	3	138	1137	54.14	3	6
A.I. Kallicharran	Warwickshire	1984	26	24	1	206	1131	49.17	3	8
K.S. McEwan	Essex	1980	25	25	3	136	1116	50.72	3	6
C.J. Tavaré	Kent	1983	25	25	3	122*	1114	50.63	1	8
B.W. Luckhurst	Kent	1974	25	24	2	129*	1055	47.95	3	8
G.A. Gooch	Essex	1983	21	21	1	176	1048	52.40	3	4
D.I. Gower	Leicestershire	1982	20	19	3	115	1036	64.75	3	6
B.C. Broad	Nottinghamshire	1986	24	24	2	104*	1011	45.95	2	5
Zaheer Abbas	Gloucestershire	1983	22	20	4	158	1003	62.68	3	6

50 WICKETS	County	Season	O	M	R	W	Average	5wkt	Best
R.J. Clapp	Somerset	1974	192.1	21	811	51	15.90	1	5-38
W.W. Daniel	Middlesex	1980	212.2	30	700	51	13.72	1	6-15

MOST ECONOMICAL BOWLING	County	Season	O	M	R	W	Runs/Over
J.K. Lever	Essex	1972	250	28	510	43	2.04

MOST DISMISSALS	County	Season	Dis	Ct	St
J.T. Murray	Middlesex	1975	44	36	8

MOST CATCHES BY A FIELDER	County	Season	Ct
C.J. Tavaré	Kent	1978	18

Records for the three national limited-overs competitions

Competition title	National Westminster Bank Trophy *(Originally the GILLETTE CUP)*	Benson and Hedges Cup	John Player Leage
Innings overs limit	60 overs	55 overs	40 overs
Season instituted	1963 Gillette Cup; 1981 NatWest Trohpy	1972	1969
Highest total	392-5 (60 overs) Warwickshire v Oxfordshire, Birmingham 1984	350-3 (55 overs) Essex v Combined Universities, Chelmsford 1979	310-5 (40 overs) Essex v Glamorgan, Southend 1983
Highest total batting second	306-6 (59.3 overs) Gloucestershire v Leicestershire, Leicester 1983	294-7 (55 overs) Gloucestershire v Somerset, Taunton 1982	301-6 (39.3 overs) Warwickshire v Essex, Colchester 1982
Lowest total	39 (26.4 overs) Ireland v Sussex, Hove 1985	56 (26.2 overs) Leicestershire v Minor Counties, Wellington 1982	23 (19.4 overs) Middlesex v Yorkshire, Leeds 1974
Highest individual score	206 A.I. Kallicharran, Warwickshire v Oxfordshire, Birmingham 1984	198* G.A. Gooch, Essex v Sussex, Hove 1982	176 G.A. Gooch, Essex v Glamorgan, Southend 1983
Highest partnership	286 (2nd wkt) I.S. Anderson and A. Hill, Derbyshire v Cornwall, Derby 1986	285* (2nd wkt) C.G. Greenidge and D.R. Turner, Hampshire v Minor Counties (South), Amersham 1973	273 (2nd wkt) G.A. Gooch and K.S. McEwan, Essex v Nottinghamshire, Nottingham 1983
Best bowling analysis	7-15 A.L. Dixon, Kent v Surrey, The Oval 1967	7-12 W.W. Daniel, Middlesex v Minor Counties (East), Ipswich 1978	8-26 K.D. Boyce, Essex v Lancashire, Manchester 1971
Wicket-keeping – most dismissals (match)	6 (5 ct, 1st) R.W. Taylor, Derbyshire v Essex, Derby 1981 6 (4ct, 2 st) T. Davies, Glamorgan v Staffordshire, Stone 1986	8 (8 ct) D.J.S. Taylor, Somerset v Combined Universities, Taunton 1982	7 (6 ct, 1 st) R.W. Taylor, Derbyshire v Lancashire, Manchester 1975
Fielding – most catches (match)	4 A.S. Brown, Gloucestershire v Middlesex, Bristol 1963 4 G. Cook, Northamptonshire v Glamorgan, Northampton 1972 4 C.G. Greenidge, Hampshire v Cheshire, Southampton 1981 4 D.C. Jackson, Durham v Northamptonshire, Darlington 1984 4 T.S. Smith, Hertfordshire v Somerset, St Albans 1984	5 V.J. Marks, Combined Universities v Kent, Oxford 1976	5 J.M. Rice, Hampshire v Warwickshire, Southampton 1978

above, Alvin
Kallicharran completed
the only double-century
in English limited-overs
cricket.
(NatWest/Bill Smith)
left, Roy Marshall
scored the fastest
Gillette Cup hundred.
(NatWest/Bill Smith)

David Gower whose 158 against New Zealand remains England's highest one-day innings.
(NatWest/Bill Smith)

John Edrich won the first match award in a one-day international. (Bill Smith)

Limited-Overs Internationals

The first one-day international was a hastily-arranged affair, played to appease the disappointed public on the final scheduled day of a rain-aborted Test match between Australia and England at Melbourne on 5 January 1971. By co-incidence, the match not only took place on the very ground where Test cricket had begun 94 years earlier, but also resulted in an Australian victory against England. More significantly it attracted 46 000 spectators, produced receipts of $33 000, and began a revolution in international cricket.

The first international man of the match was John Edrich, the Surrey and England opening batsman who scored 82 – **the first fifty in a one-day international.**

The first adjudicator was Charles Elliott, the former Derbyshire batsman and Test umpire who was in Australia on a Churchill Fellowship.

The first ball in these matches was bowled by Graham McKenzie to Geoffrey Boycott. **The first** bowler to take a wicket at this level was Jeff Thomson, who had Boycott caught by Bill Lawry.

When Australia toured England the following year, three limited-overs internationals replaced the extra (Sixth) Test previously agreed by the respective Boards.

The first century in limited-overs internationals was scored by Dennis Amiss for England against Australia at Old Trafford on 24 August 1972.

The first bowler to take five wickets in a one-day international was Dennis Lillee – for Australia against Pakistan at Headingley on 7 June 1975 in the first World Cup.

In Australia, the influence of television magnate Kerry Packer produced the dramatic advent of floodlit cricket, with such attendant innovations as white balls, black sightscreens, and coloured clothing. Skilful marketing of this instant formula produced a headlong proliferation of tournaments. The 1984-85 season saw the quite staggering total of 31 limited-overs internationals being staged in Australia during a period of just nine weeks.

Limited-overs International Records (1970-71 to 1986)

Highest Total	338-5	Pakistan v Sri Lanka	Swansea	1983
Lowest Total	45	Canada v England	Manchester	1979
Lowest Total Batting Second	297-6	New Zealand v England	Adelaide	1982-83
Highest Aggregate	626	Pakistan v Sri Lanka	Swansea	1983
Lowest Aggregate	91	England v Canada	Manchester	1979
Tied Match		Australia v West Indies	Melbourne	1983-84

Highest Individual Score for each Country

189*	I.V.A. Richards	West Indies v England	Manchester	1984
175*	Kapil Dev	India v Zimbabwe	Tunbridge Wells	1983
171*	G.M. Turner	New Zealand v East Africa	Birmingham	1975
158	D.I. Gower	England v New Zealand	Brisbane	1982-83
138*	G.S. Chappell	Australia v New Zealand	Sydney	1980-81
123	Zaheer Abbas	Pakistan v Sri Lanka	Lahore	1981-82
121	R.L. Dias	Sri Lanka v India	Bangalore	1982-83

Highest Partnership for each Wicket

1st	193	G.A. Gooch, C.W.J. Athey	England v New Zealand	Manchester	1986
2nd	221	C.G. Greenidge, I.V.A. Richards	West Indies v India	Jamshedpur	1983-84
3rd	224*	D.M. Jones, A.R. Border	Australia v Sri Lanka	Adelaide	1984-85
4th	157*	R.B. Kerr, D.M. Jones	Australia v England	Melbourne	1984-85
5th	152	I.V.A. Richards, C.H. Lloyd	West Indies v Sri Lanka	Brisbane	1984-85
6th	144	Imran Khan, Shahid Mahboob	Pakistan v Sri Lanka	Leeds	1983
7th	108	Ramiz Raja, Anil Dalpat	Pakistan v New Zealand	Christchurch	1984-85
8th	68	B.E. Congdon, B.L. Cairns	New Zealand v England	Scarborough	1978
9th	126*	Kapil Dev, S.M.H. Kirmani	India v Zimbabwe	Tunbridge Wells	1983
10th	106*	I.V.A. Richards, M.A. Holding	West Indies v England	Manchester	1984

Best Bowling Analyses for each Country

7-15	W.W. Davis	West Indies v Australia	Leeds	1983
6-14	G.J. Gilmour	Australia v England	Leeds	1975
6-14	Imran Khan	Pakistan v India	Sharjah	1984-85
5-20	V.J. Marks	England v New Zealand	Wellington	1983-84
5-23	R.O. Collinge	New Zealand v India	Christchurch	1975-76
5-26	U.S.H. Karnain	Sri Lanka v New Zealand	Moratuwa	1983-84
5-43	Kapil Dev	India v Australia	Nottingham	1983

Hat-Tricks

Jalaluddin	Pakistan v Australia	Hyderabad	1982-83
B.A. Reid	Australia v New Zealand	Sydney	1985-86

Wicket-keeping – Most Dismissals

5	(5ct)	R.G. de Alwis	Sri Lanka v Australia	Colombo (SO)	1982-83
5	(5ct)	S.M.H. Kirmani	India v Zimbabwe	Leicester	1983
5	(5ct)	R.W. Marsh	Australia v England	Leeds	1981
5	(3ct, 2st)	S. Viswanath	India v England	Sydney	1984-85

Fielding – Most Catches

4	Salim Malik	Pakistan v New Zealand	Sialkot	1984-85
4	S.M. Gavaskar	India v Pakistan	Sharjah	1984-85

THE WORLD CUP

Sponsored by Prudential Assurance, this competition was first held in 1975. It was the first attempt at organizing a world cup for cricket since the rain-ruined Triangular Test Match Tournament of 1912. Blessed by the ultimate in fine weather – not a minute of play was lost during 15 matches spread over as many days – and culminating in a rousing final played before a packed and sun-drenched Lord's on the longest day of the year, the inaugural tournament was an unqualified success. That final, which entertained from 11 am until 8.43 pm, not only made a repeat competition mandatory – subsequently they have been staged at four-year intervals – but it also marked the acceptance of one-day limited-overs cricket at international level by players, spectators and, most importantly, cricket's administrators.

Prudential sponsored similar World Cup tournaments in 1979 and 1983, the latter producing one of cricket's most sensational giant-killing epics when a rank outsider – India – defeated the firm favourites, West Indies, in another enthralling final.

The 1987 competition, sponsored by Reliance Industrial, a Bombay textile company, will be held simultaneously in India and Pakistan in October and November. The semi-finals will be played at Lahore and Bombay, and Eden Gardens, Calcutta, will have the honour of staging the final.

WORLD CUP RECORDS 1975-83

Highest total	338-5	Pakistan v Sri Lanka	Swansea	1983
Highest total batting second	288-9	Sri Lanka v Pakistan	Swansea	1983
Lowest total	45	Canada v England	Manchester	1979
Highest match aggregate	626	Pakistan v Sri Lanka	Swansea	1983
Lowest match aggregate	91	Canada (45) v England (46-1)	Manchester	1979
Biggest victories	10 wickets	India beat East Africa	Leeds	1975
	10 wickets	West Indies beat Zimbabwe	Birmingham	1983
	202 runs	England beat India	Lord's	1975
Narrowest victories	1 wicket	West Indies beat Pakistan *(with 2 balls to spare)*	Birmingham	1975
	9 runs	England beat New Zealand	Manchester	1979
Highest individual score	175*	Kapil Dev, India v Zimbabwe	Tunbridge Wells	1983
Hundred before lunch		A. Turner (101), Australia v West Indies	Oval	1975

Highest partnership for each wicket

Wkt	Runs				
1st	182	R.B. McCosker, A. Turner	Australia v Sri Lanka	Oval	1975
2nd	176	D.L. Amiss, K.W.R. Fletcher	England v India	Lord's	1975
3rd	195*	C.G. Greenidge, H.A. Gomes	West Indies v Zimbabwe	Worcester	1983
4th	149	R.B. Kanhai, C.H. Lloyd	West Indies v Australia	Lord's	1975
5th	139	I.V.A. Richards, C.L. King	West Indies v England	Lord's	1979
6th	144	Imran Khan, Shahid Mahboob	Pakistan v Sri Lanka	Leeds	1983
7th	75*	D.A.G. Fletcher, I.P. Butchart	Zimbabwe v Australia	Nottingham	1983
8th	62	Kapil Dev, Madan Lal	India v Zimbabwe	Tunbridge Wells	1983
9th	126*	Kapil Dev, S.M.H. Kirmani	India v Zimbabwe	Tunbridge Wells	1983
10th	71	A.M.E. Roberts, J. Garner	West Indies v India	Manchester	1983

Best bowling	7-51	W.W. Davis, West Indies v Australia	Leeds	1983
Most economical bowling	12-8-6-1	B.S. Bedi, India v East Africa	Leeds	1975
Most expensive bowling	12-1-105-2	M.C. Snedden, New Zealand v England	The Oval	1983
Wicket-keeping–most dismissals	5	S.M.H. Kirmani, India v Zimbabwe	Leicester	1983
Fielding–most catches	3	C.H. Lloyd, West Indies v Sri Lanka	Manchester	1975

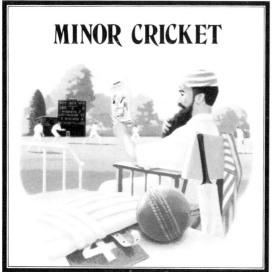

MINOR CRICKET

In theory all cricket matches which are not termed 'First-Class' have to be classified under the heading of 'Minor Cricket'. If we accept that modern first-class cricket began in 1864 when over-arm bowling was legalized, then technically all cricket before that year was 'minor'. That certainly was not the case. In 1981 the Association of Cricket Statisticians published *A Guide to Important Cricket Matches Played in the British Isles 1709-1863*, which effectively begins with the first county match on record: Kent v Surrey ar Dartford Brent on 29 June 1709. Although there are records of more than 700 'important' matches being played in the 18th century, playing conditions were so far removed from the modern game that it would be absurd to include them in records of first-class cricket. A much stronger case can be made for including all Great Matches played since 1815 when the end of the Napoleonic Wars heralded the rebirth of matches involving England, MCC and the county organizations of the day.

'Minor Cricket' is a general classification for the game at school, college, university (apart from Oxbridge), village and town club, military services, diocesan and minor county levels. It can encompass any match which does not warrant the status of first-class, great or important.

The sheer volume of minor cricket has made this area of the game a minefield for historians and statisticians. In many cases records were either not kept or have been destroyed. In listing the most important records for Minor Cricket, there can be no claim that, at some time somewhere in the world, they have not been equalled or surpassed. They are the best performances that are on record.

Batting records and outstanding performances

The highest individual innings in all cricket is 628 not out by Arthur Edward Jeune Collins, who was then a 13-year-old schoolboy at Clifton College in Bristol. Playing in a Junior house match for Clarke's (now Poole's) House against North Town, he batted for 6 hours 50 minutes spread over 5 afternoons on 22, 23, 26, 27, 28 June 1899. Opening the innings, he carried his bat throughout a total of 836 all out and hit 1 six, 4 fives, 31 fours, 33 threes, 146 twos and 87 singles. The scorer gave his total as '628 – plus or minus 20, shall we say'. Collins completed the match double by taking seven wickets in the first innings and another four in the second as his house romped home by an innings and 688 runs.

Born in India in 1885, Collins was in the Clifton XI of 1901 and 1902. Joining the Army, he was gazetted Second Lieutenant in 1904 and promoted to Lieutenant in 1907. In 1912 he scored 58 and 36 at Lord's for the Royal Engineers against the Royal Artillery. A year later he was killed in action in Flanders.

G.V.W. (Gerald) Lukehurst (Kent 2nd XI), scored **six consecutive not out hundreds** for Gore Court C.C. and F. Day's XI between 3 July and 20 July 1955, when aged 37.

Greg Beacroft scored 268 (29 sixes and 11 fours) in 92 minutes for Yass Wallaroos against Williamsdale at Canberra, Australia, on 21 January 1979, the day after his 21st birthday.

The fastest recorded double century came off only 58 balls – many of which went over a cliff on the Channel Island of Alderney on 19 June 1983. Playing for Alderney against Sun Alliance, David Whatmore scored 210 off 61 balls, including 25 sixes and 12 fours. His first hundred was made off

33 balls and his second off only 25.

D.G. (later Sir Donald) Bradman scored **a century off 22 balls in three overs** at Blackheath, New South Wales, a Blue Mountains town some 60 miles west of Sydney, on 3 November 1931. Playing for Blackheath against Lithgow in a match to celebrate the opening of an experimental malthoid pitch, Bradman, having scored 38 off the first over he received, later produced the following record-breaking sequence: 66424461/64466464/ *661*446 (*singles scored by his partner, Wendell Bill).

V.F.S (Vivian) Crawford of Surrey, scored **a century in 19 minutes** at Cane Hill, Surrey on 16 September 1899 when he was 20 years old.

S.K ('Shunter') Coen of Western Province, Orange Free State, Griqualand West and South Africa (two Tests against England in 1927-28) scored **50 runs in 7 minutes** for Gezira against the RAF in 1942. Then in his 40th year, he made all his runs in boundaries – 11 fours and a six.

Lt (later Lt-Col) Philip Mitford ran **eleven runs from one scoring stroke**, without the aid of overthrows, when playing in a Governor's Cup match in Malta on 28 May 1903.

In 1923 two naval cadets scored **174 runs in 33 minutes,** an average of over five runs per minute. K.A. Sellar (now Cdr 'Monkey' Sellar, DSO, DSC, RN) and L.K.A. Block (later Judge Block, DSC) were playing for the Royal Naval College, Dartmouth against Seale Hayne Agricultural College.

The most sixes hit off successive balls on record is nine. C.I.J. ('Jim') Smith of Wiltshire, Middlesex and England, achieved this feat in 1935 while playing for a Middlesex XI against Harrow and District at Rayner's Lane, Harrow. That season 'Big Jim' hit 50 in 14 minutes against Kent at The Mote, Maidstone, and he was to reduce that time by 3 minutes against Gloucestershire in 1938. A renowned hitter, he frequently peppered the area between the Old Tavern and 'Q' Stand at Lord's, including blows that reached St John's Wood Road.

Smith's feat was equalled in Cairo, Egypt, in 194243 by A.D. (Dudley) Nourse, the backbone of both Natal and South African batting for two decades. Playing for a South African XI against the Military Police, his nine consecutive six-hits

Jim Smith, legendary smiter, who once hit nine sixes off successive balls.

included six in one over.

Major (now Brigadier) W.M.E (Michael) White scored **two seperate hundreds on the same day** (23 July 1949) for Aldershot Services against the MCC at the Officers' Club Ground, Aldershot. After bowling unchanged throughout the MCC first innings and taking 4 for 85 in 41 overs, White had scored one run at the end of the first day's play. His innings of 112 (3 sixes and 24 fours) enabled the Services side to recover from 123 for 7 to 283 all out – a first innings lead of one run. His second century of the day carried his side to six-wicket victory against the clock. After reaching three figures in 90 minutes, White took his score to 120 not out, and won the match with two successive boundaries. Two years earlier Mike White had marked his county debut for Northamptonshire by taking three wickets in six balls on two occasions, one in each Somerset innings. He is currently President of the 'Incogs' – Incogniti Incognitis *('Unknown only to the unknown').*

The world record for most runs in one over is 62. This extraordinary feat was achieved in a Queensland country match in 1968-69. H. Morley struck 9 sixes and 2 fours off an over from R. Grubb which included four no-balls.

The world record partnership for any wicket is 641. This was established in Australia on 19 March 1914 when T. Patten (408) and N. Rippon (321) came together for Buffalo River's third wicket against Whorouly at Gapsted, Victoria.

The longest recorded time in which a batsman has failed to score is 100 minutes. Playing for the Gentlemen of Leicestershire against the Free Foresters at Oakham, Rutland, on 19 August 1963, Ian Balfour was marooned on five for his record period. He emerged from his hibernation to score another 34 runs.

Bowling records and outstanding performances

The feat of taking all 20 wickets in a match is not unique. **The first recorded instance of a bowler taking all ten wickets twice in the same match and bowling all his victims** occurred in 1881-82 in a minor match at Bendigo, New South Wales. The bowler was F.R. 'The Demon' Spofforth, whose cut and swerve at fast-medium pace had bowled Australia to victory at The Oval in 1882 and brought about 'The Ashes'.

This feat was emulated by J. Bryant (Erskine v Deaf Mutes in Melbourne on 15 and 22 October 1887) and by Albert Rimmer (Linwood School v Cathedral Grammar School at Canterbury, New Zealand, in December 1925).

W.H. ('Bill') Chinnery took all ten wickets twice for the Essex club of Orsett, on 15 and 22 May 1943 in consecutive matches against Jurgens CC and Hornchurch CC.

The only recorded instance of a bowler taking all ten wickets, all bowled, for no runs was achieved by Jennings Tune on 6 May 1922. He completed this dream rout in just five overs at Cliffe, Yorkshire, while playing for Cliffe against Eastrington in the Howden and District League.

In an inter-divisional Ships' Shield match at Purfleet, Essex, on 17 May 1924, J.W. Brockley, aged 17, took all ten wickets, clean bowled, for two runs in eleven balls, including a triple hat-trick.

Schoolboy Paul Hugo took nine wickets with nine consecutive balls in South Africa in February 1931. He was playing for Smithfield School against Aliwal North. His feat was equalled in New Zealand in December 1967 by Stephen Fleming, for Marlborough College 'A' XI against Bohally Intermediate at Blenheim.

The oldest man on record to complete a hat-trick is Lionel Deamer when he was aged 74 years 330 days. He achieved this remarkable feat on 6 July 1979 for Lloyds Bank (Midlands) C.C. against Earlswood C.C., finishing with the impressive analysis of five wickets for 14 runs.

Maurice Hanes of Bedworth 2nd XI bowled 17 overs, 5 balls (107 consecutive balls) without conceding a run against A.P. Leamington 2nd XI at Bedworth, Warwickshire, on 16 June 1979. H. Hopkinson of Mildmay C.C., London, took 99 wickets for 147 runs in 1910 – an average of only 1.48 runs per wicket.

Wicket-Keeping and fielding records

The only wicket-keeper on record to have dismissed an entire side is Welihinda Badalge Bennett on 1 March 1953. The 20-year-old Sri Lankan was a student at Mahinda College for whom he was playing when he stumped six and caught four of the Galle C.C. team on the Esplanade ground at Galle.

The highest number of recorded catches in a match is 14. Stephen Lane, a 13-year-old schoolboy, held seven catches in the field in each innings while playing for St Patrick's College, Silverstream, against St Bernard's College, Lower Hutt, in Wellington, New Zealand.

Minor Counties cricket

The Minor Counties Cricket Association was formed in 1895 and it immediately instituted the Minor Counties Championship, with seven counties competing in that first season: Bedfordshire, Durham, Hertfordshire, Norfolk, Oxford-

MINOR COUNTIES CHAMPIONSHIP RECORDS

Highest Total	621		Surrey II v Devon	Oval	1928
Lowest Total	14		Cheshire v Staffordshire	Stoke	1909
Highest Score	282	E. Garnett	Berkshire v Wiltshire	Reading	1908
Most Runs–Season	1212	A.F. Brazier	Surrey II		1949
Record Partnership	388*	T.H. Clark and A.F. Brazier	Surrey II v Sussex II	Oval	1949
Best Bowling–Innings	10-15	G.J.W. Platt	Surrey II v Dorset	Dorchester	1908
	10-15	M. Ashenden	Bedfordshire v Shropshire	Bedford	1958
–Match	18-100	N.W. Harding	Kent II v Wiltshire	Swindon	1937
Most Wickets–Season	119	S.F. Barnes	Staffordshire		1906

shire, Staffordshire and Worcestershire. The foundation dates of those clubs currently competing in the Championship are:

Bedfordshire	3 November 1899
Berkshire	17 March 1895
Buckinghamshire	15 January 1891
Cambridgeshire	6 June 1891
Cheshire	29 September 1908
Cornwall	12 November 1894
Cumberland	10 April 1948
Devon	26 November 1899
Dorset	5 February 1896
Durham	10 May 1882
Hertfordshire	8 March 1876
Lincolnshire	28 September 1906
Norfolk	14 October 1876
Northumberland	December 1895
Oxfordshire	14 December 1921
Shropshire	28 June 1956
Staffordshire	24 November 1871
Suffolk	August 1932
Wiltshire	January 1893

Minor Counties champions

The record number of titles is seven by Buckinghamshire, who also shared the honours in 1899, and Lancashire 2nd XI.

The most successive titles is three by Worcestershire 1896-98.

THE MINOR COUNTIES CHAMPIONS

1895	Norfolk	1912	In abeyance	1946	Suffolk	1968	Yorkshire II
	Durham	1913	Norfolk	1947	Yorkshire II	1969	Buckinghamshire
	Worcestershire	1920	Staffordshire	1948	Lancashire II	1970	Bedfordshire
1896	Worcestershire	1921	Staffordshire	1949	Lancashire II	1971	Yorkshire II
1897	Worcestershire	1922	Buckinghamshire	1950	Surrey II	1972	Bedfordshire
1898	Worcestershire	1923	Buckinghamshire	1951	Kent II	1973	Shropshire
1899	Northamptonshire	1924	Berkshire	1952	Buckinghamshire	1974	Oxfordshire
	Buckinghamshire	1925	Buckinghamshire	1953	Berkshire	1975	Hertfordshire
1900	Glamorgan	1926	Durham	1954	Surrey II	1976	Durham
	Durham	1927	Staffordshire	1955	Surrey II	1977	Suffolk
	Northamptonshire	1928	Berkshire	1956	Kent II	1978	Devon
1901	Durham	1929	Oxfordshire	1957	Yorkshire II	1979	Suffolk
1902	Wiltshire	1930	Durham	1958	Yorkshire II	1980	Durham
1903	Northamptonshire	1931	Leicestershire II	1959	Warwickshire II	1981	Durham
1904	Northamptonshire	1932	Buckinghamshire	1960	Lancashire II	1982	Oxfordshire
1905	Norfolk	1933	Undecided	1961	Somerset II	1983	Hertfordshire
1906	Staffordshire	1934	Lancashire II	1962	Warwickshire II	1984	Durham
1907	Lancashire II	1935	Middlesex II	1963	Cambridgeshire	1985	Cheshire
1908	Staffordshire	1936	Hertfordshire	1964	Lancashire II	1986	Cumberland
1909	Wiltshire	1937	Lancashire II	1965	Somerset II		
1910	Norfolk	1938	Buckinghamshire	1966	Lincolnshire		
1911	Staffordshire	1939	Surrey II	1967	Cheshire		

CURIOSITIES

W.G. Grace was once dismissed by the creator of Sherlock Holmes, but not before he had scored a century. Sir Arthur Ignatius Conan Doyle, a right-handed batsman and occasional slow bowler, was playing for the MCC against London County at Crystal Palace on 25 August 1900. It was his only wicket in first-class cricket.

Surrey and England fast bowler Maurice Allom played tenor and baritone saxophone in a jazz band at The Savoy in 1927. He appeared regularly in a band formed from Cambridge undergraduates by Fred Elizalde. A recording of them at Hayes in Middlesex on 22 June 1927 still survives. Allom made his England debut in New Zealand's first Test match, at Lancaster Park, Christchurch, on 10 January 1930, and took four wickets – including a hat-trick – in five balls.

The first man to hit a ball over the present pavilion at Lord's was Albert Trott. Playing for MCC and Ground against the Australians on 31 July 1899, he struck a ball from Monty Noble over the top of the roof. Its carry took it as far as one of the pots of a chimney situated above and behind it.

A marathon cricket match involving 22 pupils of St Peter's School, Bournemouth, endured for 137 hours (5 days 17 hours) on 25 June-1 July 1980. The new (then) code of laws was observed.

The only centenarian to have umpired at Lord's is Joseph Filliston, a former slow bowler and BBC Cricket Club umpire. He officiated in the Lord's Taverners v Old England match in 1962. Two years later he died following an accident.

J.G. ('Jock') Sutherland carried his bat through an innings of 21 for Wakatu C.C. against Waimea College but did not manage to score a run. The innings, played in October 1976 at Victory Square in Nelson, New Zealand, lasted 54 minutes.

Frederick Buckle had an unhappy match for Surrey against Middlesex at Lord's on 12-13 July 1869. A 19-year-old right-handed batsman, he was recorded as 'absent, not sent for in time – 0' in the first innings, and 'absent unwell – 0' in the second. Surrey were dismissed for 37 and 105, losing by 43 runs.

The only Englishman to score a hundred against Australia in England in his first Test match is Dr W.G. Grace. Opening the batting in the first Test played in England, at The Oval in September 1880, he scored 152 to record his country's first Test century. The only other player to score a hundred in similar circumstances for England was K.S. Ranjitsinhji. The first Indian to play Test cricket, he celebrated his debut by scoring 154 not out against Australia at Old Trafford, Manchester, in July 1896.

During School cricket practice at Cowell, South Australia, during the 1967-68 season, Tony Wiseman saw a 3ft 6in poisonous snake slithering up the pitch towards him as the bowler delivered the ball. He allowed the ball to pass as he left his crease to kill the snake with his bat. Surprised not to hear an appeal for a stumping, he turned round to find that the wicket-keeper had vanished.

The only animal to have an obituary notice in *Wisden's Cricketers' Almanack* is Peter, the Lord's cat. His entry on page 973 of the 1965 edition reads:

'CAT, PETER, whose ninth life ended on November 5, 1964, was a well-known cricket-watcher at Lord's, where he spent 12 of his 14 years. He preferred a close-up view of the proceedings and his sleek, black form could often be seen prowling on the field of play when the crowds were biggest. He frequently appeared on the television screen. Mr S.C. Griffith, Secretary of the MCC, said of him: "He was a cat of great character and loved publicity."'

The rival captains in the 1905 series between England and Australia, the Hon F.S. Jackson and Joe Darling, were both born on 21 November 1870.

When James Lillywhite's touring professionals challenged 22 of Goulburn in December 1876, play was disrupted for several minutes when the field was invaded by six hares and two young kangaroos. A few weeks later the Englishmen were to play representative Australian team on level terms for the first time in a game which subsequently became recognized as the first-ever Test match.

Cawood won a York Senior League match against Dringhouses in 1979 without once hitting the ball. Having dismissed their opponents for just 2 runs in the space of 39 balls, Cawood completed an emphatic victory when the first ball of their innings produced four byes.

A minor league match in Hampshire produced the following scoreline: Meonstoke 45 (Shakespeare 8 for 20); Trinity 35 (Marlow 9 for 14).

The first major match to be started on one ground and finished on another took place between London and Kent in August 1730. Begun 'at the end of Frog Lane, near Islington', it was finished on Kennington Common.

The highest number of runs scored from a single hit is 286. When a touring team from Victoria played a scratch eleven from Bunbury in Western Australia, the opening ball of the match was hit into 'a three-pronged branch of a tall Jarrah tree'. Although the home side claimed a 'lost ball', the umpire ruled that it could not be lost because it could be seen. With the Victorian batsmen continuing to run, the Bunbury players sent for an axe to cut down the tree. None could be found. Eventually someone produced a rifle and, after numerous unsuccessful attempts, the ball was shot down. The Victorians 'stood' on their score of 286 and went on to win the match.

Playing for Alexandra Park 3rd XI against Hanwell 3rd XI on 23 August 1986, Ken Hudson (born 4 June 1908) shared a brief last-

Lall Singh, the only Malaysian to play Test cricket. (Author)

wicket partnership with Dean King (b 20 July 1973). Their age difference of 65 years 46 days is believed to constitute a partnership record – certainly at Hanwell on a Saturday.

On 23 February 1976 the South Australian team went on strike. Captained by Ian Chappell and currently leading the Sheffield Shield they were angered by the selectors' decision to replace their twelfth man from the previous match with an all-rounder fresh to first-class cricket. When the selectors, chaired by Phil Ridings, threatened to select an entirely new team for the last two matches of the season, the strike, which had lasted for 18 hours, was called off.

For nearly four decades virtually every cricket reference book credited R.L. Hunte with a Test match appearance for West Indies against England at Port-of-Spain, Trinidad, in February 1930. It was E.A.C. (Errol) Hunte who actually played, the second of his three Test appearances. The error was caused by a copy typist mishearing 'Errol' as 'R.L' and it resulted in Hunte having his career record separated under the two sets of initials in many publications.

No Hampshire-born Hampshire cricketer has played Test cricket for England since March 1896 when Arthur James Ledger Hill made the last of his three appearances against South Africa at Newlands, Cape Town, and scored 124. Although 15 Hampshire players have represented England in Tests, only one other (Victor Barton v South Africa in 1891-92) was actually born within the county boundaries.

The only Malaysian to play Test cricket is Lall Singh. Born near Kuala Lumpur in 1909 and now head groundsman at the Selangor Club, he appeared in India's first Test match, at Lord's on 25-28 June 1932. Remembered as a magnificent beturbaned fielder in the covers, he scored 15 and 29, adding 74 in 40 minutes in the second innings in partnership with fast bowler Amar Singh. He proudly claims to have been the only Test cricketer to have owned a nightclub in Paris.

Seymour Nurse (West Indies) had the misfortune to be caught at deep fine-leg from a hit that rebounded off the head of a fielder at backward short-leg when he was batting against Australia in the Second Test at Melbourne in December 1968.

B.K. ('Budhi') Kunderan, a wicket-keeper, opened India's batting and bowling against England at Edgbaston, Birmingham, in July 1967. With two of India's new-ball bowlers unavailable because of injury, Kunderan (4-0-13-0) was given his only bowl in first-class matches on that tour.

During the first 'Test' between Young Sri Lanka and Young England on 6 February 1987, play was stopped by an iguana which crept menacingly across the middle of the historic Colombo Cricket Club ground.

The first team to consist of players with the same name was fielded by Surrey in July 1731. This confusing combination defeated Kent at Duppas Hill, Croydon, all eleven players being named Wood.

After scoring 224 not out for England against Surrey at The Oval on the two preceding days, Dr W.G. Grace won the 440 yards hurdles (over 20 flights of hurdles) at the first National Olympian Association meeting at the Crystal Palace on 1 August 1866.

The first man to be convicted of manslaughter on the field of play was William Waterfall at Derby Assizes in 1775.

Cricket's most bizarre record: 286 runs from a single hit. (BBC Television)

GLOSSARY

All-Rounder: a player who is worth his place either as a batsman or as a bowler. Can also refer to a batsman/wicket-keeper.

Amateur: the status of first-class cricketers who did not receive a salary or match fee but who were permitted 'out-of-pocket expenses'. This distinction from the professional was abolished by the Advisory County Cricket Committee meeting at Lord's on 26 November 1962, a decision later ratified by the MCC. The status still exists in minor cricket where clubs engage professionals.

Analysis: usually refers to bowling statistics for an innings or match, but can also describe a bowler's figures for the season or even his entire career. Innings analyses appear as 19.4-16-10-10 – but not often! That one, 19 overs and 4 balls – 16 maidens – 10 runs – 10 wickets, was achieved by Hedley Verity, Yorkshire's left-arm spin bowler, against Nottinghamshire at Leeds in 1932 and remains the record analysis in all first-class cricket.

Appeal: A call by a player to an umpire for a decision on any matter concerning play; usually refers to a call of 'How's that?' by a member of the fielding side which encompasses all ten ways of dismissing a batsman: bowled, caught, stumped, leg before wicket, hit wicket, run out, hit the ball twice, handled the ball, obstructing the field, and timed out.

Ashes: a trophy, housed in the Memorial Gallery at Lord's, which consists of a small urn supposedly containing the ashes of a bail burnt by some ladies in Sydney, and which was presented to the Hon Ivo Bligh after he had led his English team to a 2-1 victory against W.L. Murdoch's Australians in 1882-1883. The Ashes are normally at stake during Test matches between England and Australia. The trophy was conceived as a result of a mock obituary notice published in *The Sporting Times* after Australia had beaten

England in England for the first time (29 August 1882). A note at the foot of this famous obituary announced that 'The body will be cremated and the ashes taken to Australia'. Bligh, who became the eighth Earl of Darnley, retained the urn and its embroidered velvet bag until his death in 1927, when it was bequeathed to the MCC. 'The Ashes' remain at Lord's even when 'held' by Australia.

The Countess of Darnley, the Australian who jointly-conceived and finally inherited the Ashes.

Average (Batting): the mean number of runs per completed innings over a period (ie season, tour, Test series, or career) achieved by a batsman; calculated by dividing his aggregate by the number of his innings discounting any in which he was 'not out' or 'retired hurt/ill'.

Average (Bowling): the mean cost of each wicket in terms of runs over a period (as above) achieved by a bowler; calculated by dividing the number of runs conceded (excluding all extras) by the number of wickets taken.

Averages: comparative tables of batting and bowling averages.

Away-Swinger: a bowling delivery which moves in the air from leg to off (right to left as the bowler sees it). Also termed an 'out-swinger'.

Back up, to: in fielding, to prevent overthrows by standing behind the wicket-keeper or another fielder to stop the ball on its return if he misses it, or to support a fielder's throw from a long distance; in batting, the action of the non-striker in moving down the pitch immediately the ball is bowled in order to be ready for a run.

Backward Point: an offside fielding position between Point and the Slip area now usually referred to as 'Gully'.

Bails: two pieces of wood, each $4\frac{3}{8}$ inches long, which are placed end to end on top of the stumps and which must not project more than $\frac{1}{2}$ inch above them. The umpires may dispense with them during extremely windy conditions.

Ball: made of stitched leather dyed red with an interior of cork layers each bound with twine; for major cricket its circumference must not measure less than $8\frac{13}{16}$ inches nor more than 9 inches, and its weight, when new, must not be less than $5\frac{1}{2}$ ounces nor more than $5\frac{3}{4}$ ounces. Other specifications are permitted for lower grade balls and for women's and junior cricket.

Bat: its blade (striking part) must be made of wood – normally willow – and must not exceed $4\frac{1}{4}$ inches in width; and may be covered with material for protection, strengthening or repair provided that it does not exceed $\frac{1}{16}$ inch in thickness; the overall length of the bat (top of handle to bottom of blade) must not exceed 38 inches.

Beamer: a fast, head-high full pitch which is now categorically forbidden under Law 42 (Unfair Play).

Benefit: awarded by the first-class counties to players usually about ten seasons after winning their 1st XI caps. During the calendar year of their benefit, players are allowed to raise unlimited sums from subscriptions and lotteries and are usually awarded the profits of one home county match of their choosing.

Block: the mark or hole made by the batsman with the toe of his bat in the popping crease when taking guard. Also refers to totally defensive batting where the ball is merely stopped with the bat.

Blue: awarded for appearing for Cambridge or Oxford in a University Match.

Bosie: Australia's term for the googly – derived from the name of its originator, B.J.T. Bosanquet.

Bouncer: a fast short-pitched ball which is aimed to reach the batsman at shoulder height or above. An umpire has the power to prevent a bowler intimidating a batsman by bowling bouncers under the provisions of Law 42 (Unfair Play).

Boundary: the limit of the playing area on all sides which is usually marked by a rope, a white line or a fence; current playing conditions for first-class matches exhort the Ground Authority to provide the largest playing area possible, subject to no boundary exceeding a distance of 90 yards from the centre of the pitch or being closer than 50 yards. Also refers to a hit which sends the ball beyond the playing area; four runs are awarded if it touches the ground within the playing area first and six if it does not.

Bowl, to: to propel the ball fairly at the striking batsman's wicket.

Bowled: method of dismissal whereby the bowler bowls down the striker's wicket, even if the ball touches that batsman's bat or person first.

Bowling Crease: the whitewash painted line, 8 feet 8 inches in length, which extends equidistantly on either side of the stumps at each end of the pitch. Under the old no-ball law the bowler had to have part of one foot behind the bowling crease at the moment of delivery but, under the present front-foot law, it is now the popping crease which must not be overstepped.

Box: a light shield for protecting the genitals and worn by batsmen, wicket-keepers and some fielders occupying close positions. Also the old term for the fielding position which is now called 'Gully'.

Break: a ball's deviation from the straight on pitching.

Break-back: a fast off-break which is usually produced by the bowler cutting his fingers across the seam.

Bump Ball: a ball which rebounds directly from the striker's bat to the ground before being 'caught' by a fielder; to the distant spectator a 'bump ball' is usually impossible to distinguish from a genuine catch.

Bumper: a fast short-pitched ball (see 'Bouncer').

Bye: a run scored from a ball (other than a no ball or a wide) which passes the striker without touching his bat or his body.

Call: a batsman's summons to his partner to run. Also the umpire's act of announcing a no-ball, wide or dead ball.

Cap: cricketers' formal headgear. In English first-class cricket, a capped player is one who has been awarded his county 1st XI cap.

Carry One's Bat, to: the act of an opening batsman who remains at the wicket throughout his side's completed innings and is still not out at the fall of the tenth wicket. Batsmen who retire and resume their innings cannot qualify for this epithet.

Castle: colloquial term for the wicket.

Caught: method of dismissal whereby the striker has touched the ball with his bat, or his hand or glove (below the wrist) while holding the bat, and it is subsequently held by a fielder before it touches the ground.

Century: colloquial term for 100 runs.

Change Bowler: one brought on to bowl after the opening pair.

Chinaman: the left-arm bowler's off-break to the right-handed batsman.

Chop: a form of late cut, executed by bringing the bat down sharply on a ball on the off-side just as it passes the batsman, designed to steer the ball through the slip area.

Chucker: a bowler who infringes Law 24 (1) Note (a) by throwing the ball instead of bowling it.

Close Field: the fielding positions which are close to the striker such as the slips, gully, silly point, silly mid-off, silly mid-on, short-legs, and leg slip.

Closure: declaration.

Cow Shot: a rustic unorthodox stroke played across the line of the ball with a near-horizontal bat and which aims to send the ball on the leg-side.

Cradle: an apparatus made of slatted wood fixed to a concave metal frame on to which players throw the ball with a low trajectory to practise slip catching.

Creases: lines of whitewash painted on the pitch at either end and according to Law 9. They define the bowler's permitted area of delivery and also the limits within which the batsman cannot be stumped or run out. There are three types of crease at each end; the Bowling Crease, the Popping Crease and the Return Crease.

Creeper: a ball which shoots along the ground; also termed a 'shooter' or 'sneak'.

Cross-batted: a stroke made with an arc of the bat that is not perpendicular to the pitch and which is consequently aimed across the line of the ball.

Crumbling Pitch: one which is dry and disintegrating.

Cut: a stroke played with a horizontal bat at a short-pitched ball on the off-side (see 'Late Cut' and 'Square Cut').

Cutter: a batsman who cuts. Also a ball which, bowled at medium pace or above, is made to deviate off the ground on pitching.

Dead Ball: the ball becomes dead under Law 23 (1) when:

Colin Cowdrey, president of MCC in their Bicentenary year, scored a century in his hundredth Test. (UPP)

(a) It is finally settled in the hands of the wicket-keeper or the bowler.
(b) It reaches or pitches over the boundary.
(c) A batsman is out.
(d) Whether played or not, it lodges in the clothing or equipment of a batsman or the clothing of an umpire.
(e) A ball lodges in a protective helmet worn by a member of the fielding side.
(f) A penalty is awarded under Law 20 (Lost Ball) or Law 41 (1) (Fielding the Ball).
(g) The umpire calls 'over' or 'time'.
The ball ceases to be dead when the bowler starts his run-up or bowling action.

Declaration: the closing of an innings by the batting side's captain when he still has wickets standing. Declarations were not allowed until 1889 and then on the last day only. Not until 1951 were they permitted on the first day and then only as an experiment which was not incorporated into the Laws proper until 1957.

Deep: the playing area or field near the boundary which can also be described as the 'country'.

Defence: the batsman's technique in stopping the ball.

Delivery: the act of bowling the ball or the ball bowled.

Donkey Drop: a ball bowled high into the air by a slow bowler.

Drag, to: to drag the back foot when

bowling. Also to drag the ball into the wicket (play on) when batting. Also to impart back-spin on the ball when bowling.

Draw: a match which ends without a clear result. Also the name of a batting stroke (no longer played intentionally) where the batsman lifted his front leg and deflected the ball underneath it.

Drive: a stroke aimed at the pitch of the ball with a perpendicular arc of the bat.

Driver: a batsman who specializes in the drive.

Duck: a score of 0.

Extras: runs added to the side's total but which are not credited to the batsman or debited to the bowler. Extras (known in Australia as 'sundries') comprise byes, leg-byes. wides and no-balls.

Field: the playing area. Can also refer to a fielder or the positioning of the fielders.

Fine: at a narrow angle to the wicket; the opposite of square.

Finger-Spin: one method of making the ball turn.

First-Class: the highest grade of match apart from Test cricket. Officially defined (by the then Imperial Cricket Conference) for the first time in 1947 as 'a match of three or more days' duration between two sides of eleven players officially adjudged first-class'. The status of teams is decided by the governing cricket body of the country concerned. A player who appears in a match deemed to be first-class becomes a 'first-class cricketer'.

Flight: the trajectory of the ball. Slow bowlers try to deceive the batsman with subtle variations of flight so that he misjudges the pitch of the ball.

Flipper: a ball bowled by leg-break bowlers which hurries off the pitch like a top-spinner. It is delivered from a special grip involving only the tips of the first and third fingers of the right hand and is flipped out of the hand from underneath the wrist.

Fly Slip: a slightly unusual fielding position about halfway between the slips and the boundary.

Follow-On: the side which bats first and leads by 200 runs in a match of five days or more, by 150 runs in a three or four-day match, by 100 runs in a two-day match, or by 75 runs in a one-day game, has the option of requiring the other side to 'follow their innings'; ie to bat again out of turn.

Follow-Through: the path of a bowler after the act of delivering the ball.

Forward Stroke: a stroke played by advancing the front foot (left foot if the batsman is right-handed) down the wicket to play the ball as close as possible to the place where it pitches.

Full Toss (or Full Pitch): a ball that reaches the batsman without bouncing.

Gardening: the act of repairing or flattening with the bat that part of a damp pitch which has become damaged by the ball's contact.

Gate: the sum of admission money taken at the gate or turnstiles. Also the space left between a batsman's feet and his bat if he does not move to the pitch of the ball correctly.

Gentlemen: the amateur or unpaid cricketers, as distinct from the Players or professionals. The distinction was abolished from English first-class cricket after the 1962 season.

Glance: a deflection of the ball off the face of the bat, usually to fine-leg.

Go Away, to: term for a ball leaving the batsman either in the air or on pitching.

Googly: an off-break bowled with a leg-break action.

Go With the Arm, to: term for a ball that follows the course of the bowler's arm either in the air or on pitching. A right-arm bowler can thus make his 'arm ball' leave the right-handed batsman; ie make it move from leg to off.

Greasy: a pitch or outfield affected by rain or over-watering.

Green-Top: a pitch that is well grassed. As it is likely to retain overnight moisture early in the day's play, it will obviously favour the faster bowlers.

Ground-Fielding: stopping the ball hit along or via the ground, as opposed to catching.

Groundsman: the person who tends the pitches and playing area. In Australia the term is 'curator'.

Ground-Staff: junior members of the playing staff of a county (or the MCC) who assist with the maintenance of the ground and with bowling in the nets, as well as being coached.

Grub: a ball bowled under-arm along the ground. Also call a 'sneak'.

Guard: given to the batsman on coming in by the umpire at the bowler's end so that he knows the position of his bat and feet in relation to the stumps he is guarding. He will ask for middle, middle-and-leg (or two legs), or leg stump and make his block (mark the ground where his bat rests) accordingly.

Gully: a close catching position on the offside between the slips and point.

Half-Cock: a defensive stroke which is neither forward nor back made when the batsman has misjudged the length of the ball and cannot adjust his feet in time.

Half-Volley: a ball that is over-pitched, enabling the batsman to hit it off the front foot an instant after it has bounced.

Handled the Ball: either batsman (not necessarily the striker) can be out if he touches the ball with his hands while it is in play – unless he has the permission of the fielding side. The wicket is not credited to the bowler.

Harrow Bat: a size of bat smaller than normal and suitable for a teenager.

Hat-trick: the feat of taking three wickets with three consecutive balls within the same match – it can be spread over two overs or even from the first innings into the second. Three wickets with three legitimate balls but with a no-ball interrupting the sequence does not count as a hat-trick. The term evolved from the custom of presenting the bowler with a top hat for achieving this feat. The first recorded instance occurred on 8 September 1858 at the Hyde Park Ground in Sheffield when H.H. Stephenson, playing for the All-England Eleven, took three wickets in three balls in the second innings and was presented with a white hat.

Hit the Ball Twice: the batsman is out if he hits the ball twice except for the sole purpose of defending his wicket. The dismissal is not credited to the bowler.

Hit Wicket: a batsman is out if, while the ball is in play, he breaks his wicket with any part of his person, dress or bat, at any time when playing the ball or in setting off for his first run. He is not out if he breaks his wicket while trying to avoid being run out or stumped. The dismissal is credited to the bowler.

Hook: the stroke made off the back foot by which a short ball is hit to leg with a cross bat.

How's That?: the standard form of appeal.

Inswinger: a ball which moves in flight from off to leg.

King Pair: short for a 'king pair of spectacles'. If, in a two innings match, a batsman is out first ball for nought in both innings, he has 'bagged a king pair'.

Lap: a modern term for a cross-batted stroke, somewhere between a sweep and a pull, which hits the ball towards mid-wicket.

Late Cut: a wristy stroke played late and with a horizontal bat to a short ball outside the off stump and which hits it downwards and past the slips.

Leg Before Wicket (lbw): a method of dismissal credited to the bowler and defined under Law 36 as follows:

(a) **Striker Attempting to Play the Ball**
   The striker shall be out LBW if he first intercepts with any part of his person, dress or equipment a fair ball which would have hit the wicket and which has not previously touched his bat or a hand holding the bat, provided that:
   (i) the ball pitched in a straight line between wicket and wicket or on the off-side of the striker's wicket, or in the case of a ball intercepted full pitch would have pitched in a straight line between wicket and wicket; and
   (ii) the point of impact is in a straight line between wicket and wicket, even if above the level of the bails.

(b) **Striker Making No Attempt to Play the Ball**
   The striker shall be out LBW even if the ball is intercepted outside the line of the off stump if, in the opinion of the umpire, he has made no genuine attempt to play the ball with his bat, but has intercepted the ball with some part of his person and if the circumstances set out in (a) above apply.

Leg Break: a ball that turns from leg to off on pitching.

Leg-Bye: a run obtained from a ball that has been unintentionally deflected by the batsman with any part of his person other than his hand or hands holding the bat, but has not touched the bat. Leg-byes are recorded as extras and are not debited to the bowler's analysis. A leg-bye scored off a no-ball is recorded as a no-ball.

Leg-Cutter: a fast leg-break bowled by cutting the fingers across the seam of the ball.

Leg-Side: the side of the pitch and field behind the batsman as he adopts his stance at the crease, ie the side containing his legs.

Leg-Theory: a method of bowling concentrated on the leg stump and the pads with an array of fielders in catching positions on the leg-side (the 'leg-trap').

Leg-Trap: a crescent of fielders in close catching positions on the leg-side in support of inswing, off-spin or leg-theory bowling.

Length: one of the basics of good bowling. A good length ball is one which pitches at such a distance from the batsman that he is uncertain whether to play forward or back.

Light: one of three constantly varying factors affecting play (along with weather and the state of the pitch). Under the present Law 3 the umpires are sole judges of the fitness of the light for play without appeal from the batting side. Their decision can be overruled if both captains want play to continue.

Lob: a ball bowled or returned by a fielder under-arm.

Long Field: the area of the field in front of the bowler's end sightscreen where long-off and long-on patrol.

Long Handle: taken by an aggressive batsman intent on hitting out. The term derives from the batsman's grip; by moving his hands to the top of the handle he can increase the arc of his swing.

Long Hop: a short-pitched ball easily punished off the back foot on either side of the wicket.

Long-Leg: fielding position on or near the boundary behind the wicket on the leg-side – a very deep fine-leg.

Long-Off, Long-On: fielding positions on or near the boundary on either side of the sightscreen at the bowler's end.

Long-Stop: obsolete fielding position behind the wicket-keeper. It was once a vital position demanding a specialist fieldsman as wicket-keeping gloves were unknown until c 1820. The first wicket-keeper to dispense with a long-stop was Harry Phillips who kept wicket for Sussex from 1868 until 1891.

Lost Ball: an archaic provision, presumably retained for minor cricket, whereby, if the ball in play cannot be found or recovered, any fielder may call 'lost ball' when six runs shall be added to the score, or as many as have already been completed.

Maiden: an over from which no runs are scored by the batsmen. A maiden over must not include any no-balls or wides; since 1985 the penalty runs incurred by such deliveries have been debited to the bowler's analysis.

Match: a contest of two innings per side, except in one-day and limited-overs games.

Matting: an alternative to grass as a surface for the pitch. Can be made of jute (fibre from the bark of an East Indian plant), coir (coconut fibre), or of various synthetic substances. The base on which it is laid is vitally important and can very from grass to concrete.

Meat: of the bat – the middle of the blade at its thickest point.

Middle: the 'square' on which the pitches are prepared.

Mow: cross-batted hit to leg.

Nets: a 'hollow' rectangle of string netting within which players practise on prepared pitches away from the main square or on synthetic pitches at indoor schools.

New-Ball: either captain can demand a new ball at the start of each innings. Under the present Law 5, national governing bodies are left to determine the availability of a second new ball in matches of three or more days duration, but stipulate a minimum of 75 overs. In Test matches in England the captain has the option of taking a new ball after 85 overs have been bowled with the old one. In all other first-class matches, including the County Championship, the number of overs is 100.

Night-Watchman: a lower-order batsman sent in to play out time when a wicket falls shortly before close of play, and to prevent a better batsman risking his wicket.

No-Ball: an illegal delivery. For a ball to be legitimate, it must be bowled and not thrown, the bowler's back foot must land within and not touching the return crease and its forward extension, and some part of his front foot (grounded or raised) must be behind the popping crease. In addition, the bowler must notify the batsman of any change in his mode of delivery; ie from over to round the wicket, under-arm to over-arm, right-arm to left-arm. No-balls are also called for certain infringements by fielders and the wicket-keeper. A penalty of one run is awarded if no runs are made otherwise. Since 1985 such penalty runs have been debited to bowlers' individual analyses. Byes or leg-byes scored off a no-ball are recorded as no-balls. A batsman can be out off a no-ball in four ways: run out, handling the ball, hitting the ball twice and obstructing the field. An extra ball must be bowled for every no-ball called so that each completed over contains six legal deliveries.

Not Out: to not lose one's wicket. 'Not out' innings are excluded when calculating batting averages. Also an umpire's negative reply to an appeal.

Obstructing the Field: either batsman can be out if he wilfully obstructs the fielding side by word or action. If the non-striker is responsible for an act of wilful obstruction which prevents a catch from being taken, it is the striker who is out. The dismissal is not credited to the bowler.

Off-Break: a ball that turns from off to leg on pitching.

Off-Cutter: a fast off-break bowled by cutting the fingers across the seam of the ball.

Off-Drive: a drive, usually made off the front foot, which hits the ball between cover and mid-off.

Off-Side: the side of the pitch and field in front of the batsman as he adopts his stance at the crease, opposite the side where his legs are.

On-Drive: a drive, usually made off the front foot, which hits the ball between mid-wicket and mid-on.

Out-Cricket: the collective effort of the fielding team.

Out-Field: the outer part of the playing area away from the table or square.

Out of His Ground: the batsman must have some part of his bat in his hand or of his person grounded behind the line of the popping crease; on the line is out.

Outswinger: a ball which moves in flight from leg to off.

Over: the period of play, or total of balls bowled, between one changing of ends and the next. Six-ball overs have been in operation universally in first-class cricket since the 1979-80 season, although Law 22 does provide for either six or eight.

Over the Wicket: the method of bowling where the operative arm is close to or over the stumps, ie to a right-handed batsman, a right-arm bowler bowls from the off-side and a left-arm bowler delivers from the leg-side.

Overthrow: a throw-in by a fielder which is not gathered at the stumps and which enables the batsmen to take a further run or more. Runs thus taken are termed overthrows but, unless they are extras, they are credited to the striker and debited to the bowler's analysis.

Pad-Play: the act of deliberately stopping balls with the pads.

Pair: a pair of spectacles – two scores of nought in the same match.

Pitch: the specially prepared area, 5 feet in width and 22 yards (one agricultural chain) long, between the two sets of stumps.

Play: the action of the game. Also the umpire's call to begin.

Played On: term meaning to deflect the ball into the stumps with the bat. It is recorded as 'bowled'.

Plumb: a true pitch, perfect for batting. Also it can describe an lbw decision that is so obviously out (to all observers except the victim), that the batsman should have 'walked' without waiting for an appeal.

Point: a close fielding position square with the wicket on the off-side 'at the point of the bat'.

Pop: a ball which lifts sharply off the pitch is said to pop.

Popping Crease: the line across the pitch marking the forward limit of the batsman's safe ground. Painted in whitewash 4 feet in front of the stumps, it is now the line which controls the bowler's front foot.

Professional: a player employed to coach and/or play by clubs and schools. Before amateur status was abolished in English cricket at the end of the 1962 season it described a paid player.

Pull: a forceful stroke off the front foot made with a vertical bat across the line of a ball pitching on or outside the off stump, and sending the ball between mid-on and mid-wicket.

Put In, to: to ask the opposition to bat first; ie to elect to field on winning the toss.

Quickie: colloquial term for a fast bowler.

Quick Wicket: a hard pitch from which the ball bounces quickly.

Reach: the distance which a batsman can stretch forward to reach the pitch of a ball.

Retire Hurt or Ill: a batsman may retire, ie end his innings voluntarily, at any time. If his action is the result of injury or illness, it is regarded as 'not out' and he may resume his innings at the fall of a wicket or the retirement of another batsman. If he leaves the field or retires for any other reason, it is recorded as 'Retired, out' and he can only resume his

innings with the consent of the opposing captain.

Return: a throw back to the stumps at either end after the ball has been fielded.

Return Creases: the lines at each end of the bowling crease, parallel with a line between the two sets of stumps and 4 feet 4 inches from the middle stump's centre. They are marked to at least 4 feet behind the wicket but are considered to be unlimited in length. Since the introduction of the front foot no-ball law, the return crease has been extended to join the popping crease and so complete the rectangle.

Round the Wicket: the method of bowling where the operative arm is the one farther from the stumps, ie to a right-handed batsman, a right-arm bowler bowls from the leg-side and a left-arm one delivers from the off-side.

Rubber: a set of Test matches between the same two countries and played during one season. Also termed a series.

Run: the unit of scoring.

Runner: the member of the batting side allowed to run for a batsman who, during the match, is incapacitated by illness or injury. If possible, he should have already batted in that innings and, if the injured batsman is wearing gloves and pads, he must be similarly equipped.

Run Out: a method of dismissal not credited to the bowler. Either batsman can be Run Out if in running he is out of his ground and the wicket is broken by the fielding side. The batsman nearest to the broken wicket is the one dismissed if they are in the act of running. If a batsman remains in or returns to his ground and the other batsman joins him there, the latter is out if his wicket is broken. If a batsman is run out, only that run being attempted is not scored. The one exception involves an injured batsman ignoring his runner and being run out himself, when no runs are scored.

Run the Ball Away: to cause it to move away from the batsman towards the slips.

Run-Up: a bowler's approach to his delivery stride.

Score Book: the volume of printed forms on which the match is recorded.

Score Card: a printed card giving the teams and allowing space for innings and bowling details to be recorded. A document seldom available outside Britain.

Scorer: the person who records the

details of the match.

Scratch Team: a privately collected side with no bond of common membership.

Seam: the stitching around the circumference of the ball that fastens together its leather segments. It plays an important part in bowling techniques.

Seam Bowler or Seamer: any bowler of medium pace or faster who makes the ball deviate by pitching it on its seam rather than using cut or fingerspin.

Selector: in England, one of a committee of four appointed annually by the Test and County Cricket Board (TCCB) to choose England teams for that season's Test matches. For choosing tours overseas, the selectors are joined by the tour captain and manager, and by the chairman of the TCCB Cricket Committee.

Session: one of three periods of play separated by lunch and tea intervals.

Shooter: a ball that does not rise off the ground after pitching.

Short-Leg: a close catching position on the leg-side, defined more precisely by its relationship to the batsman's wicket; ie forward, square or backward.

Short Run: when either batsman fails to make good his ground at one end when running two or more runs, the umpire calls and signals 'one short', and the run is not counted. Also a quickly taken single for a short hit.

Shoulder Arms: used to describe a batsman's action when he holds the bat aloft and allows an off-side ball to pass without playing a stroke.

Sight-Screen: the screen, usually white and mobile, sited beyond the boundary behind the bowler to give the batsman the clearest possible view of the ball. For Test matches in England the TCCB has ruled that ground authorities must provide sight-screens at both ends. For night cricket which uses a white ball, the screens have to be black.

Silly: close; ie silly mid-on is synonymous with forward short leg.

Single: one run.

Skier: steepling hit.

Slip: fielding position on the off-side and adjacent to the wicket-keeper. First slip is next to the 'keeper and any others are numbered outwards towards gully.

Square-Cut: a stroke made off the back foot with a horizontal bat to a short ball outside the off stump, and which despatches it just backward of point.

Sticky Wicket: a rain-affected pitch which has begun to dry out under the sun's heat, forming a hard crust over soft, wet soil. This allows the ball to bite, turn and lift sharply. Also termed a 'glue pot'.

Stone-Waller: an extremely defensive batsman who is more concerned with safeguarding his wicket than with scoring runs.

Stumps: normally of ash. Three stumps (off, middle and leg) form the wicket when surmounted by two bails.

Stumped: a batsman is out if, in receiving a ball that is not a no-ball but which may be a wide, he is out of his ground and the wicket is put down by the wicket-keeper without the intervention of another fielder. If this happens when he is not attempting a run, he is out stumped and the dismissal is credited to the bowler.

Substitute: a substitute player may field for any member of the side who, during that particular match, is incapacitated by illness or injury. The consent of the opposing captain must be obtained for the use of a substitute if any player is prevented from fielding for any other reason. The opposing captain cannot object to any particular player acting as substitute, nor, under the 1980 code, to where he shall field apart from keeping wicket. A player may bat, bowl or field even though a substitute has acted for him. Any catches or stumpings made by a substitute are recorded as 'ct/st sub', although current books containing the full scores of Test matches do add the substitute's name in brackets. A substitute is not permitted to bat or bowl unless he is replacing a player called from a County Championship match to stand by for England's Test team. The first instance of this regulation being invoked occurred on 29 July 1982 when David Brown, the former England fast bowler who was Cricket Manager of Warwickshire, substituted for Gladstone Small in the match against Lancashire at Southport, bowled 13 overs and took a wicket before making way for the player England had not needed after all.

Sweep: a stroke played off the front foot from the crouch position with a horizontal bat usually to a ball pitched on or outside the leg stump. Denis Compton was the master and main perpetrator of the sweep and a large proportion of his runs were scored behind the wicket on the leg-side from it.

Swerve: old term for swing – lateral movement of the ball in the air.

Tail: those players who are not selected for their batting ability and who occupy the lower places in the batting order.

Team: a match is played between two sides or teams of eleven players each, one of whom is captain.

Testimonial: awarded by counties to players and, occasionally, officials, who have given long service. Unlike a Benefit, it does not include the proceeds of a county match.

Test Match: a contest of two innings per side and usually of five days duration between two full members of the International Cricket Conference.

Tie: a match which ends with an equal aggregate of runs scored by both sides and with the side batting last having completed its innings.

Top-Spin: spin which causes the ball to gain pace after bouncing but not to deviate laterally. It is an additional weapon in the leg-break bowler's armoury.

Toss: a coin is tossed by the home captain and his opposite number calls 'heads' or 'tails'. The winner has choice of innings.

Tour: a sequence of away matches played by one team without returning home. The term is usually reserved for the fixed itinerary of a team travelling abroad.

Track: colloquial term for the pitch.

Twelfth Man: the emergency (substitute) fielder and drinks waiter.

Umpire's Signals: these are laid down in Law 3 of the 1980 code and must be acknowledged by an official scorer before the game can proceed:

Boundary: by waving the arm from side to side.
Boundary 6: by raising both arms above the head.
Bye: by raising an open hand above the head.
Dead Ball: by crossing and re-crossing the wrists below the waist.
Leg-Bye: by touching a raised knee with the hand.
No-Ball: by extending one arm horizontally.
Out: by raising the index finger above the head. If not out, the umpire shall call 'not out'.
Short Run: by bending the arm upwards and by touching the nearer shoulder with the tips of the fingers.
Wide: by extending both arms horizontally.

Wicket: the three wooden stumps with two wooden bails on top that are pitched opposite and parallel to each other and 22 yards apart. Each wicket when set must be 9 inches wide with the tops of the stumps 28 inches above the ground. The bails are 4⅜ inches long and, when in position on top of the stumps, must not project more than ½ inch above them. In an extreme wind the umpires may decide to dispense with the bails. The term wicket is often, quite incorrectly, used to describe the pitch.

Wicket-keeper: the fielder who, protected by pads and gauntlets, fields behind the stumps at the batsman's end. Before the specialist position was introduced in the late 18th century, a fielder was placed in the deep behind the batsman (long-stop).

Wicket Maiden: an over in which no runs are scored by the batsmen but in which at least one wicket falls which has been credited to the bowler. It must not include any no-balls or wides.

Wide: a ball bowled so high over or so wide of the wicket that, in the opinion of the umpire, it passes out of the reach of the striker, standing in a normal guard position. It must be called and signalled by the bowler's umpire as soon as it passes the line of the striker's wicket. If no extras result from it, a penalty of one run is added to the score and another ball must be bowled to replace it in that over.

Since 1985 such penalty runs have been debited to bowlers' individual analyses. Unlike no-balls, wides are not included in the total of balls received by the batsman as he cannot score off a wide. He can, however, be out to a wide in five ways: stumped, hit wicket, run out, handled the ball, or obstructing the field. If a batsman hits a ball called 'wide', the umpire must revoke his call.

Wrong-Un: another term for the googly – an off-break bowled with a leg-break action.

Yorker: a ball pitched well up so that, at the instant the bat on its downswing reaches the vertical, it passes underneath it.

Cricket as played on the Goodwin Sands in 1894. (Mary Evans Picture Library)

POSTSCRIPT

Any book of cricket records has to have a cut-off point and, for this edition, it is the end of the 1986 English season.

During the six months in which this volume has been compiled and set all seven full member countries of the ICC have been engaged in an extraordinary excess of international activity. A total of 22 Test matches and 52 limited-overs internationals had been played before the end of March. New Zealand's hastily-arranged tour of Sri Lanka, plus yet another four-nation tournament in Sharjah, will take the final totals for the overseas season to 25 Tests and 62 internationals – a staggering case of overkill. India staged eleven home Tests, including only the second to be tied, while Australia hosted no fewer than 21 one-day internationals.

The threefold success of England's mission in Australia brought to an end a run of eleven Tests without victory. Possibly an even greater achievement was Pakistan's first series victory in India where their spinners proved more effective than the home team's on grossly underprepared pitches.

The total of triple centuries in first-class cricket was extended to 97 by Abdul Azeem (303* for Hyderabad against Tamil Nadu at Hyderabad in the Ranji Trophy) and David Hookes (306* for South Australia v Tasmania at Adelaide in the Sheffield Shield). The latter's unbroken fourth-wicket partnership of 462 with Wayne Phillips (213*) is the highest for any wicket by Australian batsmen anywhere.

Chris Broad, recalled for his first tour, confidently launched England's successful assault on three trophies, and deservedly won the International Cricketer of the Year award. (Adrian Murrell/All-Sport)

SUMMARY TEST MATCHES 1986-87 SEASON

(Excluding Sri Lanka v New Zealand)

		Tests	Won by							Tied	Drawn
			E	A	WI	NZ	I	P	SL		
England	**v Australia**	5	2	1	·	·	·	·	·	·	2
Australia	**v India**	3	·	0	·	·	0	·	·	1	2
West Indies	**v New Zealand**	3	·	·	1	1	·	·	·	·	1
	v Pakistan	3	·	·	1	·	·	1	·	·	1
India	**v Pakistan**	5	·	·	·	·	0	1	·	·	4
	v Sri Lanka	3	·	·	·	·	2	·	0	·	1
		22	2	1	2	1	2	2	0	1	11

SUMMARY ONE-DAY INTERNATIONALS 1986-87 SEASON
(Up to 1 April 1987)

		Matches	E	S	Won by WI	NZ	I	P	SL	No Result
England	v Australia	7	4	3	·	·	·	·	·	·
	v West Indies	5	4	·	1	·	·	·	·	·
	v Pakistan	2	2	·	·	·	·	0	·	·
Australia	v West Indies	5	·	2	3	·	·	·	·	·
	v Pakistan	1	·	0	·	·	·	1	·	·
	v India	6	·	2	·	·	3	·	·	1
West Indies	v New Zealand	3	·	·	3	0	·	·	·	·
	v India	1	·	·	1	·	0	·	·	·
	v Pakistan	7	·	·	5	·	·	2	·	·
	v Sri Lanka	1	·	·	1	·	·	·	0	·
India	v Pakistan	7	·	·	·	·	1	6	·	·
	v Sri Lanka	6	·	·	·	·	5	·	1	·
Pakistan	v Sri Lanka	1	·	·	·	·	·	1	0	·
		52	10	7	14	0	9	10	1	1

The sorry remnants of Sydney's famous Hill. (Sue Harley)

CRICKET QUIZ

1 Who was the oldest man to captain England?
2 What is the highest number of wickets to fall in a single day of first-class cricket?
3 Who scored the most boundaries off one over in Test cricket?
4 Which colony played its initial first-class match as Port Philip District?
5 Who was the first batsman to score a century before lunch on the first day of a Test match?
6 Which ground staged both the first Test match and the first first-class match in South Africa?
7 Who is the only wicket-keeper to have dismissed an entire side in any cricket match?
8 West Indies hold the world record for the longest sequence of matches without defeat. How many is it?
9 Who was the first Test cricketer to die?
10 Which first-class county was founded at Sidmouth in Devon?
11 Who scored the first hundred in a Women's Test match?
12 In which year did the first Indian team tour England?
13 Sir Arthur Conan Doyle took only one first-class wicket. Who was his victim?
14 Hanif Mohammad played the longest innings in any cricket match. How long did he bat?
15 Who published the first cricket annual?
16 Who holds the world record for the most first-class match appearances?
17 What first-class Test record does Sanjeeva Weerasinghe hold?
18 Who is the only bowler to take all ten wickets in a first-class innings in the West Indies?
19 Who is the only batsman to score 2000 runs in a season without making a century?
20 Who, when aged 60 years and 151 days, became the oldest man to play in a first-class match in England?

(Answers on Page 240)

21 Which teams, led by Ray Illingworth and Garfield Sobers, completed for the Guinness Trophy?

E

Ealham, Alan George Ernest b 30 Aug 1944 (Kent) 94-5
East, David Edward b 27 Jul 1959 (Essex) 92, 93, **93**, 104, 150
East, Robert John b 31 Mar 1953 (OFS) **105**, 160
Eastman, Lawrence Charles 1897-1941 (Essex; Otago) 189
Eckersley, Peter Thorp 1904-40 (Lancs) **115**
Edmonds, Philippe Henri b 8 Mar 1951 (CU; Middx; E) 50
Edrich, John Hugh MBE b 21 Jun 1937 (Surrey; E) 38, 40, 184, 186, **209**, 209
Edrich, William John DFC 1916-86 (Middx; E) 80, 82, 118, 124, 138, 154, 184, 189
Edward II, King of England 1284-1327 7
Eggar, John Drennan 1916-83 (OU; Hants; Derbys) 102
Elliott, Charles Standish b 24 Apr 1912 (Derbys) 102, 209
Elliott, Gideon 1828-69 (V) 148
Elliott, Harry 1891-1976 (Derbys; E) 102, 103, 188
Ellis, Mathew 1870-1940 (V) 143
Emburey, John Ernest b 20 Aug 1952 (Middx; W Prov; E) 69, 88, **89**
Emmett, Thomas 1841-1904 (Yorks; E) 19-20
Endean, William Russell b 31 May 1924 (T; S Afr) 154, 156
English, Edward Apsey 1864-1966 (Hants) 96
Evans, Thomas Godfrey CBE b 18 Aug 1920 (Kent; E) 39-40, **46**, 52, 54, 59, 145, 188, 191
Everett, Samuel Charles 1901-70 (NSW) 142

F

Fagg, Arthur Edward 1915-77 (Kent; E) 74, 75
Farrimond, William 1903-79 (Lancs; E) 93, 114
Faulkner, George Aubrey DSO; Major 1881-1930 (T; S Afr) 58
Fazal Mahmood b 18 Feb 1927 (N India; Punjab; Lahore; P) 25, 51, 69, **178**, 178-9
Fender, Percy George Herbert 1892-1985 (Sussex; Surrey; E) 75, 76, 92, 188, 189
Ferguson, Bill 75
Ferguson, William Henry BEM 'Fergie' 1880-1957 (Australian scorer) 11, 75
Ferris, John James 1867-1900 (NSW; S Aus; Aus; Glos; E) 62
Fielder, Arthur 1877-1949 (Kent; E) 23, 82, 137
Filliston, Joseph (umpire) 216
Findlay, Thaddeus Michael b 19 Oct 1943 (Windward Is; WI) 165, 166
Fingleton, John Henry Webb 1908-81 (NSW; Aus) 23, 32, 38, 146
Firth, Jack 1918-81 (Yorks; Leics) 117
Flavell, John Alfred b 15 May 1929 (Worcs; E) **133**, 133
Fleetwood-Smith, Leslie O'Brien 'Chuck' 1910-71 (V; Aus) 47, 87
Fleming, Stephen (Marlborough Coll; NZ) 214
Fletcher, David George William b 6 Jul 1924 (Surrey) 72
Fletcher, Duncan Andrew Gwynne b 27 Sep 1948 (Rhodesia; Zimbabwe) 211
Fletcher, Keith William Robert b 20 May 1944 (Essex; E) 41, 61, 78, 105, **105**, 184, 188, 211
Flint, Derrick b 14 Jun 1924 (Warks) 197

Flowers, Wilfred 1856-1926 (Notts; Eng) **137**, 189
Foley, Cyril Pelham Lt Col 1868-1936 (CU; Middx) 70
Ford, Francis Gilbertstone Justice 1866-1940 (CU; Middx; E) 70
Foster, Frank Rowbotham 1889-1958 (Warks; Eng) 130
Foster, Neil Alan b 6 May 1962 (Essex; E) **105**, 214
Foster, Reginald Erskine 'Tip' (OU; Worcs; E) 30, 34, 67, 158
Foulkes, Ivor b 22 Feb 1955 (Border) 160
Fowler, Graeme b 20 Apr 1957 (Lancs; E) 74, 76
Frames, AS (sec, S Afr 1929) **153**
Francis, MG (OFS) 156
Frank, Charles Newton 1891-1961 (T; S Afr) 35
Fredericks, Roy Clifton b 11 Nov 1942 (Guyana; Glam; WI) 41, 106
Freeman, Alfred Percy 'Tich' 1888-1965 (Kent; E) 84, 87, 88, 89, 100, **101**, 112, 128, 130, 186
Freeman, Eric Walter b 13 Jul 1944 (S Aus; Aus) 150
Freilinghans, HO (manager, S Afr 1929) **153**
French, Bruce Nicholas b 13 Aug 1959 (Notts; E) 122, 123
Fry, Charles Burgess 1872-1956 (OU; Surrey; Sussex; Hants; E) 74, 80, 137, 144, 156, 185

G

Gaekwad, Anshuman Dattajirao b 23 Sep 1952 (Baroda; I) 38, 68
Garlick, Paul Lawrence b 2 Aug 1964 (CU) 84
Garner, Joel b 16 Dec 1952 (Barbados; Somerset; WI) 51, 202, 206, 211
Garnett, E (Berks) 215
Garrett, Thomas William 1858-1943 (NSW; Aus) 18-20
Gatting, Michael William b 6 Jun 1957 (Middx; E) **118**
Gavaskar, Sunil Manohar b 10 July 1949 (Bombay; Somerset; I) 5, 28-9, **29**, 30, 32, 33, 34, 42, 57, 60, 61, 62, 67, 68, 210
Gaveston, Piers d 1312 7
Geary, George 1893-1981 (Leics; E) 106, 116, 117, 173, 186, 189
George IV, King of England 1762-1830 9
Ghavri, Karsan Devraj b 28 Feb 1951 (Saurashtra; Bombay; I) 51
Ghazali, Mohamad Ebrahim Zainuddin 'Ebbu' b 15 Jun 1924 (Maharashtra; Muslims; Services; P) 40
Ghulam Ahmed b 4 July 1922 (Hyderabad, I) 69
Ghulam Mahomed 1898-1966 (Muslims; Sind) **172**
Gibb, Paul Anthony 1913-77 (CU; Yorks; Essex; E) 104
Gibb, Peter JM b 17 Oct 1931 (T) 158
Gibbons, Harold Harry Ian 'Doc' 1904-73 (Worcs) 133
Gibbs, Glendon Lionel 1925-79 (Br Guiana; WI) 164
Gibbs, Lancelot Richard b 29 Sept 1934 (Guyana; Warks; S Aus; WI) 43, 51, 69, **130**, 165
Gibson, Sir Kenneth Lloyd 1888-1967 (Essex) 104

Giffen, George 1859-1927 (S Aus; Aus) 18, 50, 57, 58, 90, 91, 102, 114, 147-8, **148**, 149, 189
Giffen, Walter Frank 1861-1949 (S Aus; Aus) 72
Gifford, Norman MBE b 30 Mar 1940 (Worcs; Warks; E) **133**, 186, **201**, 201
Gilligan, Arthur Edward Robert 1894-1976 (CU; Surrey; Sussex; E) 23, 25, 28, 72, 180
Gilmour, Gary John b 26 Jun 1951 (NSW; Aus) 210
Gimblett, Harold 1914-78 (Somerset; E) **124**, 125
Gladwin, Clifford b 3 Apr 1916 (Derbys; E) 23, 103, **105**
Godambe, Shankarrao Ramachandra 1899-1969 (Bombay; Hindus; Gujarat) **172**
Goddard, John Douglas Claude b 21 Apr 1919 (Barbados; WI) 60
Goddard, Thomas William John 1900-66 (Glos; E) 108, 112, 186
Goddard, Trevor Leslie b 1 Aug 1931 (Natal; NE Transvaal; S Afr) 51, 57, 154
Gomes, Hilary Angelo 'Larry' b 13 Jul 1953 (Trinidad; Middx; WI) 41, 211
Gomez, Gerald Ethridge b 10 Oct 1919 (Trinidad; WI) 164
Gooch, Graham Alan b 23 Jul 1953 (Essex; W Prov; E) 41, **105**, 105, 206, 207, 210
Goodway, Cyril Clement b 10 Jul 1909 (Warks) **130**
Goonesena, Gamini b 16 Feb 1931 (Ceylon; Notts; CU; NSW) 138
Gordon, Norman b 6 Aug 1911 (T; S Afr) 158
Gower, David Ivon b 1 Apr 1957 (Leics; E) 40, **117**, 206, **209**, 210
Grace, Dr Henry Mills 1808-1871 (father of WG, EM, GF) 192
Grace, Dr William Gilbert 1848-1915 (Glos; E) 18, 25, 28, 54, 60, **60**, 70, 73, 76, 80, 82, 90, 108, 112, 122, 134, **136**, 137, 138, 151, 184, 185, 186, 188, 189, 193, 216, 218, **pl 2**
Grace, Edward Mills 1841-1911 (Glos; E) 193
Grace, George Frederick 1850-80 (Glos; E) 96
Grace, Martha nee Pocock (mother of WG, EM, GF) 192-3
Graham, Henry 1870-1911 (V; Otago; Aus) 72
Graveney, Thomas William OBE b 16 Jun 1927 (Glos; Worcs; Q; E) 40, 80, **132**, **133**, 145, 184, 186, 189
Gray, James Roy b 19 May 1926 (Hants) **111**
Green, David Michael b 10 Nov 1939 (OU; Lancs; Glos) 80
Greenidge, Cuthbert Gordon b 1 May 1951 (Hants; Barbados; WI) 41, 78, **110**, 185, 206, 207, 210, 211
Greenidge, Geoffrey Alan b 26 May 1948 (Barbados; Sussex; WI) 85
Greenwood, Andrew 1847-89 (Yorks; E) 19, 20
Greenwood, Julia b 1951 (Yorks; E) 198
Greetham, Christopher Herbert Millington b 28 Aug 1936 (Somerset) **125**
Gregory, Charles William 1878-1910 (NSW) 145
Gregory, David William 1845-1919 (NSW; Aus) 18, 19, 20
Gregory, Edward James 'Ned' 1839-99 (NSW; Aus) 11, 19-20
Gregory, John Morison 'Jack' 1895-1973 (NSW;

ANSWERS TO CRICKET QUIZ

1 W.G. Grace
2 39
3 Sandeep Patil
4 Victoria
5 Victor Trumper
6 St George's Park, Port Elizabeth
7 Welihinda Bennett
8 27

9 James Southerton
10 Somerset
11 Myrtle Maclagan
12 1886
13 W.G. Grace
14 16 hours 10 minutes
15 Samuel Britcher
16 Wilfred Rhodes

17 Highest career bowling average in Test cricket
18 Eddie Hemmings
19 David Green
20 Lord Harris
21 England v Rest of the World 1970

Home Studies Course in Osteopathy ..

CONTENTS

Sept. 27, 1909

INTRODUCTION TO PART FIRST

(Comprising Lessons I and II)

In this part of our course we present to the student the theory and practical principles of Osteopathy. We have endeavored, so far as was possible, to make the instruction *practical* and to the point, and have not wasted words in elaborating theories or describing the several methods, movements and forms of Osteopathic Theatment, but have, on the contrary, aimed to state everything clearly, forcibly and practically, so as to lose no time in getting to the point.

We have omitted, so far as was possible, all technical terms and expressions, and have always used the common and generally understood term in preference to the technical one.

We have endeavored to give the student specific directions for the various procedures recommended, with the reason for each, but have wished to avoid taking him into the maze of theory and speculation. We have given him in a few words the theory underlying Osteopathy, eliminating the vague generalities and the speculative vagaries of many writers upon the subject.

We might easily have padded out the instruction given herein so that it would have occupied a space at least five times as large as that occupied by what we have written, but we believe that the intelligent student, wishing to be told how to do things in as short a time and in as practical a manner as possible, has no time to waste in hunting the kernel of wheat in the bushel of chaff

We recommend that the student go over the various movements and motions very carefully, thoroughly acquainting himself with them, and then proceed to put into practice his instructions, using some friend or relative upon whom to experiment. There is nothing like getting to work and DOING things. An hour's practice will be of more benefit than days of reading. It not only is more practical, but serves to fix firmly in the student's mind the principles which he has just studied.

3

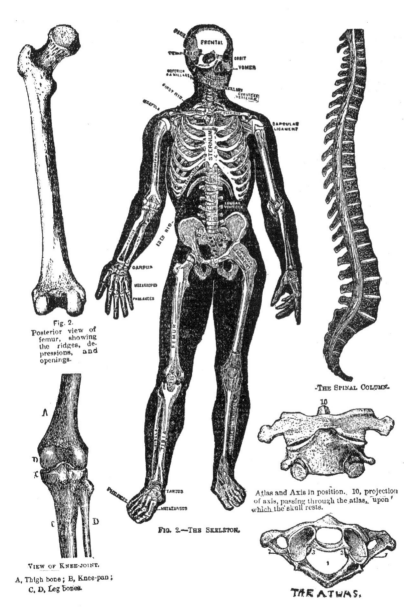

Fig. 2.
Posterior view of femur, showing the ridges, depressions, and openings.

VIEW OF KNEE-JOINT.

A, Thigh bone; B, Knee-pan; C, D, Leg bones.

FIG. 2.—THE SKELETON.

THE SPINAL COLUMN.

Atlas and Axis in position. 10, projection of axis, passing through the atlas, upon which the skull rests.

THE ATLAS.

LESSON I

THE THEORY OF OSTEOPATHY

Osteopathy is a system, method or science of healing disease without the use of drugs or medicines of any kind. It is based upon the proven laws of Anatomy and Physiology, and comprises a scientific and thorough knowledge of the structure and functions of the human mechanism. Our students are taught to understand and apply certain organic laws and natural remedial resources, within the human organism itself, and by means of scientific manipulation and adjustment assist Nature, in harmonious accord with its own mechanical principles, activities and processes, to recover from displacements, derangements, obstructions and pressures, and to regain its normal equilibrium of form, action and function, thus restoring to the patient normal Health and Strength.

Osteopathy holds to the theory that the body is a delicate mechanism, subject to the same laws of mechanics as those which regulate all mechanical structures in their construction, arrangement, position and operation. That to have perfect action in any machine, each and every part of it must be exactly in place and entirely free from obstruction. That any machine subject to great strains or shocks, such as the human body sustains from accidents, overwork, sudden atmospheric changes, bad surroundings, etc., can be so racked by these agents that some of its parts will be misplaced or dislocated and its normal action perverted or entirely destroyed. That the condition of the human body which we term Disease is due entirely to obstruction of or pressure on some of the arteries, veins, nerves or ducts of the body, from the action of which we obtain motion, sensation, digestion, assimilation, nutrition and egestion. That a removal of this obstruction or pressure will restore the circulation of the blood and other fluids of the body and bring about a condition of Ease, Strength and Health.

The aim of our students is to restore to normal action and function the organs and different parts of the body that have been manifesting along abnormal lines. The nerves, which have been likened to a great telegraphic system, passing

5

through, over, under and between the bones, muscles, ligaments, arteries and veins, are extremely sensitive and liable
to get out of order   Our student, like the skilled lineman, first
finds out where the wires are crossed or interfered with, and
starts in to adjust them   He extends the contracted muscle
or reduces the slight dislocation which has caused a pressure
upon the nerve and has shut off its current, and by so doing
he restores the line to working order and gives the suffering
organ or part the perfect service which it demands. He does
all this by scientific and intelligent manipulation. No drugs
are prescribed by the Osteopath. He does not need them. He
has something better.

The nerves convey sensations to and from the brain, and
control the various functions of the body, and it is of the ut-
most importance that they be kept free from interference and
pressure.   But the nerves themselves are dependent on the
supply of blood, as is also every organ or part of the body.
The blood is sent to all parts of the body through the arteries
and brought back to the heart through the veins, the arteries
and veins branching out through the intricate network of organs, muscles and nerves. A natural flow of blood means
Health, while a local or general disturbance of the circulation causes Disease   If the circulation is any way obstructed
the part which is thus deprived of its nourishment is soon
weakened and becomes diseased. An obstructed artery may
cause heart disease, and an obstructed vein may cause inflam-
matory rheumatism, dropsy, erysipelas, varicose veins or even
cancer   By our method of Osteopathic treatment the obstruction is located and removed, the circulation stimulated,
the parts nourished, and the impurities which have gathered
are carried off.

Our student adjusts into harmonious relation all the wonderful and intricate mechanism of the human body, thus giving free circulation of the blood to and from the heart, freeing
the nerve force, adjusting any parts of the framework which
may have become displaced, building up the system, stimulating and developing and thus effecting a cure

He accomplishes the desired result by an intelligent and
scientific method of manipulation of the different parts of the
body. By his manipulations he stimulates the several nerve
centers of action, removes the pressure from the nerves all
along the lines of their distribution, arouses nerve force, frees
and equalizes the circulation of the blood and other fluids of

the body, and, in short, equalizes the forces in every tissue, muscle, organ, nerve and cell in the body and restores harmony to every part of the system. If a muscle is contracted and tightens down on one or more nerves, trouble is sure to follow. If the nerve interfered with happens to be a sensory nerve, paralysis may ensue; if a sympathetic nerve, the nutrition is cut off; failure of any or all the various functions of the body is likely to occur. The only way to remedy the trouble and restore the normal workings of the different parts of this mighty machine is to go to the seat of the trouble, find and remove the obstruction and start the mechanism working without friction or jolting. With the obstructions to the free flow of the blood and other fluids removed, and the circulation restored through natural channels; with the removal of any and all pressure upon nerve fibers; with the adjustment of any misplaced or shifted parts of the machinery; the system must right itself and health ensue

Every bone, every drop of blood, every nerve, ligament and muscle, however small and seemingly useless, has a distinct and positive work to perform, and in a normal condition it will unerringly perform that work. The human body is perfect in its plan and action, and disease is impossible except under abnormal conditions. Osteopathy teaches how to remedy the abnormal conditions and to again start this intricate machine running smoothly, with its parts all nicely adjusted, its bearings free from friction and every detail in perfect harmony with the whole.

Osteopathy goes to the root of disease, the prime cause of the disorder, and as many of the so-called varieties of disease have one common origin, there are practically no diseases but are materially benefited or entirely cured by this form of treatment. In fact, many diseases will yield to no other form of treatment. The best results of Osteopathic treatment are, of course, obtained in cases of disease resulting from an abnormal condition of the machinery of the body, the nerves, blood vessels and fluids of the system, which effects are, almost without exception, caused by partial or complete displacement of bones, muscles, tissues, etc. Chronic cases, which are the despair of the drug-giving physician, are those in which the Osteopath makes his most remarkable cures, and, naturally, he prefers to treat such cases

The discoverer of Osteopathy, Dr. A T. Still, inclined to the theory that the majority of diseases were caused by dislo-

cated bones, and he consequently named the new science "Osteopathy," from the Greek roots "osteon" (bone) and "pathos"
(suffering). This name has been adhered to by his followers, notwithstanding the fact that the advancements in the
science have shown that the real Osteopathic treatment consists principally in a treatment of the nerves, and, strictly
speaking, the term "Neuropathy" would be far more appropriate, although the original name will probably be always
adhered to, as the public have become accustomed to it, and a
change of names at this time would create confusion.

We are inclined to the theory that there are but comparatively few cases of dislocation, and are convinced that in many
cases the dislocated bone is but a contracted muscle, which is
readily relieved by manipulation, the operator and patient both
believing that a bone was dislocated and had been "set" by the
Osteopath.

BASIC PRINCIPLES OF OSTEOPATHY

1. That Health and Normal Function depend upon the
blood and nerve supply to the tissues.

2. That impaired structure or function of an organ causes
pain to be manifested when a pressure is exerted upon or
over the organ. That the nerves supplying the organ with
its nerve current will also manifest a sensitiveness to the touch,
as does the organ itself, consequently a sensitiveness along the
course of the nerves supplying any organ is an evidence of abnormal conditions existing in the organ itself.

3. An interference with a nerve, or an irritation to the
same, will affect the functions of the organ supplied by that
particular nerve, causing it to function abnormally.

4. Alternate pressure along the course of a nerve will
stimulate the organ supplied by that nerve. Steady pressure
upon a nerve will inhibit the action of the organ supplied by
that nerve.

5 That stimulation or inhibition of a nerve is most easily
accomplished at its periphery, or at the point of its emergence
from the spinal cord.

6 The only rational method of treatment of disease is
that which removes the cause by removing physical obstructions, by stimulating or inhibiting functional activity, by restoring the normal condition of nerve current and blood supply
to every organ in the body

7. That an equalized circulation of the blood and freed
nerve-current spells H-E-A-L-T-H.

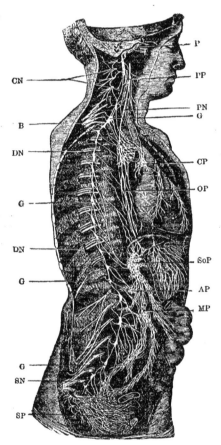

Fig. 75.

Vertical section of body, showing sympathetic nerves and ganglia of right side, and their connection with the cerebro-spinal nerves. — *Cerebro-spinal system :* CN, cervical nerves ; B, nerves distributed to the arm; DN, dorsal nerves; SN, sacral nerves, some of which are distributed to the leg ; PN, pneumogastric nerve. *Sympathetic system :* P, plexus in the head ; PP, pharyngeal plexus ; CP, cardiac plexus, OP, oesophageal plexus ; SoP, solar plexus ; AP, aortic plexus, MP, mesenteric plexus ; SP, sacral plexus ; G, some of the ganglia of the sympathetic system.

POINTS ON PRACTICE

(a) The Spinal Cord is the keyboard of a piano to the Osteopath. You will see by reference to our lesson on the Nervous System that the Spinal Column is the great cable from which branch out the spinal nerves which supply the nerve-current to each organ and part of the body. These spinal nerves escape from the Spinal Cord through openings along the length of the Spinal Column, and are often bound up, unduly pressed and interfered with by the muscles around the spine, and the nerve current to some part of the body is thereby reduced or shut off, causing pain and disease in some part or organ of the body supplied by that nerve, although that part or organ may be very far removed from the point at which the pressure or interference occurs By proper manipulation and movements the obstruction is removed, the current turned on once more and normal conditions restored

(b) The circulation of blood to and from the head is often found to be interfered with by a pressure or contraction of the muscles of the neck, and the interference often manifests itself in the shape of deafness, impaired sight, catarrh and other disorders of the sight, hearing and smell, and also in dizziness, headaches, etc, etc By proper manipulation of the neck normal conditions are restored.

(c) Interferences with the circulation and nerve-current are often removed by the free movement and manipulation of the legs and arms, which frees and softens up the muscles and releases the obstructed circulation and nerve-current and allows Nature to restore normal conditions.

(d) It is often found that contracted muscles are drawing in the ribs and exerting an undue pressure upon some of the organs of the body This condition can frequently be relieved by the simple treatment which we have described as "Chest Expansion" (see lesson on Movements), the principle of which is that the expansion is best given with the arms high above the head, and the knee of the operator pressed upon the spine, just below the shoulder blades, which treatment stretches the contracted chest muscles and springs the ribs into place.

(e) The Great Osteopathic Dysentery Treatment , (see lesson), which consists in pressing your knee against the pa-

19

tient's spine, just below the last rib, at the same time bending the patient backward, will remove the trouble almost instantly. The theory of this treatment is fully set forth in the lesson treating of this class of troubles.

(f) Osteopathy has discovered a method of reducing fevers and slowing down the heart's action in a very short time. It is most simple and consists of a pressure on the vaso-motor center, at the base of the brain, on the back of the neck, just over the upper cervical vertebræ.

SPINAL CENTRES

The following table of centres for Osteopathic Spinal Treatment will prove interesting and instructive to the student When a muscular contraction is found at one or more points along the length of the Spinal Column, it will be found that a pressure is exerted upon the nerve emerging at that point, and a corresponding trouble is manifested in the organs supplied by that particular nerve or nerves. The proper manipulation will relieve the trouble.

The sensory nerve supply to the several parts and organs are as follows:

First, second and third Dorsal—Heart.

First, second, third, fourth and fifth Dorsal—Lungs.

Sixth, seventh, eighth and ninth Dorsal—Stomach

Ninth, tenth, eleventh and twelfth Dorsal—Intestines down to upper part of rectum.

Second, third and fourth Sacral—Rectum.

Seventh, eighth, ninth and tenth Dorsal—Liver and Gall Bladder.

Tenth, eleventh and twelfth Dorsal—Kidney and Ureter.

Second, third and fourth Sacral—Neck of Bladder.

Eleventh and twelfth Dorsal, and first Lumbar—Over-dis-tension and ineffectual contraction of Bladder.

Tenth, eleventh and twelfth Dorsal, and first, second, third and fifth Lumbar—Prostate.

Tenth Dorsal—Testis, or Ovary.

Eleventh and twelfth Dorsal—Appendages, etc.

Tenth, eleventh and twelfth Dorsal, and first Lumbar—Uterus (in contraction).

First, second, third and fourth Sacral—Os Uteri,

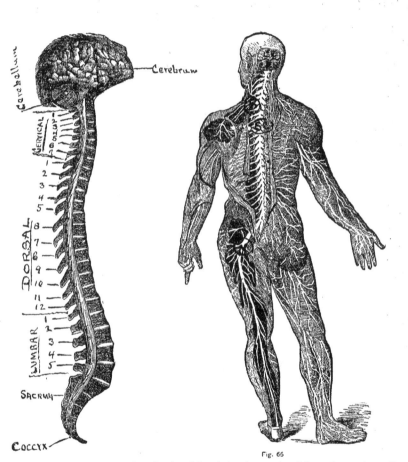

The brain and spinal col-
umn with vertebrae
classified.

Fig. 66

Posterior view of the spinal cord,—a portion of the cerebrum and cerebellum,
and some of the nerves of the cerebro-spinal system. On the left side of the
body some of the tissues are removed to show the deeper nerves, while the
right side shows certain superficial ones.—CE, cerebrum; CER, cerebellum;
B, nerves distributed to the arm; SC, spinal cord; SN, sciatic nerve.

LESION TABLE

WHERE TO LOOK FOR LESIONS

If there seems to be trouble in any particular organ or part, look carefully for lesions in the corresponding centre on the spinal column, as per following table If a lesion is found at the nerve centre of an organ, you may rest assured that there is a manifestation of disease in that particular organ. In case of trouble in any of the following organs or parts, examine the spine for lesions at the following points:

Pharynx, Larynx and Tonsils—Second and third Cervical

Thyroid Gland—Fifth, sixth and seventh Cervical and first Dorsal.

Arm—Fifth, sixth, seventh and eighth Cervical and first Dorsal

, Lungs and Bronchi—Second to eighth Dorsal

Heart—Second to fifth Dorsal; also middle of Cervical region.

Stomach—Third to eighth Dorsal

Liver—Ninth and tenth Dorsal.

Spleen—Eighth to eleventh Dorsal

Duodenum—Sixth to tenth Dorsal

Jepunum and Ileum—Lower Dorsal and Lumbar.

Colon—Second to fifth Lumbar.

Rectum—Second to fifth Lumbar; Sacral; also third and fourth Dorsal

Uterus—Second to fifth Lumbar, ninth and tenth Dorsal

Genitals, generally—Second to fifth Lumbar.

Bladder—Second, third and fourth Sacral.

Sphincter Ani—Fifth Sacral

You will understand that not only does a lesion of a centre produce disease in the organ supplied by it, but also a diseased condition of an organ will manifest itself in a tenderness at its spinal nerve centres.

LESSON II

MOVEMENTS AND MANIPULATIONS

Treatment for Dislocation of Atlas.

There are several forms of Osteopathic treatment generally known as "Movements." They have a most important physiological and therapeutic effect. The venous and lymphatic circulation is materially affected by these Movements, and a corresponding therapeutic effect is thereby obtained. Osteopathic Movements are of two general classes: Active and Passive. Active Movements are produced by the efforts of both; the operator moves the body or limb, and the patient exerts a resistive effort; in others the patient moves his body or limb, and the operator exerts the resistive effort. The principle is the same in both cases, the details differing because of convenience of handling, etc.

Raising Clavicle.

Passive Movements are produced simply by the efforts of the operator, without any assistance or resistance on the part of the patient. The patient is perfectly passive and simply allows the operator to make the Movements.

Osteopathic Movements are several in number, each particular form being capable of manifestation by Active or Passive effort. The movements are known as: Rotation, Flexion and Extension, Separating and Closing, Joint Stretching. The name of each Movement will suggest its application, but, in order that the student may readily understand each Movement, we will give a short description of the various applications of each particular movement.

Kneading the Back.

ROTATION

ROTATION OF THE FOOT.—With the patient lying on his back, take his heel in your left hand, and his toes in your right, and make a rotary movement from the ankle, pressing the foot forward. Repeat several times. (Passive.)

ROTATION OF THE LEGS.—The patient on his back, place one hand on the sole of his foot, the other under his knee, raise the leg and rotate the leg from the hip, outward. Repeat several times. (Passive or Active.)

Breast Manipulation.

ROTATION OF THE ARMS.—The patient sitting, grasp the arm below the elbows and rotate outward. Repeat several times. (Passive or Active.)

ROTATION OF THE SHOULDER.—The patient sitting, place one hand on the shoulder and the other under the elbow, and rotate. Repeat several times. (Passive.)

Kneading Forearm.

ROTATION OF. THE HAND.—The patient sitting, take his hand in one of yours, and with your other hand grasp his wrist and rotate from side to side. Repeat several times. (Passive.)

ROTATION OF THE HEAD.—The patient lying on his back, stand at his head, and place one hand on his forehead, the other under his neck, and rotate the head slowly from side to side. Repeat several times. (Passive.)

Breast Manipulation.

ROTATION OF THE BODY.—The patient sitting with hands on hips, stand behind him and place your right hand on his right shoulder-blade and your left on the left side of his chest. Rotate by pushing his right side forward with your right hand and drawing his left side backward with your left hand. Then reverse the position of the hands and rotate in an opposite direction. Repeat several times. (Passive.)

Kneading Abdominal Muscle.

ROTATION OF THE PELVIS.—The patient on his back and holding on to the table, grasp his feet and rotate his legs in such a manner as to describe a circle large enough to bring the pelvis into action. Repeat several times. (Passive.)

FLEXION AND EXTENSION

Kneading the Neck.

FLEXION AND EXTENSION OF THE FOOT.—The patient on his back, take his toes in one hand and his ankle in the other. Move the foot backward and forward. If you prefer operate on both feet at the same time. Repeat several times. (Passive or Active.)

FLEXION AND EXTENSION OF THE LEG.—The patient on his back, place one hand on the knee, the other under the sole of the foot, and move the leg up and down, flexing it against the chest. Repeat several times. (Active.)

FLEXION AND EXTENSION OF THE ARMS.—The patient sitting, stand behind him and grasp his wrists, he keeping his elbows close to his body. Move his arms up and down. Repeat several times. (Active.)

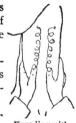

Kneading with Thumb.

FLEXION AND EXTENSION OF THE HAND.—The patient sitting, grasp his wrist with one of your hands and hold his

Wringing Movement.

Kneading Arm.

Kneading the Glutei.

Kneading Abdomen.

Kneading Abdomen.

fingers in your other hand, and move the hand up and down. Repeat several times. (Passive or Active.)

SEPARATING AND CLOSING

SEPARATING AND CLOSING THE ARMS.—The patient sitting with arms extended to the front, take hold of his wrists and separate and close his arms. Repeat several times. (Active.)

SEPARATING AND CLOSING THE LEGS.—The patient on his back, take hold of his ankles, underneath, and separate and close his legs. Repeat several times. (Active.)

SEPARATING AND CLOSING THE KNEES.—The patient on his back, stand at his side and placing one hand on each knee, separate and close. (Active.)

JOINT STRETCHING

STRETCHING THE ARM AND SHOULDER JOINTS.—The patient on his back, with head and shoulders raised on pillow, and arms extended over his head, stand at his head and take his hands in yours, passing your thumb between his thumb and forefinger, letting your fingers pass around the fleshy part of his thumb and back of his hand. Make several vigorous elastic pulls, avoiding sudden jerks. Make the pulls gradual, then withdraw the force suddenly. Repeat several times.

STRETCHING THE LEG JOINTS.—The patient on his back, take his ankles in your hands and pull straight down. Gently, but firmly. (Repeat several times.)

STRETCHING TOE AND FINGER JOINTS.—Take each toe or finger separately and pull slowly and gradually, releasing the pressure suddenly.

KNEADING

This is a leading method of Osteopathic treatment, and one frequently employed. It consists of compression of the tissues and muscles by grasping them or by pressing them against underlying bony surfaces. It differs from Osteopathic Rubbing in as much as the hand is not allowed to move along the surface of the skin, but is held firmly on the parts. We separate the different forms of Manipulation into three general classes: Superficial, Digital and Palmar.

Surface Kneading is practically an intelligent form of pinching movement, and acts solely upon the skin and the tissues immediately underlying it. The skin is gently but firmly grasped between the thumb and forefinger, and lifted from the bone or muscle, then released the moment the strain is greatest. The two hands are alternately used, the one picking up the skin as the other drops it, the surface being gone over in a systematic manner. This form of Manipulation is most valuable in emptying and refilling the blood vessels and lymph spaces and channels, and is quite stimulating. It is especially useful in affections of the skin.

Surface Kneading.

Palmar Kneading is intended to act upon the muscles. It is akin to the movement of the hand of the baker as he kneads his dough. The operator grasps the muscle with the palm of his hand, keeping the fingers close together, the thumbs out. The thumb is not used, the muscle being grasped between the fingers and the palm of the hand, the heel of the hand, or the lower fleshy part of the thumb. Do not allow the skin to slip, but maintain a firm grasp. Manipulate deeply so as to reach the deeper parts. The muscle should be compressed by the hand and at the same time gently lifted from the bone or underlying tissues, rolled and stretched. When the strain is greatest, release so as to stimulate. Work slowly and carefully, repeating the manipulations according to the requirements of the case, and the state of the patient. In the beginning, do not exert much force, but later on increase the force as the patient becomes accustomed to it. Try to individualize groups of muscles, as the best results are thus obtained. In Palmar Manipulation, use the hands alternately.

Kneading Back.

Kneading the Hand.

In some cases it is also desirable to use a rolling movement, the heel of the hand and the fleshy part of the thumb being pressed upon the muscle, which is then rolled to and fro, the fingers not being used. Use one or both hands. This rolling movement is especially useful in manipulating the upper part of the back, the hips, arms and legs. In manipulating the legs or arms, a wringing movement may be used occasionally, the movement resembling the motions of a woman's hands when she is wringing out a thick garment. In some cases deep kneading with the heel of the hand is preferable to the use of both palm and fingers, especially in manipulating the back, chest and abdomen. The operator must use his own good judgment in such cases, ascertaining which method gives the most relief. The different modes of administering Palmar Manipulation may be varied, alternated or combined. The student should thoroughly acquaint himself with the several methods above mentioned, and should practice them on himself and his friends until he is proficient.

Kneading the Neck.

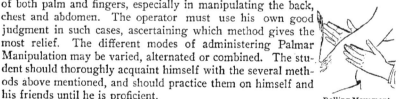

Rolling Movement,

Digital Kneading.

Digital Kneading is effected by grasping the tissue between the ends of the fingers and thumb, and then rubbing the tissue against the bone. Either the end of one finger or of several may be used in connection with the thumb. This form of Manipulation is used principally in manipulation of the spine, joints, head, face and abdomen.

RUBBING

Beating Movement.

We advocate the use of Rubbing, in connection with other Osteopathic treatment. The palm of the hand and the lower part of the fingers should be used, the tips of the fingers and the thumb being turned back. It is beneficial in stimulating the parts, and promoting the flow of the blood and lymph.

PERCUSSION

Chopping Movement.

Percussion is another form of administering Osteopathic treatment. It consists of administering blows to different parts of the body, with varying degrees of force. The wrist should be flexible and loose, as a stiff wrist gives a blow such as is used in fighting. The blow should be elastic and springy, which although penetrating deeply, does not injure the surface. Percussion can be given by several methods, which we will not briefly describe. The first method is by striking the body with the inside flat surface of the half-closed fist, the heel of the hand and the closed ends of the fingers coming in contact with the flesh. The second method is a chopping movement, made with the little finger side of the hand. The hand is likened to a butcher's cleaver in this chopping movement. The fingers are held loosely apart, coming together when the blow is struck. The third method is a slapping movement, which is best comprehended by the position and movement of the mother administering a well-merited spanking to one of her brood. The fingers are held rigid, and the body slapped. The fourth method is a clapping movement, the hand being hollowed so as to emit a hollow sound; just as one holds his hands in applauding at a theater or concert. The fifth method is a tapping movement, with the tips of the fingers, one or more fingers of one or both hands being used. Percussion in its different forms is a powerful stimulant to the nerve centers.

Slapping.

Tapping.

VIBRATION

Beating Sciatic Nerve.

This is a most important form of Osteopathic treatment, and is a very powerful stimulant. It consists of certain oscil-

latory movements, produced through a succession of rapid
individual efforts of the operator's hand. There should be
little or no perceptible strain upon the arm muscles of the
operator. The palm of the hand or the fingers must be placed
firmly upon the parts to be treated, the arm being held straight
and a fine trembling or vibrating movement communi-

Digital Vibration.

cated to the hand by the muscles of the upper part
of the arm. The movement is somewhat difficult of acquirement, but practice will make perfect, and the student
must persist in his practice until the desired movement is acquired, for this is one of the most stimulating and penetrating
of all the methods of Osteopathic treatment, its effect being
quite perceptible and almost akin to the effects of a current of
electricity. It has a stimulating and strengthening effect upon
the nerves, and acts strongly upon the venous circulation and
upon the lymphatics. Be careful not to press upon the body

Digital Vibration.

with your wrist, as you should use no greater pressure than
the weight of your hand. When properly administered by one
hand on the breast, the vibrations should be distinctly felt by
the other hand placed under the back of the patient. A useful
method of practicing this valuable method of treatment is had
by placing a goblet of water on the table and then placing the
hand on the table and making the vibratory movement. If
you have acquired the proper delicate vibratory motion, the

Deep Vibration.

water will merely quiver in the centre, and will not move from
side to side. Practice this until you perfect it. Vibration
using the fingers alone, is known as Digital Vibration: when
the palm of the hand is used it is known as Palmar Vibration:
and another method in which the knuckles of the closed hand
are used, is known as Knuckle Vibration. The principle is the
same in all three forms, the particular method to be used being
merely that which may seem best to the operator and best
adapted to the shape and form of the particular part of the

Vibration of
Liver.

body being treated.

STROKING

This form of Osteopathic treatment is useful in producing
sedative or quieting effects. It should be applied with a very
light contact, the tips of the fingers, or the palm of the hand,
just barely touching the patient. In some cases it will produce
a feeling of drowsiness on the part of the patient, and is also
very useful in relieving certain forms of nervous headache, and
in affording relief from insomnia. Patients will frequently

drop off into a light doze during this form of treatment. It is used after the more vigorous forms of Osteopathic treatment, and never fails to quiet down the patient, equalize the circulation and relieve an excess of stimulation. Stroking should always be performed in a downward and outward direction, and in one direction only, not to-and-fro. The tips of one, more or all of the fingers, or the palmar surface of one or both hands, are moved gently over the skin, with a light contact, not even the mere weight of the hand being allowed to press upon the surface of the skin. Lightness, gentleness, and airiness are the words best describing the Stroking movement. The student should acquire this most important and effective movement.

Stroking.

NERVE PRESSURE

This form of treatment consists of a pressure upon a nerve at some point in its course. It is either stimulative or sedative, according to the manner of its application. The physiological effect of a sudden, light pressure upon a nerve, followed by an immediate withdrawal of the pressure, repeated several times, is that of decided stimulation. On the other hand, a firm, steady, deep pressure desensitizes or deadens sensation, and if continued for some time will produce numbness. Remember alternate pressure and relaxing stimulates; firm, steady, continued pressure desensitizes. We will frequently refer to these two forms of nerve pressure, so be sure to get them firmly fixed in your mind. The points at which the pressure is more frequently applied are the motor points lying near the surface, where the principal nerves are easily reached by pressure. The spinal nerves are treated by placing one finger on each side of the spinal column, and exerting a pressure at points on a line with the spaces between the vertebræ.

Holding Vaso-Motor.

FREEING THE PNEUMO-GASTRIC NERVE

The patient on his back, place your hand under the chin, pull the head backward. Move from right to left, and manipulate deeply and firmly the lower part of the neck, on each side of the windpipe. This frees and stimulates the pneumo-gastric nerve, which largely influences the organs of digestion.

Freeing Pneumo-Gastric.

PRESSURE ON THE PHRENIC NERVE

Seat your patient on a stool or chair, standing behind him. Place the fingers of each hand upon the transverse processes

Pressure Phrenic Nerve.

of the third, fourth and fifth cervicals. Press the fingers forward and down in front of the transverse processes, and press upon the phrenic nerve, which controls the diaphragm.

PRESSURE ON THE VASO-MOTOR NERVE

Place the fingers on each side of the back of the neck and press with fingers on each side of the spine over the upper cervicals (vaso-motor centre) for two or three minutes. This will slow the action of the heart.

Holding Vaso-Motor.

SPINAL TREATMENT

The patient on his side, then using the palmar surface of the fingers and hand, manipulate along the right side of the spinal column, commencing at the first cervical, and moving down the entire length of the spine. Move the muscles upward and outward gently but firmly and with a deep pressure, paying special attention wherever you find a tender spot, a hot or cold spot, or a knotted condition of the muscles. Then turning him on his other side, treat the opposite side in the same manner. Take your time in giving this treatment. Avoid using the finger tips.

EXTENSION OF THE SPINE

The patient on his back, grasp his shoulders, your fingers under his armpits. An assistant holds the patient's ankles. The patient relaxes and you give a careful stretching or extension of the spine, gentle but firm, for about one minute. This frees the circulation of the spinal cord and relieves pressure upon the spinal nerves.

Spinal Extension.

NECK TREATMENT

The patient lying on his back, stand at his head and place one hand on his forehead, the other under his neck, and rotate the head slowly from side to side. Then manipulate thoroughly and deeply the muscles of the back, sides and front of the neck. Then place the hands in the first position, and give the neck a thorough extension or stretching, gently but firmly, being careful not to rotate the head. This treatment frees the circulation to the brain.

EXPANDING THE CHEST

Seat your patient on a stool or chair (if a chair, let him face its back) and stand behind him. Place your foot on the seat

Extending Neck.

of the chair, the tip of your toe being up against, or under, the body of the patient. Place your knee between the patient's shoulders, holding his wrists in each hand. Raise his arms (sideways) up and over his head, slowly but strongly, and press hard with your knee against his spine. Then maintaining the pressure of your knee, lower the arms with a backward motion. The patient should inhale, filling the lungs, while the arms are being raised; exhaling as the arms are lowered.

Expanding Chest.

THE GREAT OSTEOPATHIC DYSENTERY MOVEMENT

Seat your patient on a stool or chair (if a chair, let him face its back) and stand behind him. Place your foot on a round of the chair, grasp his shoulders, and press your knee firmly against his back, on the spinal column, just below the last rib. Draw him back by the shoulders, gently but firmly. Take your time and do not be in a hurry. In giving the treatment have him relax all his muscles. If the patient is in bed, place one hand under each of his sides, placing your fingers on each side of his spine just below the last rib. Lift him up from the bed several inches, his weight resting on the ends of your fingers, his body from shoulders to pelvis forming an arch.

ADJUSTING RIBS

In our lesson on the Skeleton and Bones we have told you that the ribs form a bony cage, containing important organs. They are quite elastic, but have only a limited field of motion, and are rather easily forced into a strained and unnatural position. In many cases it will be found that the ribs on one side are slightly depressed, and those on the other side are slightly raised. This condition will, of course, produce abnormal results, as the nerve-current and circulation will be affected, in all probability.

Dysentery Treatment.

Very fortunately, it is possible and comparatively easy to readjust these abnormal conditions, by replacing the ribs. There is a large muscle which covers the greater part of the breast (the pectoralis major, see lesson on the Muscles and accompanying cut), which is connected with the collarbone and the ribs, and also is connected by tendons with the Humerus (large upper arm bone) about three inches below the shoulder joint. You can feel the connection by raising your arm over

your head and realizing the movement of your upper ribs.
Our Chest Expansion Treatment is designed to release the
ribs and restore normal conditions.

The following movements are also useful in similar cases:

Stand beside the patient and place one hand on each side
of the thorax (the upper cavity of the trunk of the body),
pressing the ribs forward and upward, holding them in position while the patient inflates his lungs.

In some cases of Constipation we find the sixth or seventh
ribs slightly contracted and turned to the side, and either the
ribs or muscles exerting an undue pressure upon the Splanchnic
nerves, which affect the digestive organs, bowels, etc., the result of the pressure being that a portion of the nerve-current
is thus cut off. This condition is relieved by manipulation and
by placing the tips of the finger or the thumb under the middle
of the rib, while the patient inflates his lungs, and raises his
arm over his head. You will see by reference to the several
illustrations accompanying this part of the course the different
methods of raising and adjusting the ribs in their proper position. The principle is the same in each case. The raising of
the arm and inflating of the lungs should always accompany
the raising of the ribs by the ends of the fingers or thumb. A
little actual practice will give you the idea far better than can
any printed description.

Raising Eighth Rib.

Raising Ribs.

Raising Ribs.

Raising False Ribs.

Raising Ribs.

THE OSTEOPATHIC GENERAL TREAT-
MENT

This treatment contains that which goes to make up most of the leading features of the treatments recommended for special complaints. When you can give a general treatment as below described, you have practically mastered the art of Osteopathic manipulation and treatment. The General Treatment can be advantageously used in every form of complaint, as it contains within it all the elements that go to make up the special treatments. Of course, in some cases, it is well to omit some of the movements, etc, but as a rule it is as well to retain them all, unless the patient is too weak to stand them, in which case you must use your own good judgment as to how much had better be omitted.

Some of the best Osteopathic practitioners confine themselves almost altogether to the General Treatment, in all cases, and the only special treatment given by them is an accenting of the treatment of the region of the affected part. You will see by studying carefully the theory of Osteopathic practice, that this General Treatment will free and equalize the circulation of the entire body, and will free and stimulate the nerve impulse to all the parts. This being the case, a normal condition will be soon restored, and the normal condition being restored, Health must manifest itself.

Our advice to you is to always carry in mind the General Treatment, no matter in what part of the body is located the complaint. Of course, pay special attention to the region of the affected part, giving special manipulations there, as the same is needed and the patient will expect it, but work in the General Treatment somewhere, either at the beginning or the ending, or in connection with the special treatment.

The patient will feel so invigorated after a few General Treatments that he will notice if you omit any of the movements, etc, afterwards. Many patients will experience a marked improvement after the first General Treatment. When you remember that an interruption of the circulation in any one part will produce results in parts of the body far removed from the point at which the obstruction occurs, you will see the importance of the General Treatment. In case it is difficult to closely diagnose the trouble, you will get the result just the same as if you had been able to closely locate the trouble, if you will give the General Treatment. This is where you have quite an advantage over the Drug Doctor. And, then besides, you cannot do any harm in case of a mistaken diagnosis, as he is apt to do.

By all means let your hobby be General Treatments. Learn to give them thoroughly and effectively, and your success is assured.

PRELIMINARY.—Direct the patient to lie upon his face. Place a pillow under his breast, reaching up so that his chin may rest upon it. Let his arms hang loose over the sides of the table.

Examine his ribs and see if they are in place and presenting an even surface when the hand is placed over them. If a rib is turned it will present a sharp edge.

Place the first finger of the right hand upon the left side of the spinal column, close up against the spine, and the second finger upon the right side of the spinal column so that the spine is between the two fingers. Then, beginning at the first cervical, bring the fingers firmly down the entire length of the spine, *slowly* and carefully. If you find tender spots you will know that there exists a congested condition over a certain nerve center controlling some part of the body. If you find a small spot much colder, or much warmer, than the surrounding parts, you will know that some muscle is contracted and is obstructing the circulation supplying some nerve centre, which is undoubtedly causing trouble in the part of the body controlled by that nerve centre.

Go over the spine a second time, in the same way, only press your fingers in more deeply, and you will possibly find muscles manifesting a knotted feeling to the touch, which indicates a contraction, and consequent interference.

Placing the patient on his back, instruct him to place his arms to his sides and relax all over. Examine him thoroughly by passing the hands all over his body from head to feet, over all the organs and limbs, noting carefully all tender spots, contractions, swellings, etc. Do not neglect to examine the pulse to ascertain the action of the heart.

TREATMENT

(1) Begin by giving a thorough Spinal Treatment, as follows: The patient on his side, then using the palmar surface

Spinal Treatment.

of the fingers and hand, manipulate along the right side of
the spinal column, commencing at the first cervical, and moving down the entire length of the spine. Move the muscles
upward and outward gently but firmly and with a deep pressure, paying special attention wherever you find a tender
spot, a hot or cold spot, or a knotted condition of the muscles.
Then turning him on his other side, treat the opposite side in
the same manner. Take your time in giving this treatment.
Avoid using the finger tips.

(2) Then give a thorough Neck Treatment, as follows:
The patient lying on his back, stand at his head and place one
hand on his forehead, the other under his neck, and rotate the
head slowly from side to side. Then manipulate thoroughly
and deeply the muscles of the back, sides and front of the neck.
Then place the hands in the first position, and give the neck
a thorough extension or stretching, gently but firmly, being
careful not to rotate the head. This treatment frees the circulation to the brain.

(3) Then give Spinal Extension, as follows: The patient
on his back, grasp his shoulders, your fingers under his armpits An assistant holds the patient's ankles. The patient
relaxes and you give a careful stretching or extension of the
spine, gentle but firm, for about a minute. This frees the circulation of the spinal cord and relieves pressure upon the
spinal nerves.

(4) Then give Chest Expansion, as follows: Seat your
patient on a stool or chair (if a chair, let him face its back)
and stand behind him. Place your foot on the seat of the
chair, the tip of your toe being up against, or under, the body
of the patient. Place your knee between the patient's shoulders, holding his wrists in each hand. Raise his arms (sideways) up and over his head, slowly but strongly, and press hard
with your knee against his spine. Then maintaining the pressure of your knee, lower the arms with a backward motion.
The patient should inhale, filling the lungs, while the arms
are being raised; exhaling as the arms are lowered.

(5) Then give Rotation of the Shoulder, as follows:
The patient on his back or sitting up, place one hand on his
shoulder, and with your other hand take hold of his elbow
and rotate the arm around the head.

(6) Then give Stretching of the Arm and Shoulder
Joints, as follows: The patient on his back, with head and

shoulders raised on a pillow, and arms extended over his head, stand at his head and take his hands in yours, pressing your thumb between his thumb and forefinger, letting your fingers pass around the fleshy part of his thumb and back of his hand. Make several vigorous elastic pulls, avoiding sudden jerks. Make the pulls gradually, then withdraw the force suddenly. Repeat several times.

(7) Then give Rotation of the Hands, as follows: Take the patient's hand in yours, and with your other hand grasp his wrist and rotate from side to side. Repeat several times. (Passive.)

(8) Then give Flexion and Extension of the Hand, as follows: Grasp the patient's wrist with one of your hands, and hold his fingers in your other hand, and move the hand up and down. Repeat several times. (Active or Passive)

(9) Then give Flexion and Extension of the Arm, as follows: The patient sitting, stand behind him and grasp his wrists, he keeping his elbows close to his body Move his arms up and down. Repeat several times. (Active.)

(10) Then give Separating and Closing of the Arms, as follows: The patient sitting with arms extended in front, take hold of his wrists and separate and close his arms. Repeat several times. (Active.)

(11) Then give Flexion and Extension of the Legs, as follows: The patient on his back, place one hand on knee, the other under the sole of the foot, and move the leg up and down to and from the chest. Repeat several times. (Active)

(12) Then give Rotation of the Leg, as follows: The patient on his back, place one hand on the sole of his foot, the other under his knee, raise the leg and rotate from the hip outward. Repeat several times. (Active or Passive.)

(13) Then give Flexion and Extension of the Foot, as follows: The patient on his back, take his toes in one hand and his ankle in the other. Move the foot backward and forward. If you prefer, operate on both feet at the same time. Repeat several times. (Active or Passive)

(14) Then give Separation and Closing of the Legs, as follows. The patient on his back, take hold of his ankles, underneath, and separate and close his legs. Repeat several times. (Active)

(15) Then give Separation and Closing of the Knees, as follows: The patient on his back, stand at his side, and placing one hand on each knee, separate and close.

(16) Then give Stretching of the Leg Joints, as follows: The patient on his back, take his ankles in your hands, and pull straight down, gently but firmly. Repeat several times.

Manipulating Abdomen.

(17) Then give the patient a good Kneading, all over, from Head to Feet, going over every portion of the body, carefully and thoroughly, as follows: Palmar Kneading is akin to the movement of the hand of the baker as he kneads his dough. The operator grasps the muscle with the palm of his hand, keeping the fingers close together, the thumbs out. The thumb is not used, the muscle being grasped between the fingers and the palm of the hand, the heel of the hand, or the lower fleshy part of the thumb. Do not allow the skin to slip, but maintain a firm grasp. Manipulate deeply so as to reach the deeper parts. The muscle should be compressed by the hand and at the same time gently lifted from the bone or underlying tissues, rolled and stretched. When the strain is greatest, release so as to stimulate. Work slowly and carefully, repeating the manipulations according to the requirements of the case, and the state of the patient. In the beginning, do not exert much force, but later on increase the force as the patient becomes accustomed to it. Try to individualize groups of muscles, as the best results are thus obtained. Use the hands alternately. In some cases it is also desirable to use a rolling movement, the heel of the hand and the fleshy part of the thumb being pressed upon the muscle which is then rolled to and fro, the fingers not being used. Use one or both hands. Digital Kneading is effected by grasping the tissue between the ends of the fingers and thumb, and then rubbing the tissue against the bone. Either the end of one finger, or of several, may be used in connection with the thumb.

Kneading Leg.

Kneading the Arm.

(18) Then go over the entire body, and administer Percussion, using the particular form best adapted to the special part of the body upon which you are operating. A little practice will soon give you the best method of administering Percussion, but the following is the general rule: Percussion consists of administering blows to different parts of the body, with varying degrees of force. The wrist should be flexible and loose, as a stiff wrist gives a blow such as is used in fighting. The blow should be elastic and springy, which, although penetrating deeply, does not injure the surface. Percussion can be given by several methods, which we will now

Clapping.

briefly describe. The first method is by striking the body
with the inside flat surface of the half-closed fist, the heel
of the hand and the closed ends of the fingers coming in contact with the flesh. The second method is a chopping movement, made with the little finger side of the hand. The hand
is likened to a butcher's cleaver in this chopping movement.
The fingers are held loosely apart, coming together when the
blow is struck. The third method is a slapping movement
which is best comprehended by the position and movement of
the hand of the mother administering a well merited spanking to one of her brood. The fingers are held rigid, and the
body slapped. The fourth method is a clapping movement,
the hand being shaped so as to emit a hollow sound; just as
one holds his hands in applauding at a theater or concert.
The fifth method is a tapping movement with the tips of the
fingers, one or more fingers of one or both hands being used.
Percussion, in its different forms, is a powerful stimulant to
the nerve centers.

(19) Then give Vibrations over the principal organs of the
body, as follows: This form of treatment is a very powerful
stimulant. It consists of certain oscillatory movements, produced through a succession of rapid individual efforts of the
operator's hand. There should be little or no perceptible
strain upon the arm muscles of the operator. The palm of the
hand or the fingers must be placed firmly upon the parts to
be treated, the arm being held straight and a fine trembling
or vibrating movement communicated to the hand by the
muscles of the upper part of the arm. The movement is
somewhat difficult of acquirement, but you must persist until
the desired movement is acquired, for this is one of the most
stimulating and penetrating of all the methods of Osteopathic
treatment, its effect being quite perceptible and almost akin
to the effects of a current of electricity. It has a stimulating
and strengthening effect upon the nerves, and acts strongly
upon the venous circulation and upon the lymphatics. Be
careful not to press upon the body with your wrist, as you
should use no greater pressure than the weight of your hand
When properly administered by one hand on the breast, the
vibrations should be distinctly felt by the other hand placed
under the back of the patient.

(20) Finish the treatment with a gentle and soothing
Stroking, as follows: This treatment is useful in producing

sedative or quieting effects. It should be applied with a very light contact, the tips of the fingers or the palm of the hand just barely touching the patient. In some cases it will produce a feeling of drowsiness on the part of the patient. It never fails to quiet down the patient, equalize the circulation and relieve an excess of stimulation. Stroking should always be performed in a downward and outward direction, and in one direction only, not to and fro. The tips of one, more or all of the fingers, or the palmar surface of one or both hands, are moved gently over the skin, with a light contact, not even the mere weight of the hand being allowed to press upon the surface of the skin. Lightness, gentleness, and airiness, are the words best describing the Stroking movement.

In addition to the above movements and manipulations, etc., you should add the following to the General Treatment, when indicated by the requirements of the particular case treated:

(A) In cases of Stomach, Liver or Bowel trouble, Indigestion, Dyspepsia or Constipation, etc, etc, give the following treatment, which Frees the Pneumo-Gastric Nerve: The patient on his back, place your hand under the chin, pull the head backward. Move from right to left and manipulate deeply and firmly, the lower part of the neck, on each side of the windpipe. This frees and stimulates the pneumo-gastric nerve, which largely influences the organs of digestion.

(B) In cases where fever manifests itself, or where it is desirable to reduce or slow down the action of the heart, add the following treatment, which consists of a pressure upon the Vaso-Motor Centre: Place the fingers on each side of the back of the neck and press with fingers on each side of the spine over the upper cervicals (vaso-motor center) for two or three minutes. This will slow the action of the heart.

(C) In cases where Dysentery, Diarrhea, Cholera Morbus, etc., is feared, add the following treatment which is known as the Great Osteopathic Dysentery Movement: Seat your patient on a stool or chair (if a chair, let him face its back) and stand behind him. Place your foot on a round of the chair, grasp his shoulders, and press your knee firmly against his back, on the spinal column, just below the last rib. Draw him back by the shoulders, gently but firmly. Take your time and do not be in a hurry. In giving the treatment have him relax all of his muscles. If the patient is in bed place one hand under each of his sides, placing your fingers on each side of his spine just below the last rib. Lift him up from the bed several inches, his weight resting on the ends of your fingers, his body from shoulders to pelvis forming an arch.

QUIZ QUESTIONS

1. What is Osteopathy?
2. What is the theory upon which it is based?
3. What part do the nerves and the circulation play in health and disease?
4. How does an Osteopath restore normal conditions?
5. Sum up in a few words the Basic Principles of Osteopathy.
6. State in a few words the "Points on Practice" given in Lesson I.
7. Name the Spinal Centre for the Liver.
8. Where would you look for a Lesion in a case of trouble with the Bladder?
9. Name the principal Osteopathic "Movements"
10. Name and describe the different forms of Kneading.
11. Name and describe the several forms of Percussion.
12 What is the effect of Vibration, and how is it administered?
13. How do you apply Stroking, and what is its effect?
14 How do you stimulate a nerve?
15 How do you desensitize a nerve?
16. How do you free the Pneumo-Gastric Nerve, and what is its effect?
17. How do you press on the Vaso-Motor Centre, and what is its effect?
18. How do you give a Spinal Treatment?
19. How do you give a Neck Treatment?
20. How do you Expand the Chest?
21 Describe the Osteopathic Dysentery Treatment?
22 Describe the theory of Rib Raising, and tell how you accomplish it?

THE HOME STUDY COURSE

IN

OSTEOPATHY

ISSUED BY

The Columbia College of Osteopathy

3031 AUDITORIUM BLDG., CHICAGO, ILL., U. S. A.

Consists of Twelve Lessons, fully illustrated, and is issued in Five Parts, as follows:

PART FIRST—
Theory of Osteopathy.
Movements and Manipulations.
General Treatment.

PART SECOND—
Special Treatments.

PART THIRD—
Special Treatments.

PART FOURTH—
Special Treatments.
Osteopathic Anatomy.
Osteopathic Physiology.

PART FIFTH—
Osteopathic Anatomy and Physiology.
Building up and Conducting an Osteopathic Practice.
Practical Advice and Suggestions.
Miscellaneous Information.

HOME STUDY COURSE

IN

OSTEOPATHY

PART SECOND
COMPRISING LESSONS III, IV AND V

ISSUED BY

THE COLUMBIA COLLEGE OF OSTEOPATHY
3031 AUDITORIUM BUILDING
CHICAGO, ILL., U. S. A.

CONTENTS

LESSON III

LESSON IV

LESSON V

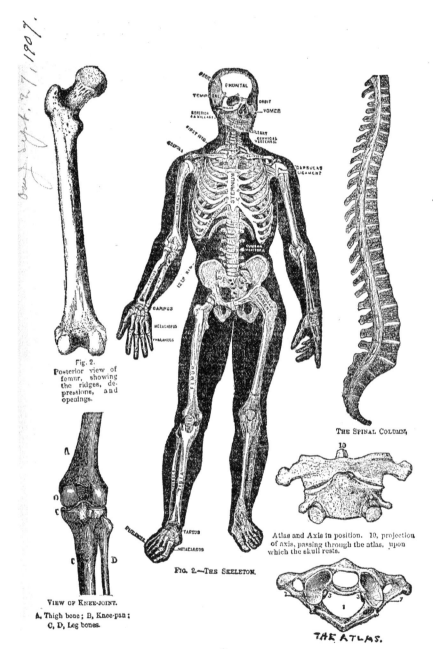

Fig. 2.
Posterior view of
femur, showing
the ridges, de-
pressions, and
openings.

THE SPINAL COLUMN.

Atlas and Axis in position. 10, projection
of axis, passing through the atlas, upon
which the skull rests.

VIEW OF KNEE-JOINT.

A, Thigh bone; B, Knee-pan;
C, D, Leg bones.

FIG. 2.—THE SKELETON.

THE ATLAS.

3

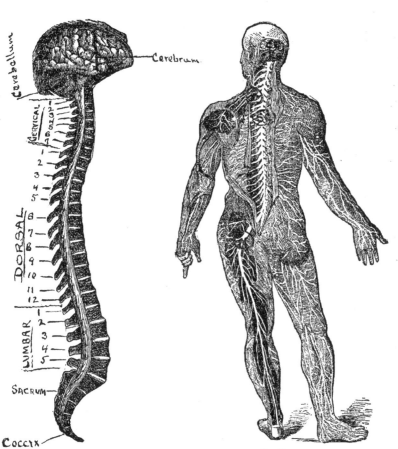

Cerebellum

Cerebrum.

CERVICAL 1 2 3 4 5 6 7

DORSAL 1 2 3 4 5 6 7 8 9 10 11 12

LUMBAR 1 2 3 4 5

SACRUM

COCCIX

Fig. 66.

Posterior view of the spinal cord, — a portion of the cerebrum and cerebellum and some of the nerves of the cerebro-spinal system. On the left side of the body some of the tissues are removed to show the deeper nerves, while the right side shows certain superficial ones. — CE, cerebrum; CER, cerebellum, B, nerves distributed to the arm; SC, spinal cord; SN, sciatic nerve.

4

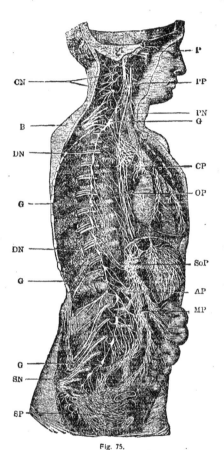

Fig. 75.

Vertical section of body, showing sympathetic nerves and ganglia of right side, and their connection with the cerebro-spinal nerves. — *Cerebro-spinal system:* CN, cervical nerves ; B, nerves distributed to the arm; DN, dorsal nerves; SN, sacral nerves, some of which are distributed to the leg ; PN, pneumogastric nerve. *Sympathetic system:* P, plexus in the head ; PP, pharyngeal plexus; CP, cardiac plexus. OP, oesophageal plexus ; SoP, solar plexus ; AP, aortic plexus, MP, mesenteric plexus ; SP, sacral plexus ; G, some of the ganglia of the sympathetic system.

5

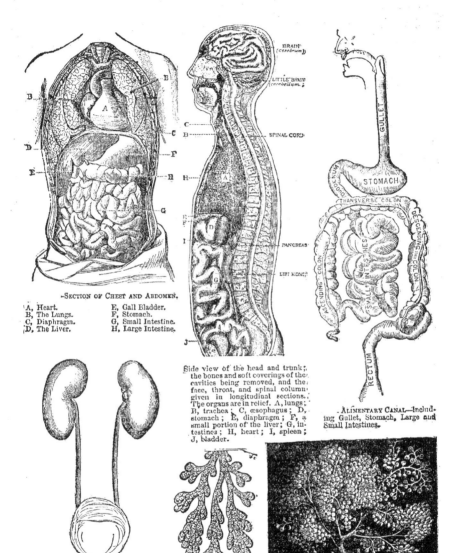

—SECTION OF CHEST AND ABDOMEN.

A, Heart.
B, The Lungs.
C, Diaphragm.
D, The Liver.
E, Gall Bladder.
F, Stomach.
G, Small Intestine.
H, Large Intestine.

BRAIN (cerebrum)

LITTLE BRAIN (cerebellum.)

SPINAL CORD

PANCREAS

LEFT KIDNEY

Side view of the head and trunk;
the bones and soft coverings of the
cavities being removed, and the
face, throat, and spinal column
given in longitudinal sections.
The organs are in relief. A, lungs;
B, trachea; C, œsophagus; D,
stomach; E, diaphragm; F, a
small portion of the liver; G, intestines; H, heart; I, spleen;
J, bladder.

GULLET

STOMACH

DUODENUM

TRANSVERSE COLON

DESCENDING COLON

ASCENDING COLON

SMALL INTESTINES

RECTUM

—ALIMENTARY CANAL—Includ-
ing Gullet, Stomach, Large and
Small Intestines.

—THE KIDNEYS AND BLADDER.

—A gastric gland.

—STRUCTURE OF A SALIVARY GLAND.

6

LESSON III.

SPECIAL TREATMENTS.

DISEASES OF THE STOMACH, INTESTINES, ETC.

CONSTIPATION.

This disease is one of the most common, and at the same time one of the most difficult diseases to cure by Drug-giving Doctors. Happily, however, it yields readily to Osteopathic treatment. Constipation carries in its train ills and disorders of many kinds, and when we once rid a patient of Constipation we have relieved him of many other complaints. When the cause is removed the effects disappear. The symptoms of Constipation are too well known to be dwelt upon here. The Osteopathic theory of the disease is that the nerve force is partly shut off from the organs, which are consequently deprived of their ability to perform their accustomed tasks. By removing the pressure on the nerves and stimulating the action of the liver and bowels by manipulation the peristaltic action of the bowels is again made normal and all the organs of nutrition and elimination perform their work, and health ensues.

TREATMENT.

(1) Give the patient a good spinal treatment, as follows: The patient on his side, then using the palmar surface of the fingers and hand, manipulate along the right side of the spinal column, commencing at the first cervical, and moving down the entire length of the spine. Move the muscles upward and outward gently but firmly and with a deep pressure, paying special attention wherever you find a tender spot, a hot or cold spot, or a knotted condition of the muscles. Then turning him on his other side, treat the opposite side in the same manner. Take your time in giving this treatment. Avoid using the finger tips.

Spinal Treatment

7

Extending Neck.

Expanding Chest.

Kneading Abdo-
men.

(2) Then give the Neck Treatment, as follows: The patient lying on his back, stand at his head and place one hand on his forehead, the other under his neck, and rotate the head slowly from side to side. Then manipulate thoroughly and deeply the muscles of the back, sides and front of the neck. Then place the hands in the first position, and give the neck a thorough extension or stretching, gently but firmly, being careful not to rotate the head. This treatment frees the circulation to the brain.

(3) Then give Chest Expansion, as follows: Seat your patient on a stool or chair (if a chair, let him face its back) and stand behind him. Place your foot on the seat of the chair, the tip of your toe being up against, or under, the body of the patient. Place your knee between the patient's shoulders, holding his wrists in each hand. Raise his arms (sideways) up and over his head, slowly but strongly, and press hard with your knee against his spine. Then maintaining the pressure of your knee, lower the arms with a backward motion. The patient should inhale, filling the lungs, while the arms are being raised; exhaling as the arms are lowered.

(4) Then give Extension of the Spine, as follows: The patient on his back, grasp his shoulders, your fingers under his armpits. An assistant holds the patient's ankles. The patient relaxes and you give a careful stretching or extension of the spine, gentle but firm, for about one minute. This frees the circulation of the spinal cord and relieves pressure upon the spinal nerves.

(5) Then give Rotation of the Pelvis, as follows: The patient on his back and holding on to the table, grasp his feet and rotate his legs in such a manner as to describe a circle large enough to bring the pelvis into action. Repeat several times. (Passive.)

(6) Then administer Kneading in the region of the Liver, as follows: Palmar Kneading is akin to the movement of the hand of the baker as he kneads his dough. The operator grasps the muscle with the palm of his hand, keeping the fingers close together, the thumbs out. The thumb is not used, the muscle being grasped between the fingers and the palm of the hand, the heel of the hand, or the lower fleshy part of the thumb. Do not allow the skin to slip, but maintain a firm grasp. Manipulate deeply so as to reach the deeper parts. The muscle should be compressed by the hand and at

the same time gently lifted from the bone or underlying tissues, rolled and stretched. When the strain is greatest, release so as to stimulate. Work slowly and carefully, repeating the manipulations according to the requirements of the case and the state of the patient. In the beginning, do not exert much force, but later on increase the force as the patient becomes accustomed to it. Try to individualize groups of muscles, as the best results are thus obtained. Use the hands alternately. In some cases it is also desirable to use a rolling movement, the heel of the hand and the fleshy part of the thumb being pressed upon the muscle, which is then rolled to and fro, the fingers not being used. Use one or both hands. Digital Kneading is effected by grasping the tissues between the ends of the fingers and thumb, and then rubbing the tissue against the bone. Either the end of one finger, or of several, may be used in connection with the thumb.

Abdominal Kneading.

Kneading Abdominal Muscle.

(7) Then give Flexion and Extension of the Legs, as follows: The patient on his back, place one hand on the knee, the other under the sole of the foot, and move the leg up and down to and from the chest. Repeat several times. (Active.)

(8) Then Rotate the Legs, as follows: The patient on his back, place one hand on the sole of his foot, the other under his knee, raise the leg and rotate the leg from the hip outward. Repeat several times. Then treat the other leg.

Manipulating Abdomen.

(9) Then administer Vibration over the Liver and the Bowels, as follows: This form of treatment is a very powerful stimulant. It consists of certain oscillatory movements, produced through a succession of rapid individual efforts of the operator's hand. There should be little or no perceptible strain upon the arm muscles of the operator. The palm of the hand or the fingers must be placed firmly upon the parts to be treated, the arm being held straight and a fine trembling or vibrating movement communicated to the hand by the muscles of the upper part of the arm. The movement is somewhat difficult of acquirement, but you must persist until the desired movement is acquired, for this is one of the most stimulating and penetrating of all the methods of Osteopathic treatment, its effect being quite perceptible and almost akin to the effects of a current of electricity. It has a stimulating and strengthening effect upon the nerves, and acts strongly upon the venous circulation and upon the lymphatics. Be careful not to press upon the body with your wrist, as you should use no greater

Vibration of Liver.

Deep Vibration.

pressure than the weight of your hand. When properly administered by one hand on the breast, the vibrations should be distinctly felt by the other hand placed under the back of the patient.

Stroking.

(10) Finish by a gentle, quieting Stroking, as follows: This treatment is useful in producing sedative or quieting effects. It should be applied with a very light contact, the tips of the fingers, or the palm of the hand, just barely touching the patient. In some cases it will produce a feeling of drowsiness on the part of the patient. It never fails to quiet down the patient, equalize the circulation and relieve an excess of stimulation. Stroking should always be performed in a downward and outward direction, and in one direction only, not to-and-fro. The tips of one, more or all of the fingers, or the palmar surface of one or both hands, are moved gently over the skin, with a light contact, not even the mere weight of the hand being allowed to press upon the surface of the skin. Lightness, gentleness, and airiness, are the words best describing the Stroking movement.

Treat frequently. Patients suffering from Constipation usually take an insufficient quantity of fluids. The perfectly healthy man drinks at least two quarts of fluids each day. Without sufficient fluids Nature finds it hard to do her work. Accordingly instruct your patient to increase his fluids each day until he drinks the normal quantity. This is important; do not neglect the fluids.

DYSPEPSIA, INDIGESTION, ETC.

These complaints are too well known to go into detail regarding symptoms, etc. Osteopathy teaches that the causes producing Dyspepsia and kindred troubles are identical with those manifesting in the shape of Constipation, Liver Complaint, etc. Consequently, the treatment is practically the same in each case. Osteopathy is very efficacious in cases of Dyspepsia, Indigestion, etc., the improvement usually being manifested from the first.

Freeing Pneumo-Gastric.

Treatment: Give the full treatment given for Constipation. In the Spinal Treatment, pay special attention to that part of the spinal column between the second and sixth dorsal vertebræ, in which region will probably be found tender spots showing an obstruction of the nerves controlling the organs of nutrition, digestion and assimilation.

Many Osteopaths treat Dyspepsia by giving the full General Treatment, in which they pay particular attention to kneading the region of the stomach, etc   Give frequent treatments

DIARRHEA, DYSENTERY, CHOLERA MORBUS, ETC.

These diseases and their symptoms are well known. Osteopathy offers a simple and effective cure. Osteopathy teaches that disorders of this class are caused by an interference with the peristaltic action of the bowels, which is controlled by the great Splanchnic and right Pneumo-Gastric nerves which together form the Solar Plexus or Abdominal Brain. Under ordinary conditions, just the right amount of nerve force is transmitted to move the bowels normally and naturally. However, occasions arise in which it would seem that Nature's "shut-off" had refused to work, or become fastened in some manner, and consequently the nerve force continues to be poured into the organs and parts until, unless checked in some way, the machine runs itself down and often collapses. It is practically a similar case to a runaway locomotive whose air brakes will not work. Every engineer knows what a terrible predicament he is placed in if his "air" refuses to work. He is very fortunate if he avoids a wreck. Now Osteopathy has discovered a way to help the Engineer of the system, when his air brakes refuse to act, and his train is threatened with destruction

As we have already stated, the bowels are controlled by the great Splanchnic and right Pneumo-Gastric nerves, and it is over these nerves that this runaway current is speeding. You will see at once that a pressure on these nerves will desensitize them and shut off the current until Nature has time to adjust her air brakes. In another part of this course, we have explained that a steady, continued pressure over a nerve centre will desensitize it, and an alternated movement will stimulate it, so you see at once the philosophy of this Great Osteopathic Dysentery Treatment. The principal trouble seems to come over the Splanchnic nerve, and a steady, firm pressure there affords instant relief and very often one simple treatment will will effect an entire cure   This is something that every man, woman and child should know   It has saved many lives, and has relieved thousands of cases of intense pain, weakness and drain upon the system

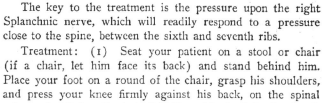

Dysentery Treatment.

The key to the treatment is the pressure upon the right Splanchnic nerve, which will readily respond to a pressure close to the spine, between the sixth and seventh ribs.

Treatment: (1) Seat your patient on a stool or chair (if a chair, let him face its back) and stand behind him. Place your foot on a round of the chair, grasp his shoulders, and press your knee firmly against his back, on the spinal column, just below the last rib. Draw him back by the shoulders, gently but firmly. Take your time and do not be in a hurry. In giving the treatment have him relax all his muscles. If the patient is in bed, place one hand under each of his sides, placing your fingers on each side of his spine just below the last rib. Lift him up from the bed several inches, his weight resting on the ends of your fingers, his body from shoulders to pelvis forming an arch.

(2) Then hold the Vaso-Motor nerves as follows: Place the fingers on each side of the back of the neck and press with fingers on each side of the spine over the upper cervicals (Vaso-Motor center) for two or three minutes. This will slow the action of the heart.

Holding Vaso-Motor.

(3) Conclude the treatment with a quieting, soothing Stroking, which will be appreciated by the patient. Give as follows: This treatment is useful, in producing sedative or quieting effects. It should be applied with a very light contact, the tips of the fingers, or the palm of the hand, just barely touching the patient. In some cases it will produce a feeling of drowsiness on the part of the patient. It never fails to quiet down the patient, equalize the circulation and relieve an excess of stimulation. Stroking should always be performed in a downward and outward direction, and in one direction only, not to-and-fro. The tips of one, more or all of the fingers, or the palmar surface of one or both hands, are moved gently over the skin, with a light contact, not even the mere weight of the hand being allowed to press upon the surface of the skin. Lightness, gentleness, and airiness, are the words best describing the Stroking movement.

Stroking.

Persons understanding the theory of the Osteopathic Dysentery Treatment, can apply the same to their own complaints, if they are where they cannot secure the services of a practitioner.

CRAMPS IN THE BOWELS.

This trouble can be readily cured by the Dysentery Treatment, coupled with a good, thorough Kneading of the bowels. Vibration over the bowels can also be used to advantage in connection with the other treatment.

CHOLERA INFANTUM.

Give the child the Dysentery Treatment, or rather that part of it in which the patient is lifted from the bed by the fingers being placed on each side of the spine. The movements should of course be more gentle than in the case of an adult. Also press on the Vaso-Motor nerve center for a minute or two. Finish by giving Stroking treatment, which will often cause the child to fall into a refreshing slumber. Osteopaths have cured many cases of this complaint, by this treatment, after the Drug Doctors had pronounced the case hopeless.

APPENDICITIS.

This disease is caused by an inflammation of the Vermiform Appendix. The symptoms are fever; pain in the affected region; nausea and vomiting.

Treatment: The patient on his back, manipulate and knead the lower right side of the abdomen, and endeavor to move any lumps of hardened fæces toward the rectum. Manipulate in a gentle, careful manner. Then Vibrate over the lower part of the abdomen. Then take the patient's right hand, having an assistant to hold his hip at the same time, and give the arm a thorough extension over his head, as described in the lesson on Osteopathic Movements. Then give him a thorough Spinal Treatment, paying special attention to any painful spots. Then press on the Vaso-Motor nerve center for two or three minutes. Finish by a gentle Stroking, from head to feet.

DISEASES OF THE HEART
AND CIRCULATION.

The principles underlying Osteopathic treatment of **Diseases** of the Heart are that the majority of troubles of this class arise not so much from any congenital weakness of the heart, but from some obstruction or impediment in some other part of the body. With the circulation obstructed, the heart must in time feel the strain. The plain remedy, therefore, is to remove the obstruction, equalize the circulation and restore a normal condition of affairs, and the heart weakness disappears. A displacement, abnormal pressure, or contraction is very often, indeed, the real cause of "heart disease," and it readily will be seen just how Osteopathy is so successful in the cure of this class of diseases. In fact, Osteopaths frequently find that after treating a patient for some other disease, and relieving it, the old heart trouble has disappeared. With this in mind, we strongly urge the student to give to the patient suffering with heart trouble, the benefit of one or more General Treatments before beginning to treat him for the heart trouble. Many cases of heart trouble disappear after the patient is cured of constipation or dyspepsia. We herewith give a general form of treatment for diseases of the heart, which the student will use in connection with the treatments for the other troubles with which the patient is suffering.

Spinal Treatment

Treatment: (1) Begin by giving the Spinal Treatment, as follows: The patient on his side, then using the palmar surface of the fingers and hand, manipulate along the right side of the spinal column, commencing at the first cervical, and moving down the entire length of the spine. Move the muscles upward and outward gently but firmly and with a deep pressure, paying special attention wherever you find a tender spot, a hot or cold spot, or a knotted condition of the muscles. Then turning him on his other side, treat the opposite side in the same manner. Take your time in giving this treatment. Avoid using the finger tips.

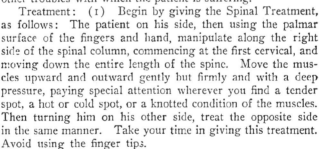

(2) Then give the Neck Treatment, as follows: The patient lying on his back, stand at his head and place

Extending Neck. one hand on his forehead, the other under his neck, and rotate

14

the head slowly from side to side. Then manipulate thoroughly and deeply the muscles of the back, sides and front of the neck. Then place the hands in the first position, and give the neck a thorough extension or stretching, gently but firmly, being careful not to rotate the head. This treatment frees the circulation to the brain.

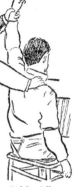

(3) Then give the following treatment designed to relieve a possible depression of the ribs which interferes with the heart's action:

Place your left hand under the right shoulder of the patient; then place the fingers of the left hand on the angle of the second rib of the patient; then take hold of his right wrist with your right hand, and draw it up slowly and steadily until it is above his head, the patient at the same time taking a long deep breath. Then lower the arm with a backward motion, at the same time pressing hard upon the angle of the rib. Then do the same with the third, fourth and fifth ribs. Then repeat on the other side of the patient's body. This treatment frequently gives instantaneous relief.

Raising Ribs.

(4) Then give Chest Expansion, as follows: Seat your patient on a stool or chair (if a chair, let him face its back) and stand behind him. Place your foot on the seat of the chair, the tip of your toe being up against, or under, the body of the patient. Place your knee between the patient's shoulders, holding his wrists in each hand. Raise his arms (sideways) up and over his head, slowly but strongly, and press hard with your knee against his spine. Then maintaining the pressure of your knee, lower the arms with a backward motion. The patient should inhale, filling the lungs, while the arms are being raised; exhaling as the arms are lowered.

(5) Then give the Spinal Extension, as follows: The patient on his back, grasp his shoulders, your fingers under his armpits. An assistant holds the patient's ankles. The patient relaxes and you give a careful stretching or extension of the spine, gentle but firm, for about one minute. This frees the circulation of the spinal cord and relieves pressure upon the spinal nerves.

(6) Then give Flexion and Extension of the Leg, as follows: The patient on his back, place one hand on the knee, the other under the sole of the foot, and move the leg up and down to and from the chest. Repeat several times. (Active.)

Expanding Chest.

ANEMIA.

This disease is caused by a deficiency of blood The symptoms are a peculiar pallor of the face, eyeballs of a bluish tint, poor appetite and imperfect nutrition, urine pale; weak heart; neuralgia, etc, etc The treatment is based upon the principle that the circulation once equalized and the organs of nutrition and assimilation stimulated so that new, rich blood can be made, the cause is removed and the patient will rapidly grow well

Treatment Give frequent General Treatments to equalize the circulation, giving especially thorough spinal treatment in the cervical and upper dorsal system which control the organs of assimilation

Also give treatment given in lesson on Dyspepsia You will see that whatever is conducive to the increase of nutrition and assimilation will result in the making of blood; and that when the blood supply is normal in quality and quantity, anemia must disappear Encourage the patient to eat good, nutritious food, and obtain as much nourishment as possible He will begin to feel hungry after your treatment for Dyspepsia, and improved appetite will do much for him, in connection · with your treatment

VARICOSE VEINS, ETC.

This disease is caused by a pressure upon some portion of the venous system The veins are unduly dilated and · are much swollen, and present a dark blue appearance

Treatment· Give a general leg treatment, employing all the Methods of Manipulation and all of the leg Movements Finish by giving a General Treatment The principal object is to free the muscles, veins and nerves of the thigh, and the student must bear this in mind in giving the treatment

Inflammation of a vein (Phlebitis) is treated by Movements and Manipulations to free the circulation at and around the affected parts

DROPSY.

Dropsy is caused by an abnormal accumulation of serum It causes swelling, beginning at the feet and extending upward. The swellings are soft and retain for some time a mark made by a pressure of a finger The treatment is designed to stimulate the skin and kidneys into renewed activity and to promote absorption. The fluids are carried off by the system and their reaccumulation is prevented by the natural functioning of the organs.

Treatment: Give the same treatment as that recommended for Diseases of the Heart, paying especial attention to the manipulation of the spine between the tenth dorsal and last sacral vertebrae, which treatment is designed to stimulate the kidneys. Also include in the treatment a thorough Vibration treatment of the kidneys, as follows:

This form of treatment is a very powerful stimulant. It consists of certain oscillatory movements, produced through a succession of rapid individual efforts of the operator's hand. There should be little or no perceptible strain upon the arm muscles of the operator. The palm of the hand or the fingers must be placed firmly upon the parts to be treated, the arm being held straight and a fine trembling or vibrating movement communicated to the hand by the muscles of the upper

Digital Vibration.

part of the arm. The movement is somewhat difficult of acquirement, but you must persist until the desired movement is acquired, for this is one of the most stimulating and penetrating of all the methods of Osteopathic treatment, its effect being quite perceptible and almost akin to the effects of a current of electricity. It has a stimulating and strengthening effect upon the nerves, and acts strongly upon the venous circulation and upon the lymphatics. Be careful not to press upon the body with your wrist, as you should use no greater pressure than the weight of your hand. When properly administered by one hand on the breast, the vibrations should be distinctly felt by the other hand placed under the back of the patient.

Deep Vibration.

In about a week the kidneys will be found to be doing their work in a normal manner, and from that time on the recovery will be rapid. Osteopathy has cured thousands of cases of Dropsy that had defied the efforts of the Drug Doctors.

LESSON IV.

SPECIAL TREATMENTS.

DISEASES OF THE LIVER.

You will see by reference to that part of the course which treats of the functions of the Liver what an important part it plays in the human economy, and how important it is that it should function normally. Osteopathy teaches that Biliousness, Jaundice and other Diseases of the Liver are occasioned by an obstruction or interruption of the circulation of the blood supplying the liver, or an interruption of the nerve current to that organ. The treatment is designed to relieve these abnormal conditions, and restore the organ to its natural condition. The following thorough Liver Treatment will apply equally to Biliousness, Jaundice, or any other affection of the Liver. Almost immediate improvement will be noticed and a speedy cure assured.

TREATMENT.

(1) Begin by giving a thorough Spinal Treatment, as follows: The patient on his side, then using the palmar surface of the fingers and hand, manipulate along the right side of the spinal column, commencing at the first cervical, and moving down the entire length of the spine. Move the muscles upward and outward gently but firmly and with a deep pressure, paying special attention wherever you find a tender spot, a hot or cold spot, or a knotted condition of the muscles. Then turning him on his other side, treat the opposite side in the same manner. Take your time in giving this treatment. Avoid using the finger tips.

Spinal Treatment

(2) Then give a thorough Neck Treatment, as follows, giving special attention to the manipulation of the lower part of the side and front of the neck, in order to free the Pneumo-Gastric nerve: The patient lying on his back, stand at his head and place one hand on his forehead, the other under his neck, and rotate the head slowly from side to side. Then

18

manipulate thoroughly and deeply the muscles of the back, sides and front of the neck. Then place the hands in the first position, and give the neck a thorough extension or stretching, gently but firmly, being careful not to rotate the head. This treatment frees the circulation to the brain.

Extending Neck.

(3) Then give a thorough Kneading of the Abdomen, as follows: Palmar Kneading is akin to the movement of the hand of the baker as he kneads his dough. The operator grasps the muscle with the palm of his hand, keeping the fingers close together, the thumbs out. The thumb is not used, the muscle being grasped between the fingers and the palm of the hand, the heel of the hand, or the lower fleshy part of the thumb. Do not allow the skin to slip, but maintain a firm grasp. Manipulate deeply so as to reach the deeper parts. The muscle should be compressed by the hand and at the same time gently lifted from the bone or underlying tissues, rolled and stretched. When the strain is greatest, release so as to stimulate. Work slowly and carefully, repeating the manipulations according to the requirements of the case, and the state of the patient. In the beginning do not exert much force, but later on increase the force as the patient becomes accustomed to it. Try to individualize groups of muscles, as the best results are thus obtained. Use the hands alternately. In some cases it is also desirable to use a rolling movement, the heel of the hand and the fleshy part of the thumb being pressed upon the muscle, which is then rolled to and fro, the fingers not being used. Use one or both hands. Digital Kneading is effected by grasping the tissue between the ends of the fingers and thumb, and then rubbing the tissue against the bone. Either the end of one finger, or of several, may be used in connection with the thumb.

Kneading.

(4) Then give Flexion and Extension of the Legs, as follows: The patient on his back, place one hand on the knee, the other under the sole of the foot, and move the leg up and down to and from the chest. Repeat several times. (Active.)

Digital Kneading.

(5) Then give Stretching of the Arm and Shoulder Joints, as follows: The patient on his back, with head and shoulders raised on a pillow, and arms extended over his head, stand at his head and take his hands in yours, passing your thumb between his thumb and forefinger, letting your fingers pass around the fleshy part of his thumb and back of his hand. Make several vigorous elastic pulls, avoiding sudden jerks.

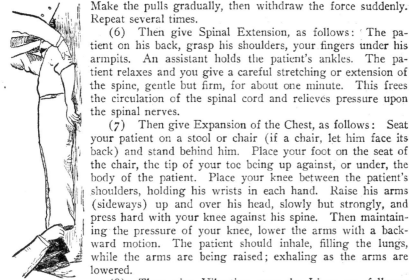

Spinal Extension.

Make the pulls gradually, then withdraw the force suddenly. Repeat several times.

(6) Then give Spinal Extension, as follows: The patient on his back, grasp his shoulders, your fingers under his armpits. An assistant holds the patient's ankles. The patient relaxes and you give a careful stretching or extension of the spine, gentle but firm, for about one minute. This frees the circulation of the spinal cord and relieves pressure upon the spinal nerves.

(7) Then give Expansion of the Chest, as follows: Seat your patient on a stool or chair (if a chair, let him face its back) and stand behind him. Place your foot on the seat of the chair, the tip of your toe being up against, or under, the body of the patient. Place your knee between the patient's shoulders, holding his wrists in each hand. Raise his arms (sideways) up and over his head, slowly but strongly, and press hard with your knee against his spine. Then maintaining the pressure of your knee, lower the arms with a backward motion. The patient should inhale, filling the lungs, while the arms are being raised; exhaling as the arms are lowered.

(8) Then give Vibration over the Liver, as follows: This form of treatment is a very powerful stimulant. It consists of certain oscillatory movements, produced through a succession of rapid individual efforts of the operator's hand. There should be little or no perceptible strain upon the arm muscles of the operator. The palm of the hand or the fingers must be placed firmly upon the parts to be treated, the arm being held straight and a fine trembling or vibrating movement communicated to the hand by the muscles of the upper part of the arm. The movement is somewhat difficult of acquirement, but you must persist until the desired movement is acquired, for this is one of the most stimulating and penetrating of all the methods of Osteopathic treatment, its effect being quite perceptible and almost akin to the effects of a current of electricity. It has a stimulating and strengthening effect upon the nerves, and acts strongly upon the venous circulation and upon the lymphatics. Be careful not to press upon the body with your wrist, as you should use no greater pressure than the weight of your hand. When properly administered by one hand on the breast, the vibrations should be distinctly felt by the other hand placed under the back of the

Expanding Chest. patient.

(9) Finish by giving a soothing Stroking, as follows: This treatment is useful in producing sedative or quieting effects. It should be applied with a very light contact, the tips of the fingers, or the palm of the hand, just barely touching the patient. In some cases it will produce a feeling of drowsiness on the part of the patient. It never fails to quiet down the patient, equalize the circulation and relieve an excess of stimulation. Stroking should always be performed in a downward and outward direction, and in one direction only, not to-and-fro. The tips of one, more or all of the fingers, or the palmar surface of one or both hands, are moved gently over the skin, with a light contact, not even the mere weight of the hand being allowed to press upon the surface of the skin. Lightness, gentleness, and airiness, are the words best describing the Stroking movement.

Stroking.

Treat every day until marked improvement is noted, then every other day, and so on, lessening the treatment, until the patient is cured.

DISEASES OF THE KIDNEYS.

Osteopathy teaches that Diseases of the Kidneys arise from an interruption or obstruction of the circulation, or an interruption of the nerve current supplying that organ. The treatment, consequently, is such as will free the circulation and nerve current. The following is a good general treatment for Diseases of the Kidneys, and will be found to relieve the majority of cases treated. You can, of course, add to, or vary this treatment, according to your own good judgment, and according to the requirements of the special case before you:

(1) Begin the treatment with a thorough Spinal Treatment, as follows, paying special attention to the lower dorsal region: The patient on his side, then using the palmar surface of the fingers and hand, manipulate along the right side of the spinal column, commencing at the first cervical, and moving down the entire length of the spine. Move the muscles upward and outward, gently but firmly, and with a deep pressure, paying special attention wherever you find a tender spot, a hot or cold spot, or a knotted condition of the muscles. Then turning him on his other side, treat the opposite side in the same manner. Take your time in giving this treatment. Avoid using the finger tips.

Spinal Treatment.

Extending Neck.

(2) Then give a thorough Neck Treatment, giving special attention to the manipulation of the lower part of the side and front of the neck, in order to free the Pneumo-Gastric nerve, as follows: The patient lying on his back, stand at his head and place one hand on his forehead, the other under his neck, and rotate the head slowly from side to side. Then manipulate thoroughly and deeply the muscles of the back, sides and front of the neck. Then place the hands in the first position, and give the neck a thorough extension or stretching, gently but firmly, being careful not to rotate the head. This treatment frees the circulation to the brain.

(3) Then give a thorough Kneading of the region of the Kidneys, as follows: Palmar Kneading is akin to the movement of the hand of the baker as he kneads his dough. The operator grasps the muscle with the palm of his hand, keeping the fingers close together, the thumbs out. The thumb is not used, the muscle being grasped between the fingers and the palm of the hand, the heel of the hand, or the lower fleshy part of the thumb. Do not allow the skin to slip, but maintain a firm grasp. Manipulate deeply so as to reach the deeper parts. The muscle should be compressed by the hand and at the same time gently lifted from the bone or underlying tissues, rolled and stretched. When the strain is greatest, release so as to stimulate. Work slowly and carefully, repeating the manipulations according to the requirements of the case, and the state of the patient. In the beginning, do not exert much force, but later on increase the force as the patient becomes accustomed to it. Try to individualize groups of muscles, as the best results are thus obtained. Use the hands alternately. In some cases it is also desirable to use a rolling movement, the heel of the hand and the fleshy part of the thumb being pressed upon the muscle, which is then rolled to and fro, the fingers not being used. Use one or both hands. Digital Kneading is effected by grasping the tissue between the ends of the fingers and thumb, and then rubbing the tissue against the bone. Either the end of one finger, or of several, may be used in connection with the thumb.

Kneading Abdomen.

Slapping.

(4) Then give Flexion and Extension of the Leg, as follows: The patient on his back, place one hand on the knee, the other under the sole of the foot, and move the leg up and down to and from the chest. Repeat several times. (Active.)

(5) Then give Stretching of the Arm and Shoulder Joints, as follows: The patient on his back, with head and

shoulders raised on pillow, and arms extended over his head, stand at his head and take his hands in yours, passing your thumb between his thumb and forefinger, letting your fingers pass around the fleshy part of his thumb and back of his hand. Make several vigorous elastic pulls, avoiding sudden jerks. Make the pulls gradually, then withdraw the force suddenly. Repeat several times.

(6) Then give Spinal Extension, as follows: The patient on his back, grasp his shoulders, your fingers under his armpits. An assistant holds the patient's ankles. The patient relaxes and you give a careful stretching or extension of the spine, gentle but firm, for about one minute. This frees the circulation of the spinal cord and relieves pressure upon the spinal nerves.

(7) Then give Expansion of the Chest, as follows: Seat your patient on a stool or chair (if a chair, let him face its back) and stand behind him. Place your foot on the seat of the chair, the tip of your toe being up against, or under, the body of the patient. Place your knee between the patient's shoulders, holding his wrists in each hand. Raise his arms (sideways) up and over his head, slowly but strongly, and press hard with your knee against his spine. Then maintaining the pressure of your knee, lower the arms with a backward motion. The patient should inhale, filling the lungs, while the arms are being raised; exhaling as the arms are lowered.

Spinal Extension.

(8) Then give Vibration over the Kidneys, as follows: This form of treatment is a very powerful stimulant. It consists of certain oscillatory movements, produced through a succession of rapid individual efforts of the operator's hand. There should be little or no perceptible strain upon the arm muscles of the operator. The palm of the hand or the fingers must be placed firmly upon the parts to be treated, the arm being held straight and a fine trembling or vibrating movement communicated to the hand by the muscles of the upper part of the arm. The movement is somewhat difficult of acquirement, but you must persist until the desired movement is acquired, for this is one of the most stimulating and penetrating of all the methods of Osteopathic treatment, its effect being quite perceptible and almost akin to the effects of a current of electricity. It has a stimulating and strengthening effect upon the nerves, and acts strongly upon the venous circulation and upon the lymphatics. Be careful not to press upon the body

Expanding Chest.

Kidney Treat-
ment.

with your wrist, as you should use no greater pressure than the weight of your hand. When properly administered by one hand on the breast, the vibrations should be distinctly felt by the other hand placed under the back of the patient.

(9) Then give the following treatment: The patient on his face, stand by his left side, and place your left hand upon the upper part of the sacrum. Place your right hand under his knees. Then, still pressing upon the sacrum, lift his knees up as high as he can stand without too much strain. Repeat several times. You will find that he will be able to stand a little higher raising of the legs each time. This is an important movement in the treatment of diseases of the Kidneys, and you should master it. (See cut.)

(10) Finish by giving a gentle, soothing Stroking, as follows: This treatment is useful in producing sedative or quieting effects. It should be applied with a very light contact, the tips of the fingers, or the palm of the hand, just barely touching the patient. In some cases it will produce a feeling of drowsiness on the part of the patient. It never fails to quiet down the patient, equalize the circulation and relieve an excess of stimulation. Stroking should always be performed in a downward and outward direction, and in one direction only, not to-and-fro. The tips of one, more or all of the fingers, or the palmar surface of one or both hands, are moved gently over the skin, with a light contact, not even the mere weight of the hand being allowed to press upon the surface of the skin. Lightness, gentleness, and airiness, are the words best describing the Stroking movement.

Stroking.

Treat every day, or every other day, as the case demands.

DISEASES OF THE PANCREAS.

Give the same treatment as that recommended for Diseases of the Liver, excepting that you will give Vibrations over the Pancreas instead of over the Liver. Diseases of the Pancreas arise from the same causes as Diseases of the Liver, i. e., an obstruction or interruption of the circulation of the blood supplying the parts, or an interruption of the nerve currents to that organ. When these obstructions or interruptions are removed by Osteopathic treatment, normal conditions return and a cure is effected. Give treatment every other day.

DISEASES OF THE SPLEEN.

Give the same treatment as that recommended for Diseases of the Liver, excepting that you will give Vibrations over the Spleen instead of over the Liver. Diseases of the Spleen arise from the same causes as Diseases of the Liver, i. e., an obstruction or interruption of the circulation of the blood supplying the parts, or an interruption of the nerve current to that organ. When these obstructions or interruptions are removed by Osteopathic treatment, normal conditions return and a cure is effected. Give treatment every day.

DISEASES OF THE BLADDER.

Treatment for Bed Wetting.

The Osteopathic treatment of diseases of the Bladder can be readily understood, when it is remembered that the nerves controlling the Bladder can be reached by pressure upon or manipulation of the sacral region. Stimulation of these nerves causes an evacuation of urine, whilst a desensitization of the same nerves will cause the opposite result. Treatment is given by administering a thorough Osteopathic General Treatment, to equalize the circulation, etc., and to stimulate the vitality of the patient, followed by such local treatment as indicated by the requirements of the case. The sacral region being the important point for treatment in diseases of this kind, you will pay more attention to it than any portion of the spinal column. In case of Retention of the Urine, you will stimulate the muscles and nerves of the sacrum and give Vibration over the same part of the body. In cases of Incontinence of Urine, or Bed Wetting of Children, after giving the Osteopathic General Treatment, press one hand firmly on the Sacrum and the other hand under the knees, and raise the knees up as far as the patient can stand without pain. This treatment has cured thousands of cases of this annoying complaint, and can be relied upon. It works like a charm, effecting the cure often after one or two treatments.

DISEASES OF THE RECTUM.

Piles and kindred diseases of the Rectum are treated by a thorough General Treatment, paying special attention to that part of the treatment recommended for Constipation. Then place your patient on his side, with his knees up against his chest, and after dipping the finger into vaseline insert it gently in the rectum and manipulate gently, carefully but thoroughly in all directions, in order to free the circulation and stimulate the parts. Do not treat too often, as the internal treatment is apt to produce a tenderness of the parts, although the General Treatment may be given daily Some remarkable results have been obtained by this treatment. A simple case of Piles may be removed by giving simply the Constipation Treatment for a week or so.

DISEASES OF THE ANUS.

Diseases of this class are successfully treated by giving the Osteopathic General Treatment, followed by dipping the finger in vaseline and placing it within the rectum, manipulating the parts gently. Also pay special attention to that part of the treatment recommended for Constipation. Do not give internal treatment oftener than one time each week

LESSON V.

SPECIAL TREATMENTS.

DISEASES OF THE RESPIRATORY ORGANS.

Osteopathy teaches us that Consumption and other diseases of the Respiratory Organs are caused by contracted muscles obstructing the circulation and nerve-impulse to the parts. Consequently, the treatment must consist of such movements and manipulations as will free the circulation and the nerve-impulse; stimulate the circulation and nerve force controlling the affected organs. You must bear in mind the fact that the several diseases of the Organs of Respiration arise from practically the same cause, and that the apparently different kinds of disease of these organs are in reality only different manifestations of the same disease. Bearing this in mind, you will have the key to the situation, and although you will vary your treatment to fit the special requirements of the particular case which you are treating, you will follow the general principles underlying the treatment. The treatment that we give below has been found most valuable in cases of Asthma, Bronchitis, etc., and other Diseases of the Respiratory Organs, including Consumption. But right here we wish to say to you that you had better not seek after cases of Consumption. The percentage of deaths from this disease is very great, and the Drug Doctors pronounce the disease incurable. The cases of Consumption offered you will be, as a rule, those which have been pronounced incurable by the Drug Doctors, and you will stand but a slight chance of success with them, as the disease will have progressed too far. It would be folly for you to take these cases, with the chances all against you and with all the Drug Doctors in town waiting to cry you down in case the patient dies, notwithstanding the fact that they lose dozens of similar cases every year. As a matter of business precaution, leave these cases for the Drug Doctors, and do not accept them yourself. This may not be a very high sentiment, but it is good business policy. Take our word for it. At the same time, if you have any one near to you who is suffering with this dread disease, you will be able to do much for them by giving the treatment below stated.

TREATMENT FOR DISEASES OF THE ORGANS OF RESPIRATION.

Spinal Treatment

(1) Start by giving Spinal Treatment, as follows: The patient on his side, then using the palmar surface of the fingers and hand, manipulate along the right side of the spinal column, commencing at the first cervical, and moving down the entire length of the spine. Move the muscles upward and outward gently but firmly and with a deep pressure, paying special attention wherever you find a tender spot, a hot or cold spot, or a knotted condition of the muscles. Then turning him on his other side, treat the opposite side in the same manner. Take your time in giving this treatment. Avoid using the finger tips.

Extending Neck.

(2) Then give Neck Treatment, as follows: The patient lying on his back, stand at his head and place one hand on his forehead, the other under his neck, and rotate the head slowly from side to side. Then manipulate thoroughly and deeply the muscles of the back, sides and front of the neck. Then place the hands in the first position, and give the neck a thorough extension or stretching, gently but firmly, being careful not to rotate the head. This treatment frees the circulation to the brain.

Expanding Chest.

(3) Then give Extension of the Spine, as follows: The patient on his back, grasp his shoulders, your fingers under his armpits. An assistant holds the patient's ankles. The patient relaxes and you give a careful stretching or extension of the spine, gentle but firm, for about one minute. This frees the circulation of the spinal cord and relieves pressure upon the spinal nerves.

(4) Then give Chest Expansion, as follows: Seat your patient on a stool or chair (if a chair, let him face its back) and stand behind him. Place your foot on the seat of the chair, the tip of your toe being up against, or under, the body of the patient. Place your knee between the patient's shoulders, holding his wrists in each hand. Raise his arms (sideways) up and over his head, slowly but strongly, and press hard with your knee against his spine. Then maintaining the pressure of your knee, lower the arms with a backward mo-

tion. The patient should inhale, filling the lungs, while the arms are being raised; exhaling as the arms are lowered.

(5) Then Rotate the Shoulders, as follows: The patient on his back or sitting up, place one hand on his shoulder, and with your other hand take hold of his elbow and rotate the arm around the head.

(6) Then administer Chopping Percussion to the Chest, as follows: With the patient on his back administer Chopping Percussion to the chest, with a flexible and springy wrist (beware of using a stiff wrist, as it will give too hard a blow). In this movement the hand is used as a butcher does his cleaver, the little finger side of the hand coming in contact with the body. The fingers are held apart, coming together with a springy movement when the blow is struck. The patient should practice deep breathing during this treatment.

Chopping Movement.

(7) Then administer Vibration to the Chest, as follows: This form of treatment is a very powerful stimulant. It consists of certain oscillatory movements, produced through a succession of rapid individual efforts of the operator's hand There should be little or no perceptible strain upon the arm muscles of the operator. The palm of the hand or the fingers must be placed firmly upon the parts to be treated, the arm being held straight, and a fine trembling or vibrating movement communicated to the hand by the muscles of the upper part of the arm. The movement is somewhat difficult of acquirement, but you must persist until the desired movement is acquired, for this is one of the most stimulating and penetrating of all the methods of Osteopathic treatment, its effect being quite perceptible and almost akin to the effects of a current of electricity. It has a stimulating and strengthening effect upon the nerves, and acts strongly upon the venous circulation and upon the lymphatics. Be careful not to press upon the body with your wrist, as you should use no greater pressure than the weight of your hand. When properly administered by one hand on the breast, the vibrations should be distinctly felt by the other hand placed under the back of the patient.

Deep Vibration.

(8) Then press upon the Vaso-Motor Nerve Center, as follows: Place the fingers on each side of the back of the neck and press with fingers on each side of the spine over the upper cervicals (Vaso-Motor Center) for two or three minutes. This will slow the action of the heart.

(9) Then administer Stroking, as follows: This treatment is useful in producing sedative or quieting effects. It

Holding Vaso-Motor.

should be applied with a very light contact, the tips of the fingers, or the palm of the hand, just barely touching the patient. In some cases it will produce a feeling of drowsiness on the part of the patient. It never fails to quiet down the patient, equalize the circulation and relieve an excess of stimulation. Stroking should always be performed in a downward and outward direction, and in one direction only, not to-and-fro. The tips of one, more or all of the fingers, or the palmar surface of one or both hands, are moved gently over the skin, with a light contact, not even the mere weight of the hand being allowed to press upon the surface of the skin. Lightness, gentleness, and airiness, are the words best describing the Stroking movement.

QUIZ QUESTIONS

1. State cause and cure of Constipation.
2. State cause and cure of Dysentery.
3. State cause and cure of Heart Disease.
4. State cause and cure of Dropsy.
5. State cause and cure of Liver troubles.
6. State cause and cure of Kidney troubles.
7. State cause and cure of Bladder troubles.
8. State treatment of diseases of the Rectum.
9. State cause and cure diseases of the Respiratory Organs.
10. State details of tenth movement in treatment of diseases of the Kidneys.

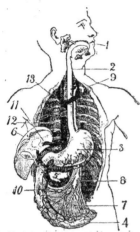

A diagrammatic representation of the various organs concerned in the conversion of food into blood. — 1, Mouth and salivary glands ; 2, the oesophagus ; 3, the stomach ; 4, a portion of the small intestine ; 5, the pancreas ; 6, the liver ; 7, mesentery with lacteals ; 8, receptacle of chyle ; 9, the thoracic duct emptying its contents into the left subclavian vein ; 10, branches of portal vein leading to liver ; 11, an hepatic vein leading from the liver to the large ascending vein ; 12, the large ascending vein cut off at its junction with the heart ; 13, the large descending vein cut off in like manner.

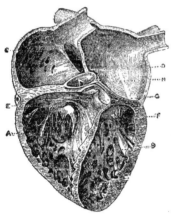

SECTION OF THE HEART.

A, Right Ventricle.   E, F, Inlets to the Ventricles.
B, Left   "   G, Pulmonary Artery.
C, Right Auricle.   H, Aorta,
D, Left Auricle.

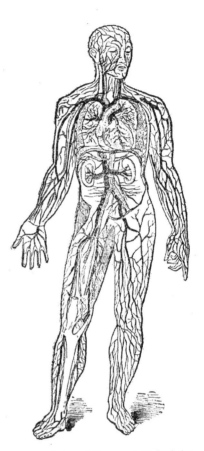

Front view of the organs of circulation. Veins, black; arteries, with transverse lines. Parts on the right side of figure are removed to show some of the deep vessels, while the left side shows superficial vessels.

THE VALVES OF THE VEINS HIGHLY MAGNIFIED.

THE HOME STUDY COURSE

IN

OSTEOPATHY

ISSUED BY

The Columbia
College of Osteopathy

**3031 AUDITORIUM BLDG.,
CHICAGO, ILL., U. S. A.**

Consists of Twelve Lessons, fully illustrated, and is issued
in Five Parts, as follows:

PART FIRST—
> Theory of Osteopathy.
> Movements and Manipulations.
> General Treatment.

PART SECOND—
> Special Treatments.

PART THIRD—
> Special Treatments.

PART FOURTH—
> Special Treatments.
> Osteopathic Anatomy.
> Osteopathic Physiology.

PART FIFTH—
> Osteopathic Anatomy and Physiology.
> Building up and Conducting an Osteopathic
>   Practice.
> Practical Advice and Suggestions.
> Miscellaneous Information.

HOME STUDY COURSE

IN

OSTEOPATHY

PART THIRD

COMPRISING LESSONS VI, VII AND VIII

ISSUED BY

THE COLUMBIA COLLEGE OF OSTEOPATHY
3031 AUDITORIUM BUILDING
CHICAGO, ILL., U. S. A.

CONTENTS

LESSON VI

LESSON VII

LESSON VIII

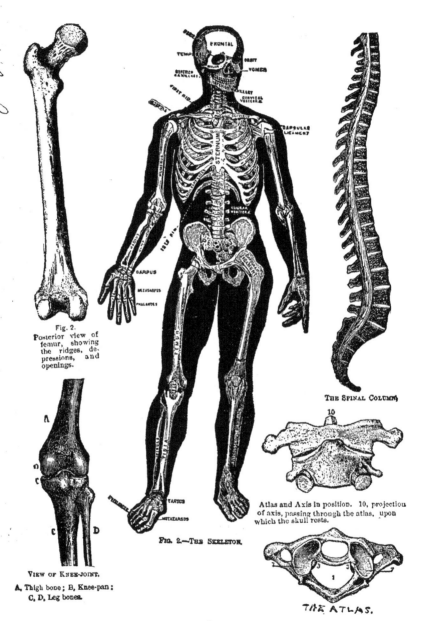

Fig. 2.
Posterior view of femur, showing the ridges, depressions, and openings.

FRONTAL
TEMP
ORBIT
VOMER
SUPERIOR MAXILLARY
FIRST RIB
CERVICAL VERTEBRA
CAPSULAR LIGAMENT
STERNUM
LUMBAR VERTEBRA
PELVIS
CARPUS
METACARPUS
PHALANGES
TARSUS
METATARSUS

FIG. 2.—THE SKELETON.

THE SPINAL COLUMN.

10

Atlas and Axis in position. 10, projection of axis, passing through the atlas, upon which the skull rests.

VIEW OF KNEE-JOINT.

A, Thigh bone; B, Knee-pan; C, D, Leg bones.

THE ATLAS.

3

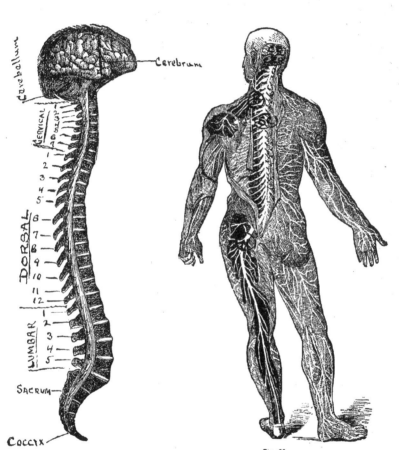

Fig. 66.

Posterior view of the spinal cord, — a portion of the cerebrum and cerebellum and some of the nerves of the cerebro-spinal system. On the left side of the body some of the tissues are removed to show the deeper nerves, while the right side shows certain superficial ones. — CE, cerebrum; CER, cerebellum, B, nerves distributed to the arm; SC, spinal cord; SN, sciatic nerve.

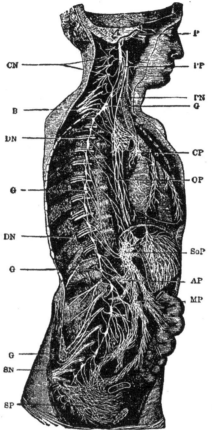

Fig. 75.

Vertical section of body, showing sympathetic nerves and ganglia of right side, and their connection with the cerebro-spinal nerves. — *Cerebro-spinal system*. CN, cervical nerves; B, nerves distributed to the arm; DN, dorsal nerves; SN, sacral nerves, some of which are distributed to the leg; PN, pneumogastric nerve. *Sympathetic system:* P, plexus in the head; PP, pharyngeal plexus; CP, cardiac plexus. OP, oesophageal plexus; SoP, solar plexus; AP, aortic plexus, MP, mesenteric plexus; SP, sacral plexus; G, some of the ganglia of the sympathetic system.

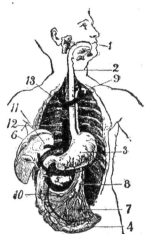

A diagrammatic representation of the various organs concerned in the conversion of food into blood. — 1, Mouth and salivary glands ; 2, the oesophagus ; 3, the stomach ; 4, a portion of the small intestine ; 5, the pancreas ; 6, the liver; 7, mesentery with lacteals ; 8, receptacle of chyle ; 9, the thoracic duct emptying its contents into the left subclavian vein ; 10, branches of portal vein leading to liver ; 11, an hepatic vein leading from the liver to the large ascending vein ; 12, the large ascending vein cut off at its junction with the heart ; 13, the large descending vein cut off in like manner.

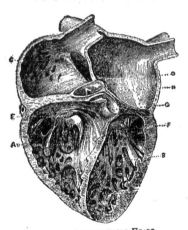

SECTION OF THE HEART.

A. Right Ventricle.
B, Left   "
C, Right Auricle.
D. Left Auricle.

E, F, Inlets to the Ventricles.
G, Pulmonary Artery.
H, Aorta.

Front view of the organs of circulation. Veins, black; arteries, with transverse lines. Parts on the right side of figure are removed to show some of the deep vessels, while the left side shows superficial vessels.

THE VALVES OF THE VEINS HIGHLY MAGNIFIED.

LESSON VI

SPECIAL TREATMENTS

RHEUMATISM AND KINDRED DISEASES

RHEUMATISM

Osteopathy teaches that every organ and part of the body will function properly, providing that there is no irregular skeleton adjustment; no interference with the circulation, no interruption of the nerve force. This being granted, Rheumatism is but one form of the manifestation of imperfect or abnormal conditions, arising from one or more of the causes indicated above.

Rheumatism in any part of the body is simply an indication that there is an interference with the circulation or an interference with the impulses reaching the part from the nervous system. We find in practice that the obstruction or interference usually comes from the contraction of certain muscles, the circulation thus being interfered with and partially shut off. The muscles the contraction of which so interfere with the circulation, are more frequently the muscles of the thigh, and the muscles of the shoulder.

A General Osteopathic Treatment is found to be most beneficial in the treatment of Rheumatism, in its several forms, although we have indicated special treatments in the more common forms You must use your own judgment, and adapt your treatment to the requirements of each particular case. Once learn the different movements and manipulations thoroughly, and you will almost instinctively use the movement or manipulation best adapted to the case

The treatment given for Rheumatism is intended to cover the several manifestations or forms of this complaint, the cause being the same in all the different forms

In the case of Stiff Neck, give the General Neck Treatment, combined with the treatment given for rheumatism In

Sciatica, give the Rheumatism treatment, together with a thorough manipulation of the lower portion of the spine. We have given a valuable special treatment for Lumbago.

RHEUMATISM IN THE LEGS

Spinal Treatment

(1) Begin with Spinal Treatment, as follows: The patient on his side, then using the palmar surface of the fingers and hand, manipulate along the right side of the spinal column, commencing at the first cervical, and moving down the entire length of the spine. Move the muscles upward and outward gently, but firmly and with a deep pressure, paying special attention wherever you find a tender spot, a hot or cold spot, or a knotted condition of the muscles. Then turning him on his other side, treat the opposite side in the same manner. Take your time in giving this treatment. Avoid using the finger tips.

Kneading with Thumb.

(2) Then give Flexion and Extension of the Leg, as follows: The patient on his back, place one hand on the knee, the other under the sole of the foot, and move the leg up and down to and from the chest. Repeat several times. (Active.)

(3) Then knead the Thigh and Leg as follows: Palmar Kneading is akin to the movements of the hand of the baker as he kneads his dough. The operator grasps the muscle with the palm of his hand, keeping the fingers close together, the thumbs out. The thumb is not used, the muscle being grasped between the fingers and the palm of the hand, the heel of the hand, or the lower fleshy part of the thumb. Do not allow the skin to slip, but maintain a firm grasp. Manipulate deeply so as to reach the deeper parts. The muscle should be compressed by the hand and at the same time gently lifted from the bone or underlying tissues, rolled and stretched. When the strain is greatest, release so as to stimulate. Work slowly and carefully, repeating the manipulations according to the requirements of the case, and the state of the patient. In the

Beating Sciatic Nerve. beginning, do not exert much force, but later on increase the force as the patient becomes accustomed to it. Try to individualize groups of muscles, as the best results are thus obtained. Use the hands alternately. In some cases it is also desirable to use a rolling movement, the heel of the hand and the fleshy part of the thumb being pressed upon the muscle which is then rolled to and fro, the fingers not being used. Use one or both hands. Digital Kneading is effected by grasping the tissue between the ends of the fingers and thumb, and then rubbing the tissue against the bone. Either the end of one finger, or of several, may be used in connection with the thumb.

(4) Then Rotate the Leg as follows: The patient on his back, place one hand on the sole of his foot, the other under his knee; raise the leg and rotate from the hip outward. Repeat several times with each leg.

(5) Then Extend Foot as follows: The patient on his back, take his toes in one hand and his ankle in the other. Move the foot backward and forward. If you prefer, operate on both feet at the same time. Repeat several times.

Treat every day until marked relief is experienced. Then treat every other day.

RHEUMATISM IN THE ARMS

(1) Begin treatment with Spinal Treatment, as follows: The patient on his side, then using the palmar surface of the fingers and hand, manipulate along the right side of the spinal column, commencing at the first cervical, and moving down the entire length of the spine. Move the muscles upward and outward gently, but firmly with a deep pressure, paying special attention wherever you find a tender spot, a hot or cold spot, or a knotted condition of the muscles. Then turning him on his other side, treat the opposite side in the same manner. Take your time in giving this treatment. Avoid using the finger tips.

Spinal Treatment

(2) Then give Neck Treatment as follows: The patient lying on his back, stand at his head and place one hand on his forehead, the other under his neck, and rotate the head slowly from side to side. Then manipulate thoroughly and deeply the muscles of the back, sides and front of the neck. Then place the hands in the first position, and give the neck a thorough extension or stretching, gently but firmly, being careful not to rotate the head. This treatment frees the circulation to the brain.

(3) Then Stretch the Arm and Shoulder Joints, as follows: The patient on his back, with head and shoulders raised

Extending Neck.

Expanding Chest.

on pillow, and arms extended over his head, stand at his head and take his hands in yours, passing your thumb between his thumb and forefinger, letting your fingers pass around the fleshy part of his thumb and back of his hand. Make several vigorous elastic pulls, avoiding sudden jerks. Make the pulls gradually, then withdraw the force suddenly. Repeat several times.

(4) Then give the Chest Expansion treatment, as follows: Seat your patient on a stool or chair (if a chair, let him face its back) and stand behind him. Place your foot on the seat of the chair, the tip of your toe being up against, or under, the body of the patient. Place your knee between the patient's shoulders, holding his wrists in each hand. Raise his arms (sideways) up and over his head, slowly but strongly, and press hard with your knee against his spine. Then maintaining the pressure of your knee, lower the arms with a backward motion. The patient should inhale, filling the lungs, while the arms are being raised; exhaling as the arms are lowered.

Kneading the Arm.

(5) Then Rotate his Arms and Shoulders, as follows: The patient on his back or sitting up, place one hand on his shoulder, and with your other hand take hold of his elbow and rotate the arm around the head.

(6) Then Knead his Arms as follows: Palmar Kneading is akin to the movement of the hand of the baker as he kneads his dough. The operator grasps the muscle with the palm of his hand, keeping the fingers close together, the thumbs out. The thumb is not used, the muscle being grasped between the fingers and the plam of the hand, the heel of the hand, or the lower fleshy part of the thumb. Do not allow the skin to slip, but maintain a firm grasp. Manipulate deeply so as to reach the deeper parts. The muscle should be compressed by the hand and at the same time gently lifted from the bone or underlying tissues, rolled and stretched. When the strain is greatest, release so as to stimulate. Work slowly and carefully, repeating the manipulations according to the requirements of the case, and the state of the patient. In the beginning, do not exert much force, but later on increase the force as the patient becomes accustomed to it. Try to individualize groups of muscles, as the best results are thus obtained. Use

Wringing Movement.

Surface Kneading.

the hands alternately. In some cases it is also desirable to use a rolling movement, the heel of the hand and the fleshy part of the thumb being pressed upon the muscle which is then rolled to and fro, the fingers not being used. Use one or both hands. Digital Kneading is effected by grasping the tissue between the ends of the fingers and thumb, and then rubbing the tissue against the bone. Either the end of one finger, or of several, may be used in connection with the thumb.

Surface Kneading.

Treat every day until a decided relief is experienced; then every other day.

RHEUMATISM IN ENTIRE SYSTEM

Treat by combining the treatments given above for Rheumatism in the Legs and in the Arms, with special Kneading and Manipulating of the affected parts. Finish with General Treatment.

LUMBAGO (BACK ACHE)

(1) Begin treatment with Spinal Treatment, as follows: The patient on his side, then using the palmar surface of the fingers and hand, manipulate along the right side of the spinal column, commencing at the first cervical, and moving down the entire length of the spine. Move the muscles upward and outward gently, but firmly and with a deep pressure, paying special attention wherever you find a tender spot, a hot or cold spot, or a knotted condition of the muscles. Then turning him on his other side, treat the opposite side in the same manner. Take your time in giving this treatment. Avoid using the finger tips.

Spinal Treatment

(2) Then give Neck Treatment, as follows: The patient lying on his back, stand at his head and place one hand on his forehead, the other under his neck, and rotate the head slowly from side to side. Then manipulate thoroughly and deeply the muscles of the back, sides and front of the neck. Then place the hands in the first position, and give the neck a thorough extension or stretching, gently but firmly, being careful not to rotate the head. This treatment frees the circulation to the brain.

(3) Then give Flexion and Extension of the Legs, as follows: The patient on his back, place one hand on the knee, the

Extending Neck.

Kneading the Back.

Kneading.

Kneading the Glutei.

Slapping.

other under the sole of the foot, and move the leg up and down to and from the chest. Repeat several times. (Active.)

(4) Then Knead the Small of the Back, as follows: Palmar Kneading is akin to the movement of the hand of the baker as he kneads his dough. The operator grasps the muscle with the plam of his hand, keeping the fingers close together, the thumbs out. The thumb is not used, the muscle being grasped between the fingers and the palm of the hand, the heel of the hand, or the lower fleshy part of the thumb. Do not allow the skin to slip, but maintain a firm grasp. Manipulate deeply so as to reach the deeper parts. The muscle should be compressed by the hand and at the same time gently lifted from the bone or underlying tissues, rolled and stretched. When the strain is greatest, release so as to stimulate. Work slowly and carefully, repeating the manipulations, according to the requirements of the case, and the state of the patient. In the beginning, do not exert much force, but later on increase the force as the patient becomes accustomed to it. Try to individualize groups of muscles, as the best results are thus obtained. Use the hands alternately. In some cases it is also desirable to use a rolling movement, the heel of the hand and the fleshy part of the thumb being placed upon the muscle, which is then rolled to and fro, the fingers not being used. Use one or both hands. Digital Kneading is effected by grasping the tissue between the ends of the fingers and thumb, and then rubbing the tissue against the bone. Either the end of one finger, or of several, may be used in connection with the thumb.

(5) Then Rub the Small of the Back, as follows: In rubbing, the palm of the hand, and the lower part of the fingers should be used, the tips of the fingers and the thumb being turned back. It is beneficial in stimulating the parts, and promoting the flow of the blood and the lymph.

(6) Then administer Percussion to the small of the back, as follows: .Percussion consists of administering blows to different parts of the body, with varying degrees of force. The wrist should be flexible and loose, as a stiff wrist gives a blow such as is used in fighting. The blow should be elastic and springy, which, although penetrating deeply, does not injure the surface. Percussion can be given by several methods, which

we will now briefly describe. The first method is by striking the body with the inside flat surface of the half-closed fist, the heel of the hand and the closed ends of the fingers coming in contact with the flesh. The second method is a chopping movement, made with the little finger side of the hand. The hand is likened to a butcher's cleaver in this chopping movement. The fingers are held loosely apart, coming together when the blow is struck. The third method is a slapping movement, which is best comprehended by the position and movement of the hand of the mother administering a well-merited spanking to one of her brood. The fingers are held rigid, and the body slapped. The fourth method is a clapping movement, the hand being shaped so as to emit a hollow sound; just as one holds his hands in applauding at a theater or concert. The fifth method is a tapping movement with the tips of the fingers, one or more fingers of one or both hands being used. Percussion, in its different forms, is a powerful stimulant to the nerve centers.

Chopping Movement.

(7) Place the patient on his side, and place your hand under his knee, and then lift up his leg with a sideways motion, at the same time using your other hand to manipulate the muscles on the side of the spinal column, commencing at the lumbar vertebra and working down to the lower part of the sacrum. (See cut.)

Treating Lumbago.

(8) Finish by stroking the entire Back, as follows: This treatment is useful in producing sedative or quieting effects. It should be applied with a very light contact, the tips of the fingers, or the palm of the hand, just barely touching the patient. In some cases it will produce a feeling of drowsiness on the part of the patient. It never fails to quiet down the patient, equalize the circulation and relieve an excess of stimulation. Stroking should always be performed in a downward and outward direction, and in one direction only, not to-and-fro. The tips of one, more or all of the fingers, or the palmar surface of one or both hands, are moved gently over the skin, with a light contact, not even the mere weight of the hand being allowed to press upon the surface of the skin. Lightness, gentleness and airiness are the words best describing the Stroking movement.

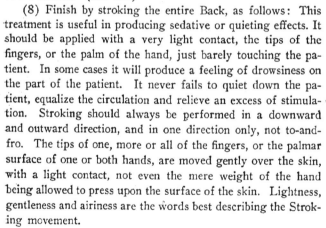

Stroking.

Treat frequently. This treatment is one of the best ever given for this very common trouble, and you should get quite satisfactory results from it. It is very thorough and effective, and you should thoroughly familiarize yourself with it, as the movements, etc., will prove useful in the treatment of other complaints, particularly Kidney Troubles and Female Complaints; in fact, this treatment alone has cured many cases of the last two named complaints.

GOUT

Spinal Treatment

(1) Begin treatment by giving Spinal Treatment, as fol·lows: The patient on his side, then using the palmar surface of the fingers and hand, manipulate along the right side of the spinal column, commencing at the first cervical, and moving down the entire length of the spine. Move the muscles upward and outward gently but firmly and with a deep pressure, paying special attention wherever you find a tender spot, a hot or cold spot, or a knotted condition of the muscles. Then turning him on his other side, treat the opposite side in the same manner. Take your time in giving this treatment. Avoid using the finger tips.

(2) Then give Neck Treatment, as follows: The patient lying on his back, stand at his head and place one hand on his forehead, the other under his neck, and rotate the head slowly from side to side. Then manipulate thoroughly and deeply the muscles of the back, sides and front of the neck. Then place the hands in the first position, and give the neck a thorough extension or stretching, gently but firmly, being careful not to rotate the head. This treatment frees the circulation to the brain.

Extending Neck.

(3) Then give Flexion and Extension of the Leg, as follows: The patient on his back, place one hand on the knee, the other under the sole of the foot, and move the leg up and down to and from the chest. Repeat several times. (Active.)

(4) Give General Treatment. Treat frequently.

LESSON VII

SPECIAL TREATMENTS

GOITRE AND TUMORS

GOITRE

Goitre is an enlargement of the thyroid gland. The thyroid gland is situated at the front of the neck, and ordinarily, attracts no attention, but when under certain conditions the gland becomes enlarged, a swelling of the neck is produced, which becomes quite noticeable This swelling sometimes attains enormous size, cases having been observed in which the size of the neck was much greater than that of the head. In some cases of Goitre, the patient suffers nothing beyond the annoyance occasioned by the impediment to the free movement of the head and neck, while in other cases, much trouble is caused by the pressure upon the windpipe, causing difficulty in breathing and swallowing, and often produces an obstinate cough, which weakens the patient. This disease has always puzzled and baffled the Drug Doctors, and many are the theories advanced in an attempt to explain the cause of the trouble. The Osteopathic theory is rational and simple, and has never been successfully contradicted. We claim that Goitre is caused by an obstruction of the circulation of the blood supplying the thyroid gland, thus occasioning a swelling or enlargement of the gland. This being granted, it follows that a removal of this obstruction and a consequent restoration of normal conditions, will cause the Goitre to be absorbed and carried off by the system. Some Osteopathic practitioners have found that in many cases of Goitre, the clavicle, or collar-bone, has been depressed and has obstructed the venous circulation from the thyroid gland, thus preventing the escape of blood and causing the enlargement of the gland Stretching the muscles in the vicinity and raising the clavicle affords immediate relief, and has effected many cures. This treatment, in connection with General Osteopathic Treatment, gives an ideal treatment for this complaint, which has baffled and routed the Drug Doctors

TREATMENT

Raising Clavicle.

(1) Standing behind the patient, place your left hand around his neck and insert the thumb of that hand under the middle of the right clavicle. Take hold of the patient's right wrist, with your other hand, and slowly raise his arm above his head, and lower with a slightly backward motion. At the time you lower the arm, press the clavicle up with the thumb that is under it. Treat the other clavicle in like manner.

Spinal Treatment

(2) Then give Spinal Treatment, as follows: The patient on his side, then using the palmar surface of the fingers and hand, manipulate along the right side of the spinal column, commencing at the first cervical, and moving down the entire length of the spine. Move the muscles upward and outward gently, but firmly, and with a deep pressure, paying special attention wherever you find a tender spot, a hot or cold spot, or a knotted condition of the muscles. Then turning him on his other side, treat the opposite side in the same manner. Take your time in giving this treatment. Avoid using the finger tips.

(3) Then give Neck Treatment, as follows: The patient lying on his back, stand at his head and place one hand on his forehead, the other under his neck, and rotate the head slowly from side to side. Then manipulate thoroughly and deeply the muscles of the back, sides and front of the neck. Then place the hands in the first position, and give the neck a thorough extension or stretching, gently but firmly, being careful not to rotate the head. This treatment frees the circulation to the brain.

Expanding Chest.

(4) Then give Chest Expansion, as follows: Seat your patient on a stool or chair (if a chair, let him face its back) and stand behind him. Place your foot on the seat of the chair, the tip of your toe being up against, or under, the body of the patient. Place your knee between the patient's shoulders, holding his wrists in each hand. Raise his arms (sideways) up and over his head, slowly but strongly, and press hard with your knee against his spine. Then maintaining the pressure of your knee, lower the arms with a backward motion. The patient should inhale, filling the lungs, while the arms are being raised; exhaling as the arms are lowered.

(5) Then place fingers under the goitre, pulling it upward and kneading it gently.

(6) Then give thorough General Treatment. Treat every other day.

FLESHY TUMORS

Fleshy Tumors originate, as do goitres, in an obstruction of the venous circulation, the veins not being able to carry off the blood on its return trip to the heart.

TREATMENT

(1) Give Goitre Treatment.

(2) Then knead the muscles and flesh in the vicinity of the tumor, as follows, also kneading and moving the tumor itself, gently, in all directions:

Manipulation,

Palmar Kneading is akin to the movement of the hand of the maker as he kneads his dough. The operator grasps the muscle with the palm of his hand, keeping the fingers close together, the thumbs out. The thumb is not used, the muscle being grasped between the fingers and the palm of the hand, the heel of the hand, or the lower fleshy part of the thumb. Do not allow the skin to slip, but maintain a firm grasp. Manipulate deeply so as to reach the deeper parts. The muscle should be compressed by the hand and at the same time gently lifted from the bone or underlying tissues, rolled and stretched. When the strain is greatest, release so as to stimulate. Work slowly and carefully, repeating the manipulations according to the requirements of the case, and the state of the patient. In the beginning, do not exert much force, but later on increase the force as the patient becomes accustomed to it. Try to individualize groups of muscles, as the best results are thus obtained. Use the hands alternately. In some cases it is also desirable to use a rolling movement, the heel of the hand and the fleshy part of the thumb being pressed upon the muscle which is then rolled to and fro, the fingers not being used. Use one or both hands. Digital Kneading is effected by grasping the tissue between the ends of the fingers and thumb, and then rubbing the tissue against the bone. Either the end of one finger, or of several, may be used in connection with the thumb.

Manipulation.

(3) Finish by giving thorough General Treatment. Treat every other day.

SCROFULA

This disease is caused by an abnormal constitutional condition, manifesting in inflammation and suppuration of the lymph-glands, ulcers, etc. Scrofula is, in fact, scarcely a specific disease, but an abnormal constitutional condition, which predisposes the system to certain diseases, and diminishes the power of recovery. This condition may be either inherited or acquired, but is most frequently manifested in children of consumptive and syphilitic parents, and in those whose youth has been passed in bad environments, and who have had insufficient and improper food, impure air and damp rooms.

TREATMENT

Give thorough General Treatment. Treat frequently.

DISEASES OF THE SKIN

Osteopathy teaches that the majority of Diseases of the Skin, if indeed not all, arise from an obstruction to the lymphatic circulation. Consequently the ideal treatment is the Osteopathic General Treatment, which will free the circulation, removing obstructions, and stimulating the entire system, and restoring normal conditions. In cases of Boils, etc., in addition to the General Treatment, you should give local manipulations in the immediate region of the Boil, moving the muscles in all directions to free the circulation.

DISEASES OF THE BONES AND JOINTS

There is no better treatment for diseases of this class, than the Osteopathic General Treatment, special attention being given to manipulation and movements of the affected parts. When the circulation is free and equalized the improvement will be speedily apparent. Treatment should be given once a day until a marked improvement is noted; then every other day.

GENERAL DEBILITY (OLD AGE)

There is no better treatment for this trouble than Osteopathy. A thorough General Treatment does much to restore normal conditions, equalize the circulation, and stimulate the system. It is a veritable Elixir of Youth to the aged and infirm, and often acts almost like a miracle.

TREATMENT

· (1) Give thorough General Treatmnt.

DISEASES OF THE EYE, EAR AND THROAT

This class of diseases yields very readily to Osteopathic treatment, and many an Osteopath has earned his first laurels in speedily curing diseases of this class after they have been pronounced incurable by the Drug Doctors, and after the patient had expended hundreds of dollars to no effect.

Diseases of the Eye, Ear, Nose and Throat are caused by a contracted condition of the muscles of the neck, and a conseqeunt obstruction to the circulation, particularly the venous circulation, by which the blood is carried back to the heart. Obstructions and interferences of this kind naturally result in a diseased condition of these organs, and the only possible cure is to free the circulation and restore normal conditions. The following treatment will prove very valuable in diseases of the Eye, Ear, Nose and Throat, and we will refer to it under each head, accompanying it with such special treatment as may be indicated. In order that it may be distinguished from other treatments, we will call it, for convenience, the COMBINED NECK TREATMENT. You will notice that this Combined Neck Treatment is merely our regular Neck Treatment combined with a few other regular movements that tend to free the circulation of the neck.

Extending Neck.

COMBINED NECK TREATMENT

(1) Begin by giving a thorough Neck Treatment, as follows:

The patient lying on his back, stand at his head and place one hand on his forehead, the other under his neck, and rotate the head slowly from side to side. Then manipulate thoroughly and deeply the muscles of the back, sides and front of the neck. Then place the hands in the first position and give the neck a thorough extension or stretching, gently but firmly, being careful not to rotate the head. This treatment frees the circulation to the brain.

(2) Then give Spinal Extension, as follows:

The patient on his back, grasp his shoulders, your fingers under his armpits. An assistant holds the patient's ankles. The patient relaxes and you give a careful stretching or extension of the spine, gentle but firm, for about one minute. This frees the circulation of the spinal cord and relieves pressure upon the spinal nerves.

Spinal Extension.

Stroking.

(3)　Then Rotate the Arm and Shoulder, as follows:
The patient on his back or sitting up, place one hand on his shoulder, and with your other hand take hold of his elbow and rotate the arm around the head.

(4)　Finish by Stroking the head and neck, and around the affected parts.

Remember that the Neck Treatment must be very thorough, as therein lies most of the virtue of the treatment. The muscles must be manipulated until they feel soft and flexible.

DISEASES OF THE EYE
GRANULATED EYELIDS

This is a most annoying disease, which comes from long continued inflammation, and shows itself in granular excrescences on the inner surface of the eyelids.

TREATMENT

(1)　Begin by giving the Combined Neck Treatment, heretofore described.

(2)　Then with the inner surface of the end of the second fingers of each hand, manipulate the eye (closed) and its muscles, gently but firmly. Press the ends of the fingers slightly under the edge of the bone and move gently. This treatment will afford relief at once, and will greatly stimulate and strengthen the eye. Then with your thumb and forefinger, gather up the eyelids, gently, and slightly press them together, or pinch them gently. This will stimulate the eyelids, and will cause the granules to be absorbed.

Extending Neck.

Treat every other day. You should be able to cure an ordinary case in one or two months. Some wonderful cures have been made by Osteopathists giving the above treatment.

INFLAMMATION OF THE EYES

Give the same treatment as that recommended for Granulated Eyelids, and also manipulate well in the neighborhood of the eye, and apply Vibration over the eye ball, the eye being of course closed.

CATARACT

Osteopathy has cured many cases of this dread disease, although considerable time is required to effect a cure, some-cases taking as much as six months, while others are relieved in say two months' time.

TREATMENT

Give the same treatment as recommended for Granulated Eyelids, and also manipulate well in the neighborhood of the eye, and apply Vibration to the eye ball, the eye being, of course, closed.

MISCELLANEOUS

Many cases of weak eyes, nearsightedness, etc., etc., have been materially benefited or cured by the treatment above recommended.

Extending Neck.

DISEASES OF THE EAR.

DEAFNESS, EARACHE, ETC.

The following treatment will be found valuable in all cases of trouble in the ear:

(1) Begin by giving the Combined Neck Treatment, heretofore described.

(2) Manipulate thoroughly all the muscles around the ear, and in its neighborhood, and insert the end of your finger in the ears, manipulating gently and carefully so as to free the circulation, finishing by taking hold of the lobe of the ear between your thumb and forefinger, and pulling it gently downward and backward, thus freeing the circulation.

Kneading Neck.

(3) Give a thorough Vibration over the Ear, as follows:

This form of treatment is a very powerful stimulant. It consists of certain oscillatory movements, produced through a succession of rapid individual efforts of the operator's hand. There should be little or no perceptible strain upon the arm muscles of the operator. The palm of the hand or the fingers must be placed firmly upon the parts to be treated, the arm being held straight and a fine trembling or vibrating movement communicated to the hand by the muscles of the upper part of the arm. The movement is somewhat difficult of acquirement, but you must persist until the desired movement is acquired, for this is one of the most stimulating and penetrating of all the methods of Osteopathic treatment, its effect being quite perceptible and almost akin to the effects of a current of electricity. It has a stimulating and strengthening effect upon the nerves, and acts strongly upon the venous circulation and upon the

Digital Vibration.

lymphatics. Be careful not to press upon the body with your wrist, as you should use no greater pressure than the weight of your hand. When properly administered by one hand on the breast, the vibrations should be distinctly felt by the other hand placed under the back of the patient.

This treatment will materially relieve, or cure, many cases of long seated troubles of the ear. The time required is from one to three months, although sometimes results are obtained in a much shorter time. Treat every day, if possible.

DISEASES OF THE NOSE
NASAL CATARRH—TREATMENT

(1)   Begin by giving the Combined Neck Treatment, heretofore described.

Holding Vaso-Motor.

(2)   Thoroughly manipulate the nose, from the corners of the eyes down to the lower part of the nose. Also manipulate the muscles in the neighborhood of the eyes and nose. Finish by giving Vibration at the upper part of the nose.

NOSE BLEED—TREATMENT

Press upon the Vaso-Motor centre, as follows:

Place the fingers on each side of the back of the neck and press with fingers on each side of the spine over the upper cervicals (vaso-motor center) for two or three minutes. This will slow the action of the heart.

DISEASES OF THE THROAT

The Combined Neck Treatment is the proper treatment for diseases of the Throat, and the Osteopathic General Treatment should also be given when possible, as the latter will stimulate the entire system, and give the patient more vitality and power to throw off abnormal conditions. In cases of Croup or Sore Throat, place the forefinger in the mouth and gently manipulate the inner parts of the throat thoroughly, loosening up any membranous substance that may have formed there.

LESSON VIII

SPECIAL TREATMENTS

DISEASES OF THE NERVOUS SYSTEM

NEURALGIA

The best treatment for Neuralgia is a thorough General Osteopathic Treatment, accompanied by special manipulation of the affected parts. The real cause of the trouble may be in conditions existing in some part of the system apparently having no connection with the trouble. By stimulating the entire system, equalizing the circulation, removing obstructions, free the nerve force, etc., normal conditions are restored, and trouble disappears. Frequent treatments should be given until a material improvement is noted.

Extending Neck.

HEADACHE

Headaches arise from a number of causes, but can nearly always be relieved by the following simple treatment:

TREATMENT

(1) Begin by giving a thorough Neck Treatment, as follows: The patient lying on his back, stand at his head and place one hand on his forehead, the other under his neck, and rotate the head slowly from side to side. Then manipulate thoroughly and deeply the muscles of the back, sides and front of the neck. Then place the hands in the first position, and give the neck a thorough extension or stretching, gently but firmly, being careful not to rotate the head. This treatment frees the circulation to the brain.

(2) Then give pressure on the Vaso-Motor Nerve Center, as follows: Place the fingers on each side of the back of the neck and press with fingers on each side of the spine over the upper cervicals (vaso-motor center) for two or three minutes. This will slow the action of the heart.

(3) Place one hand on the forehead and the other on the back of the head, and exert a firm, steady pressure; then place one hand on each side of the head, just above and slightly in

Holding Vaso-Motor.

23

front of the top of the ear, and press firmly and steadily; then place one of your middle fingers on each temple, and press firmly but not too hard upon the temple, at the same time executing a rotary motion with the tips of your fingers, not allowing them to slip over the skin, however, the motion being more in the nature of Digital Manipulation than Rubbing.

Stroking.

(4) Finish by gently Stroking the Head and Face, as follows: If you can get the patient to lie down, you had better finish the treatment with a Stroking of the entire body, from head to feet. We herewith give directions for Stroking:

(5) This treatment will usually afford great relief, or an entire cure within a few minutes. If it appears to be Nervous Headache (which usually manifest themselves at the top of the head) you should also give a thorough Spinal Treatment, as follows: The patient on his side, then using the palmar surface of the fingers and hand, manipulate along the right side of the spinal column, commencing at the first cervical, and moving down the entire length of the spine. Move the muscles upward and outward, gently but firmly, and with a deep pressure, paying special attention wherever you find a tender spot, a hot or cold spot, or a knotted condition of the muscles. Then

Spinal Treatment

turning him on his other side, treat the opposite side in the same manner. Take your time in giving this treatment. Avoid using the finger tips.

If it is what is generally known as a "Sick Headache," which arises from the stomach, you should in addition give the treatment given elsewhere for Dyspepsia.

HICCOUGH

This trouble is caused by a spasmodic contraction of the diaphragm, which is controlled by the phrenic nerve. Pressure on the phrenic nerve will relieve the most obstinate case of hiccough almost instantly.

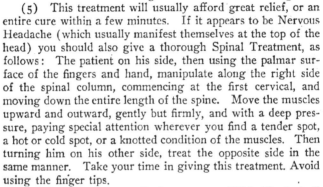

TREATMENT

(1) Begin by pressing upon the phrenic nerve, as follows: Seat your patient on a stool or chair, standing behind him. Place the fingers of each hand upon the transverse

Pressure Phrenic Nerve.

processes of the third, fourth and fifth cervicals. Press the fingers forward and down in front of the transverse processes, and press upon the phrenic nerve, which controls the diaphragm.

(2) Then give Expansion of the Chest, as follows: Seat your patient on a stool or chair (if a chair, let him face its

back) and stand behind him. Place your foot on the seat of the chair, the tip of your toe being up against, or under, the body of the patient. Place your knee between the patient's shoulders, holding his wrists in each hand. Raise his arms (sideways) up and over his head, slowly but strongly, and press hard with your knee against his spine. Then maintaining the pressure of your knee, lower the arms with a backward motion. The patient should inhale, filling the lungs, while the arms are being raised; exhaling as the arms are lowered.

(3) Finish by giving a gentle, soothing stroking of the head and face, or the whole body if deemed necessary, as follows: This treatment is useful in producing sedative or quieting effects. It should be applied with a very light contact, the tips of the fingers, or the palm of the hand, just barely touching the patient. In some cases it will produce a feeling of drowsiness on the part of the patient. It never fails to quiet down the patient, equalize the circulation and relieve an excess of stimulation. Stroking should always be performed in a downward and outward direction, and in one direction only, not to-and-fro. The tips of one, more or all of the fingers, or the palmar surface of one or both hands, are moved gently over the skin, with a light contact, not even the mere weight of the hand being allowed to press upon the surface of the skin. Lightness, gentleness, and airiness are the words best describing the Stroking movement.

Expanding Chest.

Stroking.

PARALYSIS

Osteopathy teaches that this dread disease is caused by a pressure upon certain nerves or nerve centers. The trouble can generally be traced to the spinal column, and the treatment consequently is based upon this fact. Before treating for paralysis you should make a thorough examination of the Spine, as explained in the lesson on General Treatment, paying special attention to ascertaining whether the vertebræ are all in line. In some cases you will find a slight dislocation which will have been occasioned by the contraction of a muscle, and which has resulted in a pressure on the spinal cord, causing paralysis of some particular part, or the entire body.

TREATMENT

Give a thorough General Treatment (as described under that heading), paying special attention to the Spinal Treatment, Spinal Extension, Neck Treatment, and Flexing and Extending the Legs. If a slight dislocation is found, give special

Spinal Extension.

manipulation of the surrounding muscles, and give Spinal Extension which will allow the vertebræ to slip back in place, and thus relieve the pressure.

ATROPHY

This disease is practically a starving of the muscles, causing a shrinking and withering. It is caused by an interference with the nerves controlling the arteries supplying the affected part. Osteopathy offers the only known remedy for this terrible disease.

TREATMENT

Give a thorough General Treatment, paying particular attention to the Spinal Treatment and manipulation and stretching of the afflicted part. There is nothing better than a good General Treatment, as in that treatment the entire system is stimulated, the circulation equalized and the nerves and nerve centers freed.

LOCOMOTOR ATAXIA

This disease is caused by an obstruction to the circulation and nerve current, just as is Paralysis and Atrophy. The treatment is practically the same.

TREATMENT

Give a thorough, careful General Treatment, paying particular attention to the Spinal Treatment, Spinal Extension, Flexing and Extension of the Legs.

INSANITY

Many Osteopathic practitioners have cured cases of Insanity which were undoubtedly occasioned by obstructions to the circulation and nerve current, generally some pressure upon the spinal cord.

TREATMENT

Give a good, thorough General Treatment, paying special attention to the Spinal Treatment.

EPILEPSY ("FITS")

Osteopathy teaches that this disease is frequently caused by a partial dislocation of some of the other upper cervical vertebræ, and that if such dislocation can be remedied a cure can be effected. Eminent authorities state that their experience is that about 25 per cent of cases of Epilepsy are caused by the above mentioned dislocation, but that the causes of the other 75 per cent have not yet been discovered. We believe that Osteopathy will eventually discover the cause of the majority of these cases, and the cure will follow. We believe, however, that every case of Epilepsy can be benefited by a thorough General Treatment.

TREATMENT

Treatment for Dislocation of Atlas.

. (1) The patient on his back, place your left hand upon the top of his head, your right hand and arm beneath his head and neck, your fingers two upon each side of the fourth dorsal vertebræ, pressing the muscles upward toward his head; at the same time pressing with your left hand firmly upon the top of his head and rotating it from side to side, working your right hand gradually upward until you reach the occipital.

(2) Then give thorough Neck Treatment, as follows: The patient lying on his back, stand at his head and place one hand on his forehead, the other under his neck, and rotate the head slowly from side to side. Then manipulate thoroughly and deeply the muscles of the back, sides and front of the neck. Then place the hands in the first position, and give the neck a thorough extension or stretching, gently but firmly, being careful not to rotate the head. This treatment frees the circulation to the brain.

Extending Neck.

(3) Then give Spinal Extension, as follows: The patient on his back, grasp his shoulders, your fingers under his armpits. An assistant holds the patient's ankles. The patient relaxes and you give a careful stretching or extension of the spine, gentle but firm, for about one minute. This frees the circulation of the spinal cord and relieves pressure upon the spinal nerves.

(4) Then give a thorough Spinal Treatment, as follows: The patient on his side, then using the palmar surface of the fingers and hand, manipulate along the right side of the spinal column, commencing at the first cervical, and moving down the entire length of the spine. Move the muscles upward and outward, gently but firmly, and with a deep pressure, paying special attention wherever you find a tender spot, a hot or cold spot, or a knotted condition of the muscles. Then turning him on his other side, treat the opposite side in the same manner. Take your time in giving this treatment. Avoid using the finger tips.

(5) Then give Chest Expansion, as follows: Seat your patient on a stool or chair (if a chair, let him face its back)

Spinal Extension.

Expanding Chest.

and stand behind him. Place your foot on the seat of the chair, the tip of your toe being up against, or under, the body of the patient. Place your knee between the patient's shoulders, holding his wrists in each hand. Raise his arms (sideways) up and over his head, slowly but strongly, and press hard with your knee against his spine. Then maintaining the pressure of your knee, lower the arms with a backward motion. The patient should inhale, filling the lungs, while the arms are being raised; exhaling as the arms are lowered.

(6) Finish with a gentle, soothing Stroking.

ST. VITUS DANCE

The Osteopathic General Treatment is the best possible treatment of this complaint, paying special attention to Neck and Spinal treatments.

NERVOUS PROSTRATION (NEURASTHENIA)

There is no better treatment possible than the Osteopathic General Treatment, paying special attention to the Neck and Spinal treatments.

HYSTERIA

Give Osteopathic General Treatment, paying special attention to Spinal and Neck treatments.

LOCKJAW (TETANUS)

Spinal Treatment

(1) Begin by giving a thorough Spinal Treatment, as follows: The patient on his side, then using the palmar surface of the fingers and hand, manipulate along the right side of the spinal column, commencing at the first cervical, and moving down the entire length of the spine. Move the muscles upward and outward, gently but firmly, and with a deep pressure, paying special attention wherever you find a tender spot, a hot or cold spot, or a knotted condition of the muscles. Then turning him on his other side, treat the opposite side in the same manner. Take your time in giving this treatment. Avoid using the finger tips.

(2) Then give thorough Neck Treatment, as follows: The patient lying on his back, stand at his head and place one hand on his forehead, the other under his neck, and rotate the head slowly from side to side. Then manipulate thoroughly and deeply the muscles of the back, sides and front of the neck. Then place the hands in the first position, and give the

neck a thorough extension or stretching, gently but firmly, be-ing careful not to rotate the head. This treatment frees the circulation to the brain.

(3) Then give Spinal Extension, as follows: The patient on his back, grasp his shoulders, your fingers under his armpits. An assistant holds the patient's ankles. The patient relaxes and you give a careful stretching or extension of the spine, gentle but firm, for about one minute. This frees the circulation of the spinal cord and relieves pressure upon the spinal nerves.

(4) Then give Flexion and Extension of the Legs, as follows: The patient on his back, place one hand on the knee, the other under the sole of the foot, and move the leg up and down to and from the chest. Repeat several times. (Active.)

(5) Then give Chest Expansion, as follows: Seat your patient on a stool or chair (if a chair, let him face its back) and stand behind him. Place your foot on the seat of the chair, the tip of your toe being up against, or under, the body of the patient. Place your knee between the patient's shoulders, holding his wrists in each hand. Raise his arms (sideways) up and over his head, slowly but strongly, and press hard with your knee against his spine. Then maintaining the pressure of your knee, lower the arms with a backward motion. The patient should inhale, filling the lungs, while the arms are being raised; exhaling as the arms are lowered.

Spinal Extension.

(6) Finish by a gentle stroking, as follows: This treatment is useful in producing sedative or quieting effects. It should be applied with a very light contact, the tips of the fingers, or the palm of the hand, just barely touching the patient. In some cases it will produce a feeling of drowsiness on the part of the patient. It never fails to quiet down the patient, equalize the circulation and relieve an excess of stimulation. Stroking should always be performed in a downward and outward direction, and in one direction only, not to-and-fro. The tips of one, more or all of the fingers, or the palmar surface of one or both hands, are moved gently over the skin, with a light contact, not even the mere weight of the hand being allowed to press upon the surface of the skin. Lightness, gentleness, and airiness are the words best describing the Stroking movement.

Expanding Chest.

In this treatment the greatest care and attention should be given to the manipulation of the muscles of the neck and spine,

Stroking.

the muscles being kneaded and manipulated until they are soft and flexible. Treat twice a day.

INSOMNIA

The Osteopathic General Treatment is the best possible treatment for this complaint.

IMPOTENCY (LOSS OF SEXUAL POWER)

Osteopathy teaches that this trouble is caused by an impairment of the blood supply or nerve impulse to the sexual organs. If the patient is suffering from General Debility he should be treated for that trouble and his general system built up, in addition to the following treatment for sexual weakness.

TREATMENT

Spinal Treatment

(1) Begin by giving a thorough Spinal Treatment, as follows: The patient on his side, then using the palmar surface of the fingers and hand, manipulate along the right side of the spinal column, commencing at the first cervical, and moving down the entire length of the spine. Move the muscles upward and outward gently but firmly and with a deep pressure, paying special attention wherever you find a tender spot, a hot or cold spot, or a knotted condition of the muscles. Then turning him on his other side, treat the opposite side in the same manner. Take your time in giving this treatment. Avoid using the finger tips.

(2) Then give Spinal Extension, as follows: The patient on his back, grasp his shoulders, your fingers under his armpits. An assistant holds the patient's ankles. The patient relaxes and you give a careful stretching or extension of the spine, gentle but firm, for about one minute. This frees the circulation of the spinal cord and relieves pressure upon the spinal nerves.

(3) Then give Flexion and Extension of the Legs, as follows: The patient on his back, place one hand on the knee, the other under the sole of the foot, and move the leg up Spinal Extension. and down to and from the chest. Repeat several times. (Active.)

(4) Then place the patient on his face, and (after removing your right shoe) stand on the table and place your left foot between the patient's knees, and your right foot on his sacrum. Then taking hold of his ankles, draw up his legs,

slowly but firmly, as high as can be done without causing too much pain, at the same time pressing hard with your right foot upon his sacrum. This is the great Osteopathic Impotency Cure, which is based upon the fact that the nerves supplying the sexual organs can be reached by the above movement and thereby stimulated.

(5) In some cases it is well to give Digital Manipulation to the Prostate Gland, which is often found to be enlarged. This treatment is given as follows: The patient on his side, with legs flexed, dip your forefinger in vaseline and pass it carefully up the rectum. Then gently manipulate the prostate gland.

(6) It is often well to carefully manipulate the penis and testicles, thus stimulating those parts.

Treat every day, or every other day. Marked improvement will be manifested in a week or two, and a decided change in a month, but the treatment should be kept up for two or three months if necessary. This treatment rarely fails to effect a cure.

Impotency.

QUIZ QUESTIONS

1. State cause and cure of Rheumatism.
2. State special movement (No. 7) for Lumbago.
3. State cause and cure of Goitre.
4. State cause and cure of Tumors.
5. State cause and cure of Scrofula.
6. State Osteopathic theory and treatment of Diseases of the Eye, Ear and Throat.
7. State treatment for Neuralgia.
8. State treatment for Hiccough.
9. State treatment for Paralysis.
10. State special motion (No. 1) in treatment of Epilepsy.
11. State treatment for Lockjaw.
12. State special movement (No. 4) in treatment for Impotency.

THE HOME STUDY COURSE

IN

OSTEOPATHY

ISSUED BY

The Columbia
College of Osteopathy

3031 AUDITORIUM BLDG.,
CHICAGO, ILL., U. S. A.

Consists of Twelve Lessons, fully illustrated, and is issued in Five Parts, as follows:

PART FIRST—
> Theory of Osteopathy.
> Movements and Manipulations.
> General Treatment.

PART SECOND—
> Special Treatments.

PART THIRD—
> Special Treatments.

PART FOURTH—
> Special Treatments.
> Osteopathic Anatomy.
> Osteopathic Physiology.

PART FIFTH—
> Osteopathic Anatomy and Physiology.
> Building up and Conducting an Osteopathic Practice.
> Practical Advice and Suggestions.
> Miscellaneous Information.

HOME STUDY COURSE

IN

OSTEOPATHY

— — — ——

PART FOURTH
COMPRISING LESSONS IX AND X

— — —

. . .

ISSUED BY

THE COLUMBIA COLLEGE OF OSTEOPATHY
3031 AUDITORIUM BUILDING
CHICAGO, ILL., U S A.

CONTENTS

LESSON IX

LESSON X

LESSON IX

SPECIAL TREATMENTS

FEVERS, CONTAGIOUS DISEASES, ETC.

Our advice to the student is to confine himself to chronic cases and to let acute diseases severely alone for the present We say this because we know that the public is ignorant regarding the truth underlying the various systems of therapeutics, and that the loss of a single acute case (and every physician must lose some) will hurt the Osteopath materially, whereas the public will think nothing of the loss of a dozen of the Drug-Doctors' patients. Later on, when the public becomes accustomed to Osteopathic theories and practice, things will be different. For the present the Osteopath should content himself with curing the chronic cases, most of which have been pronounced incurable by the Drug Doctors. Besides this, office practice is the most profitable, and more easily built up. By all means confine yourself to the chronic cases. We give you general treatment for use in cases of fevers, etc., as you may be called upon to use same in cases of emergency

GENERAL TREATMENT OF FEVERS

Osteopathy offers a treatment which will reduce the temperature of the body in less than one-half the time required by any other therapeutic method   The treatment consists of pressure upon the vaso-motor centre, thus reducing the general blood pressure, slowing the action of the heart, and reducing the temperature   The vaso-motor centre is reached by a pressure upon the upper cervicals, and at the same time tipping the head backward, so as to bring a pressure upon the nerves over the cervical vaso-motor centre   The following general treatment will be found efficacious in cases of fevers, although you must use your own good judgment, as no two cases of fever are exactly alike·

TREATMENT

(1)   Begin by giving a thorough Spinal Treatment, as follows   The patient on his side, then using the palmar sur-

3

Spinal Treatment

face of the fingers and hand, manipulate along the right side of the spinal column, commencing at the first cervical, and moving down the entire length of the spine. Move the muscles upward and outward gently but firmly and with a deep pressure, paying special attention wherever you find a tender spot, a hot or cold spot, or a knotted condition of the muscles. Then turning him on his other side, treat the opposite side in the same manner. Take your time in giving this treatment. Avoid using the finger tips.

(2) Then give a thorough Neck Treatment, as follows: The patient lying on his back, stand at his head and place one hand on his forehead, the other under his neck, and rotate the head slowly from side to side. Then manipulate thoroughly and deeply the muscles of the back, sides and front of the neck. Then place the hands in the first position, and give the neck a thorough extension or stretching, gently but firmly, being careful not to rotate the head. This treatment frees the circulation to the brain.

Extending Neck.

(3) Then give Spinal Extension, as follows: The patient on his back, grasp his shoulders, your fingers under his armpits. An assistant holds the patient's ankles. The patient relaxes and you give a careful stretching or extension of the spine, gentle but firm, for about one minute. This frees the circulation of the spinal cord and relieves pressure upon the spinal nerves.

(4) Then give Vibration over Abdomen, as follows: This form of treatment is a very powerful stimulant. It consists of certain oscillatory movements, produced through a succession of rapid individual efforts of the operator's hand. There should be little or no perceptible strain upon the arm muscles of the operator. The palm of the hand or the fingers must be placed firmly upon the parts to be treated, the arm being held straight and a fine trembling or vibrating movement communicated to the hand by the muscles of the upper part of the arm. The movement is somewhat difficult of acquirement, but you must persist until the desired movement is acquired, for this is one of the most stimulating and penetrating of all the methods of Osteopathic treatment, its effect being quite perceptible and almost akin to the effects of a current of electricity. It has a stimulating and strengthening effect upon the nerves, and acts strongly upon the venous circulation and upon the lymphatics. Be careful not to press upon the body with your wrist, as you should use no greater pressure than the

Spinal Extension.

weight of your hand. When properly administered by one hand on the breast, the vibrations should be distinctly felt by the other hand placed under the back of the patient.

(5) Then give Flexion and Extension of Legs, as follows: The patient on his back, place one hand on the knee, the other under the sole of the foot, and move the leg up and down to and from the chest. Repeat several times. (Active.)

Holding Vaso-Motor.

(6) Then give Pressure on the Vaso-Motor Nerve Centre, as follows: Place the fingers on each side of the back of the neck and press with fingers on each side of the spine over the upper cervicals (vaso-motor center) for two or three minutes. This will slow the action of the heart.

(7) Finish by giving a gentle, soothing Stroking, as follows: This treatment is useful in producing sedative or quieting effects. It should be applied with a very light contact, the tips of the fingers, or the palm of the hand, just barely touching the patient. In some cases it will produce a feeling of drowsiness on the part of the patient. It never fails to quiet down the patient, equalize the circulation and relieve an excess of stimulation. Stroking should always be performed in a downward and outward direction, and in one direction only, not to-and-fro. The tips of one, more or all of the fingers, or the palmar surface of one or both hands, are moved gently over the skin, with a light contact, not even the mere weight of the hand being allowed to press upon the surface of the skin. Lightness, gentleness, and airiness are the words best describing the Stroking movement.

Stroking.

Treat twice a day until a decided improvement is noted, then once a day.

SUNSTROKE

Place patient in a cool place, applying ice or cold water to the head. Give General Fever Treatment. Treat every few hours the first day.

INFLUENZA, HAY FEVER, ETC.

Give General Fever Treatment, with Digital Manipulation around the nose and inner corners of the eyes. Treat once a day.

MEASLES

Give General Fever Treatment. Treat every day.

Extending Neck.

Expanding Chest.

WHOOPING COUGH

Give General Fever Treatment. Treat every day.

MUMPS

Give General Fever Treatment. Treat every day.

CHICKEN POX

Give General Fever Treatment. Treat every day.

ERYSIPELAS

This disease is caused by an obstruction of the venous circulation between the heart and the affected part. A thorough manipulation will free the circulation and effect a cure. The General Osteopathic Treatment should always be given with the local treatment in cases of this kind.

DIPHTHERIA

The Osteopathic treatment of Diphtheria is based upon the theory that the disease is caused by certain contractions of the muscles of the neck and thorax, interfering with the circulation, thereby causing an inflamed condition. The following treatment is highly recommended by eminent Osteopathic practitioners who have found it very efficacious:

TREATMENT

(1) Begin by giving a thorough Neck Treatment, as follows: The patient lying on his back, stand at his head and place one hand on his forehead, the other under his neck, and rotate the head slowly from side to side. Then manipulate thoroughly and deeply the muscles of the back, sides and front of the neck. Then place the hands in the first position, and give the neck a thorough extension or stretching, gently but firmly, being careful not to rotate the head. This treatment frees the circulation to the brain.

(2) Then place the fingers in the patient's mouth and move the muscles of the throat gently, thus loosening the membrane which will be expelled from the mouth.

(3) Then give Chest Expansion, as follows: Seat your patient on a stool or chair (if a chair, let him face its back) and stand behind him. Place your foot on the seat of the chair, the tip of your toe being up against, or under, the body of the patient. Place your knee between the patient's shoulders, holding his wrists in each hand. Raise his arms (sideways)

up and over his head, slowly but strongly, and press hard with your knee against his spine. Then maintaining the pressure of your knee, lower the arms with a backward motion. The patient should inhale, filling the lungs, while the arms are being raised; exhaling as the arms are lowered.

(4) Then give pressure on the Vaso-Motor Center, as follows: Place the fingers on each side of the back of the neck and press with fingers on each side of the spine over the upper cervicals (vaso-motor center) for two or three minutes. This will slow the action of the heart.

Holding Vaso-Motor.

(5) Finish the treatment with a gentle, soothing Stroking, as follows: This treatment is useful in producing sedative or quieting effects. It should be applied with a very light contact, the tips of the fingers, or the palm of the hand, just barely touching the patient. In some cases it will produce a feeling of drowsiness on the part of the patient. It never fails to quiet down the patient, equalize the circulation and relieve an excess of stimulation. Stroking should always be performed in a downward and outward direction, and in one direction only, not to-and-fro. The tips of one, more or all of the fingers, or the palmar surface of one or both hands, are moved gently over the skin, with a light contact, not even the mere weight of the hand being allowed to press upon the surface of the skin. Lightness, gentleness, and airiness are the words best describing the Stroking movement.

Stroking.

Treat every few hours.

DISEASES OF WOMEN

Osteopathy teaches that this class of complaints can be relieved and cured by treatment tending to free the circulation and nerve current, thus restoring normal conditions. Osteopathic treatment, in nearly every case, gives almost immediate relief followed by a permanent cure.

DISPLACEMENT OF THE UTERUS—TREATMENT

(1) Give Spinal Treatment as follows, paying special attention to the Sacral region, as here we reach the nerves controlling the Uterus.

The patient on her side, then using the palmar surface of the fingers and hand, manipulate along the right side of the spinal column, commencing at the first cervical, and moving down

Spinal Extension.

the entire length of the spine. Move the muscles upward and
outward gently, but firmly and with a deep pressure, paying
special attention wherever you find a tender spot, a hot or
cold spot, or a knotted condition of the muscles   Then turning
her on her other side, treat the opposite side in the same manner   Take your time in giving this treatment   Avoid using the
finger tips

(2) Give Neck Treatment, as follows, thus freeing the
circulation to the brain, and enabling stronger nerve impulses
to be sent to the affected parts

The patient lying on her back, stand at her head and place
one hand on her forehead, the other under her neck, and rotate
the head slowly from side to side   Then manipulate thoroughly and deeply the muscles of the back, sides and front of
the neck   Then place the hands in the first position, and give
the neck a thorough extension or stretching, gently but firmly,
being careful not to rotate the head. This treatment frees the
circulation to the brain

(3) Give Flexion and Extension of the Legs, as follows,
thus freeing the circulation and stimulating the nerve impulse
to the weakened parts:

The patient on her back, place one hand on the knee, the
other under the sole of the foot, and move the leg up and
down to and from the chest   Repeat several times   (Active)

(4) After carefully washing the hands, insert the finger
into the vagina, and carefully press the uterus back to its
normal place   Then gently manipulate the vagina

(5) If the patient is Constipated (and she usually is) it
will be well to give her the treatment recommended for Constipation

Give treatment every day, with the exception of the vaginal
treatment, which should be given, say, every third day   It
will be as well to give an Osteopathic General Treatment the
first day, and about once a week thereafter

MENSTRUAL TROUBLES

Osteopathy has been quite successful in complaints of this
class   The freeing of the nerve supply and the equalizing of
the circulation, results in rapid improvement and usually effects
a permanent cure

TREATMENT

(1) Give thorough Spinal Treatment, as follows, giving
special attention to the lower lumbar and socral region.

The patient on her side, then using the palmar surface of the fingers and hand, manipulate along the right side of the spinal column, commencing at the first cervical, and moving down the entire length of the spine. Move the muscles upward and outward gently but firmly, and with a deep pressure, paying special attention wherever you find a tender spot, a hot or cold spot, or a knotted condition of the muscles. Then turning her on her other side, treat the opposite side in the same manner. Take your time in giving this treatment. Avoid using the finger tips.

Spinal Treatment

(2) The patient on her back, grasp her shoulders, your fingers under her armpits. An assistant holds the patient's ankles. The patient relaxes and you give a careful stretching or extension of the spine, gentle but firm, for about one minute. This frees the circulation of the spinal cord and relieves pressure upon the spinal nerves.

(3) Then give Flexion and Extension of the Limbs, as follows: The patient on her back, place one hand on the knee, the other under the sole of the foot, and move the leg up and down to and from the chest. Repeat several times. (Active.)

(4) Then give Vibration over the Uterus, as follows: This form of treatment is a very powerful stimulant. It consists of certain oscillatory movements, produced through a succession of rapid individual efforts of the operator's hand. There should be little or no perceptible strain upon the arm muscles of the operator. The palm of the hand or the fingers must be placed firmly upon the parts to be treated, the arm being held straight and a fine trembling or vibrating movement communicated to the hand by the muscles of the upper part of the arm. The movement is somewhat difficult of acquirement, but you must persist until the desired movement is acquired, for this is one of the most stimulating and penetrating of all the methods of Osteopathic treatment, its effect being quite perceptible and almost akin to the effects of a current of electricity. It has a stimulating and strengthening effect upon the nerves, and acts strongly upon the venous circulation and upon the lymphatics. Be careful not to press upon the body with your wrist, as you should use no greater pressure than the weight of your hand. When properly administered by one hand on the breast, the vibrations should be distinctly felt by the other hand placed under the back of the patient.

Spinal Extension.

We recommend that frequent Osteopathic General Treat-

Deep Vibration.

ment be given, to stimulate and build up the entire system. In cases of too profuse Menstruation it is well to hold the thumbs on each side of each of the lower vertebræ (from the first lumbar, downward) for a few seconds at each vertebra. Treat every other day.

Spinal Treatment

LEUCORRHEA (WHITES)

The following treatment usually effects a cure:

TREATMENT

Give the treatment given for Menstrual Troubles, every other day, with an occasional Osteopathic General Treatment.

OVARIAN TROUBLES—TREATMENT

Give treatment recommended for Menstrual Troubles, also give Vibration over Ovaries, and manipulation in the immediate region.

CATARRHAL VAGINITIS

This disease, which consists of an inflammation of the mucous membrane of the vagina, and kindred troubles, may be successfully treated as follows:

TREATMENT

(1) Give thorough Spinal Treatment, as follows: The patient on her side, then using the palmar surface of the fingers and hand, manipulate along the right side of the spinal column, commencing at the first cervical, and moving down the entire length of the spine. Move the muscles upward and outward gently, but firmly, and with a deep pressure, paying special attention wherever you find a tender spot, a hot or cold spot, or a knotted condition of the muscles. Then turning her on her other side, treat the opposite side in the same manner. Take your time in giving this treatment. Avoid using the finger tips.

Extending Neck. (2) Then give thorough Neck Treatment, as follows: The patient lying on back, stand at her head and place one hand on her forehead, the other under her neck, and rotate the head slowly from side to side. Then manipulate thoroughly and deeply the muscles of the back, sides and front of the neck. Then place the hands in the first position, and give the neck a thorough extension or stretching, gently but firmly, being careful not to rotate the head. This treatment frees the circulation to the brain.

(3) Then give Spinal Extension, as follows: The patient on her back, grasp her shoulders, your fingers under her armpits. An assistant holds the patient's ankles. The patient relaxes and you give a careful stretching or extension of the spine, gentle but firm, for about one minute. This frees the circulation of the spinal cord and relieves pressure upon the spinal nerves.

(4) Then give Flexion and Extension of the Legs, as follows: The patient on her back, place one hand on the knee, the other under the sole of the foot, and move the leg up and down to and from the chest. Repeat several times. (Active.)

(5) Then, after washing the hands, insert carefully the finger into the vagina and manipulate gently.

Treat every other day, occasionally omitting the vaginal treatment if the parts are tender. Also give an occasional Osteopathic General Treatment.

MENOPAUSE ("CHANGE OF LIFE")

There is no better treatment known for the troubles incident to this period of a woman's life, than the Osteopathic General Treatment, given two or three times a week.

Spinal Extension.

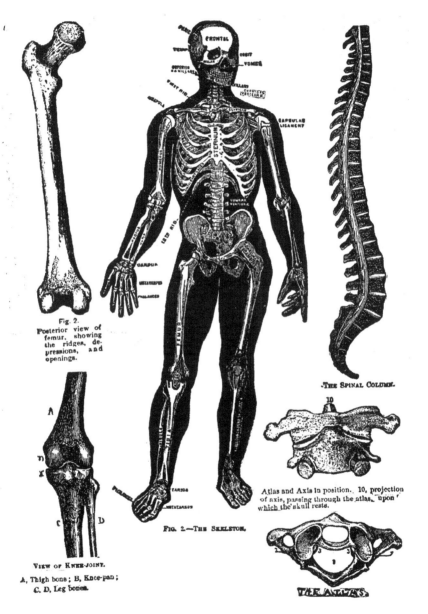

Fig. 2.
Posterior view of femur, showing the ridges, depressions, and openings.

Fig. 2.—The Skeleton.

The Spinal Column.

Atlas and Axis in position. 10, projection of axis, passing through the atlas, upon which the skull rests.

View of Knee-Joint.

A, Thigh bone; B, Knee-pan; C, D, Leg bones.

The Atlas.

The Skeleton Contains 206 Bones.

I. THE HEAD. (28 Bones).

1. THE SKULL. (8 Bones.)

1 Fron'tal (forehead).
1 Oc-cip'i-tal (back of head).
2 Pa-ri'e-tals (side of head).
2 Tem'po-rals (temples).
1 Sphe'noid ("wedge-shaped").
1 Eth'moid ("sieve-like," through which filaments of the olfactory nerve pass to the nose).

2. THE FACE. (14 Bones.)

2 "Na-sal Bones (they form the "bridge" of the nose).
2 Ma'lar (or cheek) Bones.
2 Lach'ry-mals (from a Latin word meaning "tear"; small thin bones which form a part of the inner wall of the orbits).
2 Pal'ate Bones.
2 Tur'bin-ated ("cone-shaped," one on each side of the outer wall of the nasal cavities).
2 Upper and 1 Lower Max'il-la-ry (or jaw) Bones.
1 Vo'mer ("plough-share," a thin bone which separates the nostrils).

3. THE EAR. (6 Bones.)

Mal'le-us, or "mallet."
In'cus, or "anvil."
Sta'pes, or "stirrup."

II. THE TRUNK. (54 Bones.)

1. THE SPINAL COLUMN. (26 Bones.)

7 Cer'vi-cal (or neck) ver'te-bræ.
12 Dor'sal (or back) vertebræ.
5 Lum'bar or loin vertebræ.
Sa'crum (the "sacred" bone, because used in sacrifices).
Coc'cyx (the "cuckoo" bone, because of its likeness to the bill of that bird).

2. THE RIBS. (24 Bones.)

12 on each side; the upper seven are called "true" ribs, the five lower ones are "false," or "floating" ribs.

3. THE HYOID.

A small "U-shaped" Bone in the upper part of the neck, and supports the base of the tongue.

4. THE STERNUM. Breast-Bone.

5. THE TWO HIP-BONES.

III. THE LIMBS. 124 Bones.

1. THE UPPER LIMBS. (64 Bones.)

Clav-i-cle, or Collar-bone (from "*clavis*," a key).
Scap'u-la, or Shoulder-blade.
Hu'mer-us (arm).
Ul'na (forearm), from the Greek word meaning "Elbow."
Ra'di-us (forearm), from the Latin word meaning "Spoke."
8 Car'pals, or Wrist-bones.
5 Met-a-car'pals (in the palm); *meta* "beyond" and *carpus* "the wrist."
14 Pha-lan'ges (3 in each finger, 2 in the thumb).

2. THE LOWER LIMBS. (60 Bones.)

Fe'mur (thigh-bone).
Pa-tel'la, or Knee-pan.
Tib'i-a (leg-bone), a Latin word meaning "flute."
Fib'u-la (leg-bone), a Latin word for "pin."
7 Tar'sals (forming the instep).
5 Met-a-tar'sals.
14 Phalanges (2 in the great toe, 3 in each of the others).

13

LESSON X

OSTEOPATHIC ANATOMY AND PHYSI-
OLOGY

THE SKELETON

The general figure and support of the body are furnished by the skeleton, composed of a number of bones of all sizes and shapes. The skeleton furnishes a cage-like cavity containing and protecting the vital organs; joints to facilitate motion, surfaces for the support of the softer parts of the body.

It consists of 204 distinct bones, not including the knee pans and other seed-form bones, which are situated in the tendons of certain muscles, nor does it include the teeth, 32 in number. The bones are classed as Long, Short and Flat. The long bones are hollow and have two ends, generally known as heads, to which are attached muscles and ligaments. The principal long bones are the collar-bone (clavicle), the arm-bone (humerus), the fore-arm bone (radius and ulna), the thigh-bone (femur), and the leg-bones (tibia and fibula). The Short bones are found in those parts of the body requiring strength, compactness and elasticity, and are bound together by ligaments. The wrists and ankles are good examples of Short bones. The Flat bones have flat, broad surfaces for muscular attachments, and their purpose is the protection of organs of the body. The principal Flat bones are the shoulder-blades, breast-bone, ribs, hips, etc.

The surface of the bones contain raised places and sunken places, the first being for the better attachment of the muscles, etc., and the second for the passage of blood-vessels, nerves, tendons, and muscles. Small openings are found in the bones, through which pass the blood-vessels, nerves, etc.

A Joint is the junction of two or more bones The joints of the skull are immovable; those of the spinal column are partly movable and partly immovable; the majority of the other joints are movable, such as the shoulder and hip, which are ball and socket joints, and the knee and elbow which are hinge joints.

The skull rests and moves upon the first cervical vertebra (the first vertebra) which is known as the Atlas; and upon the tooth-like process of the second bone of the spinal column, generally known as the Axis, which projects upward through a hole in the Atlas, forming a pivot upon which the head turns from side to side, the nodding movement of the skull being upon the Atlas.

The bones are held together by a strong fibrous substance called ligaments, further strengthend by muscles and tendons.

The principal support of the body is the spinal column, which bears the skull at its upper extremity, and whose lower end is wedged in between the hip-bones, and with them forms the Pelvis. In consists of 26 bones known as vertebrae, of which there are 7 in the neck or Cervical region, 12 in the back or Dorsal region, and 5 in the loin or Lumbar region The Sacrum and Coccyx are called false vertebrae Each vertebra is a disk-like bone having a bony arch projecting backward from it, and has a large hole through it When the vertebrae are in place, held by strong ligaments, this opening, or hole, in each forms a long tube extending through the entire length of the spinal column, which tube is called the Spinal Canal, and which contains and protects the Spinal Cord, which is a long cable of nerves which connects the brain with all the other portions of the body, by means of nerve branches being sent out through the apertures in the sides of each vertebra The posterior projections of the vertebrae are what we feel when we pass the hand along the spinal column.

The Ribs which branch out from each side of the spinal column, in the dorsal region, are 24 in number, 12 on each side. The upper 7 on each side are called true ribs, being fastened to the breast bone direct, the lower 5 on each side are called false or floating ribs because they are not so fastened, the upper two of them being fastened by cartilage to the other ribs, the others having no cartilages, their forward ends being free

The Pelvis is composed of the Sacrum and Coccyx behind the Hip-bones (innominates) upon the sides, and the pubic bone in front Forming joints with the Pelvis are the two thigh bones, which rest upon the bones of the lower leg, which are supported by the bones of the feet Forming joints at the upper part of the frame of the body, on each side, are the arm-bones, consisting of the collar-bone (clavicle), shoulder-blades

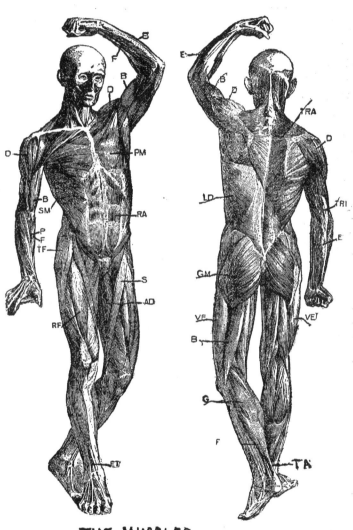

THE MUSCLES.

THE PRINCIPAL MUSCLES.

(SEE PLATE.)

THE HEAD.

Oc-cip'i-to—fron-ta'lis, moves the scalp and eyebrows.
Or-bic-u-la'ris pal-pe-bræ, closes the eyes.
Le-va'tor pal'pe-bræ, opens the eyes.
The Recti muscles (four in number) move the eye-ball.
Tem'po-ral, } raise the lower jaw.
Mas-se'ter,

THE NECK.

Pla-tys'ma My-oi'des, } move the head forwards.
Ster-no Mas'toid,
Sca-le'ni muscles move the neck from side to side.

THE TRUNK.

P.M.—Pec-to-ra'lis, moves the arm forwards.
L.D.—La-tis'si-mus dor'si, moves the arm backwards.
T.E.A.—Tra-pe'zi-us, } move shoulder-blade.
S.M.—Ser-ra'tus mag'nus,
Rhom-boi-de'us,
In-ter-cos'tals, move the ribs in respiration.
External Oblique, } move the trunk forwards.
Internal Oblique,
E-rec'tor spi'næ, move the trunk backwards.
R.A.—Rec'tus Ab-dom'i-nus, makes tense the abdominal walls.

THE UPPER LIMB.

D.—Del'toid, raises the arm.
Te'res ma'jor, lowers the arm.
Sub-scap-u-la'ris, } rotate the arm.
Spi-na'tus,
B.—Bi'ceps, bends forearm.
T.E.I.—Tri'ceps, straightens forearm.
P.—Pro-na'tor, } rotate forearm.
    Su-pi-na'tor,
F.—Flex'or car'pi ra-di-a'lis, }
   "   "   **ul-na'ris,** } move the hand.
E.—Ex-ten'sor car'pi ra-di-a'lis, }
E.—   "   "   **ul-na'ris,** }

THE LOWER LIMB.

Il-i'a-cus, }
Pso'as mag'nus, } move the thigh forwards.
Pec-tin-e'us, }
A.—Ab-duc'tor, }
G.M.—Glu-te'us, } move the thigh backwards.
    Pyr-i-form'is,
S.—Sar-to'ri-us (from *Sartor*, a tailor), crosses one thigh over the other
R.F.—Rec'tus, } move the leg forwards.
V.E.—Vas'tus,
B.—Bi'ceps, } move the leg backwards.
    Grac'i-lis.
T.A.—Tib-i-a'lis, }
    Per-o-ne'us, } move the foot.
G.—Gas-troc-ne'mi-us, }
    So-le'us,
F.—Flexors of the foot.
T.A.—Tendo Achillis.
T.F.—Moves thigh outwards.
F.T.—Extensors of the toes.

(scapula), arm-bone (humerus), the two fore-arm bones (radius and ulna), and the bones of the wrist and hand.

The four principal closed cavities within the skeleton are the Cranial, Thoracic, Abdominal and Pelvic. The Cranium (skull) is a round, bony box containing the brain, the commencement of the spinal cord, etc. Its base is composed of bones firmly wedged together, with fine openings through which the blood vessels and nerves pass. The Thoracic cavity is found from the base of the neck to the diaphragm, from spinal column to breast-bone. It contains the lungs, heart, etc. The Abdominal cavity is located between the Thoracic and Pelvic cavities, and contains the liver upon the right side, the stomach and spleen upon the left, the intestines in front, and the pancreas, kidneys, etc., behind. The Pelvic cavity is enclosed by the pelvic bones, and contains the bladder and other viscera.

The student is advised to refer frequently to the several cuts illustrating this lesson, as there is no better way of fixing the lesson in the mind than by the object lesson afforded by the pictures.

THE MUSCLES

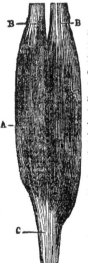

—A, Biceps muscle of the arm; B, C. Its tendons.

The Muscles number about 400, and constitute what is generally called "flesh," or in animals, "lean meat," being of a dark red color. They are divided into three classes, i. e. voluntary, involuntary and mixed. The voluntary muscles, such as those of the face, neck, abdomen, thorax, etc., are governed by the will. The involuntary muscles are indifferent of the will, and are controlled by the automatic or sub-conscious functions of the mind. The mixed muscles belong partly to both of the above named classes, the muscles of the respiratory organs being examples of this class, they being partly under control of the will, and yet capable of action independent of the same.

Voluntary muscles are connected with bones, and with cartilages, skin, ligaments, etc., by either muscular tissue or by fibrous tissue known as sinews or tendons. These tendons or sinews serve as cords to connect the remote parts of the body with the moving muscles, and their arrangement is most ingenious, one of the tendons which moves the eye passing over a pulley like loop, and one under the jaw passes through a slit in another tendon whose direction is different. Voluntary muscles are composed of bundles of fibres, each fibre being firmly enclosed in an elastic covering which does not interfere with its movement, the entire bundle of fibres being enclosed with connective tissue holding them together. Involuntary muscles are also composed of fibres which interlace and form tissues. Muscles are supplied with blood in large quantities by large blood vessels whose smaller branches pass between the fibres. The nerves accompany these blood vessels. The nerves supplying the voluntary muscles are largely motor nerves, while those supplying the involuntary muscles are principally sensory nerves. Muscles are usually contracted by the effort of the will, by means of the nerves, but contraction may also be produced by stimulation such as pinching, pricking with a needle, electricity, etc

Muscles that bend the joints are called flexors; those that restore the bent parts to a straight condition are called extensors; those that turn the parts to which they are attached upon their axis are called rotators; those that move parts toward the axis of the body are called adductors; those that move the parts from the axis of the body are called abductors; those that close or constrict certain openings of the body are called sphincters, those that control the facial expression, etc, are called muscles of expression.

Muscles to be normal and healthy need a constant supply of good blood and sufficient nerve stimulus, these being lacking disease manifests

THE CIRCULATION

The blood is the principal form taken by the nutritive constituents of food after digestion It flows through the arteries from the heart to every cell and tissue of the body, nourishing and strengthening them, and then returning through the veins to the heart, carrying with it the waste products of the system which are then expelled from the body by means of the lungs and other excretory organs. This flow of blood to and from the heart, is called the Circulation, and the organs of circulation are the heart, the arteries, the veins, the capillaries.

The heart is a hollow, muscular, pear-shaped organ, about the size of an average clenched fist. It is situated on the left side of the body, between the two lungs, the lower, pointed end resting about the fifth and sixth ribs, a little to the left of the breast bone, the broad, upper end being about on a level with the middle of the breast bone, near its junction with the cartilages of the third rib It is divided into four compart-

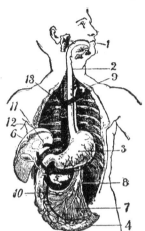

A diagrammatic representation of the various organs concerned in the conversion of food into blood. — 1, Mouth and salivary glands ; 2, the œsophagus ; 3, the stomach ; 4, a portion of the small intestine ; 5, the pancreas ; 6, the liver; 7, mesentery with lacteals ; 8, receptacle of chyle; 9, the thoracic duct emptying its contents into the left subclavian vein ; 10, branches of portal vein leading to liver ; 11, an hepatic vein leading from the liver to the large ascending vein ; 12, the large ascending vein cut off at its junction with the heart ; 13, the large descending vein cut off in like manner.

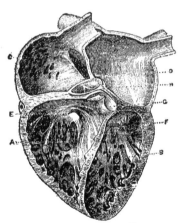

SECTION OF THE HEART.

A, Right Ventricle.   E, F, Inlets to the Ventricles.
B, Left   "   G, Pulmonary Artery.
C, Right Auricle.   H, Aorta.
D, Left Auricle.

Front view of the organs of circulation. Veins, black; arteries, with transverse lines. Parts on the right side of figure are removed to show some of the deep vessels, while the left side shows superficial vessels.

THE VALVES OF THE VEINS HIGHLY MAGNIFIED.

TABLE OF THE PRINCIPAL ARTERIES.

THE HEAD.

Internal Ca-rot'id,
Ver'te-bral, } Supply the brain.
Oph-thal'mic, supplies the eye.
External Ca-rot'id { **Lin'gual,** supplies the tongue.
    gives off .... { **Fa'ci-al,** supplies the lower part of the face.
                    { **Tem'po-ral,** supplies the upper part of the head and face.

THE TRUNK.

The A er'ta, arising from the heart, is the main arterial trunk.
Cor'o-na-ry, supplies the walls of the heart.
Bron'chi-al, supplies the lungs.
In-ter-cos'tals, supply the walls of the chest.
Gas'tric, supplies the stomach.
He-pat'ic, supplies the liver.
Splen'ic, supplies the spleen.
Re'nal, supplies the kidney.
Mes-en-ter'ics, supply the bowels.
Spi'nal, supplies the spinal cord.

THE UPPER LIMB.

Branches of the Ax-il-la'ry, supply the shoulder.
     "   "   **Bra'chi-al,** supply the arm.
     "   "   **Ra'di-al,** } Supply the forearm and fingers.
     "   "   **Ul'nar,** }

THE LOWER LIMB.

Branches of the Fem'o-ral, supply the hip and thigh.
     "   "   **Pop-li-te'al,** }
     "   "   **Tib'i-al,** } Supply the leg and foot.
     "   "   **Per-o-ne'al,** }

ments, the two upper of which are called auricles; the two
lower ventricles   The auricles have veins opening into them;
the ventricles have arteries arising from them   The auricles
receive the blood coming back through the veins   You will
understand the workings of the heart better if we show you the
course the blood follows in its circulation

The blood coming back through the veins, laden with impurities and waste product of the system, is poured into two
large veins which empty into the right auricle   When the auricle is filled to its full capacity, its walls contract and expel the
blood through an opening into the right ventricle, which in
turn contracts and forces the blood through the pulmonary
artery into the lungs, where the blood is thoroughly distributed
by numerous hair-like blood vessels among the air cells, where
it is purified by exchanging its waste products for the oxygen
of the air, and is converted into pure, red blood   This red
blood is then carried from the lungs back to the heart, this
time going into the left auricle, which in turn forces it into the
left ventricle   This ventricle then forces the pure, red blood,
laden with health-giving nutrition and life, into the arteries
through the aorta, the largest artery in the body   The arteries
carry the blood through its dividing and sub-dividing branches
to the hair-like capillaries for the nourishment and building up of the tissues   The blood, after having parted with its
life-giving properties, starts on its return journey to the heart,
through the veins, gathering up as it goes the broken down
tissues, waste products, and other refuse of the system.   On
its return journey it commences at the extremities of the venous
system, and passing on enters larger veins, then still larger
until it reaches the main venous river which pours into the
right auricle, as stated at the beginning of this paragraph.   The
beating of the heart is caused by the alternate contractions and
relaxations of the heart in performing the above work.   The
beats vary with age and temperament   At birth, the beats are
about 140 per minute, at one year, 120, two years, 110; during
middle life from 70 to 80, being ten more in women than in
men, in old age, about 60

The arteries are a series of elastic canals, which commence
with the aorta and by means of divisions and sub-divisions
convey the blood to all the vascular parts of the body.   The
larger arteries are composed of three coats; the smaller have
but two coats, the capillaries have but one

The pulsations of the aorta and its branches constitute the pulse or wave in the arteries.

The capillaries permeate the vascular organs in meshes of network bringing the blood in close contact with the tissues. They measure about one three-thousandth of an inch in diameter The nutritious ingredients in the blood transude through their walls and are appropriated by the tissues beyond. In the glandular organs they supply the substance requisite for secretion; in the villi of the intestine they take up the elements of the digested food; in the lungs they absorb oxygen and exhale carbonic acid; in the kidneys they discharge the products of destructive assimilation collected from other parts The capillary circulation thus furnishes directly or indirectly the materials for the growth and renovation of the entire body.

As before stated, after the blood has parted with nutriment to the tissues, and absorbed waste products from them, it passes on from the capillaries into larger channels called veinlets, thence to the veins, thence to the heart Other waste products not so taken up, are carried into the blood by another set of vessels called the lymphatics, which we describe later.

The veins are composed of three coats. In the limbs and external parts of the head and neck they are provided with valves, so arranged that their closure prevents a backward flow of blood

The blood is eminently "the life," for it is that constituent of the body which either directly or indirectly affords nourishment and life to all the other constituents, whether solid or fluid. If the circulation is affected, the nutrition of some part or organ of the body is thereby cut-off or reduced, and disease inevitably follows About one-tenth of a person's bodily weight is represented by his blood-supply Of this quantity, about one-fourth is distributed to the heart, lungs, large arteries and veins; about one-fourth to the liver—one-fourth to the muscles, and the remainder to the remaining organs and tissues. The brain utilizes about one-fifth of the entire quantity of blood.

Besides the blood, there is another fluid which is widely distributed throughout the body This is called the Lymph, a liquid closely resembling in composition the blood plasma, and containing some of the ingredients of the blood which have traversed the walls of the blood-vessels, and some of the products of disintegration, which, after renovation in the lymphatic sys-

tem, enter the blood and are again serviceable in the human economy. The lymph currents move in thin, delicate vessels called the lymphatics. These vessels are so fine that they cannot be seen readily until injected with quicksilver, and begin as network, or as tubes with free blind extremities, in the interspaces of the connective tissue, or of the capillary blood-vessels. These lymphatic capillaries converge and become larger as they approach the heart. The lymph empties into several of the large veins, and is thus mingled with the venous blood before its arrival at the right side of the heart.

In the course of the lymphatics, everywhere in the body, are numerous glands, called lymphatic glands, whose function is believed to be a renovating one. When these glands are hardened or otherwise altered, in large numbers, health fails and the person grows thin.

It will be seen that the blood takes up the nutritive fluids and gases, and they are by nature's processes converted into the secretions of the various organs, and the materials of the tissues. The natural constitution of the parts, though constantly changing, is maintained in its normal condition through the movement and renovation of the circulating fluids.

The student is urged to acquaint himself thoroughly with the above lesson, and to fix firmly in his mind the facts therein stated. It is necessary that he thoroughly understand the circulation of the blood, as therein lies much that goes to make up the Osteopathic theory and its practice.

Superficial lymphatics of the hand and forearm. — G, lymphatic gland.

THE NERVOUS SYSTEM

The human body has been likened to a community in which a variety of industries are carried on, each in a different way, but all conducive to the public welfare and all controlled by its official head and his subordinates. The various organs of the body are connected with the centre of operations, the Brain, by means of nerves, which are like so many electric wires running to and from the seat of government of the community. By this arrangement notice of any disturbance is at once reported to headquarters, and the remedy promptly furnished. Over these wires, or rather, over some of them, also is sent the current which furnishes the power by which the various machines are run. If any of these wires become crossed, or if the current is in any way shut off or interfered with there will be trouble manifested in that particular part of the machinery dependent upon that particular wire, and probably in other parts of the shop, as the various machines are dependent very much upon each other, and an injury to one is apt to be an injury to all in time.

The general arrangement and structure of the nervous system is as follows:

There are two divisions of the nervous system, viz., the Cerebro-Spinal nervous system and the Sympathetic nervous system. The Cerebro-Spinal division includes all that portion of the nervous system contained within the cranial cavity and the spinal canal, viz., the brain and the spinal cord, together with its nerves which branch off from each. This system presides over the functions of animal life, as volition, sensation, etc. The Sympathetic division includes all that part of the nervous system located, in the main, in the thoracic, abdominal and pelvic cavities, and which is distributed to the internal organs. Its special function is the regulation of involuntary processes, as growth and nutrition.

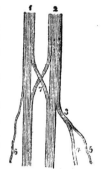

Mode of branching of nerves.—1, 2, two bundles of nerve fibres; 3, a branch of three fibres; 4, branch of two fibres; 5, 6, branches of single fibres; 7, decussation between two nerves.

The nervous system consists of two kinds of tissue, white and gray. These differ from each other not only in color but also in structure and mode of action. The white matter constitutes the bulk of the nervous tissue, and is in large quantity on the exterior of the spinal cord and in the interior and lower surface of the brain. It is a mass of white, semisolid material, mingled with delicate and transparent connective tissue, forming slender threads, which are called nervous filaments or nerve fibres. Nervous filaments are cylindrical, and running longitudinally through the centre of each is a rounded, semi-transparent band of gray color, known as the axis cylinder, which is the essential element of the nerve fibre. Through it the nerve current is transmitted. These filaments are transmitted, in a varying degree, to all the tissues, and as they emerge from the tissues they come together, forming bundles, which in turn unite with similar bundles and form nerves. The structure of a nerve is similar to that of a cable, the individual threads or wires being united into strands, and the strands into the cable itself. The nervous filaments, however, are not twisted as are the wires of a cable generally, but for the most part lie parallel to one another, each being separate from its beginning to its end. Nerves are of various

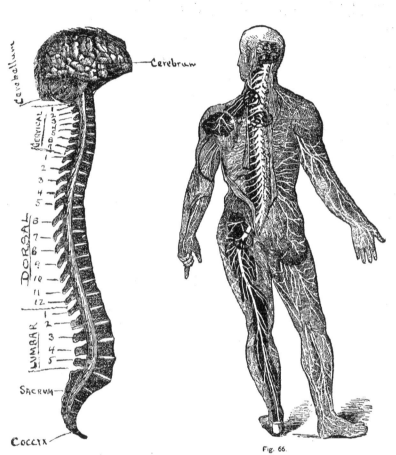

Fig. 66.

Posterior view of the spinal cord,—a portion of the cerebrum and cerebellum, and some of the nerves of the cerebro-spinal system. On the left side of the body some of the tissues are removed to show the deeper nerves, while the right side shows certain superficial ones.—CE, cerebrum; CER, cerebellum; B, nerves distributed to the arm; SC, spinal cord; SN, sciatic nerve.

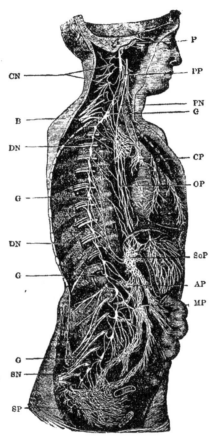

Fig. 75.

Vertical section of body, showing sympathetic nerves and ganglia of right side,
and their connection with the cerebro-spinal nerves. — *Cerebro-spinal system* :
CN, cervical nerves ; B, nerves distributed to the arm; DN, dorsal nerves;
SN, sacral nerves, some of which are distributed to the leg ; PN, pneumogastric nerve. *Sympathetic system* : P, plexus in the head ; PP, pharyngeal plexus ;
CP, cardiac plexus ; OP, oesophageal plexus ; SoP, solar plexus ; AP, aortic
plexus, MP, mesenteric plexus ; SP, sacral plexus ; G, some of the ganglia of
the sympathetic system.

sizes, ranging from a very small size to the largest, which are the sciatic nerves located in the back part of the thighs, which are as large as the circumference of the tip of the little finger of the average adult. Each nerve is sheathed with what is called the neurilemma, which also contain capillary blood-vessels. The sole function of the nerves is to transmit nervous force and impressions. The student will find it convenient to think of the nerves as electric wires supplying the different parts and organs of the body with its necessary nerve-current.

The brain is the great mass of nerve tissue which occupies the cranial cavity. It consists of three parts, viz.: The Cerebrum, or brain proper, which is the largest and occupies the upper, front, middle and back portion of the cranial cavity; next, the Cerebellum, or "little brain," which about fills the lower and back portion of the cavity; and thirdly, the Medulla Oblongata, the smallest, which is the broadened commencement of the spinal cord, lying below and in front of the Cerebellum.

Both the brain and the spinal cord are protected from shock and friction against their strong, bony encasements by membranes, by connective tissue and by fluid between certain of the membranes. The outer membrane, which is called the Dura Mater, is brown, thick and very resisting, and lines the cranial cavity and the spinal cord, and has various shelf-like expansions in the former for the support of different portions of the brain. Under the Dura Mater is the arachnoid, a closed sac of serous membrane which secretes an albuminous, lubricating fluid and which affords the brain and spinal cord considerable protection and freedom of movement with its soft and yielding liquid contents. Closely adherent to the brain and spinal cord, and dipping down into the furrows, is the third and last covering, the Pia Mater, which is really a fine network of capillary blood-vessels in the meshes of a delicate connective tissue. Through these capillaries and the large blood-vessels which enter at its base the brain is abundantly supplied with blood, receiving about one-fifth of the entire volume of blood, although it is not more than one-fortieth of the weight of the body. This large proportion of blood is needed for the active work of the brain, and unless the brain is well nourished it is unable to send forth the proper nerve impulses and consequently the entire system suffers.

The Cerebrum is the organ of the Mind, and is that part of the nervous system through which the intellectual and moral faculties act. The Cerebellum has for its function the co-ordination or harmonious regulation of the movements of the voluntary muscles. The Medulla Oblongata is the upper enlarged end of the spinal cord, which it resembles in its arrangement of gray and white matter. From its interior and from the under surface of the cerebrum arise what are known as the Cranial Nerves, which emerge from the cranial cavity through openings in the base of the skull and are distributed to various parts of the head and neck, to the organs of special sense, and to some of the thoracic and abdominal organs. In its posterior and lowermost portion nerves have their origin, which control indirectly the function of respiration.

The Spinal Cord, or spinal marrow, is continuous with the Medulla Oblongata and fills the spinal canal in the vertebral column. It is a mass of nerve tissue, which becomes enlarged in the cervical and lumbar regions, at the points where the nerves supplying the upper and lower extremities are given off, and its lower ends send forth prolongations through the sacrum, which from their fancied resemblance to the hairs of a horse's tail are called the Cauda Equina. The spinal cord is composed of a central mass of gray matter, extending nearly its whole length, surrounded by longitudinal bundles of nerve filaments, the whole being enclosed by the several membranes heretofore described. The gray matter is arranged somewhat like a double crescent united by a band of gray matter, the respective ends of these united crescents being called the Anterior and Posterior Horns. Opposite them, at regular intervals, filaments of the spinal nerves emerge from the cord. The white matter of the cord lying between the posterior horns and posterior fissure constitutes the right and left posterior columns; and that between the posterior horns and anterior horns, the right and left lateral columns; that between the anterior horns and anterior fissure, the anterior columns. These columns are connected with filaments of the spinal nerves, and thus the spinal cord is a conducting medium as well as a nerve centre. The posterior columns of the spinal cord convey sensory impressions to the cerebrum, and the antero-lateral columns convey motor impulses from the cerebrum.

The Spinal nerves consist of thirty-one symmetrical pairs of nerves, which are connected with the spinal cord by so-called Roots. Each nerve has an anterior and a posterior root. The posterior roots, upon each of which is a ganglion, with their respective nerves, are known as Sensory roots and nerves, because they convey sensations, while the anterior roots and nerves are known as the Motor roots and nerves, because they convey motor impulses

Of the Cranial nerves, one of the most important for the consideration of Osteopaths is the Pneumogastric, or twelfth pair of cranial nerves   The distribution of these nerves is wider than that of any nerves of the body, and their influence greater, for they supply the larynx, pharynx, heart and lungs, the stomach, intestines, liver and other abdominal organs, giving them sensibility and motion   The Pneumogastric nerves are connected at various points with the sympathetic system of nerves

The Sympathetic system of nerves, or as it is sometimes called, the Great Sympathetic Nerve, consists of a double chain of ganglia on the sides of the spinal column, also of scattered ganglia in the head, neck, chest and abdomen   These ganglia are connected with each other by filaments and with the Cerebro-Spinal nervous systems by motor and sensory nerves   From them numerous and very delicate fibres are distributed chiefly to the alimentary canal and its appendages, the heart, blood-vessels and other organs   The nerves distributed to the blood-vessels are known as the Vaso-Motor nerves, and the continuous muscular action they furnish is known as the "tone" or "tonic contraction" of the arteries.

At various points the sympathetic nerves, with their ganglia, form about certain large arteries matted nets of "Plexuses ' A typical one is the Solar Plexus (sometimes called the Abdominal Brain). This is situated in the abdomen, some of its filaments accompanying the branches of the aorta distributed to the stomach, intestines, spleen, pancreas, liver and other organs   The Sympathetic system controls, for the most part, the involuntary processes, such as circulation, respiration and digestion, so that we do not ordinarily notice that we have a heart, lungs and stomach, so quietly does this vital machinery work   Yet owing to the connection of the sympathetic with the cerebro-spinal nerves, the functions of the internal organs may be disarranged by apparently slight causes. The student of Osteopathy will bear this in mind as he progresses with his lessons.

The peculiar power transmitted by the nerves is known as Nerve Force (the ancients, believing it to be a fluid, called it "the nervous fluid"). In character and rapidity of movement it seems like the electric current. It is put in motion by stimuli, within or without the body, as, for example, food, waves of light and sound, the emotions, the application of electricity and other agents; and when aroused it makes itself manifest in voluntary and involuntary functions and in the various motions and sensations incident to the body.

Nerve force is sometimes said to be "transferred," i. e., pain or some other sort of sensation is felt in an altogether different part of the body from that where the stimulus really is; for example, in disease of the hip-joint, pain in the knee is a common sign, while pain at the hip is comparatively rare. An impression conveyed to a nerve centre by a sensory nerve, and thence reflected to the motor nerve, results in muscular movement or secretion, which is said to be the effect of Reflex Action.

Reflex Action occurs frequently in the body and in both divisions of the nervous system. For the most part it is performed without the knowledge of the individual, but when it occurs through the brain it becomes appreciable, and may even be voluntarily aided. For example, the act of swallowing is mainly the result of an unconscious reflex action by the mere contact of substances with the pharynx. But if an irritant, such as the end of the finger, or a feather, be introduced in the throat, an involuntary effort at expulsion is made.

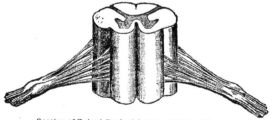

Section of Spinal Cord with roots of Spinal Nerves.

QUIZ QUESTIONS

1. State theory of treatment of fevers.
2. State how you would give pressure on vaso motor center.
3. State treatment for influenza.
4. State treatment for diphtheria.
5. State treatment for displacement of uterus.
6. State treatment for menstrual troubles.
7. How many bones are in the skeleton?
8. Upon what vertebræ does the skull rest and move?
9. How many vertebræ comprise the spinal column? Name them.
10. Describe the different kinds of muscles.
11. Describe the course of the circulation to and from the heart.
12. What is the lymph?
13. Name the two divisions of the nervous system and describe each.
14. Name and describe the three parts of the brain.
15. Describe the spinal cord.

Our concluding part, Part V, will comprise Lesson XI, continuing Osteopathic Anatomy and Physiology, and Lesson XII, containing advice as to building up and conducting an Osteopathic practice, practical advice and suggestions and miscellaneous information.

HOME STUDY COURSE

IN

OSTEOPATHY

PART FIFTH
COMPRISING LESSONS XI AND XII

ISSUED BY

THE COLUMBIA COLLEGE OF OSTEOPATHY
3031 AUDITORIUM BUILDING
CHICAGO, ILL., U. S. A.

CONTENTS

LESSON XI

LESSON XII

LESSON XI

OSTEOPATHIC ANATOMY AND PHYSIOLOGY

ORGANS OF RESPIRATION

The organs of respiration comprise the lungs and the air passages leading to them. The lungs are two in number, and are located in the thoracic cavity, one on each side of the median line, and separated from each other by the heart and its great blood-vessels, and by the larger air tubes. Each lung is cone-like in shape and extends upward to the lower border of the neck, and, excepting where the large blood-vessels and tubes enter, is covered with a strong but delicately constructed sac, known as the pleural sac These sacs are together known as the pleura, and the space inclosed by each is known as the pleural cavity. One wall of each sac is closely adherent to the lung and the other to the concave inner wall of the chest. The lining of each sac secretes a fluid that allows the inner surfaces of its walls to glide easily upon each other in the process of breathing.

The Air Passages are the interior of the nose, pharynx, larynx, windpipe or trachea, and the bronchial tubes

The Nose is lined with a mucous membrane, kept moist by the secretions of its mucous glands and warm by being richly supplied with blood, the air, therefore, in its passage through the nostrils coming in contact with a large extent of warm mucous membrane. The Pharynx is a passage for air as well as food, though the organs of respiration are sometimes said to begin with the larynx, which is located in front of and adjoining the upper end of the œsophagus. It is composed of several large cartilages controlled by muscles, and is so arranged as to form a kind of box, and has about the middle of it a dilatable opening called the glottis, through which respiration is performed, and by means of which articulate sounds are produced

The Trachea is a membranous, elastic tube which extends

3

downward from the larynx. Nearly opposite the third dorsal vertebra it divides into smaller tubes, called the right and left bronchial tubes, which enter the lungs. These in turn divide and subdivide like the branches and twigs of a tree, becoming smaller and smaller, until they finally end in lobules, i. e., oval sacs or bags. Covering the lobules, and dipping down between the adjoining walls of the air vesicles, is the network of capillary blood-vessels referred to in our lesson on the Circulation. The peculiar arrangement of the walls of the lobules affords an extensive surface of very delicate membrane for the aeration of blood, it being estimated that the extent of surface of all the vesicles is about 1,400 square feet, and that in the course of twenty-four hours about 20,000 litres (35,000 pints) of blood traverse the capillaries, the blood corpuscles passing in single file and being exposed to air on both surfaces.

The process of respiration consists of inspiration, or breathing in, and expiration, or breathing out. The changes that take place in the air during respiration are as follows: Inspired air is robbed of a large part of its oxygen, which is appropriated by the blood between the adjacent walls of the air vesicles. At the same time the air acquires various matters, the results of tissue changes which have been brought to the air cells by the circulation. Hence expired air is charged with noxious materials and will not sustain combustion or maintain life. It contains carbonic acid in excess and small quantities of various excretory products similar to those excreted by the skin and kidneys, also an animal product which is prone to putrefy and is offensive.

There are changes effected in the blood during respiration. The inhaled oxygen changes the color of the blood from the blue in the pulmonary veins to the scarlet in the capillaries of the lungs. The blood as sent from the right side of the heart to the lungs is venous, dark and impure, being laden down with waste products. But when it returns to the left side of the heart, from the lungs, it has become arterial, bright, pure and charged with nourishment for the tissues. This marvelous change is effected by the blood gaining oxygen and losing carbonic acid in the lungs.

The Animal Heat is produced in proportion to the activity of internal changes, which changes are especially indicated

by the absorption of oxygen and the exhalation of carbonic
acid. The temperature of man in health is 98½ to 99 degrees F. A temperature of 105 degrees generally marks a
severe attack of some disease; one above 105 denotes great
danger, and a temperature of 110 to 112 is very quickly fatal.
A temperature of 96 degrees denotes great danger and is a
symptom of approaching collapse. Below 92 the probability
of recovery is small.

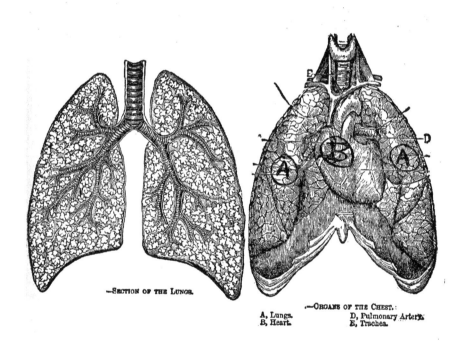

—Section of the Lungs.

.—Organs of the Chest.:

A, Lungs.   D, Pulmonary Artery.
B, Heart.   E, Trachea.

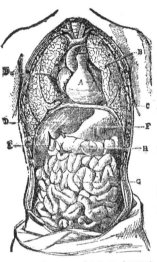

—SECTION OF CHEST AND ABDOMEN.

A, Heart.
B, The Lungs.
C, Diaphragm.
D, The Liver.
E, Gall Bladder.
F, Stomach.
G, Small Intestine.
H, Large Intestine.

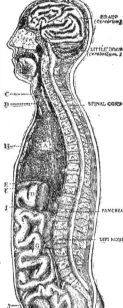

Side view of the head and trunk; the bones and soft coverings of the cavities being removed, and the face, throat, and spinal column given in longitudinal sections. The organs are in relief. A, lungs; B, trachea; C, œsophagus; D, stomach; E, diaphragm; F, a small portion of the liver; G, intestines; H, heart; I, spleen; J, bladder.

ALIMENTARY CANAL—including Gullet, Stomach, Large and Small Intestines.

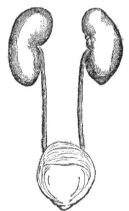

—THE KIDNEYS AND BLADDER.

—A gastric gland.

—STRUCTURE OF A SALIVARY GLAND.

THE DIGESTIVE APPARATUS

It is well known that the maintenance of life depends upon the vitality of the innumerable cells of which each body is composed, and this vitality is largely influenced by food. From the food the blood is fed; from the blood the tissues are fed. The conversion of food in the body into blood is called Digestion. The organs of Digestion consist of the Alimentary Canal and its accessory organs.

The Alimentary Canal is a muscular membranous tube, measuring in adults between 25 and 30 feet in length. It begins at the mouth and extends downward throughout the body. In it the digestion of the food is performed. It is lined throughout its entire length with a delicate but firm tissue, which is continuous with a similar lining of the air passages, the whole being known as the Mucous Membrane or "internal skin." This Mucous Membrane varies in thickness and general arrangement in different portions of the canal and contains numerous follicles for secretion and excretion, and its surface is covered with cells variously arranged. In addition to the digestive fluids which it secretes it contains a viscid fluid called mucus, which protects it and enables its opposing surfaces to glide easily upon each other in the various movements of the canal incident to digestion. The Alimentary Canal varies in size, form and structure, thereby forming the mouth, pharynx, œsophagus, stomach and intestines.

The mouth and its appendages are concerned in the earlier steps of digestion, and in health are supplied with a fluid called saliva. Behind the mouth, and at the first bend of the Alimentary Canal downward, is the pharynx, which is partly separated from the mouth by a movable curtain-like muscular flap called the soft-palate, and surrounded by three obliquely-placed muscles called the constrictors of the pharynx, which overlap each other and assist in the act of swallowing. The Oesophagus, or gullet, is the next portion of the Alimentary Canal, and connects the pharynx with the stomach. It is about nine inches long and lies upon the front and upper portion of the spinal column. Its walls contain certain muscular fibres which serve to propel the food toward the stomach. The wave-like motion caused by the alternate contraction and relaxation of these fibres is called the Peristaltic Motion, and is similar to that of the intestines

The Stomach is somewhat pear-shaped, the larger end being upon the left side of the body, beneath the ribs, in contact with the spleen, to which it is joined by a ligament of connective tissue. The smaller end is on the right side of the body, under the liver   It has two openings · one where the œsophagus enters, called the Cardiac opening because its location is near the heart, from which it is separated by the diaphragm ; the other is styled the Pyloric or "gate" opening, because it is provided with a muscular valve known as the pylorus or "gate keeper," the object of which is to prevent the premature exit of food from the stomach

The lining of the stomach is very soft and delicate and is amply supplied with blood-vessels, mucous glands and gastric tubules or follicles. These last secrete a thin, acid fluid, known as Gastric Juice. The muscles in the walls of the stomach and outside of its mucous membrane are involuntary and are arranged in three layers   Their alternate contraction and relaxation serve to agitate thoroughly the contents of the stomach   The remaining portion of the Alimentary Canal consists of the intestines, or bowels, which occupy the abdominal cavity, and are divided into the small and large intestines.

The Small Intestine is a cylindrical conduit, coiled upon itself and extending from the pylorus to the large intestine, its opening into which is guarded by the ileo-coecal valve, an arrangement which readily admits of the passage into the large intestine of refuse material, but interposes a very considerable barrier to its return   In the walls of the intestine, throughout nearly its entire length, are involuntary muscular fibres, which are abundantly supplied with a network of nerves. The lining of the intestine is very velvety, and throughout the larger part of the canal is arranged in transverse shelf-like folds, more or less circular in form, which by a winking motion sway backward and forward in the fluids of the intestines, retarding the passage of food and providing a very large surface for secretion and absorption   The velvety condition of the mucous membrane is due to its numerous cone-like elevations, presenting an appearance like plush, and known as the intestinal villi   There are more than ten million of these villi   Within them are numerous blood-vessels, which empty into a large vein called the portal vein, which conveys to the liver certain products of digestion. They contain also other vessels, known as lacteals, which are a part of the wonderful system of vessels called the lymphatics, which are fully described in our lesson on the Circulation. These lacteals commence probably as blind extremities in the intestinal villi and empty into the receptacum chyli, a pouch lying upon the lumbar vertebrae. This pouch connects with the thoracic duct, a quill-like tube extending upward and emptying into the left subclavian vein the large vein under the left clavicle or collarbone.

In the mucous membrane of the intestine are numerous follicles, some of which secrete mucus and some a digestive fluid known as intestinal juice. Within about three inches of the pylorus, the duct from the gall bladder of the liver, and that from the pancreas, open into the intestine, admitting the bile and pancreatic juice.

The large intestine begins at the ileo-coecal valve, in the right lower portion of the abdominal cavity, ascends upon the right side of the cavity, crosses over to the left underneath the stomach, and descends upon the left side, terminating the alimentary canal. Its commencement is known as the Coecum, which is a rounded cavity having a cylindrical tube from one to five inches long projecting from its lower portion, which tube is known as the vermiform appendix. Its uses are not fully known, some claiming it to be an attachment which was at one time needed to perform certain functions, but which has now outlived its usefulness; while others claim that its office is to furnish a fluid which lubricates the intestine. Its best known office seems to be to furnish Drug Doctors with cases of Appendicitis upon which to perform dangerous and expensive operations. Osteopathy affords a simple, practical, effective cure for Appendicitis without the risk of the knife.

The accessory digestive organs are the teeth, salivary glands, liver and pancreas. The spleen has been styled an accessory organ, but its function is not definitely known

The teeth are the organs of mastication, by which the food is thoroughly broken up into minute fragments and thus prepared for the softening and digestive action of the saliva.

The Salivary Glands are important accessory organs of digestion. Their secretions, together with that from the glands of the general mucous surface of the mouth, constitute the

Saliva. This secretion is a thin alkaline fluid, whose function is to dissolve the particles of food, thus enabling us to taste; to soften food so that it may be the more readily chewed and swallowed; to keep the mouth moist and lubricated; and, finally, to transform some of the starch in food. A man secretes from one to three pounds of saliva per day.

The Pancreas is an elongated fleshy organ near to and just behind the stomach, which secretes the pancreatic juice, a viscid alkaline fluid which is poured into the upper portion of the small intestine. It acts principally upon the fat in food

The Liver is the largest gland in the body. It secretes the bile, which is carried by a multitude of fine canals within the substance of the liver into a main tube which opens into the upper part of the small intestine before described. Part of this bile, however, passes through a branch of this main tube to the Gall Bladder, there to be stored for future use. This reservoir is a pear-shaped bag, about three inches in length, attached to the under side of the liver

In addition to the secretion of bile, the liver has another important function, the glycogenic function, so named from the substance called glycogen. This substance is formed in the liver from the digested materials brought to that organ by the portal vein, but is derived chiefly from the starch and sugar absorbed in the digestive process. It is formed during digestion and stored in the liver, to be gradually transformed, in the intervals of digestion, into glucose, or a sugar similar to grape sugar.

The Bile is of a yellowish-green color and is constantly secreted; but the flow is increased soon after digestion in the stomach begins. About two and one-half pounds are secreted per day. It assists the pancreatic juice in preparing fat for absorption and assists in the prevention of decomposition and putrefaction of food during its passage through the intestines and also increases the muscular action of the intestines

The various steps by which food is converted into the tissues of the body are· Mastication, Insalivation, Deglutition, Stomach and Intestinal Digestion, Absorption, Circulation and Assimilation.

When food has been received into the mouth it is masticated by the teeth, assisted by the action of the tongue, lips and cheeks. At the same time it is softened by insalivation, or a thorough mixture with saliva, and during this process part of the cooked starch in the food is changed into dextrine, and then into glucose, and is thus rendered soluble. This change is effected by the ptyaline of the saliva, which acts as a ferment and changes the chemical constitution of any substance for which it has an affinity

The food, having been properly prepared, now moves toward the pharynx to be swallowed. The passage of the food to the stomach is then effected by the peristaltic action of the œsophagus When the food reaches the stomach digestion begins. The mucous membrane becomes red from its engorgement with blood, and the gastric juice pours out in abundance. The latter dissolves the connective tissue of meat, releases fat from its envelopes by breaking them up, and transforms some of the albuminous material, such as lean meat, the gluten of wheat and white of eggs, into albuminose, in which form they are capable of being absorbed. The transformation is effected by the ferment action of an organic ingredient of the gastric juice known as pepsin, in connection with the acid ingredient.

While the above processes are being carried on, the fluid portion of the food, both that which has entered the stomach as fluid and that which has been liquefied by stomach digestion, is rapidly taken up by the absorbents of the stomach and carried into the blood, while the more solid portions are thoroughly intermingled with the gastric secretions by the churning action of the muscles of the stomach The unabsorbed food begins slowly to leave the stomach in about half an hour after its introduction, in the form of a gray semi-fluid, usually called chyme, which is a mixture of some of the sugar and salts of the food, of transformed starch or glucose, of softened starch, of broken fat and connective tissue, and of albuminose.

The chyme, upon entering the intestine, comes in contact with the bile and the pancreatic and intestinal juices, and intestinal digestion commences By means of these fluids most of the food not already softened is dissolved From the digestion in the small intestine there results three substances, viz : (1) Peptone, from the digestion of albuminous matters; (2) Chyle, from the emulsion of the fats; (3) Glucose, from the transformation of starch These substances are to a large extent carried into the blood and become a part of it, while the undigested food passes on into the large intestines or bowels.

Absorption, or the process by which liquefied and transformed food is taken up by the veins and lacteals, is effected by endosmosis. By the blood vessels of the stomach, water, and whatever is dissolved in the gastric juice, are rapidly absorbed and carried by the blood in the portal vein to the liver, together with the peptone, glucose and molecular fat which has reached the portal vein through the blood-vessels of the intestinal villi. This blood, after traversing the liver, reaches the right side of the heart. On the other hand, the chyle passes through the lacteals into the thoracic duct, together with the lymph from the lower portions of the body, and is conveyed to the left sub-clavian vein, and so into the blood. We have explained in our lesson on The Circulation the process by which the blood carries the digested materials to the various tissues of the body and by which each cell and tissue appropriates material so brought for its growth and development.

Besides the organs already described, the abdominal cavity contains other important organs, the Kidneys, two in number, located in the loins behind the intestines, one on each side of the spinal column. They are shaped like a bean, being about four inches long, two inches wide and one inch thick. The function of the kidneys is to purify the blood by removing from it a poisonous substance called urea and certain waste products. If their action is interfered with, blood poisoning takes place, on account of the accumulation of urea and effete materials in the system The watery fluid secreted by the kidneys is carried by two tubes, called ureters, to the bladder.

The Bladder is located in the pelvis, behind the pubes, and serves as a reservoir for the urine.

THE SKIN

Some writers have likened the skin to a sentinel whose duty is to guard the body from attacks of the enemy, from both within and without. It consists of two distinct layers, the Dermis and Epidermis. The Dermis is also known as the Cutis Vera, or true skin, and the latter as the Cuticle, the scarf skin and the false skin.

The Dermis, or deeper layer, is composed of a dense network of fibrous and elastic tissue, in the meshes of which are muscular fibres, blood and lymphatic vessels, nerves, sebace-ous and sweat glands, hair and hair follicles. Under it, and closely blended with it, is the sub-cutaneous tissue, which contains blood-vessels, lymphatics, nerves, muscular fibres and adipose tissue.

The Epidermis, or superficial layer of the skin, is composed entirely of cells and is devoid of blood-vessels and nerves. By attrition and chemical action, the outer cells of the epidermis are almost constantly being removed, while the deeper ones, formed from the dermis, are being pushed forward to take their place, growing harder and flatter as they approach the surface. Having no nerves, the epidermis is not sensitive; and being without blood-vessels, can not bleed. It is adapted as a covering and protection to the sensitive tissues beneath.

Classed as appendages of the skin are the sweat and sebace-ous glands (with their ducts) and the hair and nails. In the dermis and sub-cutaneous tissue are the sweat glands, consisting of numerous coils of exceedingly minute tubing, surrounded on all sides by a fine network of blood-vessels; the lower extremity of each coil being closed and turned toward its centre. From the blood in the blood-vessels the perspiration is being constantly filtered out by the tubular sweat glands. It is estimated that there are nearly three million sweat glands on the human body, and the entire length of the secreting tubes is said to be between two and three miles.

.THE SKIN

The purpose of these glands is to eliminate the debris of used-up tissues and to keep the body comfortable in varying temperatures and conditions. The amount of perspiration excreted in twenty-four hours is from two to three pounds, under ordinary circumstances, but men working in iron mills, etc., may perspire as much as three pints in an hour. The sebaceous glands secrete an oily matter which lubricates the skin and hair. They are located in the Dermis, and are simple or compound follicles.

The hair bulb or root enlargements are inserted either in special hair sacs or follicles or in sebaceous follicles. Each hair is oval or somewhat flattened, and is composed of a pith-like substance in the centre, surrounded by a fibrous tissue, and this by a so-called cuticle of epidermis-like cells. Hairs are well supplied with blood at the base of the hair follicles, and are living tissues, strong and elastic

The nails are modifications of the epidermis, identical in formation, but peculiar in appearance and manner of growth. The nail rests in a matrix, which is a fold of the dermis, particularly rich in papillæ, from which the nail cells are produced. When nails are destroyed, new ones will be formed if the matrix is uninjured.

The functions of the skin are six in number, as follows:

(1)   A covering and protection to the external surface of the body.

(2)   An organ of sensation.

(3)   An organ of excretion.

(4)   A regulator of temperature

(5)   An organ of absorption. This is its least known function, but it is a physiological fact that the skin will absorb certain drugs, poisons, oily substances, etc

(6)   An accessory organ of breathing. It absorbs a small amount of oxygen and gives out a larger amount of carbonic acid, performing, it is estimated, about one-fiftieth, or more, of the respiratory function.

Owing to the above named qualities or functions the skin is a valuable ally to the lungs, liver, bowels and kidneys, and its condition has much to do with the general health.

THE MALE GENERATIVE ORGANS

The organs of generation in the male consist of the Penis, the Testes, the Prostate Gland, Cowper's Glands and the Vesiculæ Seminales

The Penis consists of erectile tissue arranged in three cylindrical compartments, each surrounded by a fibrous sheath It is the organ of copulation, and consists of a root, body and extremity, the latter being known as the *glans penis.*

The Testes or testicles are glandular organs, suspended in the scrotum by the spermatic cords, and secrete the seminal fluid The scrotum is the pouch containing the testes and a part of the spermatic cord Its appearance differs under different aspects and influences In the young and robust man it is short, corrugated and closely surrounds the testes, while in the old or weak man it becomes extended and flabby. Warm weather causes it to extend and become loose and cold weather the reverse. The spermatic cord, which is composed of arteries, veins, lymphatics, nerves, the excretory ducts of the testicle, etc , support the testes in the scrotum.

The Prostate Gland is a muscular, glandular body located immediately in front of the neck of the bladder. It resembles in size and shape a horse chestnut, and when enlarged may be distinctly felt by the finger inserted in the rectum

Cowper's Glands consist of several lobules held together and are about the size of peas. They are situated one on each side of the membranous portion of the urethra, close above the bulb.

The Vesiculæ Seminales, or seminal vesicles, are small pouches lying between the rectum and the base of the bladder. They serve as reservoirs for the semen, also secreting a fluid to be added to the secretions of the testicles.

Erection of the penis is caused by the overfilling of the organ with blood, the size of the organ being increased very materially, and the blood pressure being largely increased. There is also a higher temperature, with at first a pulsatile movement, increased consistence and then erection of the organ. The semen passes from the testes to the Vesiculæ Seminales, and emission occurs by strong peristaltic contractions of the parts controlling the act.

It has long been known that percussion and manipulation of the sacral region and buttocks acted as a stimulant to th sexual organs, and was a valuable remedy for impotence in man and sterility in women. The ancient Romans practiced whipping of the buttocks for sexual weaknesses, and libertines have employed a vigorous spanking for the same purpose. Cases have been known where whipping of boys has given rise to involuntary action of the genital organs, and the same result has been noted in cases where men have been punished at the whipping post The explanation of the above stated phenomena is to be found in the fact that the nerves controlling these parts may be reached and stimulated by manipulation and movements applied to the sacral region, the nerves thereby being freed and stimulated and allowed to perform their natural functions.

FEMALE GENERATIVE ORGANS

The external generative organs of the female are the Mons Veneris, the Labia Majora, the Labia Minora, the Clitoris, the

Meatus Urinarius and the Orifice of the Vagina. The term Vulva, as generally applied, includes all these parts.

The Mons Veneris is a round eminence in front of the pubis symphysis, formed by a collection of fatty tissue beneath the integument.

The Labia Majora are two prominent longitudinal cutaneous folds extending downward from the Mons Veneris to the anterior boundary of the perineum.

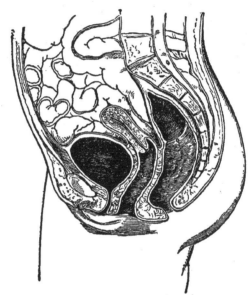

Female Pelvic Organs.

The Labia Minora, or nymphæ, are two folds of mucous membrane, hidden posteriorly in the Labia Majora, but anteriorly they embrace the Clitoris, forming its prepuce.

The Clitoris is an erectile organ, analogous to the penis in man. It is partially hidden by the Labia Minora. Its body is short and is concealed behind the Labia. Its extremity or glans is a small rounded tubercle, which is extremely sensitive and easily excited.

The Meatus Urinarius is the orifice of the urethra, and is

located near the margin of the Vagina, about an inch below the Clitoris.

The Orifice of the Vagina is below the Meatus Urinarius and is surrounded by the sphincter vaginæ muscle. It is usually partly closed by the hymen in the virgin The hymen -is a membranous fold, which closes to a greater or less extent the opening of the Vagina. Copulation and other causes rupture the hymen, although cases have been known where it remained after copulation.

The internal generative organs of the female are the Vagina, the Uterus and its appendages, the Fallopian Tubes, the Ovaries and their ligaments and the Round ligaments.

The Vagina is situated in front of the rectum and behind the bladder, and extends from the Vulva to the Uterus. It curves upward and backward.

The Uterus is a hollow, pear-shaped muscular organ, about three inches long, two inches broad and one inch thick. It is the organ of gestation, receiving the fecundated ovum in its cavity, supporting and retaining it during the development of the fetus

The Fallopian Tubes are really the ducts of the Ovaries. They convey the ova from the Ovaries to the cavity in the Uterus. They are two in number, one on each side, each tube being about four inches in length.

The Ovaries are oval-shaped bodies, about an inch and a half in length, three-quarters of an inch in width and about a third of an inch in thickness. They are analogous to the testes in the male.

Puberty in the female begins from the thirteenth to fifteenth year in temperate climates, although much earlier in the tropics. Between the ages of forty and fifty years the procreative function ceases in the female, the menses ceasing

Menstruation is the term applied to the monthly flow from the genitals of the female. It lasts usually three or four days. The normal period between periods is twenty-eight days.

QUIZ QUESTIONS

1. Name and describe the Organs of Respiration.
2. What are the changes effected in the blood during Respiration?
3 What is the temperature of a man in health?
4. Name and describe the Organs of Digestion.

5. Describe the functions of the Liver.

6. What is the Bile, and what is its purpose?

7. Describe the Kidneys, and state their purpose?

8 Describe the Skin.

9 What are the purposes of the Sweat Glands?

10. State the amount of Perspiration excreted in twenty-four hours.

11 Name the Male Generative Organs

12 State the theory of the treatment for impotence and sexual weakness.

13 Name the Female Generative Organs (external).

14 Name the Female Generative Organs (internal).

15 State the age of puberty in females.

16. When do the menses cease?

LESSON XII

MISCELLANEOUS INFORMATION

OSTEOPATHY—ITS WONDERFUL SUCCESS

Osteopathy is well known in the large cities, and the majority of people applying there for treatment by Osteopathy are acquainted with it and familiar with its merits. In the smaller cities and towns, however, it may be necessary for you to tell your prospective patients something about the new school of healing. You should be able to do this from your study of the underlying principles, theory, etc., as contained in Part I. The following lines upon the success of Osteopathy may also be used in your explanation, not forgetting to quote and exhibit the testimonials from eminent people which close this article.

A few years ago Osteopathy was an untried agency and an unproved theory. To-day it stands upon a far different basis. It has been tried and has nobly stood the test of practice. It has been used in an untold number of cases, and the result is no longer a matter for questioning. It has passed through the experimental stage, and now occupies the position of an exact science. Some of the most learned men in the medical world have adopted its principles and practice. The Osteopath has replaced the Drug Doctor in thousands of homes in this country and Europe—in fact, all over the world. A few years ago one single man, Dr. A T Still, the founder of Osteopathy was proclaiming this method of curing disease, in the face of the ridicule and opposition of the medical world. To-day hundreds of representatives—men who, by reason of their scholarship and conscientious attainment, have earned a right to the public attention and confidence—are practicing Osteopathy and proclaiming its therapeutic and scientific value. The day of false statement and popular prejudice has passed, and the people refuse to be longer bound by the narrowness and ignorance of the Drug Doctors or by the monopoly of medicine. Ten years ago there were only three or four Osteopaths

19

in the world. To-day they number thousands, and the demand is still rapidly growing. Ten years ago Osteopathy was wholly unknown to the general public. To-day it has its votaries and followers in every State, and is patronized by the most progressive, cultured and intelligent people. Governors, Senators, statesmen, clergymen and lawyers have partaken of its benefits and are loudly sounding its praises. Ten years ago the founder of Osteopathy was little more than an itinerant doctor, ostracised by his own profession and viewed with suspicion by the public. To-day Osteopathy has its dozens of colleges, schools, professors, teachers, practitioners and writers, and is enshrined in the grateful memory of the people, with a record of hundreds of thousands of cured cases. And yet it is merely in its swaddling clothes And it is no wonder that Osteopathy has made such rapid strides. Being founded on common sense, and with a rational, natural and scientific explanation for all its treatment, is it at all wonderful that, when tested by results and found able to make good its claims, the world should be willing to accept? The fact that it seldom fails, and never does harm, is enough of itself to cause the world to turn from the antiquated system of drug medication which so seldom succeeds, and which numbers its victims, wrecked by error and ignorance, as the sands of the seashore or the leaves of the forest Osteopathy has demonstrated that drugs are not essential to the cure of disease, and the people have shouted with joy at their deliverance from the knife and poison

Is Osteopathy a success? The question is answered by the number of people pouring into the offices of the Osteopaths of the land—yes, being turned away from their doors because the practitioners find it impossible to accommodate all who present themselves Will it continue to succeed? The day of Osteopathy's success is just dawning. The past and present are merely hints of its future. There is no occupation to-day that offers anything like the opportunity for an active, ambitious man or woman as does this new science of healing. The Osteopath does not have to sit down and wait for patients as does the M. D On the contrary, the supply of Osteopaths does not begin to fill the constantly increasing demand of the people for treatment Of what other profession is this true? Is it any wonder that M D's are taking down their shingles and putting up new signs bearing the magic word, "Osteopath"; that lawyers are forsaking their briefs and taking up this new profession; that clergymen are taking up the healing of bodies as well as the saving of souls? Is it any wonder that the ranks of Osteopathy are being recruited from the number of the young men and young women of to-day? It would be indeed a wonder were it otherwise Our young America is composed of young men and women too shrewd and watchful of the main chance to allow an opportunity of this kind to pass.

Read what the following prominent people have to say regarding our wonderful system of healing:

OSTEOPATHY—ITS ADVOCATES.

Hon. L V Stephens, Governor of Missouri, says: "The science of Osteopathy, as far as it has come under my observation, assists in relieving suffering humanity."

Mrs. W. M. Springer, wife of Congressman Springer, now Chief Justice of the Court of Appeals, Indian Territory: "I can never say enough in praise of Osteopathy. It relieved me from unbearable invalidism. I have seen it do the same for scores of others. I believed before I tried it that it was a scientific method, * * * and now I am convinced that Osteopathy is rational, scientific and wonderful. It will be the greatest blessing to the world."

E. H. Pratt, A.M., M. D., LL.D., a professor in one of the leading medical colleges of Chicago and one of the most prominent surgeons in the United States He took the time to investigate Osteopathy, after which he wrote an extended article indorsing it in the warmest terms, a few sentences of which are as follows: "The fact that relief can be afforded to many cases without drugs and without the knife is influential in attracting multitudes of sufferers, who are seeking for the easiest, least dangerous and cheapest possible deliverance from their afflictions. * * * There are many and astonishing cures in the multitude of patients that are patronizing Osteopathy at the present time "

"As to the method of applying Osteopathic principles in practice, it is the effort of the Osteopath to reach the sympathetic nerve centers at every available point. Its utility as a means of cure is already established beyond question. Its permanency of existence is also insured, for no truth when it is once disclosed is ever extinguished by the mind of man."

Hon. Robert L. Taylor, former Governor of Tennessee: "When a century later historians are sifting the events of this time for the epoch-making discoveries of science and civilization, there will be few chapters more important, I think, than that devoted to the reformation in medicine which will have come about through the acceptance and practice of the system known as Osteopathy "

Ex-Governor William P Dillingham, of Vermont: "I have employed practitioners of that school," said he, "to treat members of my family, and have been particularly pleased with the results I firmly believe that this practice is based on scientific principles and is an advance in medical science."

Ex-Governor Josiah Grout, of Vermont: "Osteopathy has been tried by the leading men and women of the State, and they all testify to its merits."

Governor H. S. Pingree, of Michigan "Osteopathy is a science entitled to all respect and confidence as a distinct advancement in medicine I know it is doing a vast amount of good in relieving suffering and deformity."

Opie Read, the well-known writer: "When in the future an estimative intelligence sums up the great discoveries of the nineteenth century, I believe that the science of Osteopathy will be appointed a place near the head of the list."

Governor Edwin C. Smith, of Vermont, the present official head of the State, is an ardent admirer of Osteopathy Says he· "My experience with Osteopathy has been very gratifying "

Ex-Governor John P Altgeld, of Illinois "When prescriptions and drugs were as ineffectual as empty words, it (Osteopathy) came to the rescue of myself and Mrs Altgeld, and did that which other things had failed to do Honor those to whom honor is due "

Hon. T A. Briggs, former Governor of South Dakota: "Osteopathy has helped me. It has also done good in my family, and will hurt no one "

Hon John R. Tanner, when Governor of Illinois: "There is no doubt in my mind that Osteopathy will reach and cure many chronic troubles that medicine would have little or no effect on. This is testified to by men and women in the highest walks of life and from all over the State of Illinois."

Governor B. McMillin, of Tennessee: "It is one of the greatest discoveries of the time"

Governor L. M. Shaw, of Iowa: "I am fully convinced that Osteopathy is a rational system of healing"

· Mrs Julia B. Foraker, wife of Ohio's distinguished statesman, Hon Joseph B Foraker, is a warm advocate of our system of healing. The case of her little son Arthur was the means of converting many prominent people to our teachings. Skilled' physicians of the old schools pronounced the case hopeless, but the trouble yielded satisfactorily to Osteopathic treatment. Mrs. Foraker says: "My opinion of Osteopathy has been published through the country, and I have no reason to change it. In addition to the benefits received in my own family, I have witnessed many wonderful cures resulting from this new method. This new practice is not a fad, but a science well worthy the attention of the scientific world I am a friend of Osteopathy, and shall do all in my power to promote its success everywhere."

MENTAL THERAPY AN AID TO OSTEOPATHY

Many of our readers have no doubt familiarized themselves, to a greater or lesser degree, with the effect of the mind upon the body, in health and disease. It is a well known fact that a depressed condition of mind will manifest itself in physical disorders, and that many diseases can be traced to this cause. It is likewise well known that if you can manage to inspire hope and renewed confidence in the mind of the patient, a marked improvement in his physical condition will be apparent. The Drug Doctors are becoming better acquainted with this fact, and are acting accordingly. They not only prescribe their drugs but they stimulate the mind of the patient with healthful suggestions and thus improve his chances of recovery, in fact in very many instances the cure may be credited entirely to the mental uplift, rather than to the drugs.

Osteopaths must recognize these facts, and must accordingly endeavor to supplement their work by assuming a cheerful, confident manner, which will inspire a corresponding feeling in the mind of the patient, thereby gaining his mental co-operation toward a satisfactory result. It is much easier to obtain results in a patient who is aided mentally in the recuperative work, than in the case of a patient who is pulling against you all the time by maintaining a depressed, hopeless, doubting state of mind. Give cheerful suggestions whenever possible, and endeavor to inspire the patient with hope, courage, confidence and other uplifting feelings; and be always on the lookout for "blue" depressed feelings, so that you may rout them by the proper suggestions.

We reprint, by permission, two articles originally appearing in the magazine *New Thought,* of Chicago. The first article, entitled "Osteopathy an Ally of Mental Therapy," by George M. Raleigh, D. O., M. S., points out the value of combining Osteopathy with Mental Therapy. This article has attracted much attention from adherents of both schools of drugless healing, and has done much to bring them together, combining their methods. The second article, "Mental Toxin and Anti-Toxin," by William Walker Atkinson, a well known writer upon Mental Therapy, shows the baneful effect of depressed mental states upon the body, and is worthy of careful reading by every practitioner of Osteopathy or any other branch of the healing art.

We reproduce both of these articles, without further comment, at the same time recommending that you speak upon the subject to such of your patients as seem to need it. You can show your depressed patient the importance of changing his mental attitude, as set forth in Mr. Atkinson's article, and you can win the confidence of families favoring Mental Therapy by pointing out that Osteopathy is not antagonistic to their favorite form of treatment, but, on the contrary, is in full harmony with it. There are many Mental Scientists, and others, who would gladly avail themselves of the benefits of Osteopathy, if the matter were clearly presented to them.

This is a good place to say to you that you should never assail any other system of drugless healing, but should on the contrary take the position that there is good in all of them, but that Osteopathy really accomplishes all that is claimed by the other schools, and has certain points of advantage, and accomplishes the result in a shorter time. We recently saw a few lines, which, adapted, give very good advice to the young Osteopath. The lines read as follows:

"And if you are an Osteopath, and wish to gain renown,
Just make your work perfection—don't run your rivals down."

This is good business judgment, as well as being ethical.

"OSTEOPATHY AN ALLY OF MENTAL THERAPY"

By George M. Raleigh, D O , M S.

"Close observers have noticed that the friends of Mental Science and other forms of the New Thought movement are taking quite kindly to Osteopathy, and many practitioners of Mental Healing now combine Osteopathy with their other forms of treatment. There are good reasons for this, and I am of the opinion that the future will see the two great schools of drugless healing, i. e , Mental Therapy and Osteopathy, standing shoulder to shoulder in the advance rank of the army of rational therapeutic methods.

"Mental Therapy holds that the majority of human ailments are caused by improper thinking, and that the cure lies in the correction of this improper thinking, by replacing the old thoughts with the new healthful, normal thoughts of health and vigor. Osteopathy does not dispute the mental origin of disease, but it teaches that the direct physical manifestation of the complaint is to be found in impaired or obstructed circulation, pressure upon the nerves, displacements, etc , and that by manipulation and scientific handling and stimulation of the parts, a normal condition is restored, and Health results.

"It will be noticed that there is nothing fundamentally antagonistic in the respective claims of the two schools The Osteopath sees the physical manifestation of the disease and aims to correct it; the Mental Healer seeks to remove the mental cause, and by inducing new thought action aims to remove the abnormal physical condition and prevent its recurrence. Both recognize the abnormal physical condition and seek to remove it; the one through direct physical methods, the other through mental processes acting upon the physical. The real aim of both is to get rid of the abnormal physical condition. The majority of leading Osteopaths recognize and appreciate the influence of the mind over the body, and the most successful among them combine mental treatment with their Osteopathic manipulations, and, on the other hand, many practitioners of Mental Therapy combine Osteopathic manipulations with their regular treatment Only the extremists and fanatics, on either side, refuse to admit the merits of the other school of healing.

"When it is remembered how many patients come to the Mental Healer, who are not able or willing to follow instructions, and who find it 'too hard work' to control their thoughts, or who become impatient at the apparent slowness of cure, or who want the healer to 'do something for me,' it will be seen how well Osteopathy fills the demand in these cases. And, again, the Mental Healer, by the knowledge imparted by Osteopathy, is enabled to direct his suggestions or directions more intelligently than if such knowledge is lacking. The Magnetic Healer is enabled to apply his healing methods with a greater degree of precision if he understands the principles underlying Osteopathy. And both healers are enabled to get quicker results and to please and satisfy those applying for treatment.

"In my own opinion, Osteopathy and Mental Therapy, combined, furnish the ideal drugless treatment. In my own treatment I used both methods, one or the other, or the two combined, according to the nature of the case, and the prejudices, preferences, opinions and 'notions' of the patient. By using Osteopathy, the patient experiences *immediate* relief, gains confidence, plucks up courage and has faith and hope, and after these points have been gained the road is clear for the Mental Treatment If the patient is 'blue,' discouraged, pessimistic and 'takes no stock' in Osteopathy, I always combine vigorous Mental suggestions while I am manipulating according to Osteopathic principles.

"When we understand the rationale of Mental Therapy, we see that the *way* the Mind accomplishes its results is by increasing the circulation, sending increased nerve force to the afflicted parts, etc. Now, by means of Osteopathy, this work is made much easier for the Mental Forces By the manipulations the circulation is equalized and made normal, particularly if the mind is working in the same direction The mind is not given the whole task to perform; the labor is divided Then in cases successfully treated by Mental Therapy there are always deposits, abnormal secretions, obstructions, etc , to be carried off by the circulation and other channels of elimination. The mind can do this work, but how much easier can it do this when it is actively aided by intelligent and scientific manipulation, stimulation, etc. By this division of labor only a portion of the Mind's energies is needed for this part of the task, and the energy thus saved is used to excellent advantage in rebuilding, repairing and strengthening the entire system By this combined method there is co-operation, co-ordination and reciprocity between Mind and Body and a perfect result is attained

"To Mental Science, Osteopathy comes not as an enemy, but as a brother in arms, and an ally."

"MENTAL TOXIN AND ANTI-TOXIN"

By William Walker Atkinson

"In these days of toxin and anti-toxin—of poison in sausages, oysters, canned beef, ice cream—of anti-poisoning serums (that often are more deadly than the original toxin) for the prevention and cure of tuberculosis, leprosy, pneumonia, typhoid fever, tetanus, bubonic plague, diphtheria, and the rest of the list, it requires courage to call the attention of the public to a new 'toxin,' even if at the same time we furnish an anti-toxin that 'anti-toxicates'

"We shudder at the thought of microbes and bacilli—and thereby attract them to us; we filter our drinking water, after boiling all the life out of it; we develop into microbe hunters, and see poison in everything we wear, eat, drink or breathe. But we overlook the microbes in the thoughts we think We encourage the enterprising doctor in his giddy chase after the nimble dollar, as he produces anti-toxin serums to order. The poor, broken-down cart horse is worked overtime in producing filthy pus and serum for the serum-maniac to inject into our circulation. But we overlook the pure, harmless, powerful anti-toxin obtained fresh from the cells of the brain—Right Thinking

"That Thoughts may poison is a well-proven fact Depressing thoughts interfere with the cerebral circulation, impairing the nutrition of the cells and nerve centers The result is that the organs and tissues manifest lost or impaired function—loss of general nutrition follows—and a break-down is inevitable. Fear, worry, anger, envy, jealousy and other negative thoughts reflect themselves most disastrously in the human system. Fear has paralyzed nerve-centers and turned the hair white over night. A mother's milk has been poisoned by a fit of anger Fear and Hate—father and son—have produced insanity, idiocy, paralysis, cholerina, jaundice, sudden decay of teeth, fatal anæmia, skin diseases, erysipelas and eczema. Epidemics owe their rapid spread and heavy death rate to Fear and Ignorance. Epidemics may kill their dozens—Fear kills its thousands All the brood of negative, fearful, selfish, hateful thoughts manifest themselves in physical conditions Stigmata, or marks upon the body, caused by fear or desire, are quite common in the annals of medical science and psychology.

"Professor Gates, of the Smithsonian Institution, Washington, D. C, in his investigations of the effect of mental states upon the body, found that irascible, malevolent and depressing emotions generated in the system injurious compounds, some of which were extremely poisonous, he also found that agreeable, happy emotions generated chemical compounds of nutritious value, which stimulated the cells to manufacture energy He says· 'Bad and unpleasant feelings create harmful chemical products in the body which are physically injurious Good, pleasant, benevolent feelings create beneficial chemical products which are physically healthful These products *may be de-*

tected by chemical analysis in the perspiration and secretions
of the individual. More than forty of the good, and as many
of the bad, have been detected. Suppose half a dozen men in
a room One feels depressed, another remorseful, another ill-
tempered, another jealous, another cheerful, another benevolent Samples of their perspiration are placed in the hands of
the psycho-physicist. Under his examination they reveal all
these emotional conditions distinctly and unmistakably ' Remember, this is not the 'airy fancy of some enthusiastic Mental
Scientist,' but is the testimony of a leading scientific investi-
gator in the laboratories of the Smithsonian Institution, one of
the best known scientific institutions of the world 'Chemical
analysis,' mind you—not 'transcendental imaginings '

"Now I have said enough about the toxin and some little
about the anti-toxin of the Mind I might go on for hours,
stating example after example, illustration after illustration,
but the tale would be just the same. Now what are you
going to do about it? Are you going to keep on poisoning
yourself and those around you with vile, malignant thoughts
reeking with the miasmatic effluvia of Hate—emitting the
noxious exhalation of Fear and Worry? Or will you cease
being a psychic pest-house, and begin to fumigate and dis-
infect your Mind? And after getting rid of all the microbes
of Fear and Worry and the bacilli of Hate, Jealousy and Envy,
open wide the windows of the Mind and admit the bright
Sunshine of Love and the bracing air of Confidence and Fearlessness.

"Come, friends, let us get out of this habit of poisoning
the air with Fear, Worry and Hate Thought Let us join
the ranks of the Don't Worry company—the Fearless brigade—
the invincible, conquering army of Love Let us be bright,
cheerful and happy—the other things are not worth while.
Let us be Confident, Expectant, Hopeful and Fearless—these
things are winners Let us be filled with Love for all men—
and we will find that Life is one sweet song Love, Faith
and Fearlessness are the ingredients of Life's great Anti-Toxin.
Try it and be blessed."

A FEW POINTERS

While Osteopathic treatment can be administered on a bed, couch or reclining chair, etc, the best plan is to have an Osteopathic table, measuring 2 feet 6 inches high, 2 feet 6 inches wide, and about 6 feet long. This table can be made as plain or as elaborate as the wishes and purse of the operator may indicate. A cheap pine table, of the above dimensions, with a blanket or bed-quilt spread over it, and a pillow at the head, will answer very well, where economy is desirable. The more expensive tables are upholstered with leather, or some durable material. The table should of course be strongly made, and capable of supporting the weight of the patient without a strain

The question is often asked, "Must the patient remove his or her clothing?" The answer is that the less clothing, the better the operator can reach the parts, but when the patient is of the opposite sex to the operator some discretion must be used. In all cases, sufficient clothing should be removed to enable the operator to administer the manipulations and movements without being unduly hindered. Many Osteopaths have a loose robe of some soft material, fashioned somewhat after the famous "Mother Hubbard" gowns of a few years ago, which they keep in their office for the use of their female patients. This, of course, necessitates the use of a dressing room, which is a good thing to have in any event It is not necessary to expose the person of the patient, except in very rare cases, and the operator should use delicacy in this matter, so as not to shock the sense of modesty in the patient

The operator should give his treatments in a slow, careful, gentle manner, never hurrying through The patient should be taught to thoroughly relax the muscles and take the tension off of every nerve, and lie perfectly passive and at rest.

The operator should refrain from giving vigorous treatments to a woman in pregnancy, as cases have been known in which an unduly vigorous treatment resulted in bringing on a miscarriage In fact, it is better to avoid giving treatments to women in this condition, unless it be a light treatment of the head, neck, etc. Drawing the arms above the head and pressing at the same time on the spine in the lower dorsal region, or flexing the legs against the chest, are two particularly dangerous movements at this time, and we especially caution you against giving same, under such circumstances.

BUILDING UP A PRACTICE

We are supposing that you have taken up the study of Osteopathy with a view toward changing your present occupation after you have fully acquired the working principles of Osteopathy, and have enough practice in sight to justify you in giving up your present work You begin with the first lessons, and after mastering the instruction therein imparted, you pass to the second, and so on. You should have some one upon whom you could practice the different manipulations and movements, thus familiarizing yourself with their principles and educating the hand as well as the head. You should practice the manipulations and movements until they come as natural and easy to you as any other familiar movement, such as handling the pen; knife and fork, etc. When your hands "learn to do the work themselves," thus leaving the head clear for planning out the most desirable combinations of treatment for each particular case, etc., you will be in an excellent condition to successfully treat any case that may present itself.

But you need not wait until you have attained this degree of proficiency before you take patients Your best plan is to begin treating as soon as possible. Of course you cannot expect to obtain pay patients from the very start, but invite your friends and acquaintances to come to your room to be treated in the evenings, while you are studying. The result will be that you will obtain valuable practical experience, confidence in yourself, proficiency in the various movements and manipulations, and at the same time will be advertising your work You will find that you will be able to get any amount of people who are willing to be treated, providing they do not have to pay They will be, for the most part, chronic cases that have been to doctor after doctor, without benefit You will be able to relieve a large percentage of these cases, and make a reasonable number of complete cures, in a very short time, and your fame will be spread far and wide by the persons relieved and

their friends. When you have gotten fairly started in the
work, you will be able to charge a moderate fee from those
who are able to pay, and even before you graduate you may
be in receipt of a fair income from your practice, although
until you have your diploma to show that you are fully quali
fied people will be disinclined to pay.

Remember, every person you relieve is sure to send you
another patient, and from a very small beginning (even one
charity patient) may grow an enormous practice There is
practically no limit to what you can do in the way of building
up a practice, and as the amount you earn depends entirely
upon your own efforts, you are really the master of your own
fortune. And you will know that every dollar you earn comes
to you, and no employer takes the cream and leaves you the
skim-milk for your services.

So go to work and give treatments, right and left, to any
one who will take them—pay or no pay—at the start You
will find that it is like the snowball that starts life in a small
way, but grows rapidly as it moves Remember that "nothing succeeds like success," and that "to him that hath, shall
be given." Start the ball moving at once, and before long
you will see the results Treat them all, rich and poor, young
and old, and before long your name will become a household
word in many families, and when any one comes around com-
plaining about this trouble or that, they will be recommended
to "go see Dr. ———, he cured father of his lame back, after
all the Drug Doctors had pronounced him incurable, and then
he raised old Mrs Smith out of the bed for the first time in
five years, and he cured Mrs. Brown's little Willie, and Dea-
con Jones of chronic constipation in three treatments He
will fix you up in short time." And so on, each grateful patient recommending you to some one else

Don't be afraid of taking chronic cases after the Drug
Doctors have been unable to do anything with them. This is
the very class that will be benefited by your treatments, and
the harder the case, the more credit will you get Drugs accomplish nothing in these cases, and the Drug Doctors are at
their wits' ends to know what to do with them. Osteopathy,
being based on sound scientific principles, goes right to the
cause of the trouble, and relieves it, and the symptom disappears by itself, the cause having been removed.

In small towns, the average fee for Osteopathic treatment
is $1 00, or $10 for twelve treatments; in the larger cities it is

$2.00 to $3.00 per treatment, the average arrangement being $25 for twelve treatments. When you realize how many patients you can treat in a working day, you will see the wonderful possibilities in Osteopathy, for the right kind of man or woman.

Now, we expect you to go in and win. We take an interest in the professional welfare of every one of our students, and our interest in them does not cease with the payment of the last installment of their tuition fees. We wish them to be a credit to their *alma mater,* and will always be pleased to hear of their successes.

Remember, to succeed in any field of human endeavor it is necessary to have Courage, Confidence and Energy, and we again urge upon you to cast aside all fear and lack of confidence, and "clad in the armor of a righteous cause," go boldly forth to meet the hideous dragon of Disease, confident that with the good strong sword of Osteopathy you will smite him again and again until he lies before you mortally wounded. What man has done, you can do, and we expect great things of you. GO IN AND WIN!!!

LB Ja '10

STUDY COURSE

College of Optometry

Lightning Source UK Ltd.
Milton Keynes UK
UKOW05f1105201016

285739UK00001B/107/P

CHRISTM
AN
JINGLE BELLS

By
Kelly Hambly

Thank you for purchasing Christmas Spells and Jingle Bells. Merry Christmas from my house to yours.

Chapter One

*C*hristmas and newly divorced, thought Paige as she sat at her desk staring at a blank screen. *What a combo*! For the last two hours she'd been toying with the idea of writing a new Christmas novel, but between the realisation of being divorced, finally, and browsing Instagram, all she had written so far were the words 'chapter one'. She leant back in her sumptuous leather chair cushioned with Christmas themed fleeces and blew out her frustration at not having a clue how to start it. It wasn't so much as not having a clue as she'd written many books in the past and had been a "professional" author for the last three years, but the subject was a difficult one and was sure to cause aggravation for the guilty party even though it'd be wrapped up as romantic fiction with a hint of humour. Luckily, this book wasn't intended for a publisher as she had plans to publish it herself so there were no deadlines but her own. She grinned at the prospect of causing damage to her ex-husband's reputation and sat bolt upright, fingers poised over her laptop keys. About to type, a message alert sounded on her phone. Using this as another excuse to sit, chill and daydream she lifted her phone and saw a name she hadn't seen in a very long time. A name she didn't think she'd see again, ever. Not after the last conversation they had almost ten years ago.

Hi, Paige, I hope this finds you well. I'm hoping we can talk sometime. Patrick x

'Christ on a bike,' she whispered, stunned in disbelief. She put her phone down on her desk, went to stand up in her shock and confusion but thought better of it and sat back down again, picking up the phone to check she wasn't dreaming. 'Patrick! Now there's a name I haven't heard in forever,' she blurted out to her cat Drusilla, who had strolled into her office looking unimpressed. In fact, Drusilla had a permanent annoyed look about her anyway and merely jumped up onto the windowsill to bask in the weak sunshine. The message had come through on her Instagram page, so she immediately clicked on his profile to check it was real but of course, it was set to private. With jittery hands and feeling woozy with shock, she zoomed in on his picture. Ten long years had passed since she last laid eyes on him and he looked as gorgeous as ever, if not better than when she first met him. She noted the grey in his beard and long, tousled hair and recalled his younger self waiting for her outside Paddington train station in a downpour of rain. She closed her eyes at the memory and breathed in the dampness mingling with his cologne as if she had been transported back in time. Amidst the hustle and bustle of the busy station, she saw him drawing her into his body and could almost feel the tightness of the hug that had said to her she had found 'home'. Then, the memory distorted to the last message she read from him, and her heart shattered into a million pieces yet again as the sound of her front door knocking jolted her out of it. *Thank god for that*, she thought trying hard to dampen down the shock before answering whoever it was at such a ghastly hour.

On the verge of tears, she stuffed her phone in her cardigan pocket and went down the hall to see who was at the door. Living in the countryside had its advantages, and she was usually left alone which she preferred, except she had a best friend for a neighbour who lived in a cottage five minutes down the country lane and was always turning up uninvited for a chat or a moan. No doubt today would be a moan because the local school desperately needed funds for the library after losing everything in a fire only last week.

'Bloody hell, there you are. The door was locked, and I forgot my key,' said Bryan waving a box of doughnuts. Bryan was a primary schoolteacher and her best friend since nursery school. Her family moved into the village after her great grandmother had left them the house. He stood at the door with a miffed expression on his face. 'Since when do you lock the doors?' he asked, stepping into the house, and bursting into a rock rendition of 'Phantom of the Opera'.

'I hadn't long gotten up,' she said and followed him down the hall to the living room wishing he would shut the hell up and take up singing professionally like he had always wanted to do. 'And anyway, it's very early,' she yawned despite being awake at six and spending the last two hours thinking about writing but not actually doing any.

'What's wrong?' he asked, scrutinising her face. He put the box of doughnuts on the coffee table and glared at her. 'Come on, I've known you long enough. It's definitely not the divorce and I know writing is pants right now, so it's not that. I mean, clearly you haven't written anything because you usually WhatsApp me at four in the bloody morning asking, 'does this sound all right to you?' followed by twenty bloody pages!'

Paige scoffed and sat down on the sofa. 'I don't send you twenty pages because I can't write bloody twenty pages and how can you tell there's something the matter for god's sake? I've literally just answered the door.' She reached over to the table and flipped open the box.

'You do send twenty pages and I can tell because you're looking like you've had the shock of your life. Either that or the whiteness of your face and the smudged mascara is you trying to recreate your youth. Honey, Robert Smith is so over!'

She really didn't want to have this conversation right now, but Bryan wasn't the type to give in easily.

'I got a message,' she mumbled, not really wanting to talk about it and bit into the doughnut. Jam and cream oozed out of the sides dripping down her mouth to her chin. She scooped it up with her finger and licked it off much to Bryan's disgust. 'Bloody Patrick,' she said with a mouth full.

'What was that?' He put a hand to his ear as if he couldn't hear her. 'You've had a message from whom? Sounded like catnip,' he laughed. 'Do we know a 'catnip?' he then asked seriously.

'Patrick,' she said loudly. 'He messaged me not ten minutes ago.'

Bryan slapped his forehead. 'Wow, I must be bloody psychic. See, I knew you needed someone right now.'

'Yeah, I'm sure you did. At 8 am in the bloody morning. Why are you really here?' she asked, thinking it was majorly early for him to be awake on a Saturday unless he had fallen asleep on her sofa after their Netflix binge.

'Patrick? The one who... Well, I never! What a turn up for the books. Ha, pun intended!' He laughed, then became serious again. 'What the hell does he want, anyway?' he asked.

She shrugged. 'I don't know. I haven't replied.'

'Good. But you know,' he paused and thought for a moment. 'I did really like him, and I thought it was a bloody shame that things didn't work out.'

'The story of my life, isn't it? Maybe I should write it,' she said thinking it might be a good idea. 'So what's with the free doughnuts?' She nodded to the box. 'Don't tell me. You need a favour?'

Bryan smiled. 'Well, the library is no more, and we really need books, Paige, like, desperately. So, I wondered if we could join forces, you and I and come up with a plan to raise funds.'

Thinking it was a great idea to take her mind off things she agreed. 'Want a brew? I'm sure between us we can think of something,' she got up and went into the kitchen. 'Any ideas so far?'

'Um, yes, I have actually.' Bryan followed her and leaned on the countertop with a cheesy smile on his face. 'I thought with your writing skills and my amazing voice, we could write and record a song.'

About to switch the kettle on to boil, she swung around and said, 'Really? A song? I haven't written a song, ever! Here I am struggling with a novel and you're asking me to write a song!' she chuckled thinking he couldn't be serious.

'Now's the bloody time to start then, isn't it?' he beamed. 'Oh, and I'm thinking it has to be Christmas themed.'

'Now you'll be telling me you want it next week!' she laughed, saw him smiling back at her and inwardly groaned at the prospect of becoming a songwriter. It was bad enough being an author when the words didn't flow.

'That's the plan, actually. I want to release it for Christmas. Hey, we may even get a Christmas number one. Imagine that. Remember how that used to be our dream when we were kids? We'd be dancing around the living room arguing over who was George and who was Andrew and then we'd take turns pretending to be the *Top of the Pops* presenter?'

Yes, she thought. *Imagine that*! 'Does *Top of The Pops* still exist?' she asked thinking they could be the next Slade.

'Er, No. Woman, where the hell have you been living? You need to get your head out of the books for a while. And the shed.'

Chapter Two

'Can you believe it?' Paige blew on her hot chocolate and steadied the real Christmas tree against the counter of her friend's metaphysical shop. She had bought it from the farm shop next door but parked her car too far up the street to be bothered to put it in the boot and walk back down. The village of Rhymer on the coast of Wales drew in tourists in summer and the very few shops that they had on the small road did a roaring trade thanks to the award-winning beach and coastline that served as an amazing backdrop to the dainty old cobblestone buildings. Winter was a different matter though as the pace of life slowed down which was great for the residents who could enjoy their little village and beach to themselves.

'I can't, no. It's so out of the blue, isn't it?' said Tiana her other best friend. They met at the local college when they were sixteen and have been inseparable since. 'Hey, I could always read you the tarot on him if you want?' She turned around to the shelf behind her that was packed with tarot and Oracle cards and as she was about to select a box Paige spluttered on her drink.

'No, no... I'd rather not, not after the last reading you did for me. God, woman, you predicted my divorce. I don't think I'd like to know what's next, but thanks all the same,' she chuckled nervously. No, she had to find out in her own way which meant she had to pluck up the courage and reply or leave the past in the past and try to forget about it and him. But could she do that, she thought to herself as she looked up at the crystal windchimes dangling from the ceiling.

'I'm confident you'll make the right decision,' Tiana added as though she had been listening in on her thoughts. 'And those windchimes are new. I'll give you one.' She reached under the counter and presented her with a quartz crystal chime with purple feathers. 'Oh, Bryan said you're both writing a song. Have you started?' she asked.

Have I started? The number of times she'd been asked that question when word got around she was writing a book. She rolled her eyes despairingly at the thought of coming up with a song and sighed. 'No. I haven't even given it a moment's thought if I'm honest, but I better had now I've promised him.' She thanked Tiana for the windchime, picked up her Christmas tree and trudged up the street with a tree that was taller than her 5ft 4 self. On her way up the steep road, she switched on the radio which was playing Elvis Presley's, 'Lonely This Christmas' and found herself singing along. Elvis had been her mum's favourite and the memories of the song playing on the record player when she was a kid came flooding back. Now her parents were gone and the cottage that she had grown up in was hers, the Christmas's since her dad went seven years ago had never been the same even with her ex-husband who had now gone but was still living and breathing somewhere. *And bloody good riddance to him*, she thought trying hard to push back the tears that were threatening to fall for Christmas's past. It was then that the stirrings of an idea were beginning to formulate in her head. Arriving at the cottage, she hauled the Christmas tree out of the back seat and dragged it to her front door with a plan to go up in the attic for the old decorations. This Christmas, she thought, was going to be like the good old days. A bit of childhood nostalgia to blow the cobwebs of her divorce away. Taking off her shoes and removing her coat, she saw Drusilla pounding down the stairs miaowing. 'All right, I'll feed you in a moment,' she said when she noticed an envelope by her feet. No doubt Drusilla had been playing with it after the postman dropped it through the letterbox. She bent down to pick it up and noticed a London postmark. It was from her publisher.

Pengwinn Publishers
Canary Wharf
London

We are inviting you to a Christmas party on December 22nd...

She'd been writing romance books for years and her latest one had recently become a bestseller and she was finally able to get her shelfie at the local supermarket about two miles away. At long last, she had had her 'break' and was making a good living from it. *One Autumn at the Castle* was constantly in and out of the top ten on Amazon and hit the number one spot in her category four times. There was even talk of a Netflix movie. The invite surprised her, and she thought she'd ask Bryan to go along because he loved the big city coming from a small village in the middle of nowhere. She popped the invite on her sideboard and took the tree into the living room where she placed it in the bucket she had already prepared and then went upstairs to the attic. Today was December the 2nd, and she thought she'd better get a move on with Christmas as it used to be her favourite time of year. Used to be. Pulling down the ladder the memory of ten years ago floated into her mind. Yes, she still had to decide whether to reply to Patrick or not. Their last meeting didn't end on a friendly note, and she couldn't think of why, after all these years, he'd want to get in touch now.

She paused for a moment at the top of the ladder as the past replayed in her mind and then pushed open the hatch. 'Atchoo,' she sneezed as dust motes floated around her. She hauled herself up and fumbled for the light switch cord. The attic illuminated revealing piles and piles of boxes that had been here since her parents moved in. Sifting through the boxes, she found the one she'd been looking for, the one that said 'Christmas Decs' and lifted it from the pile when she saw her mum's old record player in a box gathering dust. She dropped the box of decs down the hatch which landed with a thud on the landing and then grabbed the record player. 'Must be a sign,' she smiled to herself as she carried it down the ladder.

'Only me,' Bryan's voice rang through the hallway.

'I'm upstairs,' she yelled. 'Come and take this box down for me, will you?'

Bryan pounded up the stairs and as soon as he saw the record player he smiled. 'Oh, I remember your mother used to play all her golden oldies on this.'

'I was thinking about it today in the car and here it is. I didn't even know she kept it. Remember how you said it inspired you to take up music at university?'

'Gosh, yes that's right. It did. When I used to come here for tea after school your mam used to get the records out and we'd have a singing session in the parlour.'

Paige laughed. 'Yeah, we'd have a disco in the parlour after watching *Blue Peter*.'

'Come on, let's take it down and see if it still works. It might inspire you to write,' he winked and went downstairs whistling the *Blue Peter* theme tune.

Chapter Three

'Ah that was a trip down memory lane,' Bryan stood back to appreciate the decorations he'd hung on the tree. Silver and red baubles twinkled back from the flashing multi-coloured lights. This is the first Christmas tree she'd had in two years since her ex-husband left and now, she was feeling her old self, except the message from an old friend still plagued her mind. Well, he wasn't just an old friend he was more than that, but nothing ever happened, and nothing was ever really said but a knowing on her part and she was sure on his too though he would never admit it. Ever. He was too closed off emotionally and at times she thought he might actually be a robot, not a human being.

'What do you think I should do about this?' she asked Bryan, waving her phone around.

You still haven't made your mind up?' he asked, picking up his notepad and pen from the table. 'It's up to you but I'd be wanting to know what he wants, or it will annoy me forever. But I'm not you and I'm not the one he lied to.' He flounced down on the sofa next to her and sighed. Buddy Holly's 'True Love Ways' began on the record player and Paige rested her head on his shoulder feeling a little tipsy from the wine.

'I think our song should have a fifties vibe. What do you say?' she asked trying to delay making up her mind.

'Definitely. I can do it Elvis' style. Have you got a song title in mind yet?' he asked with the pen at the ready.

'Oh, I don't know,' she said thinking of something that rhymed. 'Christmas Spells and Jingle Bells,' she laughed not being serious at all.

Bryan turned to look at her. 'That's bloody fantastic!'

Paige sat up. 'Oh, I wasn't serious,' she said wondering what she had let herself in for.

'But it's great, I love it. Come on, Paige what's the rest of the lyrics? Best to get this done before you sober up,' he laughed.

'No can do. I'm absolutely shattered, but I will make it my mission tomorrow to get something done, promise. Oh and I totally forgot. I've been invited to London on the 22nd for a party by the publisher. You're coming with me!'

'Whoo. Really? So this will be your first professional event then? Blimey, I'd better go to town to get something smart to wear...'

'Okay, calm down. It's not for a while.'

'Time flies, babe,' he tapped the notepad. 'I need the lyrics so James and Beardo can get the music sorted,' he smiled cheekily.

'Yeah, yeah, all right.' She snatched the notepad and hummed along to the song on the record player. 'So Christmas Spells and Jingle Bells...' she looked at him for approval.

'Absolutely. It's bloody perfect.'

Bloody perfect for you because you haven't got to write it, she thought thinking of all the classic songs from her childhood like Wham's 'Last Christmas'... Ah, the last but one Christmas. Her mind went back two years ago to the Christmas that was ruined when she found her cheating husband in a pub with another woman. A woman he had been seeing for a year and she never even suspected or had an inkling about.

'Earth to Paige,' Bryan snapped his fingers.

'Sorry, I was miles away,' she said focusing on the paper in front of her. 'Okay, let's have a crack at this shall we...' She looked up and gazed around the living room at the twinkling lights and the shiny tinsel when as if like magic the words popped into her head:

'When Christmas spells and jingle bells don't work,

Take fates lending hand to start anew,

Don't look back on all those times you shared,

There's a life and many more Christmas joys ahead.'

'Oooh that's a cracking start, Paige, carry on. I literally don't know how you do it?'

'I'm not too sure either. I think it's magic,' she laughed.

She was about to give in and write more words she didn't even have yet when her phone lit up. She looked at it lying on the sofa and saw a request from Patrick on her Instagram. Bryan saw her confused expression and looked at the screen. 'He seems eager...'

'It's been years, though. He made things clear the last time we saw each other. I'm not sure I want to delve back into the past again. I've done enough of that since the twit left. Am I not entitled to look to the future instead?'

He nodded. 'Point taken.'

She hovered her finger over the decline button but thought no, just leave it and switched off her phone for the rest of the night.

Chapter Four

Being a full-time author now meant she could work from her shed in the back garden. She picked up her mug of coffee from the kitchen counter, called Drusilla and opened the back door to a frosty morning. Breathing in the chill air, she walked up the windy flagstone path to the bright blue shed surrounded by trees and stepped inside to the snug workspace she created for herself as a gift when she finally accepted her marriage was over. Drusilla hopped onto the sofa, making herself comfortable on the oversized cushion while she pulled out her chair and sat clasping the hot mug while the place warmed from the small electric fire. Her mind was swirling with everything that had happened in the past day, and she knew she needed to regain focus to get the book done. Opening the laptop and reading the chapter she wrote she decided the book needed a Christmas theme, blaming Bryan because of the song and began to make the changes. While tapping away at the keys she flinched when she caught someone walking up the garden.

'Freaking postie!' She got up and opened the door. 'Mark, you gave me a bloody fright,' she laughed as he handed her a large package.

'Sorry, love. I rang the doorbell and when you didn't answer I thought you'd be in the writing shed. You do need to get a lock for the side gate, you know...'

She signed his device, took the parcel, and agreed with him about the lock even though the area was quiet and out in the sticks. Closing the door she noted the postmark. 'Norway? Who do I know in Norway, Dru?' she said and sat down next to her. She ripped open the package to find a book, a hardback book. She received many proof copies of books from publishers asking her for a review, but it wasn't until she turned over the book to see the name on the front cover did her mouth fall open in shock. 'PATRICK GRANTHAM. You've got to be joking!' she shot out of the seat to the curious looks of Drusilla. She flipped over the book to read the back cover and yep, sure enough it was the same person. 'An exciting new thriller set in the 1940s... Jesus, I didn't know he could write,' she blurted out to nobody in particular. She flounced down on the sofa and shook her head. Was this the reason for him trying to get in contact? Putting the book to the side, she took her phone off the desk and texted Tiana.

I've only had a book delivered written by Patrick. What on earth is going on? Why does he want my approval?

She snapped a picture to go along with the message and sent it. As she sat back down at her desk, stunned and emotionally worn out, Tiana texted back:

The universe is conspiring... You should message him for god's sake, woman!

Paige rolled her eyes at the message and texted Bryan, but his response wasn't that much different either.

There's something weird going on here. You really need to talk and sort out the past... Oh and meet me in town after school to work on the song. Ciao babes x.

'Drusilla, I really need new friends, don't I? Saner ones with their heads out of the clouds.' As she picked up her coffee, she knocked the book over and looked down to see a piece of paper shoot out of the inside. She bent down to pick it up and saw her name written in ink on the envelope.

Dear Paige,

I have spent so long thinking about whether or not I should send this, but I know if I don't try to reach out now there may never be another chance. I have followed your success, and I couldn't be more proud or happy for you – in fact you inspired me to write The Devil's Cave and I just wanted to thank you for that. I wish I could talk in person about what happened that day. If you're available on December 22nd I'll be in London...

'December 22nd? She said aloud as she tried to recall the significance of the date. 'Bloody hell that's the day of the publisher's party!' She put the note down and returned to the laptop, staring at the last words she wrote: And as Sarah closed the door, she thought to herself that maybe people deserved second chances...

'Why? Why did you write this?' She laughed at herself because what else could she possibly do at this point *but* laugh? She sat back against the seat and pulled her notepad from the bag on the side feeling inspired to finish the lyrics instead.

Chapter Five

She checked her phone for the time. It was 3 pm and school was finally finished for the Christmas holidays since work had to be done on the library. She waited patiently on the pavement when a disgruntled parent walked out of the gates with a crying child whose face was covered in green glitter. As they walked past her the mother smiled tight lipped and nodded a hello at her and then she heard her say to the child: 'What possessed you to put that on your face? I know you love the Grinch, but *green glitter*. Honestly, what am I going to do with you...'

Paige laughed and waved at Bryan who had just come out of the door dressed in a Santa suit under his coat.

'Glad that's over with. Dear god, today has been mayhem!' he groaned and looking like he needed sleep.

'I can imagine, I just saw that kid with glitter on his face. The parent doesn't look happy,' she chuckled.

Bryan rolled his eyes and sighed. 'And that wasn't even the best bit... but you've got to laugh at some of the things they do. Even if we're not supposed to do it to their faces,' he giggled. 'Right, where shall we go in this crazy old village of ours? We've got the Caff, the Pine and Elm or the Rockin' Sandwich Bar... Nah that's too boring, we'll hit the Pine and Elm. My mate Beardo will be there to discuss the music side of it.'

'Brilliant. Well, I hope you liked the lyrics. Let's say I felt inspired.'

Bryan raised his eyebrows. 'I can just imagine. They were bloody brilliant, babe. I knew you had it in you. Bestselling author and now songwriter extraordinaire.'

The Pine and Elm was the oldest building in the village since the pub was inside a 14th-century castle. They walked across the drawbridge to its heavy wooden door entrance and stepped inside. The grand Christmas tree which is the highlight of Christmas in the village was lit up with hundreds of white fairy lights surrounded by red glass baubles. Paige snapped a picture and followed Bryan through the door. For a weekday it was quiet and so they took their favourite seat beside the window overlooking the moat.

'The usual? Bob the barman shouted over.

'Yes, thanks,' Paige replied and removed her coat. 'Oh yeah, I've got something else to tell you.'

Bryan rubbed his hands gleefully. He loved nothing more than gossip. 'Oh do tell.'

'Well, the book I told you about, it came with a note,' she reached into her handbag, took out her notebook and passed him the envelope from Patrick.

'Ohhh,' he smiled and whipped it out of her hands. 'Let's see...' He read it with a smile on his face. 'Well,' he folded the paper firmly and handed it back. 'If the date isn't an omen, I don't know what is...'

'Jesus, not you and all. I think you've been hanging around Tiana too much,' she laughed as the barman put their drinks on the table.

'Thanks, Bob,' Bryan said and then glared at her. 'There are no coincidences, madam. The universe is organised chaos. There are signs everywhere if you only open your eyes...'

Paige lifted her glass. 'Sure, Bry...if you say so,' she smirked. 'So, the song lyrics...' She went back into her handbag and brought out her notebook, the special one with a red leather cover she never went out without in case an idea for a novel popped in her head. It still had the original ideas for her bestseller. 'Are we going to record it tomorrow?' she asked as Beardo, the local musician strolled through the doors dressed in black. 'Hey, Beardo, how's it going?' she asked as he grunted and took a seat next to Bryan.

'Not too bad, Paige. Had a late one last night,' he said sounding exhausted. 'The after party went on 'til 4 this morning.'

'Ouch. So, you're all right for tomorrow, then?'

'Absolutely. I'm game. Anything to help the kiddos, isn't it? As soon as it's done it'll be live on iTunes by Saturday, so we're going to need promo...'

'Which I've sorted out,' said Bryan. 'The local rag are on board and the local radio and TV... I have contacts,' he said as they looked at him with surprise.

'Blimey, you have mates,' laughed Beardo. 'So how come I'm the only one who goes for a pint with you.'

Paige burst into laughter, too. 'And me. But that's great news about the promo. So the music...'

'All sorted. I got the lyrics before I went out last night and already have an idea. The only thing is that you're not going to like,' he directed it at Paige. 'Ashley will need to play bass...'

Chapter Six

'Bloody heck. So you're going to have to see him again?' Tiana scoffed over her mug of coffee. The last thing in the world Paige wanted was to see her ex-husband again. It had been over a year already since she saw him briefly on the beach despite living in the same county. She thought it was funny how you could live near someone and not see them for months sometimes years. Often, not ever.

'Yep,' she sighed, tapping her notebook that was open on the kitchen table. The book she was writing wasn't happening as her mind had been on other things, other people that didn't really warrant her time and energy. She glanced around the kitchen when her phone rang. She looked down at the screen, saw the caller ID and shot a look at Tiana.

'Answer him for god's sake, Paige.' She was serious now and not taking no for an answer. 'Or I'll do it.' She went to grab the phone when Paige plucked it up and felt pressured to accept the call.

'Hello, Patrick...' Her heart hammered against her chest as there was a slight pause before he answered.

'I didn't think you'd answer,' he said. 'But I'm glad you did...'

Paige nodded and realised he couldn't see her. 'Yes, it's been a while, hasn't it?' she replied, looking at Tiana smiling at her.

'Too long, Paige. Did you get my book?'

'I did, yes. So, you wrote a book then? Good for you. I haven't had time to read it sorry...'

'That's not why I'm calling. I mean, I was quite surprised when you answered. I didn't think you'd kept the same number after all this time.'

'Ah, change isn't my thing, you know...' she shrugged, and Tiana nodded at this agreeing with her.

He laughed. 'Yep, I remember... so I'm calling about London on the 22nd. Can you make it, *please?*'

He's practically begging, she thought and looked up at the ceiling, thinking, when she felt a thump on her leg. 'Owww,' she glared at Tiana who was nodding her head enthusiastically. 'Sorry, I hit my leg,' she said. 'Okay, I'm in London on that date anyway. I suppose I can meet you for an hour.'

'An hour?' Tiana mouthed.

'Perfect,' he said and again there was a slight pause before he said, 'I've missed you...'

At those words she almost choked on her own saliva and desperately wanted to say something back, but the words wouldn't come out or she was being obstinate but, she thought, he deserved it.

'Great, I'll be in touch to arrange a time then,' she said much to Tiana's annoyance. 'So long,' she said then hung up and threw the phone on the table. She sighed. Her heart was beating fast, and she wanted nothing more than to thump Tiana for this, but it was great to hear his voice again. Not that she was going to admit it to Tiana because she'd only rub it in that she was right.

'That sounded so bloody formal...' Tiana scolded. 'Paige, do you realise you still haven't told me what happened between you both? I mean, this was a year before you married that idiot. As I recall, you were so freaking happy that day you came back from seeing him, and then a week later you became a different person.'

Paige leant back in her chair and sighed. Hearing his voice again stirred many emotions inside her she'd forgotten about. Maybe it was time to talk about it. Ten years later. 'He... he told me he was married and couldn't get out of it as much as he wanted to because... she was pregnant.'

'What? And you didn't know this at the time?'

'Not at the time I met him, no. And there was no mention when we spoke, either. So when he finally admitted it, I walked away like anyone would. That man broke my heart, Tia. We were a perfect fit and then when I met Ashley, I tried to move on and *then* he broke my heart...'

'But it wasn't the same though, was it? I mean, the love...' She placed a hand on Paige's.

'I think we only ever get one true love in one lifetime and then everything after is just a reflection of what you once had. Oh hark at me. I have a book to finish and tomorrow I have to face that other sod.'

'You'll be fine. He owes you a massive apology. Maybe when you get it you can move on. You'll never know, maybe some things have changed for Patrick too. There's a reason for everything, honey.'

Paige smiled and rolled her eyes at Tiana's words. 'You and your witchy ways.'

Chapter Seven

'Come on, Dru, time for bed,' she said, with one foot on the stairs and a mug of cocoa in her hands. Walking up the stairs, she thought about the call and how good it was to hear his voice again. She took her mobile from her back pocket as she went into her room and clicked on his Instagram. 'Blast,' she said aloud forgetting she had to accept his request before she could have a nose at his pictures. With her finger hovering over the accept button, she gazed out of her bedroom window thinking what to do but seconds later Drusilla put a paw on her lap and before she could stop her, she had put the other on the screen and accepted it for her instead. 'Oh my god, Dru... What have you done?' Suddenly, it felt as though someone had turned the heat up in the room because she felt hot, faint, and sick but it was her own fault for being too curious. She quickly flashed the profile page in front of her and turned over her phone. *What if there's something I don't want to see?* She opened the bedroom window and welcomed the cool air on her face. Her curiosity had gotten the better of her and she looked down at the screen, her eyes drawn to the picture of him sitting at his desk in a T-shirt with a slogan that said: Don't piss me off, I'm a writer and can murder you in my novel. *Yeah*, she thought, *I can think of many I'd like to bump off.* 'Ten years,' she said to herself staring at his green eyes. Scrolling through the rest of the pictures one thing stuck out at her: for most his pictures, he was alone so where was his kid? More importantly, where was the wife?

'Maybe he doesn't like posting private stuff,' Bryan offered when he called half an hour later on video chat. 'And to be honest, you can't really blame people these days.'

'On a private page?' she responded. 'There's no relationship status, nothing. Don't you think it's unusual?' She moved the laptop off her lap and onto the bed.

'No, sometimes they do that because they don't want anyone to know their personal business. Has he contacted you since?'

She looked at her phone screen. 'No.'

'Do you want him to? You do, don't you? I can tell, Paige. You're in love with the bloody bloke.' There was silence on her end. 'See, I'm right,' he laughed, pointing at her.

She knew Bryan was right, of course. She did love him, but he was in the past now just like Ashley. 'Okay, that's enough from you. We've got an early start tomorrow, so I'm signing out...' she yawned and waved before switching off the laptop.

She got into the bed cover, switched off the lamp when her phone lit up breaking the darkness of her room. 'What now, Bry...' she groaned and grabbed the phone from the table. When her eyes adjusted to the brightness, she saw that it was a message from Patrick. 'Shit!' At that moment Drusilla snuggled against her arm. 'You know what you did, don't you?' She went into her inbox and opened the message wondering what on earth he wanted now. She'd already agreed to London.

I didn't think you'd accept my request if I'm honest.

It was the cat.

She slung the phone on her bed and put her head down on the pillow when another message came through.

Then I suppose I have the cat to thank. Am I right in thinking you're being a little short with me? Just the phone call this morning was a bit weird...

A little weird, she thought. *A little? What is wrong with the man?*

To be fair, Patrick, it's a little awkward after all this time, you know. I didn't think I'd ever see or hear from you again. You are married with a kid(s), and you left me and the friendship without so much as a word when I found out the truth. You hurt me.

Take that! She thought and pulled Drusilla close to her. There was nothing like a snuggle from the cat purring contentedly against you. Five minutes went by without another word and as she was going to switch off her phone, she saw that he was still typing. *Writing another novel, are you? I didn't think you could write in the first place...* 'God, what am I like?' she shook her head at her own stupid thoughts and realised she still held resentment over the situation despite it being ten years since she thought of him. A ping on her phone indicated the message had been sent, and she pulled the phone closer to her to read.

Paige, I can't tell you how sorry I am. When you found out I panicked and I didn't know if you wanted to hear from me again, so I stayed away thinking it was best for you to carry on with your life, but in the last year or so you've been heavily on my mind. No, I am not married now, and I don't have kids. It's a long, long story and I hope I can tell you about it sometime. We've wasted so much time as it is...

'No kids? What?' *Oh god*, she thought, *maybe something terrible had happened to them.* She gazed into the darkness of her room thinking about how to respond. She read the words again and now saw that he was online and no doubt waiting for a response from her.

Okay, I'm sorry for being snappy and I'm sorry to hear things have not worked out for you. I really must get some sleep right now because we're recording a song in the morning. And congrats again on the book release.

Recording? Wow. Are you singing? As I recall you didn't have the best voice. Joking.

I'm not singing, cheeky and to be honest you can't sing as I recall. It's to raise money for the school library. It burned down so me and Bryan put a song together. I wrote it and he's singing you'd be pleased to hear.

That's fantastic. Not about the library burning down, I mean the song. I'd love to hear it and if there's a way I can donate, let me

know... oh hang on, I just saw your post. Wow, you look beautiful still...

She rolled her eyes at this and decided she had to call it a night.

Thanks, appreciate the donation but I really have to go... Night.

Okay. Thanks for talking and good luck tomorrow. Night xxx

She switched off her phone and crashed onto the pillows again with a flutter in heart. 'He's not married, Dru...' she said and finally fell asleep.

Chapter Eight

❬ *Deck the halls with boughs of holly, fa la la la la la la la la.'*

Paige woke up to Bryan singing in the hallway and checked her phone for the time. 'Oh bloody hell,' she jumped out of bed almost tripping on Dru who was miaowing for breakfast and shouted down to Bryan to feed her.

'Okie dokie. I opened the door with my key because I wondered why you weren't answering your phone.'

'Oh, I had a late one,' she shouted down to him as she gathered her clothes from the wardrobe and dashed down the hall to the bathroom.

'Yeah, talking to you know who, was it?' he laughed and then called Dru whilst shaking her box of biscuits.

How does he know? She shook her head and opened her make-up bag. Looking in the mirror at her reflection, she pushed back her dark brown hair and remembered Patrick's words from last night. 'Beautiful, huh? You were always such a liar,' she scoffed but deep down she knew he wasn't that bad. She put on her red lipstick and then went downstairs to the smell of coffee.

'Here you go, we got fifteen minutes,' he said handing her a mug. 'I'm so excited about this.'

'I know,' she smiled. 'Is teaching really what you want, Bry?' she asked taking a seat at the table.

Bryan sighed. 'Not really. Breaking into music is so hard...'

'Yeah, like writing but I persevered and got a break. Maybe your day will come. Maybe this will be it.'

'Wouldn't that be amazing? No more kids sticking glitter to their faces,' he laughed, sipped his coffee, and urged her to get moving.

'I've never been in a recording studio before,' she said excitedly as she got into Bryan's car and then remembered Ashley would be there.

'What's with the sour face?' he asked turning on the ignition. 'Oh, Ashley. I totally forgot. Paige, it couldn't be helped. Beardo's regular bassist is away visiting family, and he was the only one we could get at short notice.'

'Oh, it's fine, I suppose. Does he know I'm going to be there?'

'Yep, your name is on the song.'

On the way to Beardo's house who was even more out in the sticks than they were Bryan blasted Christmas songs and sang along to distract her from thoughts of seeing Ashley, but he needn't have bothered because as they got on to the country road, she saw a notification from Patrick.

Good morning. I hope the recording goes well today. X

She couldn't help but smile when she read it which caught Bryan's attention.

'Don't tell me...'

'Why? What are you bloody psychic now?'

'Hah! No, I deduced and came to the only plausible conclusion Patrick?' he said and grinned.

'Yeah, he just messaged me good luck for the day that's all.'

'Sounds like you had a really good convo last night. So did he say why he never spoke to you again?'

'Sort of. Apparently, he's not married now and has no kids.'

Bryan laughed. 'Why? Did the aliens abduct them?'

'He didn't exactly say...'

'Oh,' he said dubiously.

'It's not like that. I just didn't ask, and he didn't elaborate. I should ask though, shouldn't I? I mean, he knows nothing about my marriage and divorce either. In fact, I don't think he knows me at all now so I can't really moan at him, can I?'

Bryan nodded enthusiastically. 'Of course you bloody should ask. The man completely and utterly lied to you for a whole sodding year. Anyway, have you written anything for that new book?'

'Not much but I think I know where I'm going with it now.'

'Maybe today will give you more fodder,' he smiled and turned onto the gravelly drive.

Chapter Nine

'Brr,' she shivered as she stepped out of the car. 'Do you feel like it's gotten colder all of a sudden?'

Bryan looked up at the sky. 'Yeah, on the radio this morning I think they said snow is forecast. Sure you're all right?' he asked, noticing her looking at the car next to them on the drive.

'Of course, I will meet you inside,' she said as the front door opened. Beardo stood in the doorway welcoming them inside. 'And the stars of the show have arrived,' he smiled. 'Come on in, I've got the coffee pot going.'

'Won't be a moment, Beardo,' Paige waved her phone. 'I just need to make a call.' Bryan gave her a look as if to say *oh yeah* and smirked as he went indoors. Resting against the car door she opened up her Instagram and went into her inbox.

Thanks. I'm a little bit nervy actually, you see, my ex-husband will be there playing bass.

She hit send thinking the mention of her having been married and divorced may hit him where it hurts but the moment she stepped into the house he messaged back.

I had no idea you got married. I'm sorry things didn't work out, but some things happen for a reason, honey. I should know.

Oh, she thought. *How would you know?*

'Get off the phone, Missy, we've work to do,' said Beardo as she walked into the living room. Beardo's house was enormous. He owned a few acres and had a working farm but these days he could afford farmhands while he got on with his music. All because he wrote a few hit songs for a movie.

'Wow, this is amazing,' she slipped the phone into the pocket of her cardigan while she looked at his gold discs hanging on the wall.

'Aye, not bad for a kid who was written off in comprehensive, right?'

'Oh, come on, Beardo, you were never written off. I guess you were just different, and people didn't understand. Their loss. You've done so well for yourself.'

'And so have you. Who would guess our little village in the middle of nowhere could produce such talent?'

Bryan mockingly coughed. 'My turn next, let's hope.'

'Yes, this has to be it, Bry...' she said.

With that the patio doors opened, and Paige looked up as her ex-husband's gangly frame walked in. 'Hey, we're all set and ready to go,' he said locking eyes with her. The room went silent all of a sudden as Bryan looked at Beardo and then Beardo looked at Bryan then at Paige who was standing stock still with a poker face.

'Hello again,' she said calmly. 'So, let's go and record this, shall we?' she looked at Bryan and Beardo who hadn't yet said a word and walked out of the room, brushing past Ashley without a second glance. Once she got outside, she let out a breath and walked into the garage which was larger and more expensive looking to that of an ordinary one attached to a house. This garage was kitted out with the most up-to-date music equipment in the industry. The walls were wood panels, and the reception area had a wood cabin feel to it, with leather sofas and a large fluffy rug and a coffee table.

'Hi, Paige,' said Florence at the reception desk. 'Where's everyone?' she asked.

'Oh, they won't be a minute,' she said and turned around to see the three of them walk into the building. Bryan had a look of confusion on his face, and she knew that he expected her to have more of a reaction to seeing him again, even she did but she surprised herself and couldn't believe that all the worrying was for nothing. Was she completely healed from him? She wondered about all the times he would pop into her head, and she would get emotional and spend hours moping around the house. Was it all in her head and wasn't real after all? *What a waste of time,* she thought.

Beardo and Bryan went into the studio leaving Ashley standing in front of her smiling and running a nervous hand through his blonde hair. Not a smug smile, a genuine *I am happy to see you* smile.

'You're looking really well,' he said, sincerely which she could tell from having known him as long as she did.

'Thanks, and so are you. It's great you could offer your time for this. I know it means an awful lot to Bryan.'

'Thanks. I...'

He was cut off by Beardo yelling over the speaker that everyone was to meet in the recording studio promptly.

'I guess we're being summoned,' she said and led the way through the corridor to the back room.

Chapter Ten

'Right,' said Beardo as everyone gathered in the mixing room. 'I know we haven't had long to get this together, but I must say how proud I am of how well we've worked the past twelve hours to get the score written,' he gestured to Ashley leaning against the doorframe. 'Especially Ash who wrote the majority of it,' he clapped, and everyone followed suit, even Paige much to her surprise. 'And most of all, to Paige, for it wasn't for her ability to string words together, we'd have no song to sing...' He clapped again and so did everyone.

For a split second she glanced over Bryan's shoulder at Ash and noticed him looking at her. She instantly averted her gaze on Beardo who motioned for Bryan to go and do his part. 'Take a seat next to me,' Beardo offered as he sat down at the mixing desk.

'Gosh, this is terribly exciting,' she said and got out her phone to record. When she did, she noticed Patrick had sent yet another message.

I've been scrolling through your photos and not getting much work done.

She smiled at this when she heard the thud of the microphone.

'Excuse me,' said Bryan sitting on a stool with a pair of headphones on. 'Aren't you supposed to be recording not talking to lover boy,' he said.

At this point she wanted to clout him one and felt her cheeks warm with embarrassment, but she couldn't help but laugh at his cheeky expression. 'I am recording,' she spoke into the microphone so that he could hear her.

'Alrighty then,' said Beardo. 'Take one,' he pointed to Bryan who began swaying to the music he could hear in the headset.

'*When Christmas Spells and Jingle bells don't work...*'

33

A chill went down her arm at hearing her words sung like this. Okay, so she had an audiobook, but this was on a different level combined with the music. After two takes, Beardo called it a wrap, and the job was done.

'Wow, that was so cool, Bry,' she hugged him. 'How does it feel to be George Michael at last?' she laughed.

'Bloody amazing,' he responded. 'I guess this is how the other half feels, Andrew,' he smiled.

'All back to my kitchen for snacks,' Beardo yelled at everyone.

Bryan got chatting to the guitarist and headed out the building. As she was about to look at her phone, Ashley stepped in front of her, and she looked up at him.

'That was a great song. I always knew you could write, and this proves it,' he said.

She was taken aback by the praise. This was the first time he had ever mentioned her writing. When they were married, he was always too busy with other things to pay attention to her dreams, let alone read anything she wrote.

'Thanks. That means a lot. I just hope it does well for him, and the school, of course.'

He looked down at the floor and went quiet. 'I wondered if we could talk one day you're free,' he said and then raised his eyes to hers.

She wasn't expecting this and said sure without really thinking it through. 'Well, you know the landline number anyway,' she replied and saw Bryan waving her out of the reception. 'Bryan wants me, I'd better go,' she said and quickly left him standing there.

'What does he want?' he asked pulling her down the garden.

'Oh, he asked if we could talk one day that's all. I don't see the harm I guess.'

'That's weird though, don't you think? He hasn't spoken to you since the divorce last year.'

She shrugged. 'I don't know, Bry. My head feels a little mashed right now...'

'I know, darling. That's why I'm looking out for you. Anyway, we'll be in London soon. A break at last...'

'Yeah, a break,' she said thinking about her meeting with Patrick and checking her phone again.

'Okay, Dru,' she said walking into her shed. 'We've a job to do and I want it done before the end of Christmas. Do you think that a powerful partnership like ours can produce another fantastic book?' she asked, looking at Dru's grumpy face staring back at her. 'I know, you think I'm bonkers, don't you? Well, all the best people are according to the Mad Hatter,' she smiled at this and opened her laptop. Outside, the sky was grey and threatened snow they'd forecast. Snuggled in her oversized cardigan with rips in the sleeves, she pulled them over her freezing hands and poked her fingers through the holes, so they resembled gloves. After writing a few paragraphs, she yawned and checked her phone for the time. 'Goodness, we've been here three hours already.' Turning to the window where Dru was sitting looking out the window, she gasped. 'It's snowing, Dru,' she squealed picking her up and rushing out the door. 'Whoo.' She ran into the garden swirling around when she heard Tiana calling her name. 'Hey, T, it's snowing.'

'No shit Sherlock,' she replied. 'Open the blasted door will you, it's freezing.'

'All right keep your hair on,' she said and walked down the path to the side gate to let her in. 'Go pop the kettle on and I'll rustle us up some food.'

'You been writing?'

'Yep. And it's turning out not like I hoped...'

'Oh?' she said, filling up the kettle.

'Well,' she replied, looking in the fridge. 'I was going to really let rip about what Ashley did but to be honest, T, I can't be bloody bothered and so the story has just gone in a different direction.'

'You know what they say, don't you? When you just don't care anymore, you're healed.'

'Yeah, I probably am. I actually spoke to him yesterday too, and it went better than I thought. No real awkwardness and I felt no animosity or hatred. I felt wondrously calm, T. I was even freaking myself out on the quiet.'

'That's bloody great to hear. So what about the other one?'

'Other one?' she asked, cutting into a slab of cake she bought from the bakery in town.

'The real deal, the one who has recently put a spring in your step and yes, I've noticed, madam. I notice everything,' she said, popping two tea bags into the pot.

'Why doesn't that surprise me? Well, he messaged me yesterday, and I was meant to reply but forgot to be honest. I came home after recording the song yesterday and went straight to bed exhausted. I've barely looked at the phone today.' She picked up her phone off the kitchen counter where she left it so it wouldn't distract her from her work and saw that she had several messages from him waiting for her in the inbox. Speaking of the devil,' she waved the phone.

'What does he want now?' she asked, pouring the tea into mugs.

'Hang on, I'll check.' Her fingers raced across the screen and when she saw the words staring back at her she gasped.

'What is it?'

'Um, he said he loves me.'

Chapter Eleven

After she switched on the tree lights, she sat down on the sofa in the living room not paying any attention to the Christmas movie playing on the television. She looked at his messages again and again trying desperately not to fall too hard a second time, but who was she kidding? Her feelings never really went away in the first place they just became dormant when she met Ashley.

'Paige!' came a voice from the hallway. She leapt out of the sofa in fright as Bryan burst into the room clutching a CD in his hands. 'It's here, our song is finally here,' he waved it about.

'Jesus, Bry, you gave me the fright of my life.'

'Sorry, babe, but this it, we're finally rock stars!' He went to the CD player and put the disc in and pressed play. He took her hand in his and began crying as the song started.

'Oh, Bry, this is amazing.'

'Yep, it's on iTunes now and the rag has posted an article about it. I just hope the stations will pick it up.'

'You'll never know. Stranger things have happened,' she said and took another look at the message awaiting her reply.

'What's that?' He nodded to the screen. 'He loves you... wow. I don't know why I'm surprised, I really don't but excuse me and pick my jaw up from the floor. Have you replied?'

She went over to the CD player and pressed play on the song again. 'No, I haven't.'

'I think you know what you want to say, and I fully support you in whatever you choose,' he kissed her on the cheek and produced a bottle of wine from the carrier bag he was holding.

'Thanks, Bry. I'll get some glasses.' The next thing she knew the door opened again and Tiana strolled in squealing and saying something she couldn't make out over her excitement.

'T, calm your shit down,' she laughed.

'They've played the song on the radio just now while I was on my way back from Tesco. I kid you not!'

At that moment there was a loud thud, and they both rushed into the living room to find Bryan on the floor having fainted from the shock no doubt.

'So you're doubly famous and I'm famous,' Bryan dug his fork into his eggy bread and beamed to himself as an old woman approached the table. The café was busy this morning with school kids and their parents on holidays.

'Well done, Bry. It's about time you got recognition for that voice of yours.'

'Thank you, Mrs Evans,' he replied and shook her hand.

'Yes, a job well done,' Paige raised her mug of milky tea and took a sip. 'Are you okay to hit the city today? I desperately need a dress for the publisher's party.'

'Of course. I just got overly excited that's all.'

She couldn't help but laugh and finished her bacon sandwich when their song came over the radio.

'No, Bry, don't faint again, please,' she begged as he got up off the chair to a round of applause from the customers and staff.

'Thank you, you're a wonderful audience,' he took a bow. And sat back down. 'See, I'm perfectly capable of taking it all in my stride.'

She rolled her eyes. 'Yeah, until someone asks for your autograph. Are you carrying pictures about and pens now in case someone asks?' she laughed and then took her coat off the back of the chair.

'Maybe,' he smiled, getting to his feet, and putting on his jacket. 'I'll drive...'

'No, I will, in case you get excited when the song comes on the radio. I do not want to end up in a ditch covered in snow,' she said as they said their goodbyes to the staff and walked out of the café into a flurry of snow. The pavement was white, the road was white and the cold nip in the air pinched her cheeks. 'Wow, a bad winter, I guess...'

'Yep, global warming for you. Bloody humans...' he muttered opening the car door and then throwing her the keys. 'All yours, I'll sit in the passenger seat and listen to OUR song,' he rubbed his hands gleefully.

After getting into the car she rubbed her hands for warmth and checked her phone.

Have I said something wrong?

'Jesus,' she muttered and put the phone on the dashboard.

'What is it?'

'One guess. I didn't answer his message and now he wants to know if he's said something wrong.'

She started the car and pulled out of the village and onto the main road to the city.

'And why haven't you answered him?'

'Because...'

'Because of what?'

'It's complicated, isn't it?'

'Things are only as complicated as we make them,' he responded and switched on the radio to their song playing on a national radio station.

Chapter Twelve

B ryan was right. Maybe she *was* overthinking it all. She pulled into a space in the carpark and grabbed her phone.

Can I video call you tonight?

She flashed the screen to Bryan who nodded. 'Yes, tell him yes. You two have a lot to sort out. Come on, the last one out of the carpark is a smelly old fart.' He got out, slammed the door, and zipped up his jacket. 'Where should we go first?'

'Let's get the dress out of the way first,' she said slinging her handbag over her shoulder. 'I can't stand clothes shopping...' she responded whilst typing out her message and then deleting it.

Okay, I'll let you know what time.

'Yeah, I know you hate it but if it's books...'

She switched off her phone thinking she'd leave it in the car because the last thing she wanted was to be checking it every five minutes. The man was doing her head in but in a good way. 'Oh you know me so well,' she smiled, linking his arm, and headed out of the carpark to a bustling street.

'It's manic,' she said crossing the road. They were headed to the shopping arcade, trying to navigate around people and whining kids when Paige felt someone tap her shoulder. She swung around and her jaw dropped.

'Twice in a day. We've got to stop meeting like this,' said Ashley looking down at her and smiling. Strands of hair blew across his face from under his beanie hat and he brushed them away.

'Christmas shopping?' she asked and a memory of them shopping in New York a few years ago at Christmas flashed across her eyes. Part of her wanted to cry and the other half of her hated him. The confusion mentally exhausted her.

He raised a small carrier bag and shrugged. 'Just dinner,' he said, and she sensed sadness emanating from him. 'After you've shopped could we, er, meet for a drink?'

She looked at Bryan who raised his hands as if to say, 'don't get me involved' and said yes before she gave herself too much time it think it through.

'Brilliant. If you're still around I'll be at Lexi's, you know the rock bar?'

She nodded. 'Yeah, you still go there?'

'I sort of own it now,' he said. 'Okay, I'll leave you to do your shopping. See you later then, yeah?' he said as he turned to walk away.

'Okay, later,' she said and went to join Bryan talking to a group of people who had gathered around him talking excitedly. Bryan excused himself, said his farewells and rolled his eyes at Paige once they were out of sight.

'Who were they?'

'Fans,' he said flustered. 'It's hard work being famous. So what did he want then? Don't tell me you are seriously meeting him?'

As they walked to the glass entrance to the building Paige was already having second thoughts. 'Maybe you're right. I shouldn't go but... I don't know. There's something I can't quite put my finger on.'

Bryan dragged her to the first clothes shop he saw, a little boutique by the entrance and ushered her inside pointing at a silky green dress on a mannequin. 'That would look stunning on you with your dark locks,' he enthused over the Christmas Carollers that had just begun singing 'O Christmas Tree' outside the door.

'Okay, I'll buy it,' she responded and checked the rack for her size.

'I didn't mean to buy the first thing you saw,' he laughed.

'Why not? It means more time for shopping for what we really love, doesn't it?' She checked her size, a size fourteen and went to the till. 'So what about you? Have you got a suit?' she asked him as he rifled through her purse for her card.

'Ordered it online the night you asked me to go. So where next?'

'Need you ask,' she smiled.

'Bookstore it is.'

Chapter Thirteen

'Are you sure about this?' Bryan asked getting into the driver's side of the car. 'I don't want you falling for his bullshit again, okay? Consult with me on *everything*.'

'Yeah, I think I need to do this. I can feel something is up, you know? And of course, I'll call you later. Oh before you go let me grab my phone.'

Maybe I should come...' He was about to get out of the car when she stopped him.

'No, no. It's fine, honestly. I don't intend to be there for long anyway. I've got a lot of writing to do.' He handed her the phone and despite her best efforts at hiding her worry, he got out of the car and pulled her in for a hug.

'Just remember one thing...'

'What's that?'

'He is the past, and the future is waiting for you,' he pecked her on the cheek and got back in the car and drove off leaving her standing wondering if she was indeed doing the right thing. But when she switched on her phone and saw a message from Patrick wasn't she doing just that already – re-visiting the past?

Let me know what time tonight. I can't wait to see you again. X

Walking out of the carpark she texted him back.

I will do. I have an errand to run and then I'll let you know.

She pressed send and walked across the street oblivious to the people dashing around her. Browsing through his profile, she set about searching for answers to his relationship status and read every comment she could find on his pictures but still couldn't find any mention of his wife or anyone else for that matter and figured she'd better ask him tonight. Turning into a side street of boarded up premises the hustle and bustle quieted down, and she put her phone into her coat pocket. The only noticeable sign that a business was still operating there was a placard outside Lexi's saying, 'free entry tonight'. She pushed the heavy wooden door open to the smell of stale beer and loud rock music thinking perhaps she shouldn't have come. About to walk back out the door she heard Ashley calling her name.

'Hey, Paige, glad you could make it.'

'Damn,' she muttered under her breath and turned around to see Ashley coming around the bar towards her.

'I can't stay long,' she said. 'I've got a lot of work to do.'

'Still writing?' he asked, gesturing her towards a table at the back of the room by the window.

'Yeah, I'm working on something at the minute. So what's up?' She took a seat.

Ashley opened his mouth to speak but then faltered and looked away from her towards the bar where two waitresses were cleaning. 'I never got the chance to apologise to you for everything I put you through...'

For a moment she thought she was hearing things. 'What? Are you being serious right now?' she said. *Did he just apologise? Is this the real Ashley right in front of me right now?* 'You're apologising for everything you put me through in the last few years of our marriage, are you? Why now?' she asked sceptically. He wasn't the most honest person on the planet and when it came to lying, he was a pro. But she saw something in his eyes at that moment she had never seen before. Sincerity.

'Yes. I've had a lot of time to think.'

'Really? A lot of time with a girlfriend and a club to run?' she laughed.

He looked down at the table and said nothing.

'What is it really?' she asked.

'She left me after the divorce, and I suppose it's only what I deserve for cheating on you. Truth is, Paige, she wasn't you and I feel guilty for the way I acted, and I am asking for your forgiveness because... I still love you. And I was wondering if you'd give me a second chance,' he pleaded but she didn't like this at all.

At that moment she didn't know what to say. The day was turning out to be a very strange one indeed. Panicked, she leapt from her chair and ran out of the club into the chilly air and headed to the bus station for home.

Chapter Fourteen

'Thanks,' she said to the bus driver and got off outside Tiana's shop thinking it was only she who'd have the answers to this bizarre situation taking place in her life right now. She pushed open the door to the jingles of the wind chimes she'd placed above the door and looked up from behind the counter.

'I knew you were about to pop in,' she said slamming down an Oracle deck on the counter. 'You've been on my mind all day for some reason.'

'Got time for a cuppa?' she asked as her phone pinged with notifications.

'Patrick?' Tiana nodded to the phone and went to lock the shop door. 'It's not like we're busy anyway and I've not had a lunch break. So... What's happened?'

'Uh,' she looked at her phone. It was indeed Patrick asking what time he could call her. 'Yeah, it's him.'

'God, he doesn't give up easily, does he?' she passed her a chair from behind the counter.

'No, he's not the type.' She plonked her ass down on the chair and unzipped her coat. 'I've found a dress anyway,' she lifted the bag.

'Oh, I'll have a look in a mo. Let me just go out back to put the kettle on. Keep talking, I can hear you from here...'

'Well,' she laughed nervously wondering how Tiana would react to what she had to say about Ashley because she hated his guts and even once attempted to curse him, but she was drunk and fortunately she listened to reason. 'I don't know how to say this because it's quite unbelievable and if it's not true, then it's the cruellest thing in the world...'

Tiana came back into the shop with mugs of tea. 'What's cruel?' She sat down and sipped her tea.

'I saw Ashley...'

At the mention of his name Tiana scoffed and hate flashed across her eyes. 'Oh yeah? She seethed. 'What does the prick want?'

Paige cleared her throat. 'He apologised...

'Hah! I'm sure it was to ease his guilt, love...'

'Wait, wait... he said he was sorry for what he did, and he still loves me and wants a second chance.'

A spray of tea flew out of Tiana's mouth hitting Paige in the face. 'WHAT?' she stood up, mouth open in shock and began walking around the shop shaking her head. 'What? Are you bloody serious right now?'

Paige nodded. 'Yes. He said it not an hour ago in Lexi's which he apparently bought with his father.'

'No...'

'No what? He told me he bought it.'

'No, I mean, do not listen to a word he says. Do you hear me?' She put the mug down next to a bunch of crystal rings in a trinket dish and went to the other counter and grabbed the Oracle cards she'd left lying around. 'I had a feeling...' she said looking wistfully at the shelves full of incense. She started shuffling the cards.

'I'm not that stupid, T. I'm not saying he wasn't genuine when he said it, but I know I can't go back there, can I?'

'And what about Patrick? Jesus, Paige there's two blokes admitting their love for you and they're both in the past.' She pulled a card, gasped, and clutched it to her chest. 'Oh my god...'

Paige rolled her eyes not believing in anything of the sort but respected her friend's beliefs and admired how right she was with her knowing and intuition.

'What is it?' she asked, putting the mug on the counter, and getting to her feet. Even though she didn't really believe in the occult or anything it still scared her a little especially because it predicted her divorce. 'What does it say, T? Please because you're bloody scaring me right now,' she laughed but it was just nerves.

Tiana looked at the card and then looked at Paige. 'Sure you want to know because the last time I read you were upset. I'm not saying this is bad, but this Christmas Oracle is creepily bang on.'

'Give it to me. I'm a big girl now, I can handle it,' she swallowed the spit in her mouth.

'Okay,' she looked at her whilst turning over the card. 'It says: 'When the past comes knocking, not once but twice heed this advice. One is offer is genuine and one is fake and the only way to know which one to take is by the offer of a mistletoe on Christmas Eve, but not just any old mistletoe will do. You will know. Start trusting your intuition.'

'Wow. Christmas Eve? I guess we'll have to see what happens then, won't we?' she said and asked to see the card. 'When the past comes knocking twice?' She looked at Tiana.

'I told you, bang on.'

Chapter Fifteen

Finally home, she opened the front door to Drusilla sitting on the bottom stair. 'Hey, sorry I'm late, sweetie.' She put her shopping bags down against the wall and took off her coat and boots. As she headed to the kitchen Drusilla followed behind wanting her food. 'Okay, okay, give me a moment,' she bent down to pet her head when her phone started ringing. She didn't feel like answering it and went to the cupboard for Dru's food and then popped the kettle on to boil. Not being able to resist the phone any longer she looked at it and opened the inbox.

Oh, I know what it is, you're too shy to come on camera.

She snorted. 'That's not it, you twit,' she said to herself and spooned coffee granules into her mug. *Why don't I want to give him a time?* She thought to herself and then as she opened the back door to head to the writing shed it came to her. *Fear.* 'Yes, Dru, I'm afraid to see him. Does that sound nuts to you because it does to me?'

'It doesn't sound silly to me,' said Bryan jumping over the side gate. 'You never guess what?' he said breathlessly running up the garden in his pyjama bottoms and hoodie. 'We've sold nearly five thousand copies already... Paige, FIVE BLOODY THOUSAND.'

'No way!' She squealed and was about to hug him but realised she had the mug in her hand. 'Oh my goodness, Bry that's bloody amazing.'

'That's not all. I've been approached by publishers offering free books. We've got books,' he yelled. 'This has gone better than I ever imagined and it's all thanks to your bloody writing talent.'

'And your voice. Bry, this could be it for you,' she said gesturing him to the shed.

'Oh my god, I just can't believe it,' he said flouncing down on the sofa. Drusilla glared at him for taking her spot. 'I... I mean WE have a record, an actual bloody record on the radio like we always imagined as kids.'

'Dreams can come true, Bry, I always said it.'

'Well, you're the living embodiment of making dreams come true,' he pointed to her framed book covers. 'So,' he said. 'What did I hear exactly just now?'

'Oh forget that we've got bigger things to think about now...'

'No, no. I'm your best mate and I want to know.'

She put her coffee mug down on her desk and rubbed the back of her neck. 'Well, Ash has done a U-turn and told me that he was sorry for everything and wants a second chance...'

'No, no, no absolutely not. The bloody cheek of the man. He bloody divorced you and cheated on you. What did you say?' he said incredulously.

'Nothing. I was so shocked I walked out of the club and went to see Tiana.'

'And what did she say? Did she give you a slap for being so stupid for going to meet him in the first place? 'Cos I was going to...'

At this she laughed. 'No, but...'

'Go on...'

'Okay, I'm getting to it. I just feel really confused, Bry. I never in a million years thought Ash would do this. In my head we were done. Over with...'

'Oh sweet Jesus, you're not going to tell me you have feelings?'

'No... I mean, no. I mean...'

'Oh god,' he shook his head.

'It's not like that! I spent ten years with the man. Of course there will always be something there, but it's not love... I'm sure of it.'

'And now you have Patrick nagging. What are you going to do about him?'

'I've got to video call him tonight.'

'Oh, that's what I heard in the garden just now. What are you afraid of? Don't tell me... just don't tell me. It's love, isn't it? You're afraid of looking at the man you love because you're afraid of getting hurt again, aren't you?'

'Are you sure you've no ambition of being a relationship coach as well?' she laughed. 'I think you got it, but you know, I haven't seen him since that day.'

He took her hand. 'You've got to do this. If you want, I'll be beside you and hold your hand,' he smirked.

'No, it's okay. I think I got this. Thank you.'

Chapter Sixteen

You can call me at 9 am my time if you wish. She typed pacing her bedroom and noting the time on the alarm clock. 'Bloody heck that only gives me twenty-five minutes,' she muttered and then took a seat at her desk and thought she'd check over today's work on the laptop to try to calm herself down. She read a sentence, thought it was crap and re-wrote it when a message came through.

Finally. I was getting worried that you didn't want to know me anymore. I have quite honestly gone out of my mind today thinking about how wrong it was to let our friendship dwindle like it did. But you know you are always more than that, don't you?

Her breath caught in her throat at reading this and she decided to let her guard down a touch.

I was afraid too for different reasons...

Before she had time to finish her sentence the screen said incoming call. She looked up at the ceiling, took a deep breath and hit accept.

'Hello,' Patrick said smiling back at her.

For a moment she couldn't find her voice. 'Um, hi there...' she smiled and briefly looked away from under his intense gaze. 'It is really good to see you again,' she nodded and picked Dru off the desk and settled her on her lap.

'You honestly have not changed,' he said with sadness in his voice. 'I think I should start by saying that I am sorry for the way things were left between us. It was wrong of me not to say that I was married at the time, but we had such great chemistry that I didn't know what to do when my feelings got serious...'

'It's ten years ago now, it's fine. I married, divorced and I really don't hold resentment...'

'My marriage was a sham, Paige. It wasn't real love and worst of all, the baby she had wasn't even mine. She married me for money and took me for everything in the divorce and ended up marrying the baby's father, a multi-millionaire...'

Blimey, she thought, *sounds like something out of a novel.* 'But why didn't you ever contact me after? I sent you messages, and you never replied.'

He leaned back in his chair. 'I realised I had hurt you and thought you'd be better off without me in your life. It was stupid thinking at the time because I just felt so bad for the way you found out. I had no idea she followed me to London that day for a surprise birthday present...'

'Yeah, it was a shock all right seeing her calling you from the station and introducing herself as your wife...'

'And it ended weeks later when her beau turned up at the flat and told me everything... But you've been happy, though?'

Oh if only you knew, she thought to herself, petting Dru. 'For a while I thought I was but then... you know, things happen.'

'I wish you had tried contacting me again. I thought about it for years and then when I found your book online by accident, I desperately wanted to talk to you, but I was honestly afraid of what you'd say.'

'But you did eventually contact me.'

'I had to. No choice. I am in love with you and I'm asking for a second chance.'

Oh god, I'm going to get hurt again she reasoned with herself but as she was about to speak, Dru reached out her paw and cut the connection. 'I'm... Oh, Dru, what have you done?' She texted him back.

Sorry the cat disconnected me.

It's fine. I understand.

No, the cat really did disconnect, I'm sorry. Let me call you back.

I'll be in London at the Hilton if you want to see me. Take care x. It was lovely to see you.

'Now he thinks I cut him off and I'm pissed with him,' she said to Dru. 'Oh, it's fine I don't really blame you; I mean you're just a cat and didn't know what you were doing, right? But god... it's so good to see him again. And... he loves me, Dru,' she whispered, hardly believing it.

'I've always known it,' Bryan said eating his way through her bag of crisps while lounging on her sofa in the shed. 'Has he spoken to you since?'

'I haven't heard, no. And no I didn't respond to what he said. I mean, I literally didn't have a chance to because of Dru and then he got all weird, so I don't know what to do...'

'But you love him too?' he asked chewing his crisps loudly and being annoying. 'You do because you're not screaming for me to shut up.'

Ignoring him despite having heard what he said, she deflected the conversation. 'London is only a few days away anyway,' she responded hyper focused on editing a sentence. She removed the comma and a few seconds later she put it back pushed back her chair and rubbed her tired eyes.

'Why don't you leave it for the day? You clearly can't focus on it.'

'I can't focus because there's two people bloody getting to me,' she spat, throwing her hands up in the air. 'It's like mental torture.'

'You've got to forget Ashley. I don't know what he's playing at telling you all what he did. He made his choice back then, and it wasn't you. Don't be fooled into thinking he's changed because he hasn't. He's just realising he's lost a good thing and trying to worm his way back in. As for the other one, well... I think he's worth a shot but you're not admitting it to yourself. Get your head out of the past, your and Ashley's past.'

'Yeah Bry, you're right as always... Anyway, how's the song doing?' she asked and switched off the laptop.

'Like crazy.' He looked through his phone. 'Wow,' he stood up. 'We've been invited on to a television chat show. Oh my god! The song has gone viral and there are also people singing along to it on Tik Tok. Oh my god. Oh my god.'

'Jesus, that's bloody amazing.' She never expected this reaction when she wrote it and so leapt off her chair in shock. 'Show me. Oh my god, *The Lily Van Merrick Show*! She's my idol. Bryan, I think we've both just 'made it'.'

'Made it? That's an understatement. She wants us on the show on the 23rd, so we get an extra day in London.'

'This is all fitting in nicely, isn't it?'

'Yep, like fated events. I'm telling you; something is happening right now.'

She scoffed. 'Okay, Bry whatever you say...'

Chapter Seventeen

'And I'm back to earth with a bump...' she looked out the front window and saw Ashley walking up the snow-covered drive. What could he possibly want now, she thought and considered maybe not answering the door, but she couldn't help wondering what he wanted before 9 in the morning. She went to the door to answer thanking her lucky stars Bryan didn't fall asleep on the sofa last night as he would've blocked her from answering and before he knocked, she pulled open the door and he looked up at her surprised.

'Oh, morning, hey...I,' he stammered and ran a hand through his hair. 'I was just out running, and I thought I'd say hi.'

'Hi,' she replied not believing a word of it as he never ran in his entire life.

''Do you mind if I grab a drink... I don't think I'd make it to the nearest shop. Parched,' he said.

'Okay, come in,' she said stepping aside and praying Bryan or Tiana didn't drop by unexpectedly, but they always did anyway she just hoped that it wasn't today.

'Congrats on the record by the way. I can't believe how well it's doing,' he said following her to the kitchen.

'Thanks. We're in London tomorrow. I've got a party with my publishers and then we're on the *Lily Van Merrick Show* the day after.' She couldn't believe she was telling him all this, but it wasn't like she didn't know him.

'That's amazing. I'm so proud of you, Paige.'

Gosh that's a turn up for the books she thought handing him a bottle of water. 'Thanks. Is this all right or do you want something warmer?'

'This will do, thanks. I appreciate it,' he said unscrewing the cap. 'I totally get why you ran out of the club the other day. I didn't exactly have the best approach, did I?' He laughed nervously.

'You certainly took me by surprise... Look, don't take this the wrong way...' She was about to tell him that she had no intention of ever getting back with him when she saw Dru look towards the front door.

'Helllooooo only me,' said Tiana.

Paige inwardly groaned at not knowing how to explain Ashley's presence in the kitchen at such a stupid hour, so she leaned back against the sink and folded her arms for what was to come. Tiana bounced into the kitchen smiling and when she turned her head and saw Ashley, she saw red and scowled. 'What...?' She glared at Paige and Ashley quickly thanked her for the water and said he'd see himself out. Once they heard the door close Paige stepped in first before she had to endure Tiana's wrath.

'He only wanted water, that's it.'

'Why? Doesn't he have running taps at his place?'

'He was passing, had been running, or so he says and just needed a drink. No harm done and don't worry. I am not falling for his bullshit. There's more to this I'm sure of it and I will get to the bottom of it, you mark my words.'

'Want me to do a read on it?' she asked knowing Paige would say no.

'Okay, yes,' she replied thinking any insight would be better than none right now.

'Wow, okay, I'll do it when I'm back in the shop. I actually called by for more of your signed books. We sell them like hot cakes with the tourists and now with the record doing well everyone wants one.'

'Jesus, we'll be millionaires before we know it. I'll just grab you some from the shed.' She opened the back door and walked up the path. Tiana followed behind. 'Looking forward to seeing him tomorrow?' she asked.

'Truthfully,' she said unlocking the door with her key. 'I'm terrified, T. And now he thinks I cut him off on a video call last night. I really ought to message him later.'

'I'm sure he doesn't.' What was he like?'

'Oh, his usual charming self just a bit older...' she went up to the box beside the sofa and pulled out a pile of books. 'Is this enough?'

'It'll do for now. Look, I'm sure the whole thing was awkward for him too, you know. He reached out to you not knowing how you'd react. If he weren't serious, he would not have done that after all that happened.' She handed her a pen to sign them.

'You're right, I didn't see it like that.' She took the pen and scribbled her signature thinking about how she still couldn't get used to people actually wanting her books let alone a signed one.

Chapter Eighteen

'It's two nights, Bry. I don't need all this,' she waved her hands over the pile of clothes on her bed he threw out of her wardrobe.

'You can never be too prepared,' he replied pulling a suitcase down from the top of the cupboard and throwing it on the bed.

She rifled through the clothes and held up a pair of denim shorts. 'Really? In the middle of freaking winter?'

'Oh all right, I'm just so excited. You need at least a few outfits to choose from for the television show as well. Sorry, I'm just so excited.'

'I've got that sorted,' she pointed to the suit hanging on the bedroom door. 'And don't moan, I just don't care right now.' She went into her drawers and began packing her make-up bag. With that her phone rang. It was the publisher.

'Hello, Jane.'

'Hey, Paige, sorry to give you short notice but we've had to move the party to the Hilton at Tower Bridge, don't ask, it's been a kerfuffle all right, but all sorted now. Looking forward to seeing you.'

'The Hilton? Yes, that's fine because I booked there, I'll see you tomorrow.' She ended the call and looked at Bryan. 'Isn't that where Patrick said he was?'

Bryan was holding up two T-shirts, a Duran Duran one and Wham. 'I think so, yes, but did he say which one?'

'I don't know, I can't recall if he did, just said he'd be at the Hilton if I want to see him. Why are you holding those?' she asked.

'Remember we had similar ones as kids?' He smiled. 'Here chuck one on and we can reminisce while eating our dinner,' he said pulling Wham over his shirt. 'You know I heard they've brought Top of the Pops back for a special, too. I can't wait for Christmas Day for that! Anyway, do you know what I think? I think the universe is conspiring to bring you two together. I mean, what are the odds the publisher had to change venues?'

'Oh, here we go...' she rolled her eyes at him and finished packing her case.

There was a knock on the door. 'That'll be the takeaway,' he said and went downstairs to collect it. Paige zipped up the case and sat on her bed flicking through Instagram noticing Patrick had recently put up a new post. Sitting on the edge of his bed, head lowered and eyes boring into the camera as if looking into the depths of her soul. 'Jesus...' She then read the accompanying comment he wrote.

Tomorrow will be the most important day of my professional life. I've worked so hard for this, but I realise there have been many people to thank along the way, one in which I hope to say it to personally. If they only knew the impact they had on me from that very first word they spoke... Some people are meant to be in your life for a season or a reason but only the very best end up staying for the rest of the journey.

'He means me,' she whispered, staring at the words.

'It's going cold,' Bryan hollered.

'Be there now,' she said overwhelmed to the point she thought she'd cry.

I'll see you tomorrow. She texted, got up off the bed, switched the light off and went downstairs. As she got to the bottom step he sent back:

I can't wait.

'Oh so who's making you smile now?' Bryan asked cutting the pizza. 'Actually, don't bother, it's bloody obvious. Here...' he handed her a plate of vegetarian pizza. About to eat, his phone rang. 'Blimey, we're popular tonight,' he said. 'Hello...'

'Hello there, I'm calling on behalf of the Official Charts Company. Am I speaking to Bryan Fourman?'

He gasped. 'Yes, that is me,' he said waving for Paige to come to the phone.

'I'm calling to say that your song 'Christmas Spells and Jingle Bells' will be the new Christmas number one... Congratulations.'

'Number... number...'

'We're NUMBER ONE! Oh my god...' Paige screamed, and they both danced around the kitchen.

'Paige! Oh my god, do you know what this means?'

'What?' she asked.

'We're going to be on *Top of the Pops*...'

Chapter Nineteen

'I can't bloody believe it,' Tiana announced as soon as she walked into the house at 7 am. 'I literally had to come over and see you both before you went. *Top of the Pops*, a number one! This is insane. I'm so proud you're my friends,' she began crying and hugged Paige.

'It's a shock, I must say,' Paige pulled some kitchen roll off the dispenser and handed it to her.

'And you're seeing Patrick today. It's like Christmas, Easter and Birthday's all wrapped up in one...oh my goodness, I forgot,' she suddenly became serious wiping the mascara from her cheek. 'I did the reading. Have you heard off Ashley at all?'

Take a seat,' Paige offered her a chair and popped the kettle on. 'No, thankfully. Maybe he's given up after all.'

'I saw something in the cards that I have to warn you about. Whatever Ashley says, don't believe him. I'm certain he's in debt and only after money.'

Paige gave her a look. 'What? Really? He's got a business...'

'Yeah, but that doesn't mean he's rolling in the cash. I think that slag he was with took him for most of it... Anyway, I can't fathom this next bit out because maybe it hasn't happened yet or it's showing me one possible timeline...'

Paige scooped three sugars into Ashley's cup thinking she needed it and handed it to her before he sat down next to her intrigued by what she had to say. Despite her reservations, Ashley would never tell anything she wasn't sure of herself. 'Okay, go on, I'm all ears...'

'Okay, it was a vision, and it's very weird... I saw Ashley and Patrick in the same place. Odd I know and I saw Patrick leaving and I'm not sure why but the feeling I get from it is that he saw something that upset him...'

'What do you think he saw?' She looked at her tea and thought coffee would've been better.

'I pulled a few more cards on it and I think there's a warning here, Paige. I think you need to be careful in regard to Ashley. Stay away from him because he's bad news.'

'Okay,' she nodded and took a sip of her tea. 'But what are the chances of those two ever meeting? Let's be honest.'

'That's the weirdest thing. So, just be aware when you go and remember everything I've told you.'

'Did you see an outcome?' she asked, hardly believing she was asking this.

'That's in the hands of fate or Christmas magic,' she winked.

'Righto, our taxi's here,' said Bryan in the hallway.

'Okay, won't be a second,' Paige said and got up. 'Thanks for looking after Dru as well.'

'Not a problem. She's like my god cat anyway,' she laughed. 'Just... let me know if anything happens, anything we've spoken about.'

'I will do. I will take pictures of everything.' She handed her the keys, kissed Drusilla and put her jacket on. 'Let's rock and roll then, Bry.' She waved at Tiana and got into the taxi despite the train station only being a ten-minute walk along the path at the back of her cottage.

'All right, Rob,' said Paige to the driver as she got into the back seat. 'Bloody cold, isn't it? How's Liz and the kids?'

He shook his head. 'They're all right, thanks for asking. The kids are like bottles of pop waiting for Christmas. Every morning they're up around five asking if Santa has been... it's getting tiring now.' As he pulled out, he switched on the radio and their song came on. 'Blimey, that's right I'm in the presence of pop stars now, aren't I?'

'If only,' Paige laughed. 'I just wrote it, Bryan's the star really...'

'No, you both are for what you've done for the school. I hope you know we all appreciate it.'

'Aww, that's nice of you to say.'

'Here we go then, no charge. Just an autograph will do,' he said and presented them with a copy of a Welsh magazine.

'That's us,' Paige gasped. 'I didn't know about this. When was this printed?'

'Hot off the press yesterday. Didn't you know?'

'No. I'll see if I can nab a copy in the newsagents. Seems like they got it off the local paper...' She signed the article which said: charity single written by author Paige Lockheart and sung by schoolteacher set for a Christmas number one and then got out of the taxi into an empty station.

Taking a seat on the bench Bryan checked the board. 'Four minutes to spare... Not bad.'

'This must be the cleanest station in the UK,' Paige said.

'Yeah, because nobody comes here in winter,' Bryan said, and they both laughed. Just then the train pulled in, and they got in taking a seat with a table. Paige got out her laptop thinking she'd finish the last chapter of her book while Bryan sat and watched YouTube videos on his iPad.

'We're about a mile from Paddington,' Bryan squealed.

Paige lifted her head from the laptop and looked out the window. 'I'm just wrapping up the last chapter. Perfect timing,' she began putting her stuff away and then checked her phone for the second time since they left Wales.

If you're free this afternoon I can meet you outside the Hilton Tower Bridge.

'Oh my goodness, Bry...' she showed him the message.

'That's where we're staying. What are the odds of that!'

'I know, so weird, right? What do I say?'

'You're the bloody writer, Paige, come on,' he laughed. 'It's obvious what you need to write. And the fact he's at the same hotel is even more confirmation of what I was saying – the universe is conspiring.'

'Conspiring,' she mumbled thinking there had to be something going on even if she didn't understand it.

I'm staying at the same place. I've just arrived in London so I will be at the hotel soon.

You're joking! My publisher has merged with Penngwin so I'm attending the party tonight – hey, they're your publishers too?'

YES! Omg I had no idea about the merger.

'Bry, this is getting weirder...'

'Life is weird, sweetheart. Are you only now figuring this out?' he laughed. 'Come on, let's get our bags, we're pulling in...'

Chapter Twenty

'Oh gawd,' she sighed hauling her case off the train into a throng of people whizzing by. 'Let's get a bus to the hotel. I don't fancy the underground right now,' she shouted over at Bryan who was being swept away by a tide of people.

'A coffee first,' he said, finally joining her as they made their way through the ticket machines. Heading out of the station into the overcast, snowy day, she realized in a matter of hours that she'd be face to face with Patrick again.

'Yeah, I think I need more than a coffee to be honest. I think reality has kicked in, finally, Bry and I feel sick. Oh, I can't do this,' she stopped on the pavement as people moved around her to pass.

He looked at her with sympathetic eyes. 'You can and do you know how I know?"

She shook her head.

'Because I have seen you change so much in the past year since the divorce. I see the girl I once knew standing in front of me. She was lost for a very, very long time and I never thought I'd see her again. But here she is... this strong, independent woman who is now a bestselling author who did it all herself...' he pointed to the top of the road with traffic passing by. 'Your future is a couple of miles away and I'm here to make sure you grab it with both hands. Now,' he held out his arm. 'We get a coffee; we chill and then... we PARTY!'

'Let's hope nothing spoils it, eh?'

What could possibly go wrong now?' he said leading her up the road.

She shrugged. 'I can't think of anything...' and then she remembered Tiana's warning.

'What did she say exactly?' Bryan stirred his coffee and placed the spoon on the saucer.

Sitting beside the window of a small coffee shop, Paige gazed out of the window at the hustle and bustle of Christmas shoppers and then put down her cup. 'She said this morning that she saw Patrick and Ashley in the same room together or something. I mean, how impossible is that?'

'What?' He lowered his cup. 'Are you sure they were her exact words?'

'Yep, and she said Ashley is broke and only wants me back for my money.'

'Now that I can believe, but those two in the same room is more than impossible. Maybe she misinterpreted what she saw...'

'Yeah, that's a possibility but...'

'I know, she's been right far too many times. Look, just get your meeting with Patrick over with first then worry about Ashley. I mean, what could he do here? He's a few thousand miles away sitting behind a bar serving drinks...'

'You're right. So,' she drank the last of her coffee and pulled on her coat. 'Are you ready?'

'As I'll ever be.'

Rounding the corner of the hotel Paige scoured the area for Patrick, not that she was ready to see him just yet. With her heart hammering against her chest, she followed Bryan through the glass swinging doors of The Hilton and gasped when she saw the enormous Christmas tree in the middle of the lobby.

'Welcome to The Hilton,' said a man approaching them in a black suit and gestured them towards the reception desk where a woman was waiting, smiling to take book them in.

'Hi there, Paige Lockheart and guest.'

'Hello, welcome to The Hilton. So, it's Paige Lockheart,' the woman typed it into the computer and looked up at her knowingly. 'The author?'

she asked. 'I'm sorry, I know it's unprofessional of me, but I read *One Autumn at the Castle* and I'm a big fan...'

'Aw that's so kind of you. I'll sign a copy for you and leave it at the desk tomorrow,' she said.

'Oh, would you? Thank you so much. Here you go, you're in room 11. Enjoy your stay with us.'

'Will do, thanks.'

'Oh look at you, you're known everywhere,' Bryan jibed heading for the lift.

'And that'll be you in no time too, mister,' she laughed getting into the lift as much as she disliked them.

'I wonder where he is?' Bryan asked stepping out of the lift onto the red carpeted floor. He looked up and down the hall but there was nobody around. 'You should mail him now, get it over with, rip the band aid off.'

'No, I'm not mentally ready...' she whispered looking for number 11. 'Ah here we are,' she slotted the card into the device and pushed open the door to a spacious room with a huge window with a view of the Thames and Tower Bridge. She dropped her suitcase on the bed and went to look out the window. 'Stunning view, isn't it? But not as lovely as the view from my shed...'

'You and that bloody shed. Surprised you haven't permanently moved in,' he quipped.

'Now there's an idea...'

'What?'

'I'm joking...'

'Right, I'm going to have a nose around, then get myself cleaned up and ready to party...Do you want anything from downstairs? I saw a bakery on the way here and I'm craving custard slices.'

'Oh go on then, get us something nice to eat and I'll just get myself freshened up.'

'Okie dokie. I won't be long.'

After Bryan had left, she picked up her phone and texted Tiana.

Stunning view, isn't it?

While she waited for a reply she went to her case and unpacked her clothes, careful not to crease the dress any more than she already had.

Yes, it is. I don't know how to say this, but I feel you're going to find out something you're not going to like…

Oh really? Like what?

I can't quite see it; I just feel your emotions…

Well, so far so good, T… I'll let you know the moment anything changes, okay?

You better. See you later.

A second later, the door opened, and Bryan walked in. 'Er, Paige…'

'Yeah? I'm just in the bathroom. What's wrong?' she asked.

'I was just on my way back from the shop when I swear, I swear I saw Ashley… or at least someone who looks the spit of him walking into the hotel.'

About to splash her face with water she looked up into the mirror recalling Tiana's words only moments ago. 'Oh god…'

Chapter Twenty-One

I f things couldn't get any more stressful, her phone started to ring. 'It's
Patrick.'

'Answer it then.'

'Hello.'

'Hey, I saw on your IG you're in London, so are you ready to meet
up? I'm so looking forward to it.'

'Yes, hi, I'm just having food with Bryan a moment. What time are
you thinking?'

'I'm free the rest of the day. You pick a time and I'll be in the lobby
waiting.'

'Okay then... er...' she looked at her phone screen for the time. It was
already 3.35 in the afternoon. 'How about in an hour?'

'Perfect. I'll see you soon.'

'Yes, see you soon...' She looked at Bryan looking a bit spooked and
sat down on the bed. 'Tiana said...'

'Yes, I know! But how would he even know you're here anyway?'

'Good point.' She picked up her phone and called Tiana. After a few
rings she picked up. Before Paige could utter a word Tiana said, 'Thank
goodness, I was going to call you...'

This doesn't sound good, she thought and braced herself for what she
was about to say. 'Go on, I'm all ears,' and then put her on loudspeaker
for Bryan to listen.

'Literally moments before you rang, I had a customer in the shop.
You know Mrs Goodman, Ashley's aunt, well she popped in for her
monthly card reading and she tells me that Ashley has had a total mental
breakdown and they can't find him anywhere. I hope my prediction isn't
coming true, Paige...'

Now the possibility that Ashley was here, in London at this very hotel was becoming real.

'Hello, you still there?' Asked Tiana.

'Yes, sorry... Well, not ten minutes ago Bryan thought he saw Ashley or a lookalike walking into the hotel. But if it is him, how would he even know I'm here anyway? And why would he be here, that's another thought.'

'To win you back, that's why. And I think I know how he would've found out too. I mentioned your publishing party to Beardo when he asked if you were about and I can only think he somehow mentioned it to Ashley or he got it out of him, I don't know.'

'Shit! Now what do I do? I'm meeting Patrick in less than an hour and I'm nervous enough as it is. What if he's about? Watching...'

'Let him watch, honey because he lost the best thing that ever happened to him. Don't panic. Just keep your wits about you...'

'Okay, thanks, T. I'd better go. Speak to you later.'

'Sounds like the man is desperate. I'll go and scour the hotel; you get ready for your meeting.' He pecked her on the cheek, picked up his bagel and headed to the door before turning around. 'If I see anything, I'll call you...'

'Be careful, Bry. If he's had a mental breakdown, then he's a sick man...'

'Don't worry. I've never been afraid of him. Just get ready and go and meet him. I'll watch out for you...'

'Thanks, Bry, you're a pal.'

As he left the room, he hollered, 'Yes the best girlfriend you ever had...'

She laughed before picking up her suitcase and thinking what on earth is she going to wear. All she brought besides her green dress was jeans and comfy fluffy jumpers. Oh well, jeans and a fluffy comfy jumper it was then she thought and then went to check the weather from the window. She moved the blinds aside and looked down when a familiar face caught her eye leaning against the railings to the Thames. 'Oh god...' She quickly texted Bryan but as soon as she got her phone and looked back out the window, he was gone.

Chapter Twenty-Two

'Crazy ex-husbands,' she muttered pulling her jumper over her head. She swiped red lipstick over her lips, stood back to appraise her appearance in the mirror and thougwt meh, I'll do and grabbed her bag off the bed and left the room, looking up and down the corridor before she closed the door fully. Thankfully, it was quiet and so she went to the lift praying Ashley wouldn't pop out at her. Even if he did, she was prepared for him and not afraid, just his current mental state had her a little worried. Maybe she should alert the police? Once she was safely in the lift, she pressed the button for the ground floor when her focus became entirely on the meeting. 4 3 2 1. Ping! The door to the ground floor opened into a busy lobby, so she stepped out trying to catch her breath and looked around for Patrick. Or Ashley, but her mind was on Patrick. If anything should happen, there were security guards at the entrance anyway.

'Excuse me,' said an older man and his wife trying to get into the lift.

'Oh sorry,' she moved aside and then thought she'd head outside the swinging doors and wait.

I'm here. She texted finding it even more difficult to catch her breath. It was dark now and slightly chilly but the pretty lights reflecting on the water caught her attention and the cold was soon forgotten.

I'm behind you. He texted.

She looked at her phone again and clutched it to her chest when she felt a hand rest on her shoulder and the smell of expensive, woody cologne picked up in a chilly breeze swept by her face.

'Sorry, I realise my last message sounds like something from a thriller novel.'

She laughed, wanting to burst into tears and turned around staring at a set of loving eyes soaking her all in. Without saying a word she threw her arms around him as the tears she held back burst.

'I should never have left it so long,' he whispered. 'I'm so sorry, Paige.'

She broke from the embrace and placed her hands on his face; the bristles of his unshaven face tickled her palm. 'Everything has its time.'

'And this is ours,' he said when his eyes veered to the left of her, over her shoulder.

'What is it?' she asked, turning around.

'There's a guy over there looking very threatening,' he said and slipped his hand in hers. 'We should go inside.'

'Ashley,' she muttered and searched the area for him.

'Who?'

'My ex-husband. He followed me here. I'm sorry, but I don't know what's gotten into him in the past week.'

With that Bryan came up to her. 'Hey,' he said to Patrick and shook his hand. 'Nice to see you again.'

'You too, Bryan. It's been a long time.'

It really has. I'm glad you two have finally worked things out. Listen, I just saw Ashley head down that way,' he pointed away from the hotel. 'I'm going to alert the police, so it's best to go inside, alright?'

As they went inside 'Christmas Spells and Jingle Bells' was playing low over speakers and Patrick swirled her around in the lobby announcing that she wrote the song. There were gasps and a round of applause from the staff and customers.

'Did you really have to embarrass me?' she said with a laugh.

'Not embarrassed. Proud. I'm very proud of you, Paige,' he leaned in close, brushing his nose over hers. 'I love you,' he whispered. 'Let's go get a drink in the bar and talk for old time's sake.'

'Sounds like a plan,' she smiled.

'You look stunning,' said Bryan appraising her in her green dress. 'Wait until he sees you,' he winked.

'He already has,' she laughed it off. 'So, any news about Ashley?'

'No, but I've informed the manager. Since he hasn't done anything, they can't intervene, but security has been alerted, so no worries. Ashley, despite his faults wouldn't do anything to harm you. I think he just wants to talk things out of his system...'

'Well, he now knows how he made me feel when he left, so to be honest I have no sympathy for him.'

'Too right you shouldn't. That's another thing I meant to tell you. They want to record *Top of the Pops* tomorrow according to my agent, so it means cancelling Van Merrick,' he shrugged. 'I had to tell him yes, I mean, it's *Top of the Pops*...'

Disappointed but understanding she waved it off. 'Yeah, that's fine. Oh my god, Bry, I can't wait to be in the studio when you're on the stage. It could be the start of great things to come...'

'Actually,' he sat on the end of the bed. 'I got a call when I was looking for Ash. I've been asked by Andrew Lloyd Webber to sing in his new musical... Paige, I can't believe it, even now. This is what I've always wanted, and it's happening to me right now... me, a schoolteacher from the middle of nowhere.'

She sat down next to him and put her arms around him. 'Yep, we've done all right, Bry. Two little nobodies who have been written off more times than humanely possible to digest, but we did it with perseverance and being unstoppable...I'm mighty proud of you, pal.' She kissed him on the cheek. 'Now let's go and party...'

Chapter Twenty-Three

Stepping out of the hotel room, Paige heard a commotion in the hallway and as she looked down the hall Patrick was having a heated argument with...'Ashley!' she yelled and stormed down the hall whilst hitching her dress so it didn't tear with her heels, she couldn't quite get the hang of. 'What in god's name are you doing here? Get out before I have you arrested.'

'Please,' he got on his knees in front of her and had a desperate look upon his face.

Paige looked at Patrick who took her gently by the arm and pulled her away from him.

'He's threatening me to leave you alone,' Patrick said. 'And I told him I would never leave you again.'

'Paige, please, you don't want him. Who was there for ten years, huh? We were all right, weren't we?' he said pleadingly but Paige wasn't falling for any of it. She knew his real intentions and was a pro when it came to sussing out his lies. There was something about his energy that was off.

'I don't want you, Ashley. You went behind my back after I did everything for you. I know the real reason you're here...' With that, two security guards came out of the lift and grabbed him by the arms. 'One moment, please,' she said getting on her knees. Patrick placed a protective hand on her shoulder and Bryan stepped to the side of her.

'Paige, you don't owe him anything,' said Bryan.

'No, I know I don't, but I'm not the bad person here. Ashley,' she said looking into his eyes. 'You're not well right now. I know you just want my money, and the business is in trouble, so I'm going to propose something...'

'Paige,' Bryan warned her. 'Don't do anything you'll regret.'

'No, it's okay, Bry, I won't. You see, I texted your dad a while ago and he had no idea you were here looking for me, in fact, your dad is a much better version of you, you ought to take a leaf out of his book... anyway, I spoke to him, and we came to an agreement. I buy your half of the club and keep you on as an employee... that way, you keep your job and eventually can save to buy me out. Does that sound like a deal?'

Ashley lowered his head. 'I'm sorry for this. I'm sorry for everything. I was desperate. Since we broke up my life hasn't been a bunch of roses like you thought. If we could start again...'

'No, I don't want a relation...' At that moment she saw a small mistletoe brooch on Patrick's tie. 'Oh my god,' she whispered and remembered what Tiana had said.

'A friendship,' he said. 'If you're going to be my boss, then I think we'd better get along, huh?'

She snapped out of her thoughts. 'Do you mean this?' she asked but could tell he was being genuine.

He nodded. 'You have these two as witnesses,' he said, and she looked at Patrick and Bryan for approval, but they stayed stoic. She knew what they were thinking but understood that it was her choice only.

'Paige, you're too nice,' Bryan said when he insisted Ashley find another hotel or go home. 'Why did you do this after all he's done?'

'I really can't be bothered to hold a grudge or anything, Bry. Believe me, it takes far too much energy, and you know what I've been through with him. It was mentally and emotionally draining. At least this way we all get what we want.'

'But buying his half?' he asked, perplexed.

'Well, I figured it would be a great place for my new venture,' she smiled.

'What's that?'

'Oh, didn't I tell you? I was thinking of starting writing classes and needed a venue.'

Bryan laughed. 'You're always one step ahead, aren't you.'

At the end of the hall, Bryan said he'd make sure Ashley left the premises and found another hotel as he promised and went into the lift. When all was quiet, Patrick pushed her gently against the wall and placing both hands at the side of her staring intently into her eyes. 'I've wanted to do this since the first moment I saw you...' he leaned closer and pressed his lips on hers. 'Shall we skip the first half of the party?' he said, cheekily, and she nodded her head in agreement.

'Why not? It's not like they're going to miss their two best-selling authors, is it?' she laughed.

'I couldn't really care if they do.'

News of their number one single was everywhere now and Bryan had been asked to appear on many TV shows. Waking up the next morning, Paige lifted her head off the bed and saw Patrick sitting at the bottom half looking at her. 'It's *Top of the Pops* recording today, are you ready?' he asked, handing her a mug of coffee.

'Yep, just thank goodness I'm not the one singing,' she laughed.

'I've been thinking,' he said moving up the bed closer to her. 'What are you doing for Christmas?' he asked.

'The usual, sitting at home with Bryan and Tiana eating tins of Roses and Quality Street until we're sick. Why?'

He took her hand in his. 'Why don't you come back with me to Norway? I've a cabin out in the woods that would be perfect and might inspire another Christmas novel for you,' he grinned.

A Christmas abroad? She thought. It's always been celebrated at the cottage. 'I've never spent one Christmas away from the cottage...'

'Maybe it's time for a change. What do you say?'

She didn't really have to think about her answer because it was already yes. 'I'd love to, but I need more clothes than this...' She pointed to her suitcase.

'Then we go shopping today,' he suggested.

'I'd better tell Tiana to take Drusilla for the holidays...'

'Oh, the cat that likes to switch me off,' he laughed. 'I have to meet her one day.'

'After Christmas?' She looked hopeful.

'Absolutely,' he kissed her nose. 'I'm not going anywhere this time.'

CHRISTMAS SPELLS AND JINGLE BELLS

(LYRICS)

Elvis said it would be lonely this Christmas without you
And he wasn't far off wrong
Now I'm sitting in a winter wonderland
Writing this song

(CHORUS)

When Christmas spells and jingle bells don't work
Take fate's lending hand to start anew
Don't look back on all the times you shared
There's a life and many more Christmas joys ahead

Yes, life has thrown a snowball
And you're left to mingle on your own
And Christmas feels more like a chore, and you don't know which way
to go

(REPEAT CHORUS)

If you enjoyed this book, you may also like:
One Autumn at the Castle
The Christmas Guest